# KLYSTRONS AND MICROWAVE TRIODES

# KLYSTRONS AND MICROWAVE TRIODES

*By*

## DONALD R. HAMILTON
ASSOCIATE PROFESSOR OF PHYSICS, PRINCETON UNIVERSITY

## JULIAN K. KNIPP
PROFESSOR OF PHYSICS, IOWA STATE COLLEGE

## J. B. HORNER KUPER
BROOKHAVEN NATIONAL LABORATORY

*EDITORAL STAFF*

GEORGE B. COLLINS · ALBERT G. HILL · WINIFRED McCULLOCH

OFFICE OF SCIENTIFIC RESEARCH AND DEVELOPMENT
NATIONAL DEFENSE RESEARCH COMMITTEE

*NEW YORK*
*DOVER PUBLICATIONS, INC.*

Published in Canada by General Publishing Company, Ltd., 30 Lesmill Road, Don Mills, Toronto, Ontario.

Published in the United Kingdom by Constable and Company, Ltd., 10 Orange Street, London W. C. 2.

This Dover edition, first published in 1966, is an unabridged and unaltered republication of the work first published by McGraw-Hill Book Company, Inc., in 1948. It is made available through the kind cooperation of McGraw-Hill Book Company, Inc.

This book was originally published as volume 7 in the Massachusetts Institute of Technology Radiation Laboratory Series.

*Library of Congress Catalog Card Number 66-17127*

Manufactured in the United States of America

Dover Publications Inc.
180 Varick Street
New York, N. Y. 10014

# *Foreword*

THE tremendous research and development effort that went into the development of radar and related techniques during World War II resulted not only in hundreds of radar sets for military (and some for possible peacetime) use but also in a great body of information and new techniques in the electronics and high-frequency fields. Because this basic material may be of great value to science and engineering, it seemed most important to publish it as soon as security permitted.

The Radiation Laboratory of MIT, which operated under the supervision of the National Defense Research Committee, undertook the great task of preparing these volumes. The work described herein, however, is the collective result of work done at many laboratories, Army, Navy, university, and industrial, both in this country and in England, Canada, and other Dominions.

The Radiation Laboratory, once its proposals were approved and finances provided by the Office of Scientific Research and Development, chose Louis N. Ridenour as Editor-in-Chief to lead and direct the entire project. An editorial staff was then selected of those best qualified for this type of task. Finally the authors for the various volumes or chapters or sections were chosen from among those experts who were intimately familiar with the various fields, and who were able and willing to write the summaries of them. This entire staff agreed to remain at work at MIT for six months or more after the work of the Radiation Laboratory was complete. These volumes stand as a monument to this group.

These volumes serve as a memorial to the unnamed hundreds and thousands of other scientists, engineers, and others who actually carried on the research, development, and engineering work the results of which are herein described. There were so many involved in this work and they worked so closely together even though often in widely separated laboratories that it is impossible to name or even to know those who contributed to a particular idea or development. Only certain ones who wrote reports or articles have even been mentioned. But to all those who contributed in any way to this great cooperative development enterprise, both in this country and in England, these volumes are dedicated.

L. A. DuBridge.

v

# Preface

THIS volume of the Radiation Laboratory Series attempts to cover the basic principles underlying the operation of klystrons and planar grid tubes as oscillators and amplifiers. It has been the desire of the authors to present the technical and theoretical aspects of this field as completely and as rigorously as possible, even though this meant the exclusion of a great deal of descriptive material, and has certainly added to the difficulty of a first reading. Nevertheless it was felt that the greatest need for a book on this subject at the present time was for one from which the fundamental principles for the design and understanding of microwave vacuum tubes could be obtained. No attempt has been made to describe how a vacuum tube is actually constructed. Rather the emphasis has been placed on presenting the fundamental material which the tube designer or tube user must have at his command.

Because the radio-frequency work of the Radiation Laboratory was concentrated almost entirely in the frequency region above 3000 Mc/sec, this book naturally tends to emphasize the operation of tubes in that region. However the basic principles are the same at lower frequencies although as a general rule the electrical and mechanical requirements become more difficult to attain as higher frequencies are approached. Certainly it is the authors' hope that this is a book on the principles of operation of particular types of tubes, and not a treatise on the generation of oscillations in a particular frequency band.

The wartime development of microwave radar and communications was based on three important types of amplifier and oscillator tubes: the multicavity magnetrons, the klystron family of tubes, and the planar grid tubes (also called lighthouse tubes and disk-seal tubes). The extraordinarily rapid engineering development of the multicavity magnetron as a transmitting tube is certainly one of the great advances of the war and is discussed elsewhere in the Radiation Laboratory Series. The present volume attempts to complete the story, and to cover in particular the development of microwave receiving tubes, local oscillators, and signal amplifiers. The use of klystron and planar grid tubes as transmitting oscillators, and in a few cases transmitting amplifiers, is not neglected. But up to the present their greatest use has been in receivers. It seems hardly necessary to caution the reader that the future development of microwave receiver tubes will hardly be limited to the two types discussed here.   One need only recall the announcement in June of this year of the development first at Oxford University and later at the Bell Telephone Laboratories of the traveling-wave tube, which may well revolutionize our idea of amplifier design.

This volume has been written in parts based on tube types and construction, a division in form rather than in use or purpose.   Following four introductory chapters discussing tube types and functions and basic electronic and circuit phenomena common to all types of tubes there is a part on planar grid tubes and a part on klystrons.   This division has seemed desirable to the authors since it has made the purely mathematical developments more logical than would have been the case if the division in function had been followed.   This arrangement should reduce the number of cross references, and make the reading more straightforward.   Aside from a few special cases of r-f circuits which are used solely for microwave vacuum tubes, no attempt has been made in this book to discuss the general properties of distributed constant circuits, since these problems have been discussed thoroughly elsewhere in this series.

Except for the important work of H. V. Neher and his group, most of the effort at Radiation Laboratory on microwave receivers went into the design of circuits, and the corollary tube testing and specification. We have drawn freely upon the work of other organizations both in England and in this country, and in particular upon the work of the Bell Telephone Laboratories, the General Electric Company, and the Sperry Gyroscope Company.   Since the bulk of the wartime work has just been declassified and remains unpublished, it has been necessary to refer to internal organization reports, which are not available generally.

With the increasing awareness of engineers and physicists of the relative merits of various systems of units, it has become the duty of the preface writer to mention and defend the system chosen for the book at hand.   The present volume uses the MKS system for reasons no more cogent than (1) this system is becoming more and more popular among engineers, and is making headway even among physicists; (2) amperes, ohms, and volts are units which the tube designer naturally uses.

We should like to express our thanks to Professor Eugene Feenberg, now at Washington University in St. Louis, Mr. Edward Barlow, and Dr. Marvin Chodorow, of the Sperry Gyroscope Company for many helpful comments and criticism of the manuscript.   We are indebted to our former colleagues Dr. Milton Gardner, now at the University of California, and Mr. M. C. Waltz, now at the Bell Telephone Laboratories, for a great deal of help in preparing the information for this volume. In particular we wish to thank Dr. W. G. Shepherd, of the Bell Telephone Laboratories, who has read the entire manuscript and has helped us greatly by his criticism.

ALBERT G. HILL.

CAMBRIDGE MASS.,
*July*, 1946.

# Contents

## PART III. KLYSTRONS

# PART I

# FUNDAMENTALS

# CHAPTER I

## INTRODUCTION

### By J. B. H. Kuper

During the last twenty years or so the development of radio communication and of allied techniques such as radar and television has involved the use of higher and higher frequencies. During most of this period this trend has resulted from the need for more channels in the useful frequency spectrum; on the other hand, in such notable instances as the development of radar, the use of higher frequencies arises from the need for highly directional antenna systems of reasonable size. Whatever the reason behind the upward extension of frequencies in any particular case, the pace has been set by the progress achieved in development of electron tubes capable of generating higher frequencies efficiently and reliably.

**1·1. Electron Tubes at Very High Frequencies.**—In tubes of conventional design the upper limit of the useful frequency range is fixed by one or more of the following factors: (1) the inductance of the leads to the tube elements, (2) the transit time of the electrons in the space between electrodes, (3) the losses by radiation from the tube structure and connecting leads, and (4) the necessity for small structures with limited capabilities for heat dissipation. Careful attention to these points has permitted great progress in the design of conventional tubes for frequencies up to hundreds of megacycles per second. The microwave region has been exploited, however, primarily by the use of unorthodox methods of vacuum tube construction and new principles of vacuum tube operation; these have mitigated or entirely eliminated the undesirable effects of the first three difficulties mentioned above, and the higher efficiencies resulting have tended to diminish the importance of the fourth.

The most universal difference between microwave tubes and those of conventional design is that the former incorporate cavity resonators (or at least are so constructed that they can form portions of cavities) and so avoid the effects of lead inductance and radiation losses. The properties of cavity resonators are considered in Sec. 1·3 and in more detail in Chap. 4.

An additional point of comparison arises in connection with the electronic principles that are utilized in microwave tubes. Since the same basic laws of electronic phenomena apply at all frequencies, quite different

3

aspects of these basic laws are utilized at high and at low frequencies. For one thing, the important interaction of an electron stream with a high-frequency circuit takes place not after the electron has been collected on an electrode, but rather when the electron is in an "interaction gap" between vacuum-tube electrodes of the high-frequency circuit; the interaction of electrons and electromagnetic fields is basic, the collection of electrons very minor. As a still more drastic departure in electronic behavior, the finite transit time of electrons—which has a deleterious effect as triode operating frequencies are increased—is actually utilized as an essential element in the generation of microwave power in the klystron and magnetron. These and other features of electronic phenomena at microwave frequencies are discussed in Chap. 3.

The construction of most microwave tubes is so different from that of conventional radio tubes that the sole remaining point of similarity is the standard tube base used for the d-c connections of most klystrons and microwave triodes. All in all, these methods of construction and the principles of operation of these new tubes have been so successful that during the wartime period the frequency spectrum available for radio communication and allied applications was multiplied to at least thirty times its prewar extent. Furthermore, this development made it possible, for example, to direct radiated energy into a searchlight beam of the order of magnitude of one degree in width with an antenna small enough to be installed in an aircraft. Before going into details of the relevant vacuum tube questions involved here, however, it will be necessary to discuss briefly some basic points about the microwave frequencies.

**1·2. Microwave Region.** *Frequency Range.*—At the outset it is well to emphasize that the microwave region (or centimeter-wave region) is characterized by the techniques employed and does not have precise frequency limits. In a sense it is not so much a spectral band as a frame of mind. The distinctive characteristics are the use of distributed-constant circuits enclosed by conducting boundaries in contrast to the lumped-constant elements familiar in lower frequency applications. Ordinary circuit components (condensers, coils, and resistors) are useless as lumped elements in the microwave region since they are usually so large in comparison with the wavelength that they cannot be considered as purely capacitive, inductive, or resistive elements.

In the official designations for portions of the radio frequency spectrum, the "very high frequencies" include the region from 300 to 3000 Mc/sec (wavelength from one meter to 10 cm), and the term "super high frequencies" is applied to the region above 3000 Mc/sec. This division is rather awkward since the boundary is artificial, but fortunately the term "microwaves" has been left out of the definitions, and so can be used as suggested here.

Cavity resonators may be used at frequencies in the 100 Mc/sec region or lower, the only objection being their bulk; waveguides have been used below 600 Mc/sec. On the other hand, oscillators with unenclosed circuits employing more or less lumped elements have been built for frequencies exceeding 1000 Mc/sec. It is impossible, as these examples show, to set a definite lower limit to the frequency range of the microwave region; nevertheless, in any specific case, it is easy to tell at a glance whether microwave techniques are being employed. For practical purposes, the microwave region, as defined by techniques, may be considered to start at about 1000 Mc/sec and to extend indefinitely— to more than 30,000 Mc/sec, and preferably until it merges into the infrared region. For most of the specific illustrative cases that occur at later points in this book, the frequencies lie between 1000 Mc/sec and 30,000 Mc/sec (wavelengths between 30 cm and one cm).

*Properties of Microwaves.*—Second only to the obvious advantage of offering more room for services requiring wide frequency bands, the most important property of the microwaves is their short wavelength. It is a basic principle in physical optics that radiation in a directed beam can arise only from a structure that is large in comparison to the wavelength. Therefore, in order to get narrow beams without resorting to very large antennas, it is necessary to use short waves.

The propagation of microwaves is practically limited to line-of-sight distances. Some energy, however, penetrates below the horizon because of scattering and diffraction effects. Under the right meteorological conditions, atmospheric refraction may be strong enough to guide microwave radiation along the surface of the earth to many times the horizon distance.

Microwaves are reflected strongly from bodies of water or from most metal structures, and are reflected to varying degrees by land masses and by other structures. Because of this fact, it is common to find a direct ray, and one or more reflected rays, at a given remote point. Such multipath transmission results in an interference pattern in space; any minor change in path lengths, amounting to a half wavelength or so, causes severe fading.

*Special Features of Microwave Receivers.*—As is explained in later chapters, satisfactory r-f amplifier tubes for the microwave region are not yet available; where the maximum sensitivity is required in a receiver it is necessary to use the superheterodyne principle. The nonlinear element (or mixer) is almost always a point-contact rectifier (usually a tungsten point pressing on a silicon crystal); although crystal mixers always give a conversion loss they are preferable to existing vacuum tubes. With the multigrid tubes used as converters at lower frequencies, it is usual to get amplification as well as mixing; with the microwave converters, on the other hand, the power at the "beat" or difference frequency available for amplification in the i-f amplifier is less than the incoming signal power.  Offsetting the conversion loss to some extent, the crystal mixer contributes remarkably little noise in itself.

At moderately high frequencies the useful sensitivity of a radio receiver is ordinarily limited by extraneous noise that originates outside the receiver.  The principal sources of extraneous noise are atmospheric electrical phenomena (such as distant thunderstorms) and discharges or transients in electrical machinery.  In a "noisy" location a receiver with high sensitivity will be useless for reception of very weak signals, but in a "quiet" location the full sensitivity may be useful.  The situation is markedly different at very high frequencies, however.  As the frequency is raised, the extraneous noise becomes less and less important for two reasons: (1) above the critical frequencies for ionospheric reflection only those sources of noise within (approximately) line-of-sight distances can be effective, and (2) the ordinary transients in electrical equipment do not contain components in the extreme high frequency range.  On the other hand, as the frequency is raised the receiver itself tends to become "noisier," that is, a larger portion of the total noise is generated in the early stages of the amplifier.  In the microwave region (and to a large extent at frequencies in the ultrahigh-frequency range), it is no longer true that the environment limits the useful sensitivity of a receiver; rather the limit is set in the receiver itself by the noise generated therein.

*Noise Figure.*—This generation of noise has led to the introduction of the concept of the noise figure,[1] by means of which the performance of a real receiver is measured in terms of that of a theoretically perfect receiver.  The concept is by no means limited in application to radio receivers at very high frequencies; analogous criteria could be applied to many other devices—galvanometers, for example.

In an ideal receiver the only source of noise (within the receiver) is the thermal agitation noise associated with the input impedance.  The magnitude of this noise power can be calculated from thermodynamic reasoning, given the limiting bandwidth of the receiver, $\Delta f$; the noise power is $kT \, \Delta f$ watts, where $T$ is the absolute temperature of the input impedance and $k$ is Boltzmann's constant, $1.38 \times 10^{-23}$ watt-seconds per degree absolute.  An actual receiver may have many additional sources of noise contributing to the total output noise.  For any device it is, thus, easy to assign a "noise figure"—that is, the ratio of the actual noise output power to the noise that would have been obtained if only the input impedance were contributing noise.  Alternatively, the noise figure is the ratio to $kT \, \Delta f$ of the minimum input signal for which the

---

[1] For a full discussion see H. T. Friis, "Noise Figures of Radio Receivers," *Proc. I.R.E.*, **32**, 418 (1944), and correction *ibid.* **32**, 729 (1944).

output signal and noise are equal. When several noisy devices are cascaded, their contributions may always be referred to a common point (normally the input terminals) by making allowances for the gain. The noise figure is commonly expressed in decibels; for an ideal device the noise figure is unity, or zero db.

In a straight superheterodyne receiver the noise figure is determined by the converter and the first (one or two) i-f amplifier stages. When an r-f amplifier is used before changing frequency, the amplifier noise figure is the controlling factor for the whole receiver, provided only that the gain of the amplifier is sufficient to swamp the noise of the converter.

**1·3. Microwave Techniques.** *Coaxial Lines and Waveguides.*— Because of radiation losses, parallel wires and other open transmission lines are never used (except as antennas) in the microwave region. Instead, coaxial lines and waveguides are universally employed. Although it may be said justly that a coaxial line is a waveguide, the use of the two terms in a restricted sense is well established and also convenient where it is desired to call attention to the presence or absence of a center conductor.

A coaxial line may contain a low-loss dielectric to support the center conductor; or instead of a solid dielectric it may have stub lines, short-circuited at a distance corresponding to $\frac{1}{4}$ wavelength, to support the center conductor. The latter method is favored when it is necessary to handle large amounts of power over fairly long distances; where losses are unimportant, as in low-level work with short runs, the solid dielectric lines are convenient. A waveguide may be a hollow conductor of any cross-section, or even a solid rod of dielectric, provided the lateral dimensions are not too small compared with the wavelength in air of the radiation to be handled; a waveguide may be excited in many different transmission modes. With very few exceptions, however, practical waveguides are metallic tubes of rectangular cross-section; the larger (inside) dimension lies between one-half and one air wavelength, which means that the "dominant" mode is the only one that can be propagated. Compared with coaxial lines, a waveguide has the tremendous advantage of requiring no support for a center conductor; it can handle much higher powers without insulation failures, but it is dispersive—that is, the phase velocity depends on the frequency. This can be troublesome when wide frequency ranges are to be handled.

*Cavity Resonators.*—It is a familiar fact that a piece of coaxial line or waveguide that is one-half wavelength long and is short-circuited at the ends will behave as a resonant circuit. As a result of the absence of radiation and dielectric losses, together with the relatively large areas of the conductors, the $Q$ of such a resonant circuit may be very high in comparison with typical coil-and-condenser combinations. It is possibly less commonly realized that any region bounded by a conducting surface will be a resonant cavity, and will possess an infinite number of resonant frequencies corresponding to different modes of oscillation. Usually, only the mode with the lowest resonant frequency is of interest, but it is not safe to ignore the existence of the higher modes.

In ordinary lumped-constant circuits the behavior is determined by the resistance, inductance, and capacitance. In the lumped-constant approximation an alternative specification in terms of the resonant frequency, the $Q$, and the shunt resistance is equally valid although less familiar. In microwave resonant circuits the latter representation is still possible, indeed it is generally the most useful; on the other hand, the $R$, $L$, and $C$ picture is seldom, if ever, an accurate one. In general, it is not possible to define an inductance or capacitance associated with a part of a resonant cavity in an unambiguous manner; contradictions are sure to appear sooner or later. This difficulty, which is at the heart of the difference between lumped-constant and distributed-constant circuits, is important mainly in pointing out the dangers in taking simple lumped-constant "equivalent" circuits too seriously. Although often useful in qualitative discussions, and sometimes capable of yielding quantitative results, these "equivalent" circuits for distributed-constant circuits must be used very carefully.

Obviously, many types of resonant cavities are possible. For wavemeters, in particular, higher modes in round waveguides are often employed, since they may have higher Q's than the simpler field configurations. In electron tubes, however, the cavities must satisfy two primary conditions: (1) the dimensions of the conducting walls must correspond to the desired resonant frequency, and (2) there must be a region in which there is strong interaction with an electron stream. This second condition commonly means that the cavity must have a region in which the electric field is relatively strong across a gap short enough to be traversed by an electron in a fraction of a cycle. Hence the resonators used in microwave tubes have regions (the interaction gaps) which resemble ordinary condensers. As a result of this fact it is often permissible to use the lumped-constant equivalent circuit representation in discussing these resonators.

*Reentrant Cavity Resonators.*—The necessity for an efficient interaction gap—one with a high r-f field extending over a short distance which can be traversed by an electron beam—has led to the use of a form of resonator (discussed in Chap. 4) consisting of a cylindrical box with a central post reaching almost across from top to bottom. Extreme forms of this resonator may be either a cylindrical pillbox with a vanishingly short center post, or a coaxial line short-circuited at one end and provided with an end plate close to the free end of the center conductor. The latter form may be considered as a short-circuited quarter-wavelength line loaded by a capacitance (the interaction gap) at the open end.  In any case apertures or grids are provided at the interaction gap to permit passage of the electron beam.

In the microwave region a tube can scarcely be considered apart from its cavity, so the properties of resonators, $Q$, shunt resistance, and length of interaction gap will be mentioned frequently in succeeding chapters. These four properties, with the resonant frequency, are determined by the dimensions of the resonator and by the conductivity of the material of which it is made.  To a large extent microwave tube resonator design is a compromise between the requirements for a high shunt resistance and an efficient interaction gap.

**1·4. Principal Tube Types.**—There are three principal types of vacuum tube that have been useful in the past in the microwave region: cavity magnetrons, specially designed space-charge control tubes (mostly triodes), and klystrons.  (The latter are often called velocity-modulation or velocity-variation tubes.)

*Cavity Magnetrons.*—The tremendous advance in microwave techniques during the war had as its most important ingredient the invention of the cavity magnetron.  By the end of the war it was possible to build magnetrons to deliver pulse powers in excess of a megawatt in the 3000 Mc/sec region or continuous powers approaching a kilowatt.  The magnetron is treated elsewhere in this series,[1] and this book is devoted to other types of tubes useful in applications where the power requirements are more modest.

*Special Space-charge Control Tubes.*—In view of the difficulties experienced with space-charge control tubes at high frequencies, the space-charge control tubes logically take the form of disk-seal triodes.[2]  This class of tube, the best-known members of which are popularly called "lighthouse tubes" because of their shape, has a planar structure in contrast to the cylindrical forms common at lower frequencies.  The leads to the electrodes are brought out of the vacuum envelope through disk seals (metal to glass) and the whole tube is designed for insertion in a resonator.  In the lighthouse tubes an oxide-coated cathode is mounted on the end of a cylindrical post a few thousandths of an inch from a mesh grid, and the anode is the end of a similar cylindrical post on the other side of the grid.

Two examples of the lighthouse type of microwave triode are shown (without the associated resonant circuits) in Fig. 1·1.  In Fig. 1·2 one of these tubes, the 2C40, is shown in cross-section.  The plate connection is the top cap, the grid is brought out to the intermediate disk, and the

---

[1] See Volume 6 of the Radiation Laboratory Series.

[2] E. D. McArthur, "Disk-Seal Tubes," *Electronics*, 98, February 1945.

base shell provides the r-f cathode connection. When these tubes are inserted in a coaxial-line resonator, the lead inductance is practically eliminated since the vacuum tube electrodes are integral parts of resonant

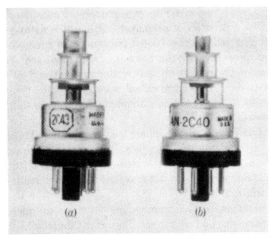

Fig. 1·1.—Typical lighthouse tubes: (*a*) the 2C43 and (*b*) the 2C40.

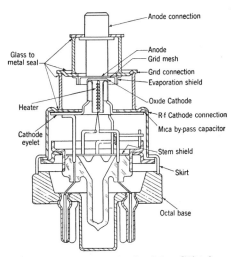

Fig. 1·2.—Mechanical details of the 2C40 tube.

cavities. At the same time this construction eliminates losses by radiation. In order to reduce transit-time effects as much as possible, the interelectrode spacings of microwave triodes must be made extremely small; thus in the 2C40, one of the examples shown in the figure, the cathode and plate have a diameter of 4.6 mm, the cathode-to-grid spacing is about 0.1 mm, and the grid-plate spacing is about 0.3 mm.

Figure 1·3 shows the 2C43 (one of the tubes of Fig. 1·1) mounted inside a coaxial-line type of cavity resonator.

Microwave triodes thus represent the logical development of the conventional triode to adapt it to operation at very high frequencies—a development that is limited mainly by purely mechanical difficulties inherent in maintaining the necessary close spacings in manufacture.

*Klystrons.*—Klystrons stand in sharp contrast to the lighthouse tubes, which are the logical adaptations of low frequency design principles to microwave requirements; the klystrons[1] are the result of the

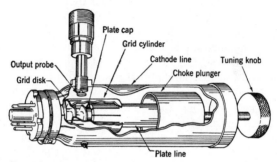

Fig. 1·3.—Cutaway drawing of a cavity for the 2C43 tube.

utilizing of, instead of minimizing, comparatively long transit times. In the two-resonator klystron amplifier, the simplest type for purposes of discussion, a beam of electrons from a gun is first accelerated to a high velocity. The beam then passes through the interaction gap of the input resonator (sometimes called the "buncher"), where each electron receives an additional acceleration (positive or negative) depending on the phase and magnitude of the gap voltage during the passage of the electron. The beam, now containing electrons of various velocities, next traverses a "drift space" in which the variations in velocity of the electrons give rise to density modulation. Since the velocity of each electron depends on the instant at which it crossed the buncher gap, an electron which was accelerated will overtake one which started out earlier and was retarded,

[1] R. H. Varian and S. F. Varian, "A High-Frequency Oscillator and Amplifier," *J. App. Phys.*, **10**, 321 (1939); D. L. Webster, "Cathode-ray Bunching," *J. App. Phys.*, **10**, 401 (1939); D. L. Webster, "The Theory of Klystron Oscillations," *J. App. Phys.*, **10**, 864 (1939); A. E. Harrison, "Klystron Technical Manual," Sperry Gyroscope Co., Inc., Great Neck, Long Island, N. Y. 1944 (contains a good bibliography of early papers); J. R. Pierce, "Reflex Oscillators," *Proc. I.R.E.*, **33**, 112 (1945); E. L. Ginzton and A. E. Harrison, "Reflex-Klystron Oscillators," *Proc. I.R.E.*, **34**, 97P, (1946).

and in this manner the electrons tend to form bunches in the beam. The bunched beam passes through the interaction gap of the output resonator (sometimes called the "catcher"); here the high frequency component of the beam current, as represented by the bunches and intervening regions of low density, drives the output resonator into oscillation. This resonator and its output coupling act as a step-down transformer to deliver useful power to the load. If a portion of the output power from such an amplifier is fed to the input resonator in the correct phase, self-sustained oscillations will be obtained.

In the type of operation thus described, control over the density of the electron stream is exercised not by direct density modulation in a single cathode-grid control region, but rather by a more indirect process occurring in a control region composed of three parts: the region of d-c acceleration, the velocity-modulating input gap, and the drift space in which velocity modulation is converted to density modulation. The most basic advantage of this new method of modulation lies in the fact that the initial (velocity) modulation is applied after d-c acceleration, rather than before d-c acceleration as in the triode. Thus, although there must be somewhat less than one cycle transit time through either the cathode-grid region of the triode or the input gap of the klystron, in the latter case the transit is made at high velocity. The requirements on electrode spacings are thus greatly relaxed for the klystron, and the upper limit of attainable frequencies is increased by at least an order of magnitude.

In the discussion of klystrons in Chap. 9 and subsequent chapters it will be seen that at first glance satisfactory klystron operation might be expected with a very small input-gap r-f voltage and a long drift space; more careful consideration shows that space-charge debunching forces become harmful with a long drift space. The resulting short drift spaces and sizable r-f gap voltages have as a consequence the need for cavity resonators with high shunt impedances. In a general way this means high-$Q$ circuits, and the ensuing complications of keeping two or more such circuits in tune.

This question of tuning contributes strongly to the fact that of all the various forms of klystrons by far the most common is the reflex klystron oscillator; this tube differs from the other forms mainly in the fact that a single resonator serves as both buncher and catcher. Instead of traversing a straight drift space the beam is turned back on itself by a retarding field, produced by a reflector electrode maintained at a potential negative with respect to the cathode. The reflected beam contains bunches, which result from the variation of transit time with velocity in a process formally similar to that occurring in the two-resonator klystron. The end result of the process of bunching in a retarding field differs by a phase factor of 180° from the field-free drift-space bunching mentioned in the discussion of the klystron amplifier. The faster electrons penetrate more deeply into the retarding field and therefore take longer to make a round trip; hence the electrons which made their first transit through the interaction gap early and were accelerated are overtaken by those which came later and were retarded. Oscillations may be produced in the reflex klystron provided the bunches in the beam return to the interaction gap at the proper phase to deliver energy to the

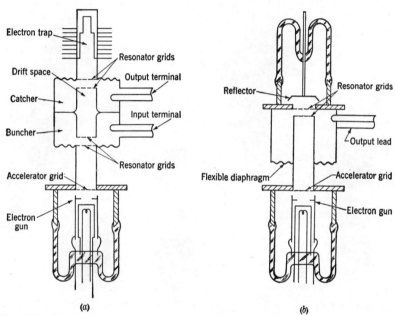

(a)                                    (b)

FIG. 1·4.—Cross sections illustrating principal features of (a) the 2-cavity klystron and (b) the reflex klystron.

resonator. This requirement can be met by adjustment of reflector voltage or spacing.

The general construction of the reflex klystron oscillator and a two-resonator klystron amplifier is indicated schematically in Fig. 1·4. Figure 1·5 shows several commercial klystrons which furnish many of the examples in later chapters.

**1·5. Points of Comparison between Low-power Microwave Tubes.**—Although differing in structure and in principle of operation, microwave triodes and klystrons have many characteristics in common. Among these are the fields of application, the use of similar types of cavity resonators, and the fact that the tubes usually have axial symmetry with one-dimensional electron flow.

*Application.*—By far the most common use of microwave triodes and reflex klystrons has been as local oscillators in microwave receivers. Other applications have been as signal generators or low-power transmitters. The microwave triodes lend themselves well to pulse operation; but klystrons are also useful, particularly where the duty ratio is high. Reflex klystrons are well adapted as frequency-modulated transmitters, especially where large frequency deviations are required.

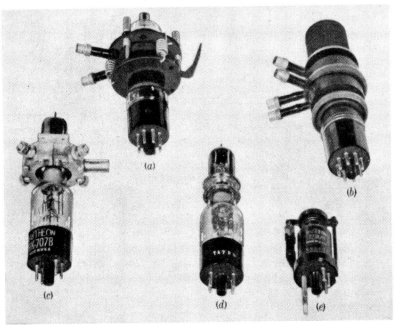

Fig. 1·5.—Representative commercial klystrons: (a) the 417A reflex klystron; (b) the 410R two-resonator klystron; (c) the 707B reflex klystron with external cavity; (d) the 707B reflex klystron without external cavity; (e) the 723A/B reflex klystron with internal cavity.

Klystrons and microwave triodes can be used as superregenerative receivers, of course, but these receivers have not found wide application in the microwave region.

*Resonators.*—It should be noted, as a point of similarity between the klystrons and the microwave triodes, that the requirements of each of these types lead to the use of the reentrant resonator which is discussed in more detail in Chap. 4. For purely mechanical reasons, however, the microwave triodes are ordinarily used in cavities which resemble capacitance-loaded coaxial lines, usually not operated in the fundamental mode but in the three- or five-quarter-wavelength mode. Most of the klystrons have integral cavities of a simple form; the 707B, an external-cavity type, is sometimes used also in a coaxial line resonator.

*Symmetry.*—Almost all microwave triodes and klystrons have structures that are figures of revolution about an axis.[1] The electron beam is located on or near the axis of symmetry, and apart from focusing effects the paths of the electrons are essentially one-dimensional. This permits a considerable simplification of the theoretical treatment of the two classes of tubes. Extremely simple theories, in which only rectilinear motions in uniform fields are discussed, are able to furnish surprisingly useful results.

*Fundamental Differences.*—On the other hand there are deep fundamental differences between microwave triodes and klystrons; as discussed earlier, these are concerned mainly with the manner of production of density variations in the electron beam. This difference is often emphasized by classifying the two types as "space-charge control" tubes and "velocity-variation" or "velocity-modulation" tubes respectively. In the space-charge control tubes, the field at a virtual cathode (potential minimum) is varied, usually by changing the potential of a grid; the electron density in the beam traversing the output circuit is varied correspondingly. Although there is, of course, a slight variation in velocity of the electrons as the grid potential is changed, this is of no practical consequence; the primary effect is density variation. In the velocity-variation tubes, on the other hand, there are space-charge effects which noticeably alter conclusions based on simple bunching theory; but here, in turn, these space-charge effects are secondary.

Partly as a result of this fact that space-charge and velocity-variation effects often are present in the same tube, it may be useful to employ a different classification scheme depending on the velocity of the electrons in the control region. Thus the space-charge control tubes may be referred to as "low-velocity" types, since the control is applied to electrons that are at rest or moving only very slowly. In the velocity-modulation types the electrons are first accelerated to a high velocity and then enter the input interaction gap, so it is natural to call them "high-velocity" tubes.

**1·6. Plan of This Book.**—Attention is devoted primarily to those specific types that have been widely used during the war and are therefore comparatively well understood. These types are the lighthouse tubes and the reflex klystrons. The amounts of space devoted to these two types indicate very roughly their relative importance to wartime applications; this ratio will very likely carry over into peacetime work.

---

[1] Exceptions are some British double-gap single resonator tubes that have not been widely used and therefore are not discussed in this book except in Sec. 2·4.

The book is divided into three main parts.   The first is devoted to general discussions of tube types and a survey of the fundamental principles of resonators and electronics applicable to both categories of tubes. The space-charge control or low-velocity types are discussed in the second part, with most of the illustrative material referring to the lighthouse tubes.   The third part is concerned with the klystrons, with two chapters on multiresonator tubes and the balance devoted to the reflex klystrons.

# CHAPTER 2

# SUMMARY OF MICROWAVE TUBE TYPES AND FUNCTIONS

## By D. R. Hamilton

As noted in the preceding chapter, the main emphasis of this book is upon reflex klystrons and microwave triodes. Numerous other types of microwave tubes exist, however, and in order to clarify the background and significance of the microwave triodes and reflex klystrons it is necessary to discuss the principal features and characteristics of these other tube types. This is most easily done by considering the various functions which vacuum tubes might be expected to fulfill at microwave frequencies; in this chapter the discussion of these functions is therefore used as a means of introducing the subsidiary tube types, comparing them with the tubes with which most of the remainder of the book is concerned, and indicating why they are not of paramount importance. At the same time this procedure serves to provide a bird's-eye view of the situation in the various possible microwave vacuum-tube applications, and provides some indication of future trends in this field.

**2·1. Mixers.**—The type of mixer used in any microwave application depends strongly on the requirements placed on this mixer. Thus, in radar application the received signals are very weak and the noise properties of the mixer are of prime importance. At frequencies of 2500 Mc/sec and higher, crystal mixers have much lower noise than any vacuum-tube mixer; this fact has resulted in the practically exclusive use of crystal mixers in radar development in this frequency range. Such mixers are discussed in detail in Vol. 16 of this series.

On the other hand, in the future there may well be applications in which noise questions lose the transcendent importance which they have in radar; this fact opens up the possibility of the use of thermionic mixers. The most promising of such mixers have been the diodes. In designing a diode mixer there apply the same considerations which have led to the "lighthouse" type of construction for triodes, as discussed in Chap. 1. The best diode so far developed has been the British CV58; at 3000 Mc/sec this tube used as a mixer has a noise figure of about 18 db, as compared to 9 db for the better crystal mixers. The 2B22, an American lighthouse diode, and the 2C40 lighthouse triode, give noise figures of 21–22 db when used as mixers at 3000 Mc/sec.

Klystron mixers were constructed in the early days of microwave development, before measurement techniques were refined to the degree of giving accurate noise figures; they were found to be too noisy for radar application.

Since thermionic microwave mixers have received very little attention in recent years, and since comparatively little is known about them, they will not be discussed further in this book.

**2·2. Amplifiers.**—In the development of wartime microwave radar there was no great utilization or intensive development of microwave amplifiers. This was the result of two primary factors: the lack of a good low-noise r-f amplifier for receiver work, and the excellence of the cavity magnetron as a transmitter for pulse radar. The post-war broadening of the types of microwave applications and the fuller utilization of the available frequency ranges will result in a greatly increased need for and development of microwave amplifiers in both the signal-amplifier and power-amplifier categories.

As an illustration of this latter point there may be noted the announcement, just as the manuscript for this book goes into final form, of the development at the Bell Telephone Laboratories of the "traveling-wave" amplifier, originally invented at the Clarendon Laboratory, Oxford, England. Typical data quoted for an initial sample of this tube are as follows: at a frequency of 3600 Mc/sec, a gain of 23 db, a bandwidth of 800 Mc/sec, output power 200 milliwatts, beam voltage 1600 volts, beam current 10 ma. Thus, although it will be seen shortly that klystrons and microwave triodes provide amplification suitable for many purposes, it is apparent that current postwar development will markedly change the amplifier situation from that to be described here.

In this postwar development, voltage or low-level amplifiers will be required for the same reasons that have made their utilization so widespread in receivers designed for the broadcast and familiar short wave bands. Among the important advantages gained by using an r-f amplifier at the input to a receiver are: reduction of local oscillator radiation and image sensitivity in superhyterodyne receivers; isolation of receiver circuits from detuning effects of an antenna (in microwave parlance this would be called "pulling"); and, especially where remote cut-off tubes are used, reduction of cross modulation by nearby powerful transmitters on neighboring channels. In radar receivers the greatest possible sensitivity, determined by the noise figure, is required; in this respect the amplifiers so far developed cannot compete with the crystal converter at frequencies above about 1000 Mc/sec. In addition, it has been found helpful in pulse radar to utilize automatic frequency control for keeping the receiver correctly tuned to the radar transmitter; this tuning process is tremendously complicated by an r-f amplifier. These considerations clearly do not apply to a communication system where, for example, fixed frequency operation is necessary and the avoidance of interference may be more important even than the noise figure. It thus seems that the development of suitable amplifiers will be a major project in the postwar era.

In transmitter practice the use of a master oscillator-power amplifier arrangement is standard except at microwave frequencies. In the latter instance, the cavity magnetron used as a self-excited osillator is capable of generating enough power to make an amplifier following the oscillator a rather undesirable complication. Although the frequency stability of this arrangement is sufficient for the wide bands needed in pulse radar it is not up to the standards customary in communication systems at lower frequencies; in addition, the master oscillator-power amplifier possesses the advantage of providing clean modulation, that is, amplitude modulation free of frequency modulation, or *vice versa*.

The further discussion of the requirements imposed upon amplifiers, and the prospects of meeting these requirements, is broken up into separate discussions of signal or voltage amplifiers, and power amplifiers.

*Signal Amplifiers.*—The requirements placed upon a signal amplifier for a specific receiver use depend upon the relative importance of noise figure and amplifier gain. As the amplifier gain is increased, a point is reached where the noise from the input stage of the amplifier swamps the noise from any subsequent devices; beyond this point any additional amplifier gain is welcome but not required, since the noise figure of the r-f amplifier now determines the ultimate sensitivity of the entire receiver.

In addition to the noise and gain requirements imposed on a signal amplifier, the requirements for bandwidth, stability, and ease of tuning should be noted. The bandwidth must be great enough to accept the desired modulation with a reasonable allowance for inexact tuning, and the tuning must not be unduly sensitive to variations in temperature or voltages. The device must be sufficiently free from regeneration to avoid loss of bandwidth, or radiation of local-oscillator power fed back from the output circuit. Relatively low gains, by usual radio engineering standards, would be preferable to instability and the need for neutralization of feedback.

Among the klystrons and microwave triodes in the 3000 Mc/sec frequency range there are no commercially available amplifiers whose performance approaches these requirements. There seems, however, some promise of the eventual availability of such klystrons or triodes; hence the present performance and future possibilities will be discussed in some detail.

The behavior of microwave triodes as low-level amplifiers is discussed in detail in Chap. 6. The most nearly appropriate microwave triode for low-level use at 3000 Mc/sec is the 2C40 lighthouse tube. It is seen in Sec. 6·6 that typical noise figures for the 2C40 are 21 db at 3000 Mc/sec and 16 db at 2000 Mc/sec. This is to be compared with a typical figure of 10 db for a 3000 Mc/sec receiver with a good commercially obtainable crystal converter. It is immediately apparent that the 2C40 tube is not useful as an r-f amplifier. It is of some interest, nevertheless, to note the values of the gain-bandwidth product, for this amplifier. (Since gain and bandwidth are both commonly desirable features, and since for a given tube the gain-bandwidth product remains approximately constant when either of these quantities is changed, the gain-bandwidth product is often referred to as the "figure of merit" of the amplifier.) Measuring bandwidth, $\Delta f$, in Mc/sec, and meaning by the gain $G$ the power gain, $G \Delta f$ has a value of approximately 20; adjusting load for maximum gain gives, typically, $G = 5$ and $\Delta f = 4$ Mc/sec for operation with plate voltage 250 volts, plate current 30 ma. The gain would be approximately unity if no regenerative feedback were used.

The performance just quoted has been considerably improved upon with experimental triode and tetrode amplifiers at 3000 Mc/sec. (See Sec. 6·3.) The best performance obtained gave a noise figure of 9 db with a power gain of 20, bandwidth 6 Mc/sec, or a figure of merit of 120. This performance involves refinements in construction which have so far prevented consistent production on a laboratory scale or any production at all on a commercial scale.

Klystron amplifiers may be divided into two categories, the two-resonator or single-stage type, and the three-resonator or cascade type; in performance, the latter type is distinguished by its high gain. This distinction is discussed below in connection with power amplifiers, and in somewhat more detail in Chap. 10 (particularly in Sec. 10·8). Since the distinction involves mostly matters of gain and bandwidth, it is not basic to the present discussion. This comes about because klystrons normally have high-impedance input circuits, in comparison to microwave triodes; this in turn means that the important factor in klystron noise is the shot excitation of the input circuit and the subsequent amplification of this noise; any increase in gain merely increases signal and noise equally. Just as in triodes, excessive noise has always been the limiting factor which prevents the use of klystrons as r-f amplifiers; hence there is little value, at this point, in distinguishing between single-stage and cascade amplifiers.

Data are presented in Sec. 10·4 for a typical klystron amplifier in which, just as in the 2C40 triode, no attempt has been made to design for low-noise operation. In this tube the noise figure showed a minimum value of 25 db at a beam voltage of 275 volts and beam current 2 ma; at the same time the power gain was 6 and the bandwidth about 1.5

Mc/sec. This low gain is not characteristic of klystron amplifiers of the cascade type, and resulted simply from the minimizing of noise figure with respect to beam voltage in this particular tube; at the expense of 10 db in noise figure the gain was raised from 6 to 1000. As discussed in Sec. 10·4, it appears possible to design for r-f amplifier service a klystron in which noise is very greatly reduced below the above figure by a reduction in current, while at the same time maintaining high gain by a reduction in voltage. Such a tube would operate at less than 100 volts with several tens of microamperes beam current. As in the case of the triode, the prime difficulty to be overcome is the necessary refinement of constructional technique to allow the use of the small dimensions which correspond to low voltages; but the klystron under discussion would not rely upon uniformity of the cathode emission properties and, as is usual, the constructional refinements are probably not as great as for the corresponding triode.

The fact that in the klystron there is a relatively large input r-f gap, and the fact that the input cavity is not subjected to certain loading by the presence of the cathode in this gap, contribute to giving the klystron a normally higher gain and smaller bandwidth than the triode amplifier. The gain-bandwidth product (as usual, a constant with respect to loading changes) is, however, large under normal circumstances (1500 at one point in the above-quoted example); one would not expect this property to be changed too drastically in a low-noise amplifier.

*Power Amplifiers.*—Noise, which is the most important feature in a signal amplifier for receiver use, becomes quite unimportant in a power amplifier intended for transmitter application. Bandwidth, ease of modulation, frequency stability, output power, gain become more important; the exact relative importance of these factors depends on the application.

A number of lighthouse-like triodes are available as excellent power amplifiers at 1000 Mc/sec. The most nearly satisfactory tube at 3000 Mc/sec has been the 2C43. This has been used primarily as a pulsed oscillator; in c-w amplifier service it would probably be limited by plate dissipation to powers of the order of one watt, which would not be very useful. Methods of modulating such triodes have not been given much study, primarily because of lack of urgent application.

As already noted, klystron amplifiers exist in two forms. Historically, the earliest form of power-amplifier klystron was the two-cavity single-stage type typified by the 410R, the characteristics of which are discussed in some detail in Sec. 10·7. This particular tube is characterized (in c-w operation at 3000 Mc/sec) by 10 per cent efficiency, 18 watts output power, power gain of 10 at maximum output, and power gain of 25 at small-signal operation. The bandwidth corresponding to these operating characteristics, as estimated from the circuit $Q$'s, is about 2.5 Mc/sec.

Such values of gain are, however, insufficient for such applications of the klystron power amplifier as the generation of microwave power at quartz-crystal-controlled frequencies. In these applications, the frequency of a crystal oscillator is multiplied in successive stages, the last one of which is a frequency-multiplier klystron. Since the output power of high multiplication frequency-multiplier klystrons is low (commonly, a few tens of milliwatts), it is necessary to have a rather large power gain in the klystron power amplifier which follows the frequency multiplier. It was primarily for this purpose that the high-gain cascade power-amplifier klystron was developed. The cascade amplifier which is directly comparable with the type 410R is the type 2K35; at a beam voltage of 2000 volts and with tuning and loading for maximum gain this amplifier has a power gain of 600 at maximum output power, small-signal power gain 1500, and bandwidth (again, calculated from known $Q$'s) of 1.3 Mc/sec.

Other klystron amplifiers (primarily cascade amplifiers) have been developed at frequencies from 1000 to 5000 Mc/sec with output powers ranging from 75 to 750 watts. Since there was no great wartime demand for such devices, none of them has been manufactured in quantity. The general characteristics of these tubes are quite similar to those quoted for the two specific examples given above. These two examples were cited primarily to indicate orders of magnitude and to illustrate the basic difference between the two-resonator amplifier, which has a figure of merit comparable to the triode (25 in this case), and the cascade amplifier with a figure of merit of 800.

A price is paid, of course, for this increase in $G \Delta f$; primarily, the price is a decrease in bandwidth and an increase in tuning inconvenience in adding an additional high-$Q$ resonator. This same increase of tuning inconvenience occurs in going from the microwave triode, which has one low-$Q$ circuit, to the two resonator klystron. In either case, the presence of more than one high-$Q$ circuit makes a simultaneous tuning of these circuits difficult and makes tuning adjustments sensitive to changes in surroundings. This difficulty is greatly reduced if some gain is sacrificed by use of stagger-tuning or additional loading; and a sacrifice of gain is much more palatable in a cascade amplifier than in a single-stage amplifier. These considerations of tuning also suggest that klystron amplifiers are particularly adapted to fixed-frequency application.

A klystron power amplifier may easily be amplitude modulated by modulation of the beam current, with no accompanying phase modulation, although no klystron amplifiers have been constructed with high-mu control grids for this purpose. Phase modulation may be obtained by modulating the beam voltage and thus the time of transit of the bunches from the input circuit. If beam current modulation accompanies the voltage modulation, amplitude modulation is present in the output signal.

**2·3. Frequency Multipliers.**—The ultimate standard of frequency at conventional wavelengths has long been the quartz-crystal oscillator, by means of which frequencies are referred back to the mechanical vibration frequency of a quartz crystal. Much of the work that has been done on frequency multipliers at microwaves has been motivated by the need for microwave frequency standards, the output frequency of which is an integral multiple of a quartz-crystal frequency. Such an arrangement provides the best primary frequency standard at present; as a secondary standard, the frequency multiplier has strong competition in arrangements by which frequencies are controlled with reference to a standard cavity.

A second and more transient application of frequency multipliers has been their use as a source of signal-generator power in the initial stages of exploring a new band of microwave frequencies. In several instances when oscillators have not been immediately available at new frequency bands, it has proved practical to obtain useful amounts of power by frequency doubling or tripling from previously established bands.

Frequency multipliers with output frequencies up to 1000 Mc/sec have commonly utilized various combinations of triode doublers and triplers. Frequency multipliers at higher output frequencies have usually been either frequency-multiplier klystrons or arrangements utilizing the nonlinearities of detecting crystals; but in at least one instance the British have used a CV90 (planar triode), driven at 18 cm, to provide useful output power at 6 cm. As between klystrons and detecting crystals, the klystron is a more high-powered device which possesses the capability of electronic control and may be modulated advantageously. Multipliers using detecting crystals do not involve the development of a new vacuum tube, and hence are especially suited to use as emergency signal generators at new frequencies.

Since very little work has been done on the use of microwave triodes as frequency multipliers with output frequencies at 3000 Mc/sec or above, further discussion will be confined to the utilization of klystrons and crystals for this purpose.

*Frequency Multiplication by Klystrons.*—As is discussed in Sec. 9·2, the basic feature that makes the klystron an excellent frequency multiplier is the presence of a driving-current waveform which has sharp discontinuities and which is, therefore, very rich in harmonics; this is in marked contrast to the triode. The amplitude of the $m$th harmonic in the klystron driving current should drop off, theoretically, as $m^{-\frac{1}{3}}$; in one experimentally observed case, as noted in Sec. 11·2, it appears to decrease as $m^{-3/4}$ for $10 \leq m \leq 30$. The harmonic content is high enough so that practical applications have utilized frequency-multiplier klystrons working on the twentieth harmonic.

These applications have not, so far, involved quantity production. Most of the work done on multiplier klystrons has been aimed at the development of tubes which, in association with cascade-amplifier klystrons, would provide tens of watts of crystal-controlled power for c-w transmitters. The nature of the klystrons developed for this purpose is dependent on the gain of the amplifiers to which the output of the multiplier is fed, and is dependent on the tubes which are available for the preceding stages of multiplication. In the present state of high-frequency triode development, the optimum input frequency for a klystron multiplier is probably in the 750–1000 Mc/sec range; many of the earlier klystron multipliers have an input frequency in the vicinity of 300 Mc/sec. Such multipliers provide tens of milliwatts output power on the tenth to twentieth harmonics, at efficiencies of the order of one-half per cent. This output power provides sufficient drive for a high-gain cascade amplifier.

The input r-f power required to drive a multiplier klystron is, however, quite appreciable, and may be of the order of watts for the tubes in question. It has, therefore, been found economical in some cases to use a second cascade amplifier at the output frequency. This allows a large reduction in total d-c power consumption; it also allows loading and stagger-tuning for increased bandwidth and stability.

*Utilization of Reference Cavities as Frequency Standards.*—While this subject does not strictly come under the heading of "frequency multipliers," it is nevertheless relevant as an alternative means of accurate frequency control. Reference cavities derive their absolute calibration from multiplied quartz-crystal frequencies as the primary standard; but they appear, in many cases, to be rather more convenient than the latter for use as practical secondary standards. This fact depends in large measure on the circuits that have been developed for controlling the frequency of an electronically-tuned oscillator with reference to a resonant cavity; for further details on this subject the reader is referred to Chap. 2 of Vol. 11 of this series.

*Frequency Multiplication in Detector Crystals.*—The rectified current that flows in a detector crystal possesses harmonics of the input frequency. With proper circuit arrangements these harmonic current components may be made to deliver appreciable power to a transmission line. A typical arrangement for accomplishing this is shown in Fig. 2·1. The input line to the crystal is so dimensioned that it supports only the lowest coaxial mode at the frequency in question; it is then fitted with chokes which prevent any harmonic power from flowing into this line. The output line, on the other hand, is a waveguide which transmits the harmonic but does not transmit the fundamental frequency. The adjustable shorts are necessary to adjust the standing waves in the vicinity of the crystal. Such an arrangement, with optimum adjustment, has given 10 mw output power at 20,000 Mc/sec with an input power of 100 mw at 10,000 Mc/sec.

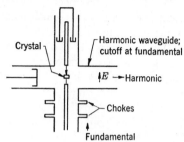

Fig. 2·1.—R-f circuit for frequency doubling in crystal detector.

In some instances—as for reference frequency standards—a much smaller amount of output power is satisfactory. For such applications, silicon crystals have been used to generate a few microwatts of power at 5000 Mc/sec when driven by about one watt of power at 100 Mc/sec.

**2·4. Oscillators.**—As has been already noted, the principal application of the tubes with which this book is primarily concerned has been as free-running oscillators. The various applications have placed rather varied requirements on oscillator performance; hence the discussion will be turned immediately to the tube types, without further generalization about oscillators as a class in themselves.

*Triode Oscillators.*—One of the primary advantages of these oscillators is that they provide a signal which is stable in frequency without the necessity for complicated regulation of the power supply. The vacuum tube is in itself basically simple in form; but this fact is offset by a number of complications which arise in connection with the external circuit. Typical of microwave triodes which are adaptable for use up to 3500 Mc/sec are the 2C40 and the 2C43 lighthouse tubes; numerical data for these two tubes will serve to indicate several characteristics of triode oscillators.

Of the two tubes mentioned, the 2C40 has the smaller dimensions and therefore lends itself to low voltage applications such as a receiver local oscillator or a bench signal generator. At 3000 Mc/sec and 250 volts the 2C40 provides about 100 milliwatts output power at 2 per cent efficiency. It may also be pulsed to 1500 volts with a peak output power up to 150 watts. The 2C43 is intended primarily for higher-voltage operation; at 3000 Mc/sec it operates with 20 to 25 per cent efficiency when pulsed with a plate voltage of 3000 volts. These tubes are most commonly used in an external "reentrant" circuit which is described in some detail in Chap. 7; this circuit provides a strong feedback from tank circuit to input r-f gap, as is made necessary by the fact that at 3000

Mc/sec these triodes have a gain not much greater than unity when they are operated as amplifiers with no feedback.

Little work has been done on the modulation of microwave triode oscillators, aside from pulse modulation. Since the phase of the electronic transadmittance is determined by the finite electron transit time in the grid-cathode and grid-plate regions, this phase varies with plate voltage and a corresponding small variation of frequency with plate voltage is present; but since the total transit time is small (only about $\pi$ radians at 250 volts plate voltage in the 2C40), a large voltage change is required for a small frequency change. This is, in fact, one of the great advantages of triode oscillators for many applications. Frequency modulation by means of reactance tubes seems to have possibilities, but this question has not been investigated in detail. Amplitude modulation of microwave triodes is even more an unknown field. It is to be expected that post-war applications will bring about a thorough exploration of these modulation questions.

*Two-cavity Klystron Oscillators.*—These are a simple generalization of the klystron amplifier, with feedback provided from output to input circuit. Since klystron amplifier gain is sizable, a much weaker feedback is required than in triode oscillators, and the two circuits do not lose their identity. Both circuits possess an inherently high $Q$; hence the adjustment of these two circuits to the same frequency, and their simultaneous tracking in any subsequent tuning, present practical difficulties in tunable operation.

Early in the development of pulse radar there was some development in Britain of two-resonator klystron oscillators as fixed-tuned pulsed transmitters. Efficiencies of 20 per cent and peak output powers of tens of kilowatts were obtained at 12 kv and 3000 Mc/sec; but further development was overshadowed by pulse magnetron development. Typical c-w operation at lower voltages is provided by the type 410R, a general-purpose tube which has external feedback and hence may be used also as an amplifier. This operates at 2000 volts and 3000 Mc/sec with 15 watts output power and 8 per cent efficiency, when loaded and tuned for maximum efficiency. (See Chap. 11.)

Klystron oscillators in general are characterized by the existence of discrete "modes of oscillation"; "mode" is used here not in the coupled circuit sense, but in the sense of denoting certain limited regions of electrode voltage within which oscillation occurs. (In a two-resonator oscillator this electrode voltage is the beam voltage.) Within a given mode the frequency of oscillation changes continuously from one end of the mode to the other as electrode voltage is changed; the total change in frequency thus available between the two half-maximum-power points of a mode is called the "electronic tuning range" for that mode.

This feature lends itself to frequency modulation; the only disadvantage is that the modulation must be applied to a low-impedance electrode. By variation of relative resonator tuning and feedback a given oscillator may be adjusted either for maximum efficiency and minimum electronic tuning range (maximum stability) or for a lower efficiency and a larger electronic tuning range. There are enough adjustable parameters available so that, in the latter case, the amplitude of oscillation may be made practically independent of frequency over most of the electronic tuning range. Thus for the above example of the 410R, with adjustment for maximum output power, the electronic tuning range between half-power points is 5 Mc/sec; adjustment of feedback and relative tuning of the resonators reduces the output power to $8\frac{1}{2}$ watts but allows electronic tuning over a range of 11 Mc/sec with only a 15 per cent decrease in output power below maximum.

*Reflex Klyston Oscillators.*—The reflex klystron oscillator utilizes only one resonant circuit; in this feature, as already noted in Chap. 1, lies one of its greatest advantages.

One consequence of this change to a single resonator is an efficiency which is inherently lower than in the two-resonator oscillator. Thus in the 723 family of reflex klystrons, the category manufactured in the largest quantity during the war, the output powers for the most commonly used mode at 300-volt operation range from 30 milliwatts at 9000 Mc/sec to 150 milliwatts at 3000 Mc/sec, corresponding to efficiencies of 0.5 and 2.3 per cent respectively. These powers are, however, quite adequate for receiver local-oscillator operation; and the input d-c power is small enough so that the low efficiency is of no importance.

An additional consequence of the change from two to one resonator, and one which is intimately related to the decrease in efficiency, is an increase in electronic tuning range. Furthermore, electronic tuning may now be accomplished by changing the voltage of the reflector, a high-impedance electrode which draws no current. To continue with numerical characteristics for the 723 family, electronic tuning ranges of approximately 45 and 30 Mc/sec are obtained at operating frequencies of 9000 and 3000 Mc/sec; these tuning ranges require reflector voltage changes of 20 and 33 volts respectively.

This electronic tuning behavior is the second great advantage of the reflex klystron. Its most useful contribution in the past has been to make possible automatic frequency control in radar receivers; by means of continuous automatic control of the local oscillator frequency, the receiver is constantly tuned to the transmitter. The electronic tuning properties of the reflex klystron also make it very adaptable to frequency-modulation communications work at microwaves. The reflex klystrons which were developed for quantity production during the war were intended to be used as local oscillators; progress on other types initiated at a later date has shown that performance with efficiencies of 6 or 8 per cent, output powers of 10 watts, and percentage electronic tuning ranges larger than those quoted above, is quite possible. This suggests strongly the future use of reflex klystrons as frequency-modulated communications transmitters.

*Secondary-emission Reflex Oscillators.*—The reflex klystron will often operate with the reflector at voltages positive as well as negative with respect to the cathode. Under these conditions the normal process of bunching is interrupted and some or most of the electrons collide with the reflector instead of being reflected; any secondary electrons resulting from this process will form a secondary beam which returns to the resonator. The primary beam, when it strikes the reflector, will be already amplitude-modulated by the usual velocity-modulation and bunching action; and if the reflector is a strong secondary emitter, a similarly amplitude-modulated and much intensified secondary beam will be returned through the resonator.

This principle has been utilized in developing an oscillator which operates at 3000 Mc/sec and 2000 volts, with output powers from 5 to 25 watts and efficiencies from 3 to 5 per cent.[1] The primary current is controlled by a high-mu control grid; modulation of this grid voltage produces output modulation which may be largely amplitude or largely frequency modulation, depending on the particular operating point.

In view of the fact that the properties of secondary emitters are not completely stable with respect to time, and since it appears that conventional reflex klystrons with similar output powers and efficiencies and cleaner modulation characteristics will shortly become available, it is not anticipated that these secondary-emission oscillators will receive extensive development. They will not be discussed further in this book.

*Oscillator-buffer Klystrons.*—As in low-frequency practice, it is often useful to have a free-running oscillator separated from the eventual load by an intermediate buffer stage; such an arrangement will, for example, prevent changes in the load from having any effect on the frequency of oscillation. Such isolation may be obtained with the two-resonator klystron oscillator by adding a third resonator through which the electron beam passes after leaving the two resonators which constitute the free-running oscillator. Any detuning of the third resonator, which is not coupled to the first two, will have no effect on oscillation frequency. On the other hand, if the length of the drift space between second and third resonators is small, the harmonic content of the beam is not greatly

---

[1] C. C. Wang, "Velocity Modulation Oscillators with Secondary Emission Current," Engineering Report 185, Westinghouse Electric and Mfg. Corp., Bloomfield, N.J., Oct. 10, 1944.

altered as the beam passes from second to third resonator; and with proper adjustment the maximum power obtainable by coupling a load to the third cavity is nearly as great as the maximum obtainable (with different adjustments!) from the second cavity. The prototype of the oscillator-buffer klystron is the type 2K34, which is derived from the type 410R in the manner described above.

Because of its basic connection with the two-resonator klystron oscillator, the oscillator-buffer klystron is not further discussed in this book.

*Floating-drift-tube Klystron Oscillators.*—By fusing into a single two-gap resonator the first and second resonators of a two-resonator klystron oscillator—as, for example, by removing the conducting walls that separate these two resonators—many of the circuit tuning problems which beset the two-resonator oscillator are dispensed with. The resulting oscillator should have the tuning convenience of the reflex klystron; at the same time, by choice of gap dimensions when the tube is designed, the ratio of input-gap to output-gap voltage may be adjusted to any desired value and the oscillator may thus be given the electrical characteristics of either the reflex or the two-resonator klystron. On the other hand, the drift-tube must still be provided with mechanical and thermal contact with the external tube envelope although there should be no r-f electrical connection. This latter point introduces difficulties, such as parasitic resonances in the various means used for supporting the drift tube.

The most commonly known example of a floating-drift-tube oscillator is the 2K40, formerly the 1280CT, which utilizes an external cavity and is thus tunable over a wide frequency range up to 10,000 Mc/sec.

While this category of oscillator seems to have many advantages, it has not received any extensive development; and since the operating principles are straightforward modifications of those used with reflex and two-resonator klystron oscillators, the floating-drift-tube oscillator will not be further discussed in this book.

*The Heil Tube.*—This designation is applied to a klystron which is closely related to the floating-drift-tube oscillator. A ribbon-like electron beam is maintained in this form by magnetic focussing and is passed through a coaxial line, the axis of which lies in the plane of the electron beam. The electrons of the beam thus enter the coaxial line in a direction perpendicular to the axis, passing from outer to inner conductor; they then pass through the interior of the center conductor, during which time they are shielded from any r-f fields which exist in the coaxial line; and finally they pass from inner to outer conductor. The coaxial line thus serves as input and output gap, and the interior of the center conductor serves as field-free drift space. In one direction from the electron beam the coaxial line is short-circuited at a point approximately a quarterwave away; in the other direction it leads, through appropriate transformer section of line, to the external load.

When operated in the manner described, with a single one-way transit of the coaxial line, performance is obtained which is comparable to that of a reflex klystron operating at the same frequency, voltages, and transit time. The oscillator may, however, be operated with the electron beam reflected for multiple transits of the coaxial line. This gives rise, in a typical case, to an increase in efficiency by a factor of four; but it also adds considerable noise component to the output signal.

The development of Heil tubes has been limited to Standard Telephones and Cables, Ltd., England; the initial tube type, from which many others have followed, is the Type S22A. Since these tubes have not been used at all in the United States, and since their principles of operation are basically similar to those of other klystrons, the Heil tubes will not be further discussed in this book.

*Monotrons.*—This is a general name given to devices based upon the principle that a d-c electron beam, passed once through a single resonant cavity, may excite oscillations in this cavity.[1]

Oscillation may occur when the number of cycles transit time through the resonator is between $n$ and $(n + \frac{1}{4})$ cycles, where $n$ is an integer. The monotrons that have been constructed have had low efficiency; and although they have certain interesting theoretical aspects, including the possibility of high efficiency, no work has been done on them in recent years. They are not discussed further in this book.

---

[1] F. B. Llewellyn and A. E. Bowen, "Ultra-high-frequency Oscillations by Means of Diodes," *Bell System Tech. Jour.*, **18**, 280 (1939). J. Marcum, "Interchange of Energy between an Electron Beam and an Oscillating Electric Field," *J. App. Phys.*, **17**, 4 (1946).

# CHAPTER 3

## BASIC ELECTRONIC PHENOMENA AT HIGH FREQUENCIES

### By J. K. Knipp

A simple electronic device is composed of several circuits coupled by an electron beam. At microwave frequencies the circuits are cavity resonators. One part of each resonator is a gap that forms the capacitance of the circuit; the remainder is a space that provides the inductance and usually contains a loop, a probe, or a window for the introduction or removal of r-f power.

Most microwave tubes have planar grid structure. In the usual triode or tetrode the gap of the input circuit is formed by a plane cathode and a parallel grid; the gap in the output circuit is formed by a plane grid and a parallel anode. In klystrons the gaps are constructed of parallel grids or of parallel plates containing one or more holes to allow for the transmission of the beam; a common grid is the radial fin grid illustrated in Fig. 4·1.

In addition to gaps formed by closely spaced grids, which are integral parts of the circuits, the electronic portion of the tube can have regions that are relatively free from r-f fields. Thus the tetrode has a grid-separation region between input and output circuits; this region is formed by the grid of the input terminal and the grid of the output terminal and can serve to shield the input circuit from the output circuit. In the klystron an electron gun accelerates the electrons before they enter the first gap. Between the two gaps of a two-cavity klystron there is a drift space in which bunching occurs. A reflex oscillator has a reflector region where electrons are reflected by a negative field and in which bunching takes place.

The gaps of all such planar tubes are lined up along the axis of the tube. The electron beam extends along the axis and passes through the various regions. The resonator fields produce a number of effects in the gaps. The gap voltage in the input terminal of a triode or tetrode generates an r-f beam current that can be used to excite the output circuit with a net gain of r-f power, the extra power being supplied by the d-c fields. An r-f field is introduced by feedback at the first gap of a two-cavity klystron oscillator, which modulates the high velocity of the electrons of the beam; in the drift region this velocity modulation generates density modulation, and the resulting r-f current excites the output

31

circuit.    The net effect is that some of the d-c energy of the beam is converted into r-f energy of the output circuit.    In a reflex oscillator the same effect is obtained with a single resonator by returning the electrons to the gap after the initial velocity modulation has had time to generate sufficient density modulation; feedback is unnecessary.

Since the gaps are regions in which the electric fields are strong, a tube is so designed that the beam must pass through the gaps rather than elsewhere in the resonators; thus large coupling between beam and resonator is obtained.    In addition, the use of narrow gaps shortens the time spent by the electrons in the r-f fields.    This short transit time is desirable since a time of transit of any gap greater than half a cycle considerably reduces the coupling between beam and resonator.

The basic phenomena occurring in circuits composed of cylindrical reentrant cavity resonators—the type used in klystrons and microwave triodes and tetrodes—are discussed in Chap. 4.    One important characteristic of such a circuit is that the response of the resonator (as measured, for instance, by the amplitude of the gap voltage) to the beam regarded as a driving current can be represented by the use of a circuit admittance, or impedance, which is determined by the nature of the cavity and its connections.    Moreover, the beam current that is effective in driving the resonator is the current actually present in the gap.    The circulating current in the cavity is the sum of the conduction and displacement currents in the gap.    This sum of the electron current and the time rate of change of the electric flux in the gap is the total current; it is directly proportional to the magnetic field at the edge of the gap and thereby determines the degree of excitation of the resonator fields.

The effect of the beam on the resonator has its counterpart in the action of the resonator on the beam.    The beam currents generated by gap voltages are described with the use of electronic admittances and impedances.    The gap fields are effective during the entire transit of the gap.    The total current is space-constant in a uniform gap.    The driving current bears a simple relation to the total current and the gap voltage.

In addition, there are a number of purely electronic effects that enter into the description of the beam.    The most striking of these are phenomena associated with finite times of passage and velocity modulation.

**3·1. Phenomena of Particular Importance at High Frequencies.—** In microwave tubes the important electronic effects arising from the high frequencies used are all related in one way or another to the fact that the time of passage of the beam electrons through any part of the tube is at least comparable to, and in many cases much larger than, the period of oscillation of the tube.

As examples, some possible three-centimeter tubes, with a frequency of

$10^{10}$ cycles/sec and a period of one ten-thousandth of a microsecond, might be considered. In the input terminal of an r-f amplifier a gap spacing of $2 \times 10^{-3}$ cm might be used. The average velocity of electrons reaching the grid would not be more than a few multiples of the mean thermal velocity of electrons from the cathode, which is $1.65 \times 10^7$ cm/sec at $1160°$ K. Hence the average time of transit is about the same as the period of the r-f oscillation. In the output terminal of the amplifier, the gap spacing might be $10^{-2}$ cm. The average velocity of the electrons while in the gap might correspond to an effective beam potential of 300 volts, which is a velocity of $10^9$ cm/sec. The time of transit of the output circuit would be one-tenth the period of oscillation. It is probable that a gap spacing which is somewhat larger would be desirable in order to reduce resonator losses. In klystrons effective gap spacings of $5 \times 10^{-2}$ cm are common, which at a beam potential of 300 volts have a time of transit of one-half cycle. The length of the drift tube between the gaps of a two-cavity klystron depends on the number of cycles of drift time needed to produce the desired bunching. At 300 volts the electrons drift $\frac{1}{10}$ cm per cycle. In the reflector region of the reflex oscillator the depth of penetration is about $\frac{1}{40}$ cm per cycle spent in the region; the extra factor of $\frac{1}{4}$ arises from the fact that the distance is covered twice and the average velocity is one-half the velocity at entry.

*Transit Angle.*—It is customary to express transit-time effects in terms of the transit angle,

$$\theta = 2\pi f T = \omega T,$$

where $f$ is the frequency of the oscillation, $T$ is the transit time under discussion, and $\omega = 2\pi f$ is the angular frequency. If the transit time is one cycle, the transit angle is $2\pi$ radians, or $360°$.

*Density Modulation and Beam-coupling Coefficient.*—A beam composed of electrons, all of which have the same velocity, contains only a d-c current if the charge density is uniform. If, however, the charge density, at any instant of time, varies periodically down the beam, and if the electric forces tending to change the electron velocities are negligible, the entire periodic configuration of the beam moves along unchanged with the electrons. The current passing through any plane perpendicular to the axis undergoes periodic changes; the frequency is given by the rate at which density maxima pass that plane. The phase difference between the currents at two parallel planes is the transit angle for the passage of the electrons from the first to the second plane. Such a beam is said to be "density-modulated."

Because of the finite gap transit time, the current of a density-modulated beam has a spread in phase in the gap equal to the transit angle of the gap. The driving current is the beam current that is effective in the interaction with the gap fields.    In a uniform gap it is the average current in the gap at any instant, provided the resonator is excited in the principal mode; the average is a space average.    Because of the phase difference of the contributions of the different elements of the current, partial cancellation takes place in the driving current.    For a simple density-modulated beam the driving current has the effective phase of the current at the center of the gap and an amplitude reduced from the amplitude of the density modulation by the beam-coupling coefficient

$$M = \frac{\sin \frac{\theta}{2}}{\frac{\theta}{2}}.$$

The beam-coupling coefficient is unity for zero transit angle, decreases to zero at $\theta = 2\pi$, becomes negative, and oscillates about zero with decreasing amplitude for increasing $\theta$; see Fig. 3·3.    The fact that the driving current is zero at $\theta = 2\pi$ is understandable because, for this value of the transit angle, half the beam current in the gap is exactly out of phase with the other half.    As the number of cycles of transit time is increased, there is a general trend such that less and less of the current is left uncanceled, causing the beam coupling to fall off inversely with the transit angle.    In addition, the cancellation is periodically complete, and the driving current is periodically zero.

*Velocity Modulation.*—Consideration is now given to the action of an oscillating gap field on a beam whose charge density is uniform and whose electrons initially (that is, on injection into the gap) have the same velocity.    If the gap transit angle is negligibly small, the electrons make the transit in the instantaneous field, which is essentially static. They gain or lose energy in an amount equal to the electron charge times the instantaneous voltage across the gap.    The beam emerges from the gap uniform in density but velocity-modulated; that is to say, the velocity of the electrons leaving the gap varies periodically with the frequency of the gap voltage above and below the velocity of the electrons on entering the gap.

If, on the other hand, the transit angle is not negligible—that is, if the transit time of the electrons is comparable to the period of oscillation of the gap field—the electrons of the beam no longer move in a field that is approximately static.    Instead they move in a field that changes during the time of transit of the gap.    The energy change on emerging from the gap is no longer given by an instantaneous potential difference. However, if extreme values of the energy change are small compared with the total energy of the electron, a voltage that is effective in the energy change, and hence in the velocity modulation, has the phase of the field when the electron is at the center of the gap and an amplitude equal to the gap-voltage amplitude reduced by $M = \dfrac{\sin (\theta/2)}{\theta/2}$, that is, by the beam-coupling coefficient.   Since this factor enters in the modulation of the beam, it is sometimes referred to as the "modulation coefficient."   That the same factor enters in the beam coupling as in the velocity modulation is not surprising, since in each case an average of a periodic quantity is effective.

During the passage of an electron through the gap the phase of the gap voltage changes by an amount equal to the transit angle.   If the energy change is small, the average of the gap voltage during the time of transit is effective.   If the transit angle is $2\pi$, the electron spends one complete cycle in the gap and is decelerated by the gap field for the same length of time that is it accelerated; hence the effective gap voltage is zero.   As the number of cycles spent in the gap is increased, there is a general trend to leave a shorter and shorter time for the net acceleration or deceleration; in terms of voltages a smaller fraction of the total gap-voltage amplitude is effective, and the modulation falls off inversely with the transit angle.   In addition it is periodically zero since the times of acceleration and deceleration are periodically equal.

*Generation of Density Modulation by Drift Action.*—Two high-frequency effects arising from the finite transit angles occurring in microwave tubes have been described thus far: the reduction in coupling between beam and resonator caused by partial cancellation in phase of the gap current, and the reduction in modulation of the beam by the gap voltage because of the change in the acceleration of the electrons during their transit.

A third effect, that is fundamental to all klystron operation, is the generation of density modulation within a beam that is velocity-modulated.   The density modulation is produced through drift action.   Such a process, which is called "bunching," is based on the fact that a beam of electrons that are periodically slower and faster than the average will, during the passage of time, tend to undergo density changes.   Bunches are formed about alternate groups of electrons having the average velocity.   Those groups form the centers of the bunches for which the electrons in advance are moving more slowly than average and the electrons to the rear are moving more rapidly than average.   The resulting density modulation has the periodicity of the velocity modulation; hence the density modulation gives an r-f current of frequency equal to the frequency of the voltage that produced the velocity modulation, as well as the harmonics of this frequency.   It is significant that, except for complicating effects that are due to space charge, density modulation tends to persist down the stream and does not, in itself, produce velocity modulation; it is significant also that velocity modulation tends to persist down the stream, though not unchanged, and generates density modulation.

*Influence of Electrons on Electrodes.*—A fourth effect—one that is also closely associated with the finite time of transit of electrons—is the effect that the electrons exert on the opposite grid or anode as soon as they enter the gap, and which continues as long as the electrons remain in the gap. It is entirely misleading to think of a grid current as being formed by the electrons collected by that grid, because a charge within a gap induces a charge on the grid in an amount that increases as it draws nearer to the grid. As it moves about in the gap the amount of induced charge changes; the rate of change is the current flowing to or from the grid. If the electron hits the grid, the current stops; if it passes through the grid, a charge is induced on the opposite side of the grid, the rate of change of which depends on the motion in the region where it now finds itself; the current to the grid reverses on passing through the grid. Also, if instead of reaching the grid the electron is reflected, the current to the grid is reversed.

*Displacement Current.*—The rate of change of electric flux through any plane in the gap is called the "displacement current" in the gap. If the gap is empty, the flux arises from the charges collected on the electrodes, and its rate of change is the current flowing to and from those electrodes. However, if there are electrons in the gap, some of the flux has its source in the additional charge induced on the electrodes, and lines flow from that charge to the charge in the gap. As the electrons move about in the gap, the total flux through any plane changes, as indeed does the division between the electrodes of the charge induced by the electrons. Hence the flux through any plane changes; this change is an additional contribution to the displacement current.

*Total Current.*—The sum of the conduction current and displacement current through any plane in the gap is the total current through that plane. It has the remarkable property that in a narrow gap it is very nearly space-constant across the gap and is equal to the current that flows along the walls of the resonator to the electrodes. It is sometimes called the circulating current or the current in the outside circuit. Any deviation from constancy in the gap is due to fringing of the electric field at the edges of the gap, and corresponds to current flowing not to the gap but to areas on the walls of the cavity outside the gap.

The total current has additional significance for a circuit formed of a cavity resonator in that, if the gap is narrow, the total current through the gap is equal in magnitude to the magnetic field at the edge of the gap. This follows from the field equations giving relations between the fields and the currents and charges in the resonator. From this relation between total current and magnetic field, the cavity excitation is established, as is shown in Chap. 4.

The total current density at any point of a vacuum is

$$\mathbf{J} + \epsilon_0 \frac{\partial \mathbf{E}}{\partial t},$$

where $\mathbf{J}$ is the conduction-current density in amp/meter², $\epsilon_0$ is $(1/36\pi) \times 10^{-9}$ farad/meter, and $\mathbf{E}$ is the electric field in volts/meter. It is of interest to compare the two current densities in a particular case. Suppose that an r-f current of $2 \times 10^{-3}$ amp flows in a uniform beam with a cross-sectional area of $5 \times 10^{-2}$ cm². The r-f conduction current density is 400 amp/meter². Suppose also that the r-f gap voltage is 36 volts and that the gap depth is $10^{-2}$ cm. The average field is $36 \times 10^4$ volts/meter. Let the frequency be $10^{10}$ cps. Then the displacement-current density is $2 \times 10^5$ amp/meter². It is very large compared with the electron current density because of the numbers chosen, and in particular because of the high frequency.

Even if the total current in the gap is space-constant, the conduction and displacement currents separately need not be, for they can vary across the gap in such a manner that their sum is space-constant.

**3·2. Current Induced by a Moving Charge.**—The presence of charge in a region between parallel conducting planes causes charge to be

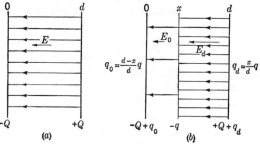

Fig. 3·1.—Lines of electric flux in uniform gap containing (*a*) no charge and (*b*) in same gap containing uniform sheet of charge of total amount $-q$.

induced on those planes in total amount equal to the negative of the charge between the planes. Unless the charge is symmetrically distributed on both sides of the midplane, the induced charge is not equally divided between the two planes. If the planes are connected through an outside circuit, the charge between the planes in moving about in the gap causes the induced charge to redistribute itself, and current flows through the circuit.

*Charge on Electrodes.*—If, for example, the potential between the planes is fixed and the gap is so narrow that fringing is negligible, and if $-Q$

and $Q$ are the total charge on the plane electrodes in the absence of charge in the region (see Fig. 3·1), the total flux is $A\epsilon_0 E = -Q$, where $A$ is the area of the gap and $E$ is the electric field.   If a uniform sheet of total charge $-q$ is introduced at the plane $x$ and the gap voltage is the same as before introduction, additional charges $q_0$ and $q_d$ are induced on the two planes with $q = q_0 + q_d$.   If $E_0$ is the field to the left of the sheet, the total flux to the left is $A\epsilon_0 E_0 = -Q + q_0$; similarly, if $E_d$ is the electric field to the right, $A\epsilon_0 E_d = -Q - q_d$.   The gap potential is $-E_0 x - E_d(d - x) = -Ed$, where $d$ is the separation distance of the electrodes.   From these relations it follows that

$$q_0 = \frac{d-x}{d}\, q, \qquad q_d = \frac{x}{d}\, q. \tag{1}$$

Thus, the charge induced is greater on the near plane and that on either plane is proportional to the distance to the other plane.

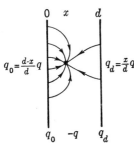

$$q_0 = \frac{d-x}{d}\,q \qquad\qquad q_d = \frac{x}{d}\,q$$

$$q_0 \qquad -q \qquad q_d$$

Fig. 3·2.—Lines of electric flux to point charge $-q$.

If instead the charge in the gap is concentrated in the neighborhood of a point a distance $x$ from the first electrode, the lines of flux are not parallel, as in the above case, but converge upon the point as illustrated in Fig. 3·2 (in this figure the gap voltage is assumed to be zero).   However, the distribution of induced charge between the two electrodes is unchanged, although the charge on either electrode is no longer uniformly distributed.   In this case also the additional charges on the electrodes are given by Eqs. (1), as can be shown by the method of images.

*Current Induced in the Circuit.*—As the charge in the gap moves, induced charge flows from one to the other of the electrodes through the circuit.   The current in the circuit is

$$I = \frac{d}{dt}\left[-Q + q_0\right] = -\frac{d}{dt}\left[Q + q_d\right] = -\dot{Q} - \frac{v}{d}\, q, \tag{2}$$

where $v = dx/dt$ is the velocity of motion of the charge in the gap and $\dot{Q}$ is a current which is determined by the outside circuit and the initial conditions (the gap voltage is merely $Qd/A\epsilon_0$).

*Conduction and Displacement Currents in the Gap.*—Consider first the displacement current in a plane to the left of the plane $x$, which is the plane containing either the sheet of charge or the point charge $-q$.   The displacement current is $\displaystyle\int dS\epsilon_0\,\frac{\partial E_x}{\partial t}$, where the integration is over the plane to the left of $x$ and $E_x$ is the component of the electric field perpendicular to that plane. Now $\int dS \epsilon_0 E_x$ is the electric flux through that plane; since the lines of flux either end up on the first electrode or return through the plane in passing to the second electrode, the total flux is just the charge on the first electrode. Hence the displacement current in a plane to the left of $x$ is $-\dot{Q} - \dfrac{v}{d} q$, by Eqs. (1). Similarly, it can be shown that the displacement current to the right of $x$ is also $-\dot{Q} - \dfrac{v}{d} q$. Thus it is seen that, in any plane to the left or right of the charge, the displacement current is just the current in the circuit.

The fixed plane through which the charge $-q$ is moving at the moment is considered next. Suppose the charge moves a distance $\Delta x$ in time $\Delta t$ and is at the plane $x - \Delta x/2$ at time $t - \Delta t/2$. The average conduction current, regarded as spread over a time $\Delta t$, is $-q/\Delta t$. The change in flux through the plane $x$ is

$$-\Delta Q + \frac{d - x - \dfrac{\Delta x}{2}}{d} q + \frac{x - \dfrac{\Delta x}{2}}{d} q = -\Delta Q + \left(1 - \frac{\Delta x}{d}\right) q.$$

Hence the average displacement current—that is, the rate of change of flux regarded as spread over a time $\Delta t$—is

$$-\frac{\Delta Q}{\Delta t} + \frac{q}{\Delta t} - \frac{v}{d} q.$$

The sum of the average conduction current and average displacement current is $-\dot{Q} - \dfrac{v}{d} q$, since the conduction current is just canceled by an opposite term in the displacement current, a term arising from the interception by the plane of all the lines of flux to the charge as it passes through the plane.

*Total Current.*—This simple example illustrates the proposition that the total current, whether it is the current in the circuit or the sum of the conduction and displacement currents in the gap, is space-constant across the gap and has the same value all the way around the circuit, with the gap as the closing element in the circuit.

**3·3. Modulation of the Beam.**—The beam as it enters a gap has properties that are dependent on the time, for it may have been modulated in passage through other resonators and, in any case, it contains fluctuations that are due to noise. Likewise, as it leaves a gap, its properties are dependent on the time. A description of the properties of the beam at any place in the gap is given by the distribution in the velocity of the passing electrons. This distribution depends on the time. A discussion of the beam explicitly in terms of the velocity distribution is given in Chap. 5.

The most important time-varying properties of a beam are its density modulation and its velocity modulation. Density modulation is the harmonic portion of the electron current; density modulation is current modulation. Velocity modulation is the harmonic portion of the average electron velocity.

These two properties can change from place to place in the beam. As has been indicated in Sec. 3·1, a density-modulated beam contains bunches. If the velocities of the electrons are the same, these bunches move along with the electron velocity, undisturbed except by outside fields and spreading forces resulting from space charge. A velocity-modulated beam becomes bunched even though originally smooth because, in such a beam, the velocities vary periodically above and below the average velocity and, therefore, the electrons tend to gather into bunches as they move down the stream. Hence a velocity-modulated beam becomes density-modulated by drift action alone. If the velocity spread is negligible and if the velocity modulation is but a small fraction of the average velocity, the velocity modulation tends to persist down the stream, disturbed only by outside fields and forces that are due to space charge. It is, however, accompanied by a changing density modulation. Thus, both density and velocity modulations tend to persist down the stream, and velocity modulation generates density modulation.

In passing across a gap the time-varying properties of the beam change because of its initial velocity modulation and also because of the electric field of the gap. In its effect on the momentum of the electrons, the r-f gap field produces velocity modulation and, in modulating the time of passage of the electrons, it bunches the electrons and in this manner produces density modulation.

In a gap the sources of modulation are two-fold: (1) that present in the beam on entering the gap, and (2) that produced by the gap field. The density modulation results from (1) density modulation at injection, (2) velocity modulation at injection generating density modulation through drift action, and (3) modulation of the time of passage by the gap field producing density modulation. The velocity modulation results from (1) velocity modulation at injection, and (2) the periodic acceleration and deceleration of the electrons by the gap field.

The coupling between the beam and the resonator takes place through the modulations of the beam, for the density—that is, current—modulation excites the resonator fields, and the resonator fields produce both the velocity and the density modulations. The modulation of the beam as it leaves the gap determines, at least in part, the modulation that it

has as it enters the next region, just as its modulation in the gap is determined in part by that which existed in the beam at injection.

   *Importance of Transit Angle.*—The transit angle, $\theta = 2\pi fT = \omega T$,
is a small fraction of a radian if the transit time $T$ is much smaller than
the period of oscillation $1/f$. At microwave frequencies it is difficult to
build tubes with small transit angles. Closely spaced grids and high
beam potentials help to keep the transit angles small, but they are not
always obtainable and other considerations sometimes make them undesirable. Large transit angles are therefore not uncommon in microwave
tubes—for example a 3-cm reflex tube with a grid spacing of 1/20 cm
and beam potential of 300 volts has a gap transit angle of $\pi$ radians.

   The importance of the transit angle is as follows. If it is very small,
each electron moves through the gap in an essentially static field and its
motion is easily described and is practically identical with the motion of
all other electrons in the gap at the moment (unless there is more than
one velocity group). On the other hand, if the transit angle is large,
the field varies with time during the passage through the gap and the
electron motion is greatly complicated; in particular the electron energy
is no longer obtainable immediately from the gap potential, and the
motion of some of the electrons can be completely out of phase with the
motion of other electrons in the gap at the moment.

   *Beam Coupling.*—The beam excites the resonator through the harmonic components of the beam current that have frequencies near the
resonant frequencies of the cavity resonator. All of the beam that is
actually in the gap participates in this excitation, and equal elements
are equally effective if the r-f field in the absence of the beam is space-
constant, which is approximately the case in most resonators operating
in the principal mode (see Chap. 4).

   A particular component of the beam current, having a given frequency of modulation, is simply constituted if it arises only from density
modulation at injection and if the velocities are the same and space-
charge spreading is negligible. At a plane a fixed distance down the
stream from the plane of entry of the gap, the component differs only
in phase from its value at the plane of entry for, since the current at the
plane arises from electrons that earlier composed the injected current,
by particle conservation their contribution to the flow of charge in corresponding intervals of time is the same. The phase difference is the
transit angle for the passage of the electrons from the plane of entry
to the indicated plane down the stream.

   If the frequency is sufficiently low—that is, if the period of the modulation is long compared with the transit time of the gap—the transit
angle is nearly zero, and the current elements within the gap arising
from the injected current modulation are practically in phase. How-

ever, if the period is comparable to the transit time, the transit angle is not small and the current elements are not in phase. As has been pointed out in Sec. 3·1, a partial cancellation results and the coupling between beam and resonator is reduced.

Suppose $i_\omega(0)e^{j\omega t}$ is the current modulation at the plane of injection and $\theta'$ is the transit angle to a plane part way across the gap; then $i_\omega(0)e^{j(\omega t-\theta')}$ is the current modulation at that plane arising from the injected current modulation under the conditions stated above. If the electrons are not accelerated, the driving current is the average over the phase

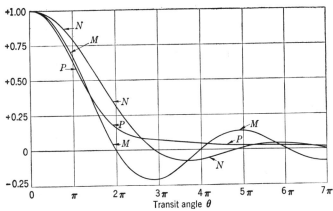

Fig. 3·3.—Beam-coupling coefficient $M$, beam-loading coefficient $N$, and the function $P$ plotted as functions of transit angle $\theta$. $M = \dfrac{\sin \theta/2}{\theta/2}$; $N = \dfrac{24}{\theta^3}\left(\sin\dfrac{\theta}{2} - \dfrac{\theta}{2}\cos\dfrac{\theta}{2}\right)$; $P = \dfrac{6}{\theta^3}(\theta - \sin\theta)$.

because in uniform motion space average and phase average are the same. Hence the driving current is

$$\frac{1}{\theta}\int_0^\theta d\theta'\, i_\omega(0)e^{j(\omega t-\theta')} = i_\omega(0)\frac{\sin \theta/2}{\theta/2}\,e^{j\left(\omega t-\frac{\theta}{2}\right)} = i_\omega(0)Me^{j\left(\omega t-\frac{\theta}{2}\right)}.$$

This is the current that is effective in the excitation of the resonator. The factor $\dfrac{\sin (\theta/2)}{\theta/2} = M$ is the beam-coupling coefficient already mentioned in the first section of this chapter, and is shown plotted as a function of $\theta$ in Fig. 3·3. It has the value unity for zero transit angle and oscillates about zero with decreasing amplitude as $\theta$ increases, the zeros occurring at $2\pi$, $4\pi$, etc. It is seen that the driving current for such a density-modulated beam has the effective phase of the current at the center of the gap and an amplitude reduced from the amplitude of the density modulation by the beam-coupling coefficient.

*Current Modulation Arising from Velocity Modulation.*—The density modulation generated by the velocity modulation that is present in the beam at the time of injection also depends on the phase, and the effective current is a function of the transit angle of the gap.

Let $v_\omega(0)e^{j\omega t}$ be the velocity modulation at the plane of injection and let $\theta'$ be the transit angle to a plane part way across the gap. In Sec. 3·5 it is shown that the component of the current at that plane arising through drift action from the initial velocity modulation, if the velocity modulation is small and the drift angle $\theta'$ not large, is

$$v_\omega(0)\left(\frac{-I_0}{v}\right)j\theta' e^{j(\omega t-\theta')},$$

where $-I_0$ is the direct current and $v$ is the average velocity of the electrons. This expression merely states that the current generated is the product of the velocity modulation at the time of injection, the charge density per unit length of the beam, and the transit angle, and, in addition, that it leads the velocity modulation by 90°.

If the electrons are not being accelerated, the space average of the current is given by the average in phase. Hence the driving current from this source is

$$\frac{1}{\theta}\int_0^\theta d\theta'\left[v_\omega(0)\left(\frac{-I_0}{v}\right)j\theta' e^{j(\omega t-\theta')}\right].$$

When evaluated, this average becomes

$$v_\omega(0)\left(\frac{-I_0}{v}\right)\frac{j\theta}{2}\left(M-\frac{j\theta N}{6}\right)e^{j\left(\omega t-\frac{\theta}{2}\right)},$$

where $N$, the beam-loading coefficient, is a function of the transit angle $\theta$. The effective current here calculated is zero for zero transit angle, a fact that is understandable since little density modulation can develop in times that are short compared with the period of modulation.

The beam-loading coefficient is an important factor in expressions for beam loading. It is defined by

$$N=\frac{24}{\theta^3}\left(\sin\frac{\theta}{2}-\frac{\theta}{2}\cos\frac{\theta}{2}\right)$$

and is plotted in Fig. 3·3, together with $M$ and a function $P$, which occurs in first-order bunching theory (see Chaps. 9 and 12). The beam-loading coefficient is unity for zero transit angle and does not become zero until $\theta$ is almost $3\pi$, after which it oscillates about zero with a period of about $4\pi$ and with a rapidly decreasing amplitude.

From the above expression for the driving current caused by velocity modulation at injection, it is seen that, for very small transit angles, the effective current is the same as the actual current from this source at the center of the gap. However, for large transit angles, this value is modified by the factor $(M - j\theta N/6)$, which affects both the magnitude and the phase of the driving current.

*Current Modulation Arising from Gap Voltage.*—In Sec. 3·5 it is shown that the density modulation arising from the action of the gap voltage is produced through the modulation of the time of passage of the electrons. Suppose that the d-c field is zero, the r-f field is space-constant, the velocity spread is negligible, and the velocity change produced by the field is small. Let $V_\omega e^{j\omega t}$ be the potential across the gap, and let $M'$ and $N'$ be the beam-coupling coefficient and beam-loading coefficient for the transit angle $\theta'$ to a plane part way across the gap. It is found that the component of the current at that plane arising from the gap voltage is

$$- \frac{V_\omega}{2V_0} \frac{I_0}{j\theta} \frac{(j\theta')^2}{2} \left( M' - \frac{j\theta'N'}{6} \right) e^{j\left(\omega t - \frac{\theta'}{2}\right)},$$

where $V_0 = mv^2/2e$ is the beam potential ($-e$ is the electron charge, $-1.6 \times 10^{-19}$ coulomb; $m$ is its mass, $0.9 \times 10^{-30}$ kgm.) From this expression it is seen that the current generated for very small $\theta'$ is proportional to the square of the time of passage and follows the potential by $\pi/2 + \theta'/2$. As $\theta'$ increases, the magnitude and phase of the current are affected, in addition, by the factor $(M' - j\theta'N'/6)$.

The driving current is again given by the average in phase

$$- \frac{1}{\theta} \int_0^\theta d\theta' \frac{V_\omega}{2V_0} \frac{I_0}{j\theta} \frac{(j\theta')^2}{2} \left( M' - \frac{j\theta'N'}{6} \right) e^{j\left(\omega t - \frac{\theta'}{2}\right)}.$$

On carrying out the integration this expression becomes

$$- V_\omega \frac{G_0}{2} \frac{j\theta N}{6} e^{j\left(\omega t - \frac{\theta}{2}\right)},$$

where $G_0 = I_0/V_0$ is the beam conductance. Thus the driving current in the gap arising from the action of the gap voltage is proportional to the beam conductance and, for small gap transit angles, is proportional to the transit angle, lagging behind the potential by $\pi/2 + \theta/2$; as the transit angle increases the magnitude is affected by the additional factor $N$.

*Beam Loading.*—Since the current of the last paragraph is produced by the gap voltage, it has a definite phase relation to that voltage and gives rise to a subtraction or addition of energy from that stored in the resonator. The power in is one-half the real part of the product of the driving current and $V_\omega^* e^{-j\omega t}$; it is

$$\frac{|V_\omega|^2}{2} \left( - \frac{G_0}{2} \frac{\theta N}{6} \sin \frac{\theta}{2} \right).$$

The combination $\dfrac{\theta N}{6} \sin \dfrac{\theta}{2}$ is shown plotted in Fig. 3·4. It reaches a maximum of about 0.4 at a transit angle somewhat greater than $\pi$, drops to zero at $2\pi$, and oscillates about zero with decreasing amplitude with a period of $2\pi$. The negative intervals correspond to the addition of energy to the resonator fields.

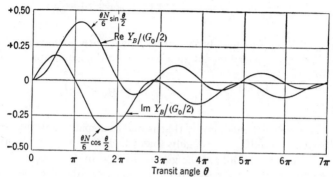

Fig. 3·4.—Real and imaginary parts of beam-loading admittance divided by $G_0/2$ as functions of the transit angle.

The coefficient of $-V_\omega e^{j\omega t}$ in the driving current,

$$\frac{G_0}{2} \frac{j\theta N}{6} e^{-j\theta/2} = Y_B,$$

is called the "beam-loading admittance." The real part of $Y_B$ is the beam-loading conductance, $\dfrac{G_0}{2} \dfrac{\theta N}{6} \sin \dfrac{\theta}{2}$, and the imaginary part,

$$\frac{G_0}{2} \frac{\theta N}{6} \cos \frac{\theta}{2},$$

is the beam-loading susceptance. The latter has the effect of changing the resonant frequency of the cavity resonator. The combination $\dfrac{\theta N}{6} \cos \dfrac{\theta}{2}$ is also plotted in Fig. 3·4; it has a small maximum near $\pi/2$, is zero at $\pi$, has an extreme negative value of about $-0.35$ before reaching $2\pi$, returns to zero and is very slightly positive before $3\pi$, where it is zero again, after which it becomes negative and has very small intervals where it is positive just before $5\pi$, $7\pi$, etc.

One-half the product of $|V_\omega|^2$ and the beam-loading conductance is the average power absorbed by a smooth beam in passing through the gap. This quantity when positive has the effect of a load on the resonator and when negative can serve to drive the resonator, as in a monotron.

*Velocity Modulation Arising from Gap Voltage.*—The velocity modulation produced by a space-constant r-f field is easily calculated under the conditions of the preceding paragraphs. If $d$ is the gap spacing, the force on an electron is $(eV_\omega/d)e^{j\omega t}$. Suppose the electron enters the gap at time $t'$ and leaves at time $t$; its change in momentum is

$$\int_{t'}^{t} dt'' \frac{eV_\omega}{d} e^{j\omega t''} = \frac{eV_\omega}{j\omega d} [1 - e^{-j\omega(t-t')}]e^{j\omega t};$$

but $\omega(t - t')$ is approximately the transit angle since the modulations are small; hence the velocity modulation on leaving the gap is approximately

$$\frac{eV_\omega}{mv} \frac{\sin \theta/2}{\theta/2} e^{j\left(\omega t - \frac{\theta}{2}\right)} = v \frac{V_\omega}{2V_0} M e^{j\left(\omega t - \frac{\theta}{2}\right)}.$$

Thus, in the velocity modulation that is due to a space-constant r-f field, the effective gap voltage is roughly that which the electron experiences when it reaches the middle of the gap multiplied by the factor $M$.

This effect is also easily seen from the energy of the electron. If the time of passage is negligible compared with the period of oscillation of the field, the energy change results from the field at the moment of passage and is given by the product of the electron charge and the gap potential at that moment. However, if the time of passage is comparable to the period of oscillation, the energy change must be calculated from a field acting on the electron which varies in time during the transit. If the r-f field is weak, the work done by the field is approximately

$$\int_{0}^{d} dx \frac{eV_\omega}{d} e^{j\left(\omega t - \frac{d-x}{d}\theta\right)} = eV_\omega \frac{\sin \theta/2}{\theta/2} e^{j\left(\omega t - \frac{\theta}{2}\right)} = eV_\omega M e^{j\left(\omega t - \frac{\theta}{2}\right)}.$$

This work represents the energy change of the electron; hence this change can be calculated approximately from the gap voltage by using the gap voltage at the time of midpassage and reducing it by the factor $M$.

*Effects of D-c Gap Field.*—The presence of a d-c field in the gap has the effect of making the electron motion nonuniform even in the absence of the r-f field. Transit angles are usually defined under d-c conditions by using time intervals calculated in the absence of all modulation; these of course are affected by the d-c field present. Moreover, the beam potential, $V_x = mv^2(x)/2e$, and beam conductance, $G_x = I_0/V_x$, change across the gap. However, as long as the d-c field does not cause negative velocities or lead to high concentrations of space charge, the form of the r-f relations for the behavior of the gap is not greatly modified beyond introducing factors and adding certain acceleration terms. As is seen later in the chapter, these changes are often conveniently expressed in terms of the two parameters,

$$r' = \frac{v(x)T'}{x}, \qquad \delta' = \frac{a(x)T'^2}{2x},$$

where $v(x)$ and $T'$ are the d-c values of the velocity of an electron at the plane $x$ and the time of passage to that plane from $x = 0$ and $a(x)$ is the d-c value of its acceleration at the plane $x$. If the d-c field is everywhere zero in the gap, $r'$ is unity and $\delta'$ is zero.

If the d-c field causes the reflection of electrons, and if the current densities are so low that the effects of space charge are still negligible, the behavior of the gap is somewhat complicated by the two-way motion of the electrons, but it can be treated in a straight forward manner since the field is approximately space-constant.

When the d-c fields are associated with high concentrations of space charge, as in the potential minimum outside a space-charge-limited cathode, the r-f problem becomes very complicated because the space charge affects the motion of the electrons, which in turn affects the space charge. Certain aspects of this phenomenon are treated in Chap. 5.

**3·4. General Relations in a Narrow Gap.**—The electronic phenomena under discussion are governed by three fundamental laws. The first of these is the law of conservation of charge. Since the charge is carried by electrons, all having the specific charge $-e$, and the number of electrons is also conserved, conservation of charge is the same as particle conservation. From the conservation of charge is derived the continuity relation, which states that the divergence of the current density is equal to the negative of the time rate of change of the charge density. The second relation is the divergence relation for the electric flux, which states that the divergence of the electric flux is equal to the charge density; since the electric flux is proportional to the electric field, the divergence of the electric field is proportional to the charge density. The third law is Newton's law governing the motion of the electrons. The only force acting on the electrons which is considered is that due to the electric field; by Newton's law the time rate of change of the momentum of an electron is equal to the product of the electron charge and the electric field.

*Assumption of Uniformity.*—The tubes that are discussed in this book have simple geometry. The electron beam passes down the axis of a tube through a succession of regions separated by plane grids. Some of these are regions of acceleration, drift, and reflection, which are relatively free from r-f fields. Others are gaps forming the capacitive portions of the resonator circuits. These gaps have depths that are usually small compared with the diameters of the gap areas. Moreover, the excitation of the resonators is generally such that the electric fields in the gaps are directed parallel to the axis of the tube and are nearly uniform over the gap areas. If, in addition, the beams are nearly uniform and fill the gaps, phenomena in the gaps are approximately one-dimensional.

The idealization of gap phenomena to uniform fields and a uniform beam composed of electrons moving parallel to the axis of the tube is a tremendous simplification to the analysis and discussion of tube behavior. It has considerable validity in all tubes discussed in this book. This simplification makes possible much of the theoretical treatment of these tubes.

There are, of course, many limitations to a treatment of gap phenomena based on the assumption of uniformity. Since all gaps have finite areas and all beams have limited cross sections, there are edge effects. Uneven cathodes, fluctuations in emission, nonparallel grids, grid structure, and uneven reflector fields make the beams nonuniform. In addition, the conduction current is carried by the electrons, which are finite charges with local fields and hence contribute to the unevenness in the gap currents and fields. Electrons have transverse velocities, and the electron velocities must be well below the velocity of light if magnetic forces are to be neglected. Some of these effects are discussed in other chapters.

*Total Current.*—Consider such a gap, in which variations parallel to the grids are negligible. Let $x$ be the distance from the first plane to a parallel plane within the gap and $d$ the separation of the bounding planes; let $t$ be the time. The current density and charge density are dependent on $x$ and $t$ alone and are related through the continuity equation. It is convenient to use the electron current $i(x,t)$ for the entire area of the gap; then the current density is $i(x,t)/A$, where $A$ is the area of the gap; using the charge density $\rho(x,t)$, the continuity equation becomes

$$\frac{\partial}{\partial x} \frac{i(x,t)}{A} + \frac{\partial}{\partial t} \rho(x,t) = 0.$$

Now the electric field also depends only on $x$ and $t$, and by the divergence relation

$$\epsilon_0 \frac{\partial}{\partial x} E(x,t) = \rho(x,t),$$

where $\epsilon_0$ is $(1/36\pi) \times 10^{-9}$ farad/meter.

The charge density can be eliminated between these two equations to give

$$\frac{\partial}{\partial x}\left[ i(x,t) + A\epsilon_0 \frac{\partial}{\partial t} E(x,t) \right] = 0.$$

The quantity,

$$i(x,t) + A\epsilon_0 \frac{\partial E(x,t)}{\partial t} = I(t) \tag{3}$$

is the total current, which depends only on the time.  It is the sum of the electron and displacement currents in the gap.  Sometimes the total current is known from the rest of the circuit; if the electric field is also known, this expression gives the electron current.

*Circuit Representation of a Gap.*—The total current can be written in terms of the gap voltage and the driving current by averaging Eq. (3) across the gap, for

$$I(t) = \frac{1}{d} \int_0^d dx \left[ i(x,t) + A\epsilon_0 \frac{\partial}{\partial t} E(x,t) \right];$$

the gap voltage is

$$V(t) = - \int_0^d dx\, E(x,t);$$

and the driving current is the space average of the electron current,

$$i(t) = \frac{1}{d} \int_0^d dx\, i(x,t).$$

Hence

$$I(t) = i(t) - C \frac{dV(t)}{dt}, \tag{4}$$

where $C = A\epsilon_0/d$ is the capacitance of the empty gap.  This simple relation can be interpreted in terms of a circuit in which the current $i(t)$ passes through the shunt combination of the capacitance and an external circuit across which the potential is $V(t)$ and through which the current $I(t)$ flows.  Consider the components of these quantities that have the time dependence $e^{j\omega t}$.  Let $i_\omega$, $V_\omega$, and $I_\omega$ be the amplitudes of the driving current,

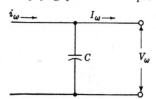

FIG. 3·5.—Circuit representation of gap in terms of driving current.  $i_\omega = I_\omega + j\omega C V_\omega$.

gap potential, and total current, respectively.  From Eq. (4) it follows that

$$i_\omega = I_\omega + j\omega C V_\omega, \tag{5}$$

which is the equation for the circuit represented in Fig. 3·5.

*Shunt Formulation.*—If all modulations are so small that quadratic and higher-order phenomena can be neglected, a clear-cut distinction can be made between effects that are produced by the gap voltage and effects arising from the condition of the beam as it enters the gap.  Such a distinction has been made in defining the beam-loading admittance $Y_B$.  Suppose such is the case; let

$$i_\omega = - V_\omega Y_B + i_m, \tag{6}$$

where $-V_\omega Y_B$ is that part of the driving current which arises from the gap voltage and $i_m$ is that part which comes from the condition of the beam as it enters the gap. The current $i_m$ could contain terms resulting from density and velocity modulation in the injected beam. It might be called the transexcitation current, or simply the exciting current.

As has been indicated in Sec. 3·3, it is possible to go further and carry out the separation for the density and velocity modulations at any place within the gap. Thus, if $i_\omega(x)$ is the density modulation and $v_\omega(x)$ is the velocity modulation at the plane $x$,

$$\left.\begin{aligned} i_\omega(x) &= -V_\omega y_m(x) + i_m(x), \\ v_\omega(x) &= -V_\omega \left(\frac{v(x)}{-I_0}\right) f_m(x) + v_m(x), \end{aligned}\right\} \tag{7a}$$

where $-V_\omega y_m(x)$ is the density modulation arising from the gap voltage, $i_m(x)$ is the density modulation due to modulations present in the beam at injection, $-V_\omega \left(\dfrac{v(x)}{-I_0}\right) f_m(x)$ is the velocity modulation arising from the gap voltage, and $v_m(x)$ is the velocity modulation that results from modulations present in the beam at injection. The coefficient $y_m(x)$ is an internal electronic transadmittance and $f_m(x)$ is a similar function for the velocity modulation. They are referred to as the density and velocity modulation admittances, respectively. On averaging the first of these equations across the gap and comparing the result with Eq. (6), it is seen that

$$Y_B = \frac{1}{d} \int_0^d dx\, y_m(x), \qquad i_m = \frac{1}{d} \int_0^d dx\, i_m(x). \tag{8}$$

An equation that supplements Eqs. (7a) is obtained from Eqs. (5) and (6) by eliminating the driving current; it is

$$I_\omega = -V_\omega Y_g + i_m, \tag{7b}$$

where $Y_g = j\omega C + Y_B$ is a quantity that will be called "the gap admittance." This equation suggests a circuit representation in terms of the exciting current as illustrated in Fig. 3·6. The exciting current $i_m$ passes through the *shunt* combination of beam-loading admittance, capacitance, and external circuit across which the potential is $V_\omega$ and through which the current $I_\omega$ flows. In this representation a current source $i_m$, having an internal admittance $Y_B$, can be regarded as exciting the resonator circuit.

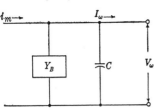

Fig. 3·6.—Circuit representation of gap in terms of exciting current. $i_m = I_\omega + V_\omega(j\omega C + Y_B)$.

*Series Formulation.*—A series representation is obtained by writing

$$Z_g = \frac{1}{Y_g}, \qquad e_s = i_m Z_g;$$

and hence

$$V_\omega = -I_\omega Z_g + e_s. \tag{9a}$$

A beam-loading impedance $Z_B$ can be defined from

$$\frac{1}{j\omega C} + Z_B = \frac{1}{j\omega C + Y_B}. \tag{10}$$

In the circuit for this representation (see Fig. 3·7) an internal voltage source $e_s$ with internal impedance $Z_B$ causes the current $I_\omega$ to flow through the *series* combination of capacitance and external circuit across which the voltage is $V_\omega$.

The density and velocity modulations, $i_\omega(x)$ and $v_\omega(x)$, can each be regarded as the sum of a term that is proportional to $I_\omega$ and a term that is due to modulations at injection. These are written in the form

$$\left. \begin{aligned} i_\omega(x) &= -I_\omega \alpha(x) + i_s(x), \\ v_\omega(x) &= -I_\omega \left( \frac{v(x)}{-I_0} \right) \beta(x) + v_s(x) \end{aligned} \right\} \tag{9b}$$

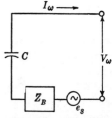

FIG. 3·7.—Circuit representation of gap in terms of internal voltage source and internal impedance.

$$V_\omega = -I_\omega \left( \frac{1}{j\omega C} + Z_B \right) + e_s.$$

On averaging the first of these across the gap and comparing the result with Eq. (9a), it is seen that

$$Z_g = \frac{1}{j\omega C} \frac{1}{d} \int_0^d dx [\alpha(x) + 1], \qquad e_s = \frac{1}{j\omega C} \frac{1}{d} \int_0^d dx\, i_s(x). \tag{11}$$

*Relations between Shunt and Series Elements.*—The shunt and series representations are, of course, equivalent. The following six equations give the relations between the elements of Eqs. (7) and Eqs. (9):

$$\left. \begin{aligned} Y_g Z_g &= 1, & e_s &= i_m Z_g \\ \alpha(x) &= -y_m(x) Z_g, & i_s(x) &= -e_s y_m(x) + i_m(x), \\ \beta(x) &= -f_m(x) Z_g & v_s(x) &= -e_s \left( \frac{v(x)}{-I_0} \right) f_m(x) + v_m(x). \end{aligned} \right\} \tag{12}$$

There is little to choose between the two representations except a possible convenience of expression in a particular problem. In most high-velocity gaps the driving current is easily calculated and from it the beam-loading admittance and exciting current; thus the shunt representation seems to be particularly convenient in the discussion of the high-velocity gap. In low-velocity gaps space charge is important; it usually is necessary first to calculate the field by some self-consistent method in terms of the total current and the modulations at injection; from the field the gap voltage and other quantities are obtained in a form that is often most easily expressed in the series representation.

A considerable portion of the theory of electron tubes is concerned with the calculation of elements of the shunt or series formulations for the conditions encountered. Of the six elements occurring in the shunt formulation,

$$
\left.
\begin{aligned}
i_\omega(x) &= -V_\omega y_m(x) + i_m(x), \\
v_\omega(x) &= -V_\omega \left( \frac{v(x)}{-I_0} \right) f_m(x) + v_m(x), \\
I_\omega &= -V_\omega Y_g + i_m, \qquad Y_g = j\omega C + Y_B,
\end{aligned}
\right\}
\tag{3·7}
$$

only four, $y_m(x)$, $i_m(x)$, $f_m(x)$, $v_m(x)$, are basic since $Y_B$ and $i_m$ are derived from the first two by integration [see Eqs. (8)]. In any particular problem not all of these are of primary interest. For example, in the input of a small-signal amplifier the important quantity is $y_m(d)$ because it is the leading term of the transadmittance of the tube; however, some drift action may be present, requiring the knowledge of $f_m(d)$. In the output, $i_m$ is the important quantity since it determines the excitation of the output and hence enters into the gain of the tube. Discussions of klystron theory usually consider the driving current,

$$
i_\omega = -V_\omega Y_B + i_m,
\tag{3·6}
$$

which is calculated for the output circuit directly from the modulation produced by the input circuit. The effect of this modulation is expressed as an electronic transadmittance, for which the symbol $Y_e$ is usually employed.

*Electron Motion.*—The electron motion is governed by Newton's law which, under the assumption of uniformity, takes the form

$$
m \frac{d^2 x}{dt^2} = -eE(x,t),
$$

where $m = 0.9 \times 10^{-30}$ kgm is the mass of the electron and

$$
-e = -1.6 \times 10^{-19} \text{ coulomb}
$$

is its charge. The energy integral is obtained by multiplying by

$$
\frac{dx}{dt} = v(x,t)
$$

and integrating with respect to the time;

$$
\frac{m}{2} [v(x,t)^2 - v(x',t')^2] = -e \int_{t'}^{t} dt'' \, v(x'',t'') E(x'',t'').
$$

If, for example, the electron is injected at the first grid and its motion is not reversed, the energy integral becomes

$$\frac{m}{2} \left[ v(x,t)^2 - v(0,t')^2 \right] = -e \int_0^x dx'' \, E(x'',t'').$$

This integral is calculated from the instantaneous field experienced by the electron and is not, of course, the integral defining the electric potential

$$V(x,t) = - \int_0^x dx'' \, E(x'',t),$$

since in the latter integral the field everywhere at the time $t$ is used. The momentum integral is obtained by the direct integration of Newton's law;

$$m \left[ v(x,t) - v(x',t') \right] = -e \int_{t'}^t dt'' \, E(x'',t'').$$

The energy and momentum integrals give the identity:

$$\int_{t'}^t dt'' \, v(x'',t'') E(x'',t'') = \frac{1}{2} \left[ v(x,t) + v(x',t') \right] \int_{t'}^t dt'' \, E(x'',t'').$$

The integration of the momentum integral gives

$$m(x - x') = mv(x',t')(t - t') - e \int_{t'}^t dt''' \int_{t'}^{t'''} dt'' \, E(x'',t'').$$

The velocity and the time of arrival at the plane $x$ of an electron injected at $x = 0$ at time $t'$ with velocity $v'$ are given, therefore, by the following formal expressions:

$$v(x,t) = v(0,t') - \frac{e}{m} \int_{t'}^t dt'' \, E(x'',t''),$$

$$t = t' + \frac{x}{v(0,t')} + \frac{e}{mv(0,t')} \int_{t'}^t dt''' \int_{t'}^{t'''} dt'' \, E(x'',t'').$$

An alternative expression for the second of these is

$$t = t' + \int_0^x \frac{dx''}{v(x'',t'')}.$$

The time rate of change of $t - t'$ is of interest in considering particle conservation; it is

$$\frac{\partial}{\partial t'} (t - t') = -\frac{1}{v(x,t)} \left\{ v(x,t) - v(x',t') - (t - t') \left[ a(x',t') - \frac{\partial}{\partial t'} v(x',t') \right] \right\}$$

where $a(x',t') = -eE(x',t')/m$.

**3·5. High-velocity Gap.**—If the electron velocities are very high, the effects of space-charge and thermal velocity spread are usually negligible. If the space charge is negligible, the field is approximately constant across the gap. The approximation is far from perfect, however, for if the field were completely space-constant, the electron current would be also —which is certainly not the case in a modulated beam.

In order to simplify the discussion, suppose that there is no d-c gap field. (A gap with a constant d-c field is considered briefly at the end of this section.) Let

$$E(x,t) = \frac{-V_\omega}{d} e^{j\omega t}, \tag{13}$$

where $V_\omega$ is the amplitude of the gap voltage and $d$ is the gap spacing. Under this assumption, the field at any particular moment is the same everywhere within the gap. The gap fields in most klystron resonators are well represented by this formula.

If the resonator is unexcited and the beam unmodulated, the electrons traverse the gap in the time, $T = d/v$, where $v$ is the velocity of the electrons in the absence of all modulation. The beam potential is defined by $V_0 = mv^2/2e$ and is constant across the gap, as is the electron velocity, because there is no d-c field. With $-I_0$ as the d-c beam current, the beam conductance is $G_0 = I_0/V_0$; and it, too, is constant across the gap.

Suppose, however, that the beam as it enters the gap is both density- and velocity-modulated with the angular frequency $\omega$. Let the current and velocity at the plane of injection, $x = 0$, be

$$\left. \begin{array}{l} i(0,t) = -I_0 + i_\omega(0)e^{j\omega t}, \\ v(0,t) = v + v_\omega(0)e^{j\omega t}; \end{array} \right\} \tag{14}$$

$i_\omega(0)$ is the amplitude of the modulation of the injected current and $v_\omega(0)$ is the amplitude of the velocity modulation at injection. If these amplitudes are small compared with the corresponding d-c quantities, if the transit angle is not too large, and if the gap voltage is a small fraction of the beam potential, the modulations everywhere in the gap are small. Such is assumed to be the case, and quadratic and higher-order terms in the modulation amplitudes are discarded. In particular, *d-c values of the transit time are used in calculating r-f coefficients.*

Let $T(x)$ be the transit time to the plane $x$ from the plane of injection, calculated in the absence of all modulation. Suppose that an electron at the plane $x$ at time $t$ was injected at $x = 0$ at time $t'$. Because of the velocity modulation at injection and because of the action of the gap field, the time of passage, $T(x,t) = t - t'$, is modulated. Let

$$T(x,t) = T(x) + T_\omega(x)e^{j\omega t}, \tag{15}$$

where $T_\omega(x)$ is the amplitude of the modulation of the time of passage. For brevity, the abbreviations, $T' = T(x)$, $T = T(d)$, $\theta' = \omega T'$, $\theta = \omega T$, are used.

The current and velocity at the plane $x$ can be written in the form

$$
\left.
\begin{aligned}
i(x,t) &= -I_0 + i_\omega(x)e^{j\omega t}, \\
v(x,t) &= v + v_\omega(x)e^{j\omega t},
\end{aligned}
\right\}
\tag{16}
$$

where $i_\omega(x)$ and $v_\omega(x)$ are the amplitudes of the density and velocity modulations, respectively.

The quantities, $v(x,t)$ and $T(x,t)$, are calculated from $v(0,t')$ with the aid of Newton's law. The current $i(x,t)$ is obtained from particle conservation by using

$$
i(x,t) = \frac{i(0,t')dt'}{dt}.
$$

Since

$$
\frac{dt'}{dt} = 1 - \frac{\partial T(x,t)}{\partial t},
$$

the expression for the current can be written in the form

$$
i(x,t) = i(0,t')\left[1 - \frac{\partial T(x,t)}{\partial t}\right].
\tag{17}
$$

The procedure is to calculate first $v_\omega(x)$ and $T_\omega(x)$. From Eq. (17), $i_\omega(x)$ is obtained in terms of $i_\omega(0)$ and $T_\omega(x)$;

$$
i_\omega(x) = i_\omega(0)e^{-j\theta'} + I_0 j\omega T_\omega(x).
\tag{18}
$$

The amplitude of the driving current $i_\omega$ is found by averaging $i_\omega(x)$ over the gap. The results are conveniently expressed in terms of the six elements of the shunt formulation,

$$
\left.
\begin{aligned}
i_\omega(x) &= -V_\omega y_m(x) + i_m(x), \\
v_\omega(x) &= -V_\omega \left(\frac{v(x)}{-I_0}\right) f_m(x) + v_m(x), \\
I_\omega &= -V_\omega Y_g + i_m, \qquad Y_g = j\omega C + Y_B.
\end{aligned}
\right\}
\tag{3·7}
$$

These elements serve to characterize the gap to this approximation.

*Velocity Modulation.*—The momentum integral, which follows from Newton's law, is

$$
m[v(x,t) - v(0,t')] = \frac{eV_\omega}{j\omega d}\left(e^{j\omega t} - e^{j\omega t'}\right)
\tag{19}
$$

On substituting $v(0,t')$ as given by Eq. (14) and comparing the result with Eq. (16), it follows that

$$
v_\omega(x) = v_\omega(0)e^{-j\theta'} + \frac{V_\omega}{2V_0}\frac{x}{T}M'e^{-\frac{j\theta'}{2}},
\tag{20}
$$

where $V_0$ is the beam potential and $M' = \dfrac{\sin{(\theta'/2)}}{\theta'/2}$ with

$$\theta' = \omega T' = \omega T(x).$$

Hence

$$f_m(x) = \frac{G_0}{2} \frac{x}{vT} M' e^{-\frac{j\theta'}{2}}, \qquad v_m(x) = v_\omega(0)e^{-j\theta'}. \tag{21}$$

The quantity $f_m(x)$ is the velocity-modulation admittance and $v_m(x)$ is the velocity modulation arising from modulations at injection. It is seen that the velocity modulation at the plane $x$ is the sum of the velocity modulation at the plane of injection at the time the electrons at $x$ were injected and the modulation caused by the action of the gap field. In the latter the effective field is that experienced by the electrons when at $x/2$ reduced by the corresponding modulation coefficient.

*Modulation of the Time of Passage.*—Integration of the momentum integral gives

$$mx = mv(0,t')(t - t') + \frac{eV_\omega}{(j\omega)^2d} [e^{j\omega t} - e^{j\omega t'} - e^{j\omega t'}j\omega(t - t')]. \tag{22}$$

From this equation is obtained the following expression for the time of passage:

$$T(x,t) = \frac{x}{v}\left[1 - \frac{v_\omega(0)}{v} e^{-j\theta'}e^{j\omega t}\right] - \frac{eV_\omega}{mv(j\omega)^2d} [1 - e^{-j\theta'} - j\theta'e^{-j\theta'}]e^{j\omega t}. \tag{23}$$

From a comparison with Eq. (15), it is seen that

$$T_\omega(x) = -\frac{v_\omega(0)}{v} T'e^{-j\theta'} - \frac{V_\omega}{2V_0} \frac{1}{T(j\omega)^2} [1 - e^{-j\theta'} - j\theta'e^{-j\theta'}]. \tag{24}$$

It is convenient to rewrite this expression by using the identity

$$1 - e^{-j\theta'} - j\theta'e^{-j\theta'} = \frac{(j\theta')^2}{2}\left(M' - \frac{j\theta'N'}{6}\right)e^{-\frac{j\theta'}{2}}.$$

Equation (24) becomes

$$T_\omega(x) = -\frac{v_\omega(0)}{v} T'e^{-j\theta'} - \frac{V_\omega}{2V_0}\frac{T'^2}{2T}\left(M' - \frac{j\theta'N'}{6}\right)e^{-\frac{j\theta'}{2}}. \tag{25}$$

The modulation of the time of passage to the plane $x$ that is due to velocity modulation at injection is proportional to the transit time to the plane $x$; for small distances the modulation that is due to the field is proportional to the square of the transit time to the plane $x$ and the phase of the effective gap voltage is that experienced by the electrons when they were at $x/2$; as the distance $x$ increases, the magnitude and phase are altered by the additional factor $(M' - j\theta'N'/6)$.

The factor $\left( M - \dfrac{j\theta N}{6} \right) = H e^{-i\eta}$,

where

$$H = \left( M^2 + \frac{\theta^2 N^2}{36} \right)^{\frac{1}{2}}, \qquad \eta = \tan^{-1} \frac{\theta N}{6M},$$

occurs frequently in transit-time phenomena. The quantities $H$ and $\eta$ are shown as functions of $\theta$ in Fig. 3·8.

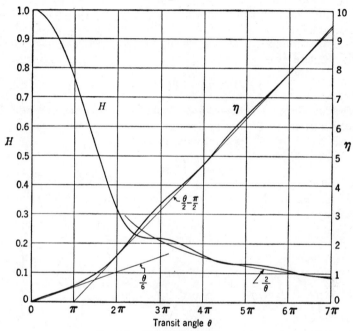

Fig. 3·8.—$H$ and $\eta$ as functions of $\theta$.

*Density Modulation.*—The amplitude of the density modulation is obtained by substituting Eq. (25) in Eq. (18); there results

$$i_\omega(x) = i_\omega(0)e^{-i\theta'} + v_\omega(0) \left( \frac{-I_0}{v} \right) j\theta' e^{-i\theta'}$$

$$- V_\omega \frac{G_0}{2} j\omega \frac{T'^2}{2T} \left( M' - \frac{j\theta' N'}{6} \right) e^{-\frac{j\theta'}{2}}, \quad (26)$$

where $G_0 = I_0/V_0$ is the beam conductance. Hence

$$\left. \begin{array}{l} y_m(x) = \dfrac{G_0}{2} j\omega \dfrac{T'^2}{2T} \left( M' - \dfrac{j\theta' N'}{6} \right) e^{-\frac{j\theta'}{2}}, \\[3mm] i_m(x) = i_\omega(0)e^{-i\theta'} + v_\omega(0) \left( \dfrac{-I_0}{v} \right) j\theta' e^{-i\theta'}. \end{array} \right\} \quad (27)$$

It is seen that the density modulation at the plane $x$ is the sum of three terms: (1) modulation arising from density modulation at injection, (2) modulation generated through drift action from velocity modulation at injection, and (3) modulation caused by the action of the gap field.   The third can be expressed in terms of the internal transadmittance, or density-modulation admittance $y_m(x)$, whereas the first two are contributions to the density modulation from the modulations in the beam as it enters the gap, $i_m(x)$.

The internal transadmittance at $x = d$ is of importance in triode and tetrode amplifiers because it is a factor in the transadmittance of these tubes.   If the input has a high-velocity gap with zero gap bias, which is rarely the case, it is

$$y_m(d) = \frac{G_0}{2}\frac{j\theta}{2}\left(M - \frac{j\theta N}{6}\right)e^{-\frac{j\theta}{2}}. \tag{28}$$

*Driving Current, Beam-loading Admittance, Exciting Current.*—The driving current is the space average of the electron current.   Since $x = vT'$ and $T = d/v$, its amplitude is simply

$$i_\omega = \frac{1}{\theta}\int_0^\theta d\theta'\, i_\omega(x).$$

In calculating the three terms in the driving current, the following three integrals are used:

$$\left.\begin{array}{c} \dfrac{1}{\theta}\displaystyle\int_0^\theta d\theta'\, e^{-i\theta'} = Me^{-\frac{j\theta}{2}}, \\[2mm] \dfrac{1}{\theta}\displaystyle\int_0^\theta d\theta'\, j\theta'\, e^{-i\theta'} = \dfrac{j\theta}{2}\left(M - \dfrac{j\theta N}{6}\right)e^{-\frac{j\theta}{2}}, \\[2mm] \dfrac{1}{\theta}\displaystyle\int_0^\theta d\theta'\, \dfrac{(j\theta')^2}{2}\left(M' - \dfrac{j\theta'N'}{6}\right)e^{-\frac{j\theta'}{2}} = \dfrac{(j\theta)^2}{6}\,Ne^{-\frac{j\theta}{2}}. \end{array}\right\} \tag{29}$$

These give

$$i_\omega = i_\omega(0)Me^{-\frac{j\theta}{2}} + v_\omega(0)\left(\frac{-I_0}{v}\right)\frac{j\theta}{2}\left(M - \frac{j\theta N}{6}\right)e^{-\frac{j\theta}{2}}$$
$$- V_\omega\frac{G_0}{2}\frac{j\theta N}{6}e^{-\frac{j\theta}{2}}. \tag{30}$$

Hence the beam-loading admittance and the exciting current amplitude are, respectively,

$$\left.\begin{array}{c} Y_B = \dfrac{G_0}{2}\dfrac{j\theta N}{6}e^{-\frac{j\theta}{2}}, \\[4mm] \text{and} \\[2mm] i_m = i_\omega(0)Me^{-\frac{j\theta}{2}} + v_\omega(0)\left(\dfrac{-I_0}{v}\right)\dfrac{j\theta}{2}\left(M - \dfrac{j\theta N}{6}\right)e^{-\frac{j\theta}{2}}. \end{array}\right\} \tag{31}$$

These quantities have already been discussed in Sec. 3·3.

*High-velocity Gap with Constant D-c Field.*—The effects of a space-constant d-c gap field that does not produce slow electrons will be summarized briefly. If $V_0$ is the beam potential at the injection plane and $V_d$ is the beam potential at the exit plane, the d-c field is $-(V_d - V_0)/d$ and the gap field can be represented by

$$E(x,t) = -\frac{1}{d}(V_d - V_0 + V_\omega e^{j\omega t}).$$

Let $v(x)$ be the velocity at the plane $x$ in the absence of all modulation. The beam potential at the plane $x$ is $V_x = mv(x)^2/2e$ and the beam conductance at that plane is $G_x = I_0/V_x$. Additional parameters are

$$r' = \frac{v(x)T'}{x}, \qquad r = \frac{v(d)T}{d}, \qquad \delta' = r' - 1 = \frac{aT'^2}{2x}, \qquad \delta = r - 1 = \frac{aT^2}{2d}$$

where $a = e(V_d - V_0)/md$ is the acceleration produced by the d-c field. In the limit of zero d-c field, $r'$ and $r$ become unity and $\delta'$ and $\delta$ become zero.

The details of the calculation are similar to those just given. The velocity modulation is

$$v_\omega(x) = v_\omega(0)\frac{v(0)}{v(x)}e^{-j\theta'} + \frac{V_\omega}{2\sqrt{V_xV_d}}r\frac{x}{T}\left(M' + \delta'\frac{j\theta'N'}{6}\right)e^{-\frac{j\theta'}{2}}. \quad (32)$$

The modulation of the time of passage is

$$T_\omega(x) = -\frac{v_\omega(0)}{v(x)}T'e^{-j\theta'} - \frac{V_\omega}{2\sqrt{V_xV_d}}r\frac{T'^2}{2T}\left(M' - \frac{j\theta'N'}{6}\right)e^{-\frac{j\theta'}{2}}. \quad (33)$$

The density modulation is

$$i_\omega(x) = i_\omega(0)e^{-j\theta'} + v_\omega(0)\left[\frac{-I_0}{v(x)}\right]j\theta'e^{-j\theta'}$$
$$- V_\omega\frac{\sqrt{G_xG_d}}{2}rj\omega\frac{T'^2}{2T}\left(M' - \frac{j\theta'N'}{6}\right)e^{-\frac{j\theta'}{2}}. \quad (34)$$

These expressions are to be compared with Eqs. (20), (25), and (26).

The six elements of the shunt formulation are

$$y_m(x) = \frac{\sqrt{G_xG_d}}{2}rj\omega\frac{T'^2}{2T}\left(M' - \frac{j\theta'N'}{6}\right)e^{-\frac{j\theta'}{2}}, \quad \Bigg\}$$
$$i_m(x) = i_\omega(0)e^{-j\theta'} + v_\omega(0)\left(\frac{-I_0}{v(x)}\right)j\theta'e^{-j\theta'}; \quad \Bigg\} \quad (35)$$

$$f_m(x) = \frac{\sqrt{G_xG_d}}{2}\frac{rx}{v(x)T}\left(M' + \delta'\frac{j\theta'N'}{6}\right)e^{-\frac{j\theta'}{2}}, \quad \Bigg\}$$
$$v_m(x) = v_\omega(0)\frac{v(0)}{v(x)}e^{-j\theta'}; \quad \Bigg\} \quad (36)$$

$$Y_B = \frac{G_d}{2} r^2 \frac{j\theta N}{6} e^{-\frac{j\theta}{2}},$$

$$i_m = i_\omega(0)\left(M - \delta\frac{j\theta N}{6}\right)e^{-\frac{j\theta}{2}} + v_\omega(0)\left(\frac{-I_0}{v(d)}\right)r\frac{j\theta}{2}\left(M - \frac{j\theta N}{6}\right)e^{-\frac{j\theta}{2}}. \tag{37}$$

It must be emphasized that there is an inherent inconsistency in the treatment of the high-velocity gap by the methods of this section, which comes from the neglect of space charge. Because of the presence of space charge the field is not space-constant. If Eq. (3) had been used to find the density modulation, the result would have been

$$i_\omega(x) = j\omega C V_\omega + I_\omega.$$

By Eq. (5) the right member of this equation is just $i_\omega$. This result is not right, for the density modulation certainly is not space-constant. The equations of this section are essentially correct for a beam containing very low charge densities; however, their justification lies in a more careful analysis of the effects of space charge. Such an analysis is presented in the next section. It should be mentioned that the residual gas in an actual tube is positively ionized by the bombardment of the electrons. Because of their large mass the ions contribute only a static positive charge density and tend to reduce the over-all space-charge effects.

**3·6. Low-velocity Gap, Neglecting Velocity Spread.**—It has been shown by Llewellyn[1] that the effect of space charge on the small-signal behavior of a uniform gap can be easily included if there are no negative velocities and the velocity spread is negligible. Under such conditions all the electrons at a given plane at a given moment have the same velocity, and therefore the current and charge density bear the simple relation

$$i(x,t) = v(x,t)\rho(x,t)A, \tag{38}$$

where $v(x,t)$ is the velocity of the electrons and $A$ is the area of the gap.

This relation begins to lose its validity when the thermal spread in velocity becomes comparable to the average velocity. Also, the relation is not applicable for a region containing a modulated beam if the thermal spread is such that electrons entering at the same time arrive at the opposite side out of phase by an appreciable fraction of a radian. Suppose a spread in velocity $\Delta v$ gives a spread in transit time $\Delta T$; cancellation in phase becomes appreciable unless $\omega \Delta T \ll 1$. In terms of the velocity, this condition is $\theta \Delta v/v \ll 1$, and in terms of the electron energy, $E = mv^2/2$, it is $\theta \Delta E/2E \ll 1$. Thermal energies are of the order of magnitude of $\frac{1}{10}$ electron volt at cathode temperatures. The condition is well satisfied in the usual high-velocity gap and also in a high-velocity

[1] F. B. Llewellyn, *Electron-inertia Effects*, Cambridge University Press, Cambridge, England, 1941.

drift region with a drift time of many cycles. For example, if $\theta$ is 60 radians and the beam voltage is 300 volts, $\theta \, \Delta E/2E$ is only $\frac{1}{100}$. If the thermal spread in energy is of the same order as the average energy, the condition is no longer satisfied in the usual high-frequency gap, and Eq. (38) is a poor approximation. Such is certainly the situation in a high-frequency space-charge-limited region, especially in the neighborhood of the cathode minimum. For this reason and also because of the presence of reflected electrons, the considerations of this section cannot be expected to apply to such a region.

The theory of Llewellyn gives an exact treatment of space charge in the uniform high-velocity gap. It also provides an account of electronic phenomena in the low-velocity gap that is valid to the extent that the velocity spread is negligible. A complete theory of the low-velocity gap must be formulated in terms of the velocity distribution of the beam; a partial account of velocity-distribution phenomena is presented in Chap. 5. In that chapter, as in this, only small-signal effects are discussed. Large-signal theory introduces an entirely new set of complications. The most important of these in klystron theory is the nonlinear nature of electron bunching. As may be seen in Chap. 9 and subsequent chapters, the bunching theory is successfully treated by the expansion of the phase of the bunched current in a series of Bessel functions, the argument of which contains the product of the drift angle and bunching voltage divided by the beam potential.

*Llewellyn's Equation.*—Equation (38) makes it possible to express the conduction current in terms of the electric field by the direct use of the divergence relation;

$$i(x,t) \,=\, v(x,t)A\epsilon_0 \, \frac{\partial E(x,t)}{\partial x}.$$ (39)

When this relation is substituted in the expression for the total current, Eq. (3), the result is

$$I(t) \,=\, A\epsilon_0 \left[ v(x,t) \, \frac{\partial E(x,t)}{\partial x} + \frac{\partial E(x,t)}{\partial t} \right].$$ (40)

Llewellyn observed that, if $x$ is regarded as the coordinate of a particular electron, $v(x,t) = dx/dt$ and the total current in Eq. (40) becomes equal to the total rate of change of electric flux through the plane moving with the electron

$$I(t) \,=\, A\epsilon_0 \, \frac{dE(x,t)}{dt}.$$ (41)

This observation is particularly significant because $I(t)$ is independent of the position of the electron and because the field is itself the second total derivative of the position, for by Newton's law

$$E(x,t) = -\frac{m}{e}\frac{d^2x}{dt^2}.$$

Hence, by substitution in Eq. (41), there is obtained

$$\frac{d^3x}{dt^3} = -J(t), \qquad J(t) = \frac{eI(t)}{mA\epsilon_0}. \tag{42}$$

This is *Llewellyn's equation* for the motion of the electrons in a uniform gap in which all electrons at a given plane at a given moment have the same velocity.

The usual procedure in the discussion of phenomena in connection with Llewellyn's equation is to assume for the total current a known function of the time, such as a constant, a constant plus harmonic terms, or a pulse of some sort; also, conditions that are consistent with the nature of the problem are imposed on the velocity and acceleration at the plane of injection. If $a(x,t)$ is the acceleration $[a(x,t) = -eE(x,t)/m,]$ Eq. (3) can be put in the form

$$\frac{\partial a(x,t)}{\partial t} = -J(t) + j(x,t), \qquad j(x,t) = \frac{ei(x,t)}{mA\epsilon_0}. \tag{43}$$

If it is desired to express the results in terms of currents alone, this equation can be used to eliminate $a(x,t)$.

When only small signals are being considered, two sets of equations are obtained. One set is time-independent and gives the d-c conditions in the gap. The other is linear in the r-f amplitudes, which are functions of the d-c parameters, and this set describes the time-varying phenomena in the gap.

*D-c Relations.*—The solution of the Llewellyn equation for a time-independent total current provides a very convenient description of d-c conditions in a gap in which the electrons at a given plane all have the same velocity. Let

$$J_0 = \frac{eI_0}{mA\epsilon_0},$$

and suppose that the electrons enter at the plane $x = 0$. Let $T'$ be the transit time from the plane of injection to the plane $x$, and $T$ the transit time across the gap.

Successive integrations of Llewellyn's equation give the acceleration, velocity, and position of the electrons in terms of $J_0$, $T'$, and the acceleration and velocity at injection:

$$\left.\begin{aligned}
a(x) &= J_0T' + a(0), \\
v(x) &= \frac{J_0T'^2}{2} + a(0)T' + v(0), \\
x &= \frac{J_0T'^2}{6} + \frac{a(0)T'^2}{2} + v(0)T'.
\end{aligned}\right\} \tag{44}$$

The third of these equations can be used to find $T'$; but since it is a cubic in $T'$, it is more convenient to regard $T'$ as a parameter in terms of which d-c phenomena are expressed.

On putting $T' = T$ and eliminating $a(0)$ from the second and third relations, there is obtained

$$d = -\frac{J_0 T^3}{12} + \frac{[v(d) + v(0)]T}{2}. \tag{45}$$

This is a cubic equation for $T$ as a function of $J_0$. For $J_0 = 0$, it gives of course, $T = 2d/[v(d) + v(0)]$. Examination shows that $J_0$ has a maximum, $2[v(d) + v(0)]^3/9d^2$, at $T = 3d/[v(d) + v(0)]$. This is $\frac{3}{2}$ the transit time for $J_0 = 0$; at the maximum $J_0 T^3/6d = 1$.

The discussion of solutions outside the range,

$$\frac{2d}{[v(d) + v(0)]} \leqq T \leqq \frac{3d}{[v(d) + v(0)]},$$

involves the possibility of the reflection of electrons and questions of the stability of the space-charge configuration. In fact, the question of stability arises for $J_0$ greater than one-half the value at the maximum, and $T > (\sqrt{3} - 1)3d/[v(d) + v(0)]$, if $v(d) < v(0)$, and arises for

$$J_0 > \frac{2[v(d)^{3/2} + v(0)^{3/2}]^2}{9d^2},$$

and a somewhat larger value of $T$, if $v(d) > v(0)$.[1]

At the current maximum, since $J_0 T^3/6d = 1$, it is easily shown that $a(0) = -2v(0)[v(d) + v(0)]/3d$ and that the velocity in the gap has a minimum, which is $v(0)v(d)/[v(d) + v(0)]$ and occurs at

$$T' = \frac{Tv(0)}{[v(d) + v(0)]}.$$

Two d-c quantities that enter in the discussion of the r-f behavior of the gap are

$$\frac{\epsilon_0}{\epsilon} = 1 - \frac{J_0 T^3}{6d} \quad \text{and} \quad \sigma = 1 - \frac{J_0 T^2}{2v(d)}. \tag{46}$$

As $J_0$ goes from zero to its maximum, $\epsilon_0/\epsilon$ goes from unity to zero; simultaneously $\sigma$ goes from unity to $-v(0)/v(d)$ and is zero when

$$\frac{\epsilon_0}{\epsilon} = \frac{1}{1 + \dfrac{2v(d)}{3v(0)}}.$$

[1] For details, see J. K. Knipp, "Space Charge Between Parallel Plane Grids," RL Report 534, Mar. 22, 1944.

If the velocity of injection is zero, the maximum current occurs when the field at the first plane is zero.   The current has the value given by

$$J_0 = \frac{2v(d)^3}{9d^2}.$$

This is Child's law for a space-charge-limited diode.   In such a diode the a-c impedance, $\rho = dV_d/dI_0$, is

$$\rho_0 = \frac{J_0 T^4}{12A\epsilon_0}. \tag{47}$$

This is a useful combination of symbols, whether Child's law is obeyed or not.

The capacity, $C = A\epsilon_0/d$, the beam conductance, $G_d = I_0/V_d$, and $\rho_0 = J_0 T^4/12A\epsilon_0$ are related as follows:

$$\frac{2C\rho_0}{T} = \frac{G_d r^2 T}{12C} = \frac{J_0 T^3}{6d} = 1 - \frac{\epsilon_0}{\epsilon}, \tag{48}$$

where $r = v(d)T/d$.

*R-f Relations.*—In order to find the conditions for steady oscillations in the gap, let

$$J(t) = -J_0 + J_\omega e^{j\omega t}, \qquad J_\omega = \frac{eI_\omega}{mA\epsilon_0}, \tag{49}$$

where $I_\omega$ is the r-f amplitude of the total current.   Llewellyn's equation becomes

$$\frac{d^3x}{dt^3} = J_0 - J_\omega e^{j\omega t}. \tag{50}$$

This is integrated for a particular electron with the condition that at injection the acceleration is $a(0,t')$ and the velocity is $v(0,t')$.

The first integration gives

$$a(x,t) - a(0,t') = J_0(t - t') - \frac{J_\omega}{j\omega}(e^{j\omega t} - e^{j\omega t'}). \tag{51}$$

The second integration gives

$$v(x,t) - v(0,t') = J_0 \frac{(t - t')^2}{2} + a(0,t')(t - t')$$
$$- \frac{J_\omega}{(j\omega)^2}[e^{j\omega t} - e^{j\omega t'} - e^{j\omega t'}j\omega(t - t')]. \tag{52}$$

The third integration gives

$$x = J_0 \frac{(t - t')^3}{6} + a(0,t')\frac{(t - t')^2}{2} + v(0,t')(t - t')$$
$$- \frac{J_\omega}{(j\omega)^3}\left[e^{j\omega t} - e^{j\omega t'} - e^{j\omega t'}j\omega(t - t') - e^{j\omega t'}(j\omega)^2\frac{(t - t')^2)}{2}\right]. \tag{53}$$

Suppose that

$$a(x,t) = a(x) + a_\omega(x)e^{j\omega t},$$
$$v(x,t) = v(x) + v_\omega(x)e^{j\omega t},$$
$$T(x,t) = T' + T_\omega(x)e^{j\omega t}, \tag{54}$$

and

$$i(x,t) = -I_0 + i_\omega(x)e^{j\omega t}.$$

From Eq. (43),

$$j\omega a_\omega(x) = -J_\omega + j_\omega(x), \qquad j_\omega(x) = \frac{ei_\omega(x)}{mA\epsilon_0}. \tag{55}$$

On substituting from Eqs. (54) in Eq. (51) and writing $e^{j(\omega t - \theta')}$ for $e^{j\omega t'}$, an expression is obtained from which the purely d-c terms can be eliminated by the use of the first of Eqs. (44). The result is

$$a_\omega(x) - a_\omega(0)e^{-i\theta'} = J_0 T_\omega(x) - \frac{J_\omega}{j\omega}(1 - e^{-i\theta'}). \tag{56}$$

By using Eq. (55), the r-f acceleration amplitudes can be eliminated. Terms containing $J_\omega$ drop out. The resulting relation is

$$j_\omega(x) - j_\omega(0)e^{-i\theta'} = J_0 j\omega T_\omega(x), \tag{3·18}$$

which was found in Sec. 3·5 by assuming particle conservation.

Substitution from Eqs. (54) in Eq. (52) gives, in a similar manner,

$$v_\omega(x) - v_\omega(0)e^{-i\theta'} = a(x)T_\omega(x) + a_\omega(0)e^{-i\theta'}T'$$
$$- \frac{J_\omega}{(j\omega)^2}(1 - e^{-i\theta'} - j\theta' e^{-i\theta'}). \tag{57}$$

On eliminating the acceleration amplitude, this equation becomes

$$v_\omega(x) - v_\omega(0)e^{-i\theta'} = a(x)T_\omega(x) - \frac{J_\omega T'}{j\omega}M'e^{-\frac{j\theta'}{2}} + \frac{j_\omega(0)}{j\omega}T'e^{-i\theta'}. \tag{58}$$

The last term in this expression should be noted for, together with contributions from $T_\omega(x)$, it gives a dependence of $v_\omega(x)$ on $i_\omega(0)$.

Finally, substitution from Eqs. (54) in Eq. (53) gives

$$0 = v(x)T_\omega(x) + a_\omega(0)e^{-i\theta'}\frac{T'^2}{2} + v_\omega(0)e^{-i\theta'}T'$$
$$- \frac{J_\omega}{j\omega}\frac{T'^2}{2}\left[\left(M' - \frac{j\theta'N'}{6}\right)e^{-\frac{j\theta'}{2}} - e^{-i\theta'}\right]. \tag{59}$$

This equation determines the amplitude of the modulation of the time of passage. On eliminating the acceleration amplitude, it becomes

$$v(x)T_\omega(x) = \frac{J_\omega}{j\omega}\frac{T'^2}{2}\left(M' - \frac{j\theta'N'}{6}\right)e^{-\frac{j\theta'}{2}}$$
$$- \frac{j_\omega(0)}{j\omega}\frac{T'^2}{2}e^{-i\theta'} - v_\omega(0)T'e^{-i\theta'}. \tag{60}$$

This expression is used to eliminate $T_\omega(x)$ from Eqs. (18) and (58).

*Llewellyn Electronic Equations.*—The results of the foregoing calculation are most easily given in terms of the series formulation:

$$
\left.
\begin{aligned}
i_\omega(x) &= -I_\omega \alpha(x) + i_s(x), \\
v_\omega(x) &= -I_\omega \left( \frac{v(x)}{-I_0} \right) \beta(x) + v_s(x), \\
V_\omega &= -I_\omega Z_g + e_s, \qquad Z_g = \frac{1}{j\omega C} + Z_B.
\end{aligned}
\right\}
\tag{3·9}
$$

and

When the six elements of these three equations have the form given by the calculations of this section, they are known as the "Llewellyn electronic equations."

A number of parameters are introduced in order to simplify the form and interpretation of the equations. The first of these are

$$
r' = \frac{v(x)T'}{x}, \qquad r = \frac{v(d)T}{d}, \qquad \delta' = \frac{a(x)T'^2}{2x}, \qquad \delta = \frac{a(d)T^2}{2d}.
$$

They come from the presence of a d-c field in the gap. If the d-c field were zero, $r'$ and $r$ would be unity and $\delta'$ and $\delta$ would be zero. Additional but not independent parameters are

$$
\frac{\epsilon_0}{\epsilon'} = 1 - \frac{J_0 T'^3}{6x}, \qquad \frac{\epsilon_0}{\epsilon} = 1 - \frac{J_0 T^3}{6d},
$$

$$
\sigma' = 1 - \frac{J_0 T'^2}{2v(x)}, \qquad \sigma = 1 - \frac{J_0 T^2}{2v(d)}.
$$

These come from the presence of current and space charge in the gap and would be unity if current and space charge were completely absent. The quantity $\epsilon$ plays the role of a low-frequency dielectric constant that is due to the electron beam. It occurs in the equation for the velocity modulation of the beam as it leaves the gap and the equation for the gap voltage. The quantity $\sigma$ is a smoothing factor. The smoothing, or debunching, comes from the spreading forces caused by the uneven disposition of space charge in a density-modulated beam. This parameter occurs in the equations for the current and velocity modulations of the beam as it leaves the gap. For a high-velocity gap in which the space charge is small, both $\epsilon_0/\epsilon$ and $\sigma$ are only slightly less than unity. However, as the space charge becomes appreciable, these quantities become considerably less than unity. As $J_0$ approaches $2[v(d) + v(0)]^3/9d^2$, which is its maximum, $\epsilon_0/\epsilon$ approaches zero and $\sigma$ approaches $-v(0)/v(d)$.

The four parameters $r'$, $\delta'$, $\epsilon_0/\epsilon'$, $\sigma'$, are related as follows:

$$
1 - \frac{\epsilon_0}{\epsilon'} = 1 - r' + \delta', \qquad 1 - \sigma' = (1 - r' + \delta') \frac{3}{r'}.
$$

Similarly,

$$1 - \frac{\epsilon_0}{\epsilon} = 1 - r + \delta, \qquad 1 - \sigma = (1 - r + \delta)\frac{3}{r};$$

also

$$\frac{a(0)}{a(d)} = 1 - (1 - \sigma)\frac{r}{\delta}.$$

The first electronic equation follows from Eq. (18) after substituting for $T_\omega(x)$ from Eq. (60). It is

$$i_\omega(x) - i_\omega(0)e^{-i\theta'} = I_\omega(1 - \sigma')\left(M' - \frac{j\theta' N'}{6}\right)e^{-\frac{j\theta'}{2}}$$
$$- i_\omega(0)(1 - \sigma')e^{-i\theta'} + v_\omega(0)\left(\frac{-I_0}{v(x)}\right)j\theta'e^{-i\theta'}. \quad (61)$$

Hence, by comparison with the first of Eqs. (9),

$$\left.\begin{array}{l} \alpha(x) = (1 - \sigma')\left(M' - \dfrac{j\theta' N'}{6}\right)e^{-\frac{j\theta'}{2}}, \\[3mm] i_s(x) = i_\omega(0)\sigma'e^{-i\theta'} + v_\omega(0)\left(\dfrac{-I_0}{v(x)}\right)j\theta'e^{-i\theta'}. \end{array}\right\} \quad (62)$$

It is significant that the presence of space charge magnifies $\alpha(d)$ and reduces the first term of $i_s(d)$, and that either can be made very small by the proper choice of $\sigma$.

The second electronic equation follows from Eq. (58). It is

$$v_\omega(x) - v_\omega(0)\frac{v(0)}{v(x)}e^{-i\theta'} = \frac{-I_\omega}{j\omega C}\frac{r}{2\sqrt{V_x V_d}}\frac{x}{T}\left(\frac{\epsilon_0}{\epsilon'}M' + \delta'\frac{j\theta' N'}{6}\right)e^{-\frac{j\theta'}{2}}$$
$$+ \frac{i_\omega(0)}{j\omega C}\frac{r}{2\sqrt{V_x V_d}}\frac{x}{T}\frac{\epsilon_0}{\epsilon'}e^{-i\theta'} - v_\omega(0)(1 - \sigma')e^{-i\theta'}. \quad (63)$$

Hence, by comparison with the second of Eqs. (9),

$$\left.\begin{array}{l} \beta(x) = -(1 - \sigma')\dfrac{2}{j\theta' r'}\left(\dfrac{\epsilon_0}{\epsilon'}M' + \delta'\dfrac{j\theta' N'}{6}\right)e^{-\frac{j\theta'}{2}}, \\[3mm] v_s(x) = -i_\omega(0)\left(\dfrac{v(x)}{-I_0}\right)(1 - \sigma')\dfrac{2}{j\theta' r'}\dfrac{\epsilon_0}{\epsilon'}e^{-i\theta'} \\[3mm] \qquad\qquad + v_\omega(0)\left[\dfrac{v(0)}{v(x)} - (1 - \sigma')\right]e^{-i\theta'}. \end{array}\right\} \quad (64)$$

The beam-loading impedance and voltage source in the third electronic equation are obtained from Eq. (62) by using the integrals of Eq. (11). It is found that

$$\left. \begin{aligned}
Z_B &= -\frac{1}{j\omega C}\left(1 - \frac{\epsilon_0}{\epsilon}\right)Ne^{-\frac{j\theta}{2}}, \\
e_s &= \frac{i_\omega(0)}{j\omega C}\left(\frac{\epsilon_0}{\epsilon}M - \frac{a(0)}{a(d)}\,\delta\frac{j\theta N}{6}\right)e^{-\frac{j\theta}{2}} \\
&\qquad + \frac{v_\omega(0)}{j\omega C}\left(\frac{-I_0}{v(d)}\right)r\frac{j\theta}{2}\left(M - \frac{j\theta N}{6}\right)e^{-\frac{j\theta}{2}}.
\end{aligned} \right\} \quad (65)$$

The presence of space charge tends to magnify the beam-loading impedance and to reduce that part of the voltage source which comes from the density modulation of the beam at injection.

*Exact Shunt Formulation.*—The Llewellyn electronic equations can, of course, be written in shunt form by using the transformation of the elements given in Eqs. (12). The following two identities are of interest in this connection:

$$\left. \begin{aligned}
j\omega C\left(1 - \frac{\epsilon_0}{\epsilon}\right) &= \frac{G_d r^2}{2}\frac{j\theta}{6}, \\
j\omega C(1 - \sigma') &= \frac{\sqrt{G_x G_d}}{2}\,rj\omega\,\frac{T'^2}{2T}.
\end{aligned} \right\} \quad (66)$$

The gap admittance is

$$Y_g = j\omega C\left[1 - \left(1 - \frac{\epsilon_0}{\epsilon}\right)Ne^{-\frac{j\theta}{2}}\right]^{-1}, \quad (67)$$

and therefore the beam-loading admittance is

$$Y_B = j\omega C\left(1 - \frac{\epsilon_0}{\epsilon}\right)Ne^{-\frac{j\theta}{2}}\left[1 - \left(1 - \frac{\epsilon_0}{\epsilon}\right)Ne^{-\frac{j\theta}{2}}\right]^{-1}. \quad (68)$$

As $\epsilon_0/\epsilon$ approaches unity, this expression becomes identical with the first of Eqs. (37). The exciting current is

$$i_m = \left[i_\omega(0)\left(\frac{\epsilon_0}{\epsilon}M - \frac{a(0)}{a(d)}\,\delta\frac{j\theta N}{6}\right)e^{-\frac{j\theta}{2}} \right. $$
$$\left. + v_\omega(0)\left(\frac{-I_0}{v(d)}\right)r\frac{j\theta}{2}\left(M - \frac{j\theta N}{6}\right)e^{-\frac{j\theta}{2}}\right]\left[1 - \left(1 - \frac{\epsilon_0}{\epsilon}\right)Ne^{-\frac{j\theta}{2}}\right]^{-1}. \quad (69)$$

It goes over into the second of Eqs. (37) as $\epsilon_0/\epsilon$ approaches unity, since at the same time $a(0)$ becomes equal to $a(d)$.

The internal electronic transadmittance, or density-modulation admittance, is

$$y_m(x) = j\omega C(1 - \sigma')\left(M' - \frac{j\theta'N'}{6}\right)e^{-\frac{j\theta'}{2}}\left[1 - \left(1 - \frac{\epsilon_0}{\epsilon}\right)Ne^{-\frac{j\theta'}{2}}\right]^{-1}. \quad (70)$$

On comparison with the first of Eqs. (35), it is seen that that equation is obtained by putting $\epsilon_0/\epsilon = 1$ in the above. The density modulation that is due to modulations in the beam at injection is

$$i_m(x) = i_\omega(0)\sigma' e^{-i\theta'} + v_\omega(0)\left(\frac{-I_0}{v(x)}\right) j\theta' e^{-i\theta'}$$

$$+ (1 - \sigma')\left(M' - \frac{j\theta'N'}{6}\right) e^{-\frac{j\theta'}{2}} \left[ i_\omega(0)\left(\frac{\epsilon_0}{\epsilon} M - \frac{a(0)}{a(d)} \delta \frac{j\theta N}{6}\right) e^{-\frac{j\theta}{2}}\right.$$

$$\left. + v_\omega(0)\left(\frac{-I_0}{v(d)}\right) r \frac{j\theta}{2}\left(M - \frac{j\theta N}{6}\right) e^{-\frac{j\theta}{2}}\right]\left[1 - \left(1 - \frac{\epsilon_0}{\epsilon}\right)Ne^{-\frac{j\theta}{2}}\right]^{-1}. \quad (71)$$

By putting $\sigma'$ equal to unity, the second of Eqs. (35) is obtained.

The coefficient of $-V_\omega\left(\dfrac{v(x)}{-I_0}\right)$ in $v_\omega(x)$ is the velocity-modulation admittance

$$f_m(x) = j\omega C(1 - \sigma')$$
$$\frac{2}{j\theta'r'}\left(\frac{\epsilon_0}{\epsilon'} M' + \delta' \frac{j\theta'N'}{6}\right) e^{-\frac{j\theta'}{2}}\left[1 - \left(1 - \frac{\epsilon_0}{\epsilon}\right)Ne^{-\frac{j\theta}{2}}\right]^{-1}. \quad (72)$$

It takes the same form as the first of Eqs. (36) when $\epsilon_0/\epsilon'$ and $\epsilon_0/\epsilon$ are unity. Finally, the velocity modulation that is due to modulations in the beam at injection is

$$v_m(x) = -i_\omega(0)\left(\frac{v(x)}{-I_0}\right)(1 - \sigma') \frac{2}{j\theta'r'} \frac{\epsilon_0}{\epsilon'} e^{-i\theta'}$$

$$+ v_\omega(0)\left[\frac{v(0)}{v(x)} - (1 - \sigma')\right] e^{-i\theta'} + (1 - \sigma') \frac{2}{j\theta'}\left(\frac{\epsilon_0}{\epsilon'} M'\right.$$

$$\left. + \delta' \frac{j\theta'N'}{6}\right) e^{-\frac{j\theta'}{2}}\left[ i_\omega(0)\left(\frac{v(x)}{-I_0}\right)\frac{1}{r'}\left(\frac{\epsilon_0}{\epsilon} M - \frac{a(0)}{a(d)} \delta \frac{j\theta N}{6}\right) e^{-\frac{j\theta}{2}}\right.$$

$$\left. + v_\omega(0)\left(\frac{Tx}{T'd}\right)\frac{j\theta}{2}\left(M - \frac{j\theta N}{6}\right) e^{-\frac{j\theta}{2}}\right]\left[1 - \left(1 - \frac{\epsilon_0}{\epsilon}\right)Ne^{-\frac{j\theta}{2}}\right]^{-1}. \quad (73)$$

This expression reduces to the second of Eqs. (36) when $\sigma'$ is put equal to unity.

It is thus seen that, in order to transform the elements of the exact shunt formulation into the elements calculated for the high-velocity gap with constant d-c field, $j\omega C\left(1 - \dfrac{\epsilon_0}{\epsilon}\right)$ and $j\omega C(1 - \sigma')$ in $Y_B$, $y_m(x)$, $f_m(x)$ are first replaced by their equivalent expressions as given by Eqs. (66), and then $\dfrac{\epsilon_0}{\epsilon}$ and $\dfrac{\epsilon_0}{\epsilon'}$ are put equal to unity in $Y_B$, $i_m$, $y_m(x)$, $f_m(x)$, and $\sigma'$ is put equal to unity in $i_m(x)$, $v_m(x)$. Hence the effect of space charge in $Y_B$, $i_m$, $y_m(x)$, $f_m(x)$ is essentially a dielectric effect while in $i_m(x)$, $v_m(x)$ it is a debunching effect. However, the two effects are not completely separable.

## CHAPTER 4

## BASIC CIRCUIT PHENOMENA AT HIGH FREQUENCIES

### By J. K. Knipp

Microwave circuits are built of resonators connected by waveguides and coaxial lines rather than of coils and condensers. Radiation losses are eliminated by the use of such closed elements and ohmic losses are reduced because of the large surface areas that are provided for the surface currents. Radio-frequency energy is stored in the resonator fields. The linear dimensions of the usual resonator are of the order of magnitude of the free-space wavelength $\lambda$ corresponding to the frequency of excitation, $f = c/\lambda$, $c = 3 \times 10^8$ m/sec.

**4·1. Cavity Resonators.** *Free Oscillations.*—A simple cavity completely enclosed by metallic walls can oscillate in any one of an infinite number of field configurations. The free oscillations are characterized by an infinite number of resonant frequencies corresponding to specific field patterns or modes of oscillation. Among these frequencies there is a smallest one, $f_0$; for it the free-space wavelength,

$$\lambda_0 = \frac{(3 \times 10^8 \text{ m/sec})}{f_0},$$

is of the order of magnitude of the linear dimensions of the cavity, and the field pattern is unusually simple; for instance, there are no internal nodes in the electric field and only one surface node in the magnetic field.

The free oscillations of such a cavity are damped by energy lost to the walls in the form of heat. This heat comes from the currents circulating in the walls and is due to the finite conductivity of the metal of the walls. The total energy of the oscillations is the integral over the volume of the cavity of the energy density,

$$\tfrac{1}{2}(\epsilon_0\mathbf{E}^2 + \mu_0\mathbf{H}^2),$$

where $\mathbf{E}$ and $\mathbf{H}$ are the electric and magnetic field vectors, in volts/meter and ampere-turns/meter, respectively, and $\epsilon_0 = \dfrac{1}{36\pi} \times 10^{-9}$ farad/meter, $\mu_0 = 4\pi \times 10^{-7}$ henry/meter. The cavity has been assumed to be empty. The total energy $w$ in a particular mode decreases exponentially in time

70

according to the expression,

$$w = w_0 e^{-\frac{\omega_0 t}{Q}},$$

where $\omega_0 = 2\pi f_0$. In this formula $Q$ is a quantity characteristic of the mode; it is defined by

$$\frac{1}{Q} = \frac{\text{energy lost in one cycle}}{2\pi \text{ energy stored in the cavity}}.$$

The fields and currents decrease in time with the factor $e^{-\frac{\omega_0 t}{2Q}}$.

*Reasons for Reentrant Cavities.*—The cavities of most klystrons and microwave triodes and tetrodes are reentrant cylindrical structures with circular cross sections (see Fig. 4·1). They are reentrant for two reasons. When the cavity is excited, the gap, namely the region between the post and the opposite end-plate, is a region of high electric field. It is through this gap that the beam passes, the electrons moving parallel to the axis of the resonator and therefore normal to the defining planes of the gap. These planes are usually grids that allow the passage of electrons while serving to maintain a fairly uniform field in the region. A high electric field is desired for large interaction between the beam and the field. The second reason for a reentrant cavity is that the gap, being small, requires a relatively short time for the transit of electrons. Transit times greater than a fraction of a cycle are almost always undesirable because of the reduced effectiveness of the gap potential in modulating the beam and of the electron current in exciting the cavity.

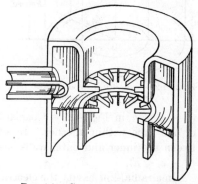

FIG. 4·1.—Cut away view of a reentrant resonator with radial fin grids and coaxial loop coupling.

*Principal Mode.*—The principal, or fundamental, mode of oscillation of such a cavity, and the one with the longest free-space wavelength $\lambda_0$, has electric and magnetic fields that do not depend on the angle defining the half plane through both the axis and the point at which the fields are being considered (see Fig. 4·2). In addition, the electric field is zero only at the wall farthest removed from the gap and the magnetic field is zero only at the center of the gap.

In this mode the magnetic field is everywhere perpendicular to the plane passing through the axis and the electric field lies in that plane. Lines of magnetic flux form circles about the axis and lines of electric flux pass from the inner to the outer surfaces.

The cavities that are used in microwave tubes almost always have a narrow gap, that is, the depth of the gap is small compared with the radius of the post ($d \ll a$ in Fig. 4·2). If the radius of the post is much less than one-quarter of the wavelength, and if the rest of the cavity is not small, the electric field in the gap is relatively strong and approximately uniform over the gap. It is directed parallel to the axis and falls off only slightly as the edge of the gap is approached. On the other hand, the magnetic field increases from zero at the center of the gap in such a manner that it is nearly linear with the radius.

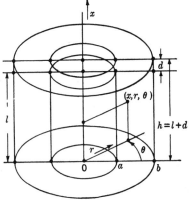

Fig. 4·2.—Cylindrical coordinates and resonator dimensions.

The proportions of the toroidal region outside the gap vary widely in tubes of different design. It is convenient to distinguish two types of cavities. Radial-line cavities have the general shape of flat pillboxes with a center post. In such a cavity the radial distance between the inner and outer walls is larger than the height of the cavity ($b - a > h$ in Fig. 4·2). Coaxial-line cavities have the general shape of one tube within another. In such a cavity the radial distance between the inner and outer walls is smaller than the height of the cavity ($b - a < h$).

In a radial-line cavity the electric field outside the gap tends to remain parallel to the axis, aside from some distortion of the field that is caused by fringing near the gap; it is weaker than in the gap and tends to become zero as the outer circular wall is approached. The magnetic field, on the other hand, increases from its value at the edge of the gap and has its maximum value at the outer circular wall.

In a coaxial-line cavity the electric field outside the gap changes its direction in relation to the axis from parallel in the region near the gap to perpendicular on going away from that region. Thus, in the coaxial portion of the cavity, the electric field tends to be directed from the inner circular wall toward the outer circular wall. It is weaker than in the gap, and as the end wall away from the gap is approached it tends to become zero. The magnetic field, on the other hand, increases from its value at the edge of the gap on moving parallel to the axis away from the gap and has its maximum value at the end wall away from the gap.

It is thus seen that, whereas the gap is a region of very large electric field and small magnetic field, the reentrant portion of the cavity is a region of large magnetic field and small electric field. The gap is the capacitive region of the circuit, and the reentrant portion is the inductive region. The direction of surface currents lies in the plane through the axis. Charge flows from the inner to the outer conducting surface of the gap by passing along the inner wall, across the end, up the outer wall, and across the outer end. The current links the magnetic flux and the magnetic flux links the current, as required by the laws of Faraday, Biot and Savart.

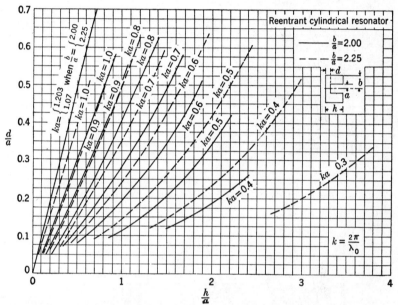

Fig. 4·3.—Curves for determining resonant wavelength $\lambda_0$ of fundamental mode of reentrant cylindrical resonator for $b/a = 2.00$ and $b/a = 2.25$.

*Resonant Wavelength for Principal Mode.*—The resonant wavelength of a particular mode is found from a proper solution of Maxwell's equation, that is, one that satisfies the boundary conditions imposed by the cavity. When the walls of the cavity conduct perfectly, these conditions are that the electric field must be perpendicular to the walls and the magnetic field parallel to the walls over the entire surface, where these fields are not zero.

The resonant wavelength $\lambda_0$ has been calculated by W. W. Hansen[1] for the principal mode of the simple reentrant cavity illustrated in Fig. 4·2. Results based on these calculations are given in Figs. 4·3 to 4·7

[1] W. W. Hansen, "A Type of Electrical Resonator," *J. Appl. Phys.* **9**, 654 (1938). The curves are from *Microwave Transmission Data*, Sperry Gyroscope Co., New York, 1944.

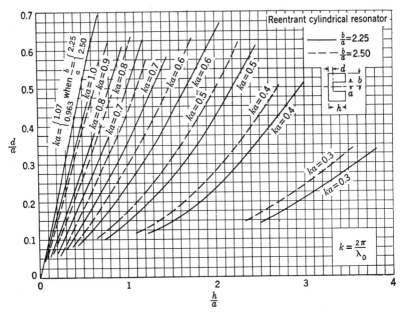

FIG. 4·4.—Curves for determining resonant wavelength $\lambda_0$ of fundamental mode of reentrant cylindrical resonator for $b/a = 2.25$ and $b/a = 2.50$.

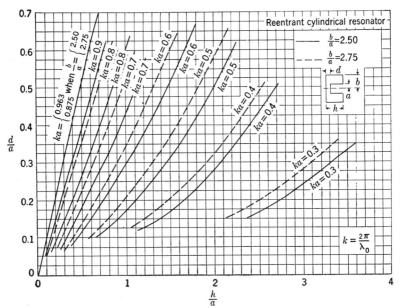

FIG. 4·5.—Curves for determining resonant wavelength $\lambda_0$ of fundamental mode of reentrant cylindrical resonator for $b/a = 2.50$ and $b/a = 2.75$.

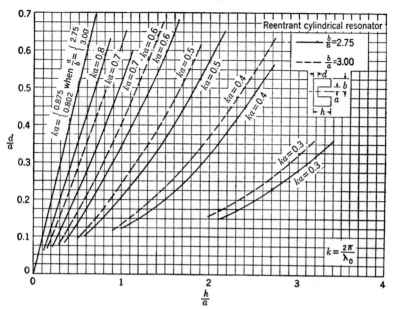

FIG. 4·6.—Curves for determining resonant wavelength $\lambda_0$ of fundamental mode of reentrant cylindrical resonator $b/a = 2.75$ and $b/a = 3.00$.

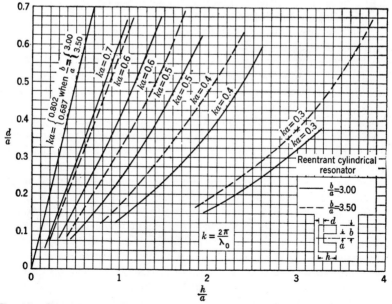

FIG. 4·7.—Curves for determining resonant wavelength $\lambda_0$ of fundamental mode of reentrant cylindrical resonator for $b/a = 3.00$ and $b/a = 3.50$.

in the form of curves for particular values of the ratio of outer to inner radius, $b/a$. The height of the resonator is $h$ and the gap depth is $d$. Sets of curves for two values of $b/a$ are given in each figure; the larger is the same as the smaller in the next figure. Curves for $d/a$ are plotted against $h/a$ for particular values of $ka$, where $k = 2\pi/\lambda_0$. By interpolating between the curves, $\lambda_0$ can be determined if the four dimensions $a$, $b$, $d$, $h$ are known; or if three dimensions and $\lambda_0$ are known, the fourth is obtainable. The curves are believed accurate to within a few per cent.

In using these curves to determine the resonant wavelength of a cavity it must be remembered that the bounding conducting surfaces of the gap region have been assumed to be solid. It has been found, for example, that two coarse grids constructed of radial fins (as shown in Fig. 4·1) for the purposes of wavelength determination have an equivalent spacing some 30 per cent greater than the physical spacing and that two fine-mesh grids have an equivalent spacing some 10 per cent greater than the physical spacing.

*Unloaded Q and Shunt Conductance.*—In a cavity undergoing free oscillations, the fields and surface currents all vary linearly with the degree of excitation, that is, a change in one quantity is accompanied by a proportional change in the others. The stored energy and the energy losses to the walls vary quadratically with the degree of excitation. Since the $Q$ of the resonator is the ratio of these two quantities, it is independent of the degree of excitation.

The resonator losses per second, besides being proportional to the degree of excitation, are inversely proportional to the product of the effective depth of penetration of the fields and currents into the walls, the skin depth, and the conductivity of the metal of the walls. Since the skin depth is itself inversely proportional to the square root of the conductivity, the losses are inversely proportional to the square root of the conductivity [see Eqs. (20) and (21)]. The losses are also roughly proportional to the total internal surface area of the cavity; and this area is proportional to the square of the resonant wavelength for geometrically similar resonators. The skin depth is proportional to the square root of the wavelength, and hence the losses per second are proportional to the three-halves power of the resonant wavelength.

The loss per cycle, which is the quantity that enters in $Q$, is proportional to the five-halves power of the resonant wavelength. Since the energy stored is roughly proportional to the volume, or the cube of the wavelength, the $Q$ varies as the square root of the wavelength for geometrically similar cavities, a relationship that is exact if the mode is unchanged because the field patterns are the same [see Eq. (23)]. In general, large cavities, which have large resonant wavelengths in the principal mode, have large values of $Q$. Cavities that have a surface area that is unusually high in proportion to the volume, such as reentrant cavities, have $Q$'s that are lower than those of cavities having a simpler geometry.

The shunt conductance $G$ as given by the expression,

$$G = \frac{\text{energy lost per second}}{\overline{V(t)^2}},$$

is defined only when the voltage $V(t)$ is specified. In a reentrant cavity the potential across the gap varies only slightly over the gap if the gap

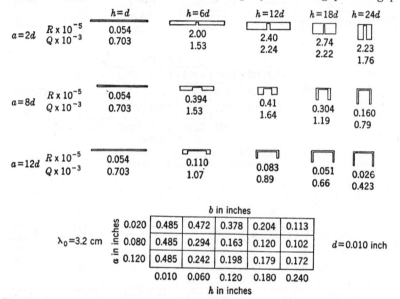

Fig. 4·8.—Shunt resistance $R$ in ohms and $Q$ for copper resonators having 3.2-cm resonant wavelength and 0.01-in. gap depth.

is narrow and the rest of the cavity is not small. A unique definition is obtained for $G$ by using for $V(t)$ the potential across the center of the gap. The gap voltage is proportional to the degree of excitation, and hence the shunt conductance is independent of the degree of excitation, as expected.

For geometrically similar cavities the shunt conductance varies inversely as the square root of the resonant wavelength for the same mode of excitation. This relationship exists because for the same excitation $\overline{V(t)^2}$ is proportional to the square of the wavelength and the loss per second to the three-halves power of the wavelength.

Both the unloaded $Q$ and the reciprocal of the shunt conductance vary as the square root of the conductivity of the metal of the walls.

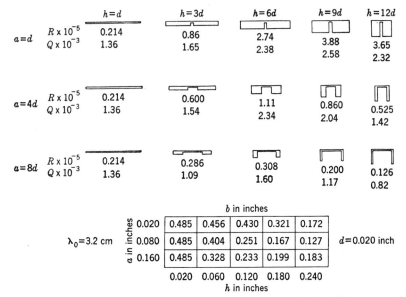

|  |  | $h=d$ | $h=3d$ | $h=6d$ | $h=9d$ | $h=12d$ |
|---|---|---|---|---|---|---|
| $a=d$ | $R \times 10^{-5}$ | 0.214 | 0.86 | 2.74 | 3.88 | 3.65 |
|  | $Q \times 10^{-3}$ | 1.36 | 1.65 | 2.38 | 2.58 | 2.32 |
| $a=4d$ | $R \times 10^{-5}$ | 0.214 | 0.600 | 1.11 | 0.860 | 0.525 |
|  | $Q \times 10^{-3}$ | 1.36 | 1.54 | 2.34 | 2.04 | 1.42 |
| $a=8d$ | $R \times 10^{-5}$ | 0.214 | 0.286 | 0.308 | 0.200 | 0.126 |
|  | $Q \times 10^{-3}$ | 1.36 | 1.09 | 1.60 | 1.17 | 0.82 |

$\lambda_0 = 3.2$ cm     $d = 0.020$ inch

| $a$ in inches | $b$ in inches | | | | |
|---|---|---|---|---|---|
| 0.020 | 0.485 | 0.456 | 0.430 | 0.321 | 0.172 |
| 0.080 | 0.485 | 0.404 | 0.251 | 0.167 | 0.127 |
| 0.160 | 0.485 | 0.328 | 0.233 | 0.199 | 0.183 |
|  | 0.020 | 0.060 | 0.120 | 0.180 | 0.240 |
|  | | | $h$ in inches | | |

Fig. 4·9.—Shunt resistance $R$ in ohms and $Q$ for copper resonators having 3.2-cm resonant wavelength and 0.02-in. gap depth.

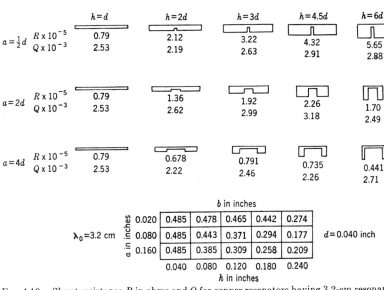

|  |  | $h=d$ | $h=2d$ | $h=3d$ | $h=4.5d$ | $h=6d$ |
|---|---|---|---|---|---|---|
| $a=\frac{1}{2}d$ | $R \times 10^{-5}$ | 0.79 | 2.12 | 3.22 | 4.32 | 5.65 |
|  | $Q \times 10^{-3}$ | 2.53 | 2.19 | 2.63 | 2.91 | 2.88 |
| $a=2d$ | $R \times 10^{-5}$ | 0.79 | 1.36 | 1.92 | 2.26 | 1.70 |
|  | $Q \times 10^{-3}$ | 2.53 | 2.62 | 2.99 | 3.18 | 2.49 |
| $a=4d$ | $R \times 10^{-5}$ | 0.79 | 0.678 | 0.791 | 0.735 | 0.441 |
|  | $Q \times 10^{-3}$ | 2.53 | 2.22 | 2.46 | 2.26 | 2.71 |

$\lambda_0 = 3.2$ cm     $d = 0.040$ inch

| $a$ in inches | $b$ in inches | | | | |
|---|---|---|---|---|---|
| 0.020 | 0.485 | 0.478 | 0.465 | 0.442 | 0.274 |
| 0.080 | 0.485 | 0.443 | 0.371 | 0.294 | 0.177 |
| 0.160 | 0.485 | 0.385 | 0.309 | 0.258 | 0.209 |
|  | 0.040 | 0.080 | 0.120 | 0.180 | 0.240 |
|  | | | $h$ in inches | | |

Fig. 4·10.—Shunt resistance $R$ in ohms and $Q$ for copper resonators having 3.2-cm resonant wavelength and 0.04-in. gap depth.

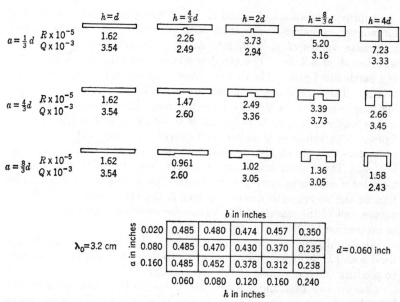

FIG. 4·11.—Shunt resistance $R$ in ohms and $Q$ for copper resonators having 3.2-cm resonant wavelength and 0.06-in. gap depth.

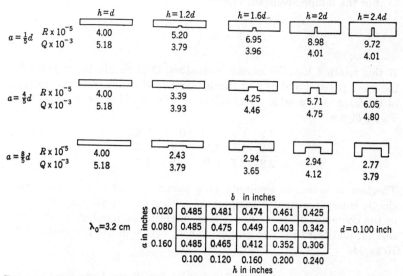

FIG. 4·12.—Shunt resistance $R$ in ohms and $Q$ for copper resonators having 3.2-cm resonant wavelength and 0.10-in. gap depth.

Approximate values of $Q$ and $R = 1/G$ are given in Figs. 4·8 to 4·12 for copper cylindrical resonators with circular cross sections having particular values of $a$, $b$, $d$, $h$.[1] All the resonators have a resonant wavelength of 3.2 cm. The gap depth is constant for all the resonators of a particular figure. The three resonators in any column have the same height. The first resonator in any row is a pillbox cylinder; the remaining four resonators in the row have the same inner radius. The outer radius required to give $\lambda_0 = 3.2$ cm is to be found in the table in each figure. The values of $Q$ and $R$ are believed accurate to 10 per cent for resonators that are highly reentrant and to 25 per cent for those that are less so. The values are exact, however, for the pillbox resonators. Cavities of similar proportions are obtained by scaling $a$, $b$, $d$, $h$ in proportion to the wavelength desired; $Q$ and $R$ are then proportional to the square root of the wavelength. Values for metals other than copper are in proportion to the square root of the conductivity.

An examination of the values of $R$ shows that $R$ increases with $d$ for fixed $a$ and $h$, as expected because of the reduced current flow necessary to produce the same value of the gap voltage.

*Comparison with Lumped-constant Circuit.*—In many respects the behavior of a resonant cavity resembles that of a low-frequency shunt $LRC$-circuit. For such a circuit, $\omega_0 = 1/\sqrt{LC}$ and $Q = \omega_0 CR$. In a highly reentrant cavity the effective capacitance is given approximately by $C = \epsilon_0 \pi a^2/d$, and $L$ can be assumed to be defined by $\omega_0$ and $C$.

For the lumped-constant circuit,

$$\frac{Q}{R} = \omega_0 \left( \frac{\epsilon_0 \pi a^2}{d} \right).$$

If this relation held for cavity resonators, $Q/R$ should be constant for the rows (fixed $d$ and $a$) and should vary as $a^2$ in the columns (fixed $d$) of the Figs. 4·8 to 4·12. The values of $Q/R \times 10^2$ mhos obtained from Fig. 4·11 are:

| | | | | |
|---|---|---|---|---|
| 2.2 | 1.1 | 0.79 | 0.61 | 0.46 |
| 2.2 | 1.8 | 1.3 | 1.1 | 1.3 |
| 2.2 | 2.7 | 3.0 | 2.2 | 1.5 |

The lack of complete similarity in behavior to that of a low-frequency circuit is apparent and is the greatest with regard to the change with $a$ in the columns; if the similarity were perfect, the numbers in the first, second, and third rows of any column would be in the proportion 1 to 16 to 64.

[1] Diagrams are from *Microwave Transmission Data*, Sperry Gyroscope Co., New York, 1944, and are based on the calculations of W. W. Hansen.

The main value of the analogy between resonators and lumped-constant circuits lies not in the extension of characteristic parameters to other geometries, in which the analogy is not very reliable, but in the fact that *the equations for the forced excitation of resonators and lumped-constant circuits are of the same general form.*

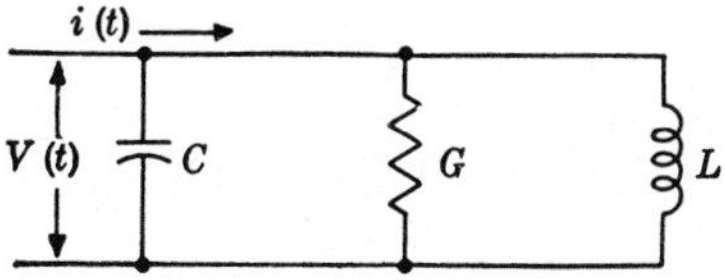

If, for example, it is assumed that the current $i(t)$ passes into the shunt

Fig. 4·13.—Lumped-constant circuit; $\omega_0 = 1/\sqrt{LC}$, $Q = \omega_0 C/G$.

combination of $L$, $C$, and conductance $G$ (see Fig. 4·13), by Kirchhoff's laws,

$$i(t) = C \frac{dV(t)}{dt} + \frac{1}{L} \int dt\, V(t) + G V(t).$$

On taking the derivative and eliminating $L$,

$$\frac{di(t)}{dt} = C \left[ \frac{d^2 V(t)}{dt^2} + \omega_0^2 V(t) \right] + G \frac{dV(t)}{dt}. \tag{1}$$

For forced oscillation with the frequency $\omega$,

$$i_\omega = \left[ G + j\omega_0 C \left( \frac{\omega}{\omega_0} - \frac{\omega_0}{\omega} \right) \right] V_\omega.$$

Thus, there is defined the circuit admittance

$$Y = G + j\omega_0 C \left( \frac{\omega}{\omega_0} - \frac{\omega_0}{\omega} \right).$$

These equations describe the excitation of the lumped-constant circuit. Similar equations, with appropriate parameters, are obtained in the description of the excitation of a particular mode of the resonator [see for example Eq. (43)]. The parameters are best evaluated by the investigation of the fields of the resonator. It is to be expected that they depend on the frequency.

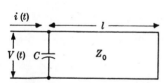

Fig. 4·14.—Short-circuited transmission line of length $l$ and characteristic impedance $Z_0$ terminated by lumped capacitance $C$.

*Coaxial-line Resonator as Short-circuited Line Terminated by a Lumped Capacitance.*—A cylindrical reentrant cavity having $b - a \ll h$ can be represented approximately as a transmission line, of characteristic impedance $Z_0$, short-circuited at one end and terminated at the other by a lumped capacitance $C$ (see Fig. 4·14). This is a natural representation since the reentrant portion of the cavity is shaped like a coaxial line and the capacitive region is well localized if the gap is narrow.

The input admittance of a short-circuited lossless transmission line of length $l$ is

$$Y_i = \frac{1}{jZ_0 \tan kl} \tag{2}$$

where $k = 2\pi/\lambda = \omega/c$, $c = 3 \times 10^8$ m/sec. Hence, the input admittance of the shunt combination of capacitance and line is

$$Y = j\omega C + \frac{1}{jZ_0 \tan kl}. \tag{3}$$

At resonance the total susceptance is zero. Therefore the resonant frequency is given by the expression,

$$\omega_0 C = \frac{1}{Z_0 \tan (\omega_0 l/c)}. \tag{4}$$

If $Z_0 \omega_0 C \ll 1$, as is possible if the capacitance is small,

$$\frac{\omega_0 l}{c} = \frac{2\pi l}{\lambda_0} \approx \frac{\pi}{2}$$

(or $3\pi/2$, etc.) and the wavelength in the principal mode is very nearly four times the line length. Such a cavity is called a "quarter-wave coaxial" resonator. If the characteristic impedance and length of line are not changed but the capacitance is increased, the resonant wavelength in the principal mode becomes greater than four times the line length, and consequently the resonant frequency is reduced. The characteristic impedance of a coaxial line of inner radius $a$ and outer radius $b$ is simply

$$\frac{1}{2\pi} \sqrt{\frac{\mu_0}{\epsilon_0}} \ln \frac{b}{a},$$

where it has been assumed the line contains no dielectric material.

The resonance condition can be used to eliminate the characteristic impedance in the expression for the input admittance of the resonator; thus is obtained the expression,

$$Y = j\omega_0 C \left( \frac{\omega}{\omega_0} - \frac{\tan k_0 l}{\tan kl} \right), \tag{5}$$

which for $k_0 l$ and $kl \ll 1$ reduces to

$$Y = j\omega_0 C \left( \frac{\omega}{\omega_0} - \frac{\omega_0}{\omega} \right).$$

It is clear that a lumped conductance $G$ at the same end as the capacitance would merely add $G$ to this equation. Losses distributed along the line, and input or output connections at a particular point in the line, could be introduced in terms of conductances and susceptances and treated by the methods usual to transmission line theory.

In a similar manner, a cylindrical reentrant cavity having $b - a \gg h$ can be represented approximately as a transmission line, with a varying characteristic impedance, short-circuited at one end and terminated at the other by a lumped capacitance. The appropriate line is a radial transmission line. It is formed of parallel metal disks between which fields are established, which travel in and out from the center. The short circuit is a circular metal wall at the outer circumference of the disks and the lumped capacitance is a gap at the center between a post and one of the disks. The quantitative description of radial transmission lines is best given with the aid of a chart such as is found in the book by Ramo and Whinnery.[1]

**4·2. Resonator Fields in Principal Mode.** *Fields, Currents, and Space Charge.*—For a cavity containing no dielectric material Maxwell's equations are the two divergence relations,

$$\mu_0 \text{ div } \mathbf{H} = 0, \qquad \epsilon_0 \text{ div } \mathbf{E} = \rho, \tag{6}$$

and the two laws of induction

$$\text{curl } \mathbf{E} = -\mu_0 \frac{\partial \mathbf{H}}{\partial t}, \qquad \text{curl } \mathbf{H} = \epsilon_0 \frac{\partial \mathbf{E}}{\partial t} + \mathbf{J}. \tag{7}$$

Rationalized mks units are used. The magnetic field $\mathbf{H}$ is in ampere turns/meter, electric field $\mathbf{E}$ in volts/meter, charge density $\rho$ in coulombs/meter³, current density $\mathbf{J}$ in amperes/meter². The dielectric constant $\epsilon_0$ is $(1/36\pi) \times 10^{-9}$ farad/meter and the permeability $\mu_0$ is $4\pi \times 10^{-7}$ henry/meter. The magnetic flux density $\mu_0\mathbf{H}$ is in webers/meter²; magnetic flux changing at the rate of one weber/sec generates one volt. There is frequent use for the two relations:

$$\frac{1}{\sqrt{\epsilon_0\mu_0}} = c = 3 \times 10^8 \qquad \text{meters/sec}, \qquad \sqrt{\frac{\mu_0}{\epsilon_0}} = 120\pi \qquad \text{ohms}.$$

The laws of electrodynamics can be expressed in differential form by Maxwell's equations or in integral form by applying the divergence theorem and Stokes's theorem to Maxwell's equations. By the divergence theorem the volume integral of the divergence of a vector is equal to the integral over the surface of its outward normal component. By Stokes's theorem the integral of the normal component of the curl of a vector over a surface bounded by a closed contour is equal to the integral around the contour of the tangential component of the vector, the direc-

---

[1] S. Ramo and J. R. Whinnery, "Fields and Waves in Modern Radio," Wiley, New York, 1944.

tion of the integration corresponding to right-handed motion with regard to normals to the surface.

When applied to Maxwell's two divergence equations, the divergence theorem gives the result that the total magnetic flux passing through any closed surface is zero and the total electric flux is equal to the charge interior to the surface; these are forms of Gauss's law. From Stokes's theorem, when applied to the two induction equations, it follows that the line integral of the tangential component of the electric field about any closed path, that is, the induced voltage, is the negative of the rate of change of the magnetic flux that has been linked by the path, and that the line integral of the tangential component of the magnetic field about any closed path is equal to the rate of change of the electric flux that passes through any area bounded by the path plus the total conduction current that passes through that area. These are Faraday's law and the law of Biot and Savart modified to include the displacement current, which is the rate of change of electric flux through the area.

The total current density is the sum of the displacement current density and the conduction current density,

$$\epsilon_0 \frac{\partial \mathbf{E}}{\partial t} + \mathbf{J};$$

and, since the divergence of the curl of a vector is zero, the total current density is without divergence. The line integral of the tangential component of the magnetic field around any closed path is equal to the total current linked by the path. The continuity equation,

$$\frac{\partial \rho}{\partial t} + \operatorname{div} \mathbf{J} = 0, \tag{8}$$

can be obtained by writing the divergence of the total current density equal to zero and replacing $\epsilon_0 \operatorname{div} \mathbf{E}$ by the charge density.

The fields $\mathbf{E}$ and $\mathbf{H}$ are zero in perfectly conducting walls. From the laws in integral form it follows that, at the surface of the cavity, $\mathbf{E}$ and $\mathbf{H}$ must be, respectively, normal and tangential to the walls where these fields are not zero. Also it follows that there is on the walls a surface current equal in density to $\mathbf{H}$ at the surface and perpendicular to $\mathbf{H}$ and a surface charge density equal to $\epsilon_0 \mathbf{E}$.

*Fields in Empty Coaxial-line Cavity.*—Microwave tubes are built with cavities of both the radial-line and coaxial-line types. Most klystron cavities are radial-line cavities. The Neher r-f amplifier and most lighthouse tube circuits have coaxial-line cavities.

It is possible to give for both types of cylindrical reentrant cavities a crude but instructive mathematical description in terms of approximate solutions of Maxwell's equations. In this chapter the coaxial-line cavity is so treated. It is selected because the fields outside the gap can be approximately represented in terms of sines and cosines rather than Bessel functions. The difference in degree of simplicity is just the greater simplicity of coaxial transmission lines over radial transmission lines.

The mathematical analysis of this chapter is illustrative rather than exact. Formulas are derived that apply only to coaxial line cavities and are only approximate. They serve to illustrate, however, the kind of relation that might be expected for other less easily treated cavity types.

In the principal mode of both radial-line and coaxial-line cavities only $E_x$, $E_r$, and $H_\phi$ are different from zero and these quantities are independent of $\phi$ (see Fig. 4·2 for cylindrical coordinates and dimensions of the cavity). The magnetic field automatically satisfies the condition of having no normal component at the walls. If the cavity is empty, $\rho$ and **J** are zero.

If the gap is narrow, the electric field in the gap is practically space-constant. Thus

$$E_x = -\frac{V}{d}, \qquad E_r = 0, \tag{9}$$

where $V$ is the gap voltage. Since $2\pi r H_\phi$ is equal to the displacement current $\pi r^2 \epsilon_0 \, dE_x/dt$,

$$H_\phi = \frac{-r\epsilon_0}{2d}\frac{dV}{dt}. \tag{10}$$

The magnetic field in a uniform gap is proportional to $r$.

In a coaxial-line cavity, $E_x$ is practically zero outside the gap except for the fringing field. Maxwell's equations are very simple. Of the two divergence equations there remains only

$$\frac{1}{r}\frac{\partial}{\partial r}(rE_r) = 0. \tag{11}$$

The first curl equation gives

$$\frac{\partial E_r}{\partial x} = -\mu_0\frac{\partial H_\phi}{\partial t}; \tag{12a}$$

and the second gives

$$-\frac{\partial H_\phi}{\partial x} = \epsilon_0\frac{\partial E_r}{\partial t}, \qquad \frac{1}{r}\frac{\partial}{\partial r}(rH_\phi) = 0. \tag{12b}$$

It can be concluded at once that in the coaxial portion the electric and magnetic fields are proportional to $1/r$.

At the end of the cavity near the gap both $E_x$ and $E_r$ are present and the field equations are more complicated. If both $d$ and $b - a$ are small compared with $l$, however, it can be assumed that the fields in the gap out to $r = a$, and in the coaxial portion of the cavity up to $x = l$, are given approximately by the preceding equations.

In the coaxial portion there is the boundary condition that $E_r$ is zero at $x = 0$. If the form,

$$H_\phi = \frac{\cos kx}{r} h(t),\tag{13}$$

where $h(t)$ is an amplitude factor, is assumed, then from the first curl equation

$$\frac{\partial E_r}{\partial x} = -\mu_0 \frac{\cos kx}{r} \frac{dh}{dt},$$

and the condition is satisfied if

$$E_r = -\frac{\mu_0}{k} \frac{\sin kx}{r} \frac{dh}{dt}.\tag{14}$$

The second curl equation is satisfied if

$$\epsilon_0\mu_0 \frac{d^2h}{dt^2} + k^2h = 0.\tag{15}$$

Hence, if $h(t)$ is proportional to $e^{j\omega t}$,

$$k^2 = \omega^2\epsilon_0\mu_0.\tag{16}$$

*Resonant Frequency.*—The condition at resonance is found by expressing the potential between inner and outer circular walls at $x = l$ in terms of the gap potential and matching the magnetic fields at $x = l$, $r = a$. The magnetic flux linked by the closed path across the center of the gap, along the metal end wall to $r = b$, down the side wall to $x = l$, and radially inward to the axis is neglected because both the magnetic field at this end of the cavity and the enclosed area $db$ are small. Hence, the line integral of the tangential electric field around this path is approximately zero. Since the tangential electric field is zero on the walls,

$$\int_l^h dx E_x + \int_b^a dr E_r = 0;$$

and therefore, using Eqs. (9) and (14),

$$V = \frac{\mu_0}{k} \sin kl \ln \frac{b}{a} \frac{dh}{dt}.\tag{17}$$

From Eqs. (10) and (13),

$$\frac{-a\epsilon_0}{2d} \frac{dV}{dt} = \frac{\cos kl}{a} h.\tag{18}$$

On eliminating $V$ from the last two equations and using Eq. (15),

$$k_0 \frac{a^2}{2d} \tan k_0 l \ln \frac{b}{a} = 1, \tag{19}$$

in which $k_0$ has been written for $k$. This is an approximate condition for $k_0$ from which the resonant frequency can be determined. On comparing with Eq. (4), it is seen that, with $C = \epsilon_0 \pi a^2/d$ and

$$Z_0 = \frac{1}{2\pi} \sqrt{\frac{\mu_0}{\epsilon_0}} \ln \frac{b}{a},$$

the equation for resonance derived by considering the resonator as a short-circuited coaxial transmission line of characteristic impedance $Z_0$ terminated by the capacitance $C$ is the same as that just derived from approximate field considerations. By using the exact solution of Maxwell's equations, the resonant frequency can be determined exactly. A calculation based on a fairly exact solution was used in computing the curves of Figs. 4·3 to 4·7.

*Unloaded Q.*—Because of the finite conductivity $\sigma$ of the metal of the walls, the fields penetrate to an average depth

$$\delta = \sqrt{\frac{2}{\omega\mu\sigma}}. \tag{20}$$

This distance is called the "skin depth." The fields and currents fall off exponentially from the surface into the metal walls according to $e^{-\frac{y}{\delta}}$, where $y$ is the perpendicular distance from the surface into the metal. The conductivity of copper is $\sigma = 5.7 \times 10^7$ mhos/m; and, since copper is nonmagnetic, $\mu = \mu_0$. Hence, in copper, for $\lambda = 3$ cm, $\delta = 0.67 \times 10^{-4}$ cm.

The surface current, which is equal in magnitude to $H_\phi$ at the wall, can be considered concentrated in a layer of resistive material of thickness $\delta$. The instantaneous power lost per unit area is

$$\frac{1}{\delta\sigma} H_\phi^2 = \frac{\omega\mu_0\delta}{2} H_\phi^2.$$

The total energy lost per cycle is the surface integral

$$\pi\mu_0\delta \int dS \overline{H_\phi^2} \tag{21}$$

over the interior walls of the cavity. The quantity $\overline{H_\phi^2}$ is the short-time average (average over one cycle) of the square of the magnetic field and is equal to one-half the square of the peak value.

The energy stored in the resonator is the volume integral

$$\mu_0 \int dV \overline{H_\phi^2}. \tag{22}$$

Hence the unloaded $Q$ of the resonator, as defined in Sec. 4·1, is given by

$$\frac{1}{Q} = \frac{\delta}{2} \frac{\int dS \overline{H_\phi^2}}{\int dV \overline{H_\phi^2}}. \tag{23}$$

Since, in general, $H$ has a loop at the surface, the mean surface value of $\overline{H_\phi^2}$ might be thought to be roughly twice the mean value throughout the volume. In a reentrant cavity, however, it is probably a better approximation to assume equal mean values, and to write

$$\frac{1}{Q} \approx \frac{\delta S}{2V},$$

where $S$ is the total interior surface and $V$ is the total volume of the cavity.

If the approximate fields derived in this section are used, the surface and volume integrals occurring in the unloaded $Q$ are easily calculated. To simplify the result, the losses and magnetic energy stored in the gap are neglected, and in the integration over the inner post $l$ is replaced by $h$. There is then obtained the expression,

$$\frac{1}{Q} = k\delta \left[ \frac{1 + \cos^2 kh}{kh + \sin kh \cos kh} + \frac{1}{2 \ln b/a} \left( \frac{1}{ka} + \frac{1}{kb} \right) \right]. \tag{24}$$

The terms in this formula are the relative contributions of the bottom and top, inner, and outer walls, respectively.

If the resonator is approximately a quarter wavelength, $kh \approx \pi/2$, the formula simplifies to

$$\frac{1}{Q} \approx \frac{4\delta}{\lambda} \left[ 1 + \frac{1}{8 \ln b/a} \left( \frac{\lambda}{a} + \frac{\lambda}{b} \right) \right]. \tag{25}$$

For fixed $b$, the highest $Q$ is found for $a = 0.28b$, for which

$$\frac{1}{Q} \approx \frac{4\delta}{\lambda} \left( 1 + \frac{\lambda}{2.2b} \right).$$

In the limit $b/\lambda \ll 1$, $1/Q = 1.88\delta/b$; the losses in the bottom are negligible.

*Shunt Conductance.*—The gap potential can be expressed as a surface integral by taking the line integral of the electric field over a closed path that crosses the gap at the axis and links all the magnetic flux of the cavity by remaining in the metal walls on the return path.    Thus the following equation is obtained:

$$V = -\mu_0 \frac{d}{dt} \int dS' H_\phi. \tag{26}$$

The area over which the integration extends is one-half the cross-sectional area cut by a plane through the axis.

The energy lost per second is

$$\frac{\omega\mu_0\delta}{2} \int dS \overline{H_\phi^2} \tag{27}$$

and therefore the shunt conductance is given by the expression,

$$G = \frac{\dfrac{\omega\mu_0\delta}{2} \int dS \overline{H_\phi^2}}{\left(\mu_0\omega \int dS' H_\phi\right)^2} = \frac{\delta}{2\mu_0\omega} \frac{\int dS \overline{H_\phi^2}}{\left(\int dS' H_\phi\right)^2}. \tag{28}$$

If the integrals are assumed proportional to the areas,

$$G \approx \frac{\delta\lambda}{4\pi} \sqrt{\frac{\epsilon_0}{\mu_0}} \frac{S}{S'^2},$$

where $S$ is the total interior surface of the cavity and $S'$ is one-half its cross-sectional area defined by a plane through the axis.

With the simplified fields used in calculating $Q$, the shunt conductance of the coaxial-line cavity is given by

$$G = \pi k\delta \sqrt{\frac{\epsilon_0}{\mu_0}} \left[ \frac{1 + \cos^2 kh}{\sin^2 kh \ln b/a} + \frac{1}{2(\ln b/a)^2} \left(\frac{1}{ka} + \frac{1}{kb}\right) \left(\frac{kh}{\sin^2 kh} + \frac{1}{\tan kh}\right) \right]. \tag{29}$$

The values of $Q$ and $R$ in Figs. 4·8 to 4·12 were calculated from formulas similar to Eqs. (24) and (29).   It is to be noted that Eqs. (4), (24), and (29) do not satisfy the lumped-constant circuit relation $QG = \omega_0 C$ since in Eq. (4) $C$ is defined as $\epsilon A/d$.

If the resonator is approximately a quarter wavelength, Eq. (29) simplifies to

$$G \approx \frac{2\pi^2\delta}{\lambda} \sqrt{\frac{\epsilon_0}{\mu_0}} \frac{1}{\ln b/a} \left[ 1 + \frac{1}{8 \ln b/a} \left(\frac{\lambda}{a} + \frac{\lambda}{b}\right) \right]. \tag{30}$$

*Damped Oscillations.*—The cavity losses have the effect of introducing a damping factor into the equation governing the time variation of the oscillations. Instead of Eq. (15) the equation for the amplitude $h(t)$ becomes

$$\frac{d^2h}{dt^2} + \omega_0^2 h + \frac{\omega_0}{Q}\frac{dh}{dt} = 0. \tag{31}$$

If the form $h = h_0 e^{i\omega t}$ is assumed, it is found that $\omega$ is complex and is given by the expression,

$$\omega = \pm\omega_0\sqrt{1 - \frac{1}{4Q^2}} + j\frac{\omega_0}{2Q}. \tag{32}$$

Therefore the fields have the time factors

$$e^{-\frac{\omega_0 t}{2Q}} e^{\pm j\omega_0\sqrt{1 - \frac{1}{4Q^2}}t}. \tag{33}$$

Since any quantity linear in the fields contains $h$ or its derivative, such a quantity obeys this amplitude equation because the equation is homogeneous. In particular, the gap voltage satisfies the amplitude equation, which can be written in the form

$$C\left(\frac{d^2V}{dt^2} + \omega_0^2 V\right) + G\frac{dV}{dt} = 0, \tag{34}$$

where $C$ is defined as $QG/\omega_0$.

**4·3. Cavity Excitation in Principal Mode.** *Excitation by the Beam.*— If a beam passes through the gap, conditions are altered by the presence of current and space charge in the cavity. Because of the space charge, the electric field is no longer constant in the gap. If the beam is uniform as assumed in Chap. 3, the electric field is still directed parallel to the axis and the gap voltage is the integral,

$$V = -\int_l^h dx E_x, \tag{35}$$

where $E_x$ is a function of $x$ as well as $t$, its space derivative being determined by the charge density through the divergence equation.

The total current $I$ passing through a uniform gap is a function only of $t$ because it is without divergence. But the total current is equal to the line integral of the magnetic field around the edge of the gap; thus

$$I = 2\pi a H_\phi. \tag{36}$$

Because of the fringing of the field at the edge of the gap, neither $I$ nor $H_\phi$ is completely constant across the edge of the gap; if the gap is narrow, however, the effect of fringing on both is small.

The total current is the integral over the area of the gap of the sum of the displacement-current density and conduction-current density, and is given by the expression,

$$I = \int dS \left( \epsilon_0 \frac{\partial E}{\partial t} + J \right). \tag{37}$$

In a uniform gap the right side can be averaged across the gap and $V$ introduced; thus

$$I = -C \frac{dV}{dt} + i, \tag{38}$$

where in this equation $C = \epsilon_0 A/d$ and $i/A$ is the average conduction-current density in the gap. This fundamental relation for the uniform gap was derived in Chap. 3 from the divergence relation and the continuity equation. By combining Eq. (38) with Eq. (36), there is obtained the expression,

$$i = C \frac{dV}{dt} + 2\pi a H_\phi, \tag{39}$$

where $H_\phi$ is the magnetic field at the edge of the gap.

It is seen that the presence of the beam has two primary effects: the effect of space charge on the electric field, which is sometimes negligible, and the addition of the conduction current to the displacement current. Outside the gap the fields are essentially unchanged except in amplitude.

Just as in the empty cavity, the gap voltage and the magnetic field at the edge of the gap for a coaxial-line cavity are, respectively,

$$V = \frac{\mu_0}{k} \sin kl \ln \frac{b}{a} \frac{dh}{dt},$$

$$H_\phi = \frac{\cos kl \, h}{a}.$$

Hence, at the edge of the gap

$$\frac{\partial H_\phi}{\partial t} = \frac{k}{a\mu_0} \frac{1}{\tan kl \ln b/a} V, \tag{40}$$

which can be substituted in the derivative of Eq. (39). There is obtained the expression,

$$\frac{di}{dt} = C \frac{d^2V}{dt^2} + \frac{k}{\mu_0} \frac{2\pi}{\tan kl \ln \dfrac{b}{a}} V. \tag{41}$$

To take into account cavity losses, a term of the form $GdV/dt$ should be added to the right member of this equation. The factor $2\pi/\ln (b/a)$ can be eliminated by using the resonance condition, Eq. (19). When these changes are made,

$$\frac{di}{dt} = C\left(\frac{d^2V}{dt^2} + \frac{\omega\omega_0 \tan k_0 l}{\tan kl}\,V\right) + G\frac{dV}{dt}. \tag{42}$$

The equation just obtained serves to determine the excitation of the cavity by the beam. Consistent with the approximations made,

$$\frac{\omega\omega_0 \tan k_0 l}{\tan kl}$$

can be replaced by $\omega_0^2$. Hence

$$\frac{di}{dt} = C\left(\frac{d^2V}{dt^2} + \omega_0^2 V\right) + G\frac{dV}{dt}. \tag{43}$$

This equation has exactly the same form as Eq. (1), which was derived for a lumped-constant circuit. If $i$ contains the component $i_\omega e^{j\omega t}$,

$$i_\omega = \left[j\omega_0 C\left(\frac{\omega}{\omega_0} - \frac{\omega_0}{\omega}\right) + G\right]V_\omega.$$

The response of the resonator to the driving current is that of a circuit with the admittance

$$Y = j\omega_0 C\left(\frac{\omega}{\omega_0} - \frac{\omega_0}{\omega}\right) + G.$$

*The Output.*—The output lead of the resonator can be a metal loop or probe in the cavity connected to a coaxial line or directly to another cavity or a window looking into a waveguide or another cavity. The output contributes to the power losses and also affects the resonant frequency. The general effect is to add terms of the form,

$$A_L\frac{d^2V}{dt^2} + B_L V + G_L\frac{dV}{dt},$$

to the equation describing the excitation of the cavity. Such terms depend on the nature of the load and are frequency-dependent. For a particular frequency they add an admittance, $j\omega A_L + (1/j\omega)B_L + G_L$, to the gap admittance, which then becomes an expression of the form,

$$j\omega_0 C\left(\frac{\omega}{\omega_0} - \frac{\omega_0}{\omega}\right) + G_{BR} + G_L.$$

In this expression, $\omega_0$ is the new resonant frequency and $C$ is the new effective capacitance and $G_{BR} = G_B + G_R$ is the sum of conductances due to resonator and beam losses. The power output is $G_L\overline{V^2}$. Because of the resonator losses and losses to the beam the power output is only a fraction of the total power produced; this fraction is called the circuit efficiency.

A detailed description of the coupling between the output lead and the resonator is beyond the scope of this chapter and only a few qualitative remarks will be made on the subject.[1]

A simple example of coupling from a resonator is an output lead composed of a small loop on the side of the cavity connected to a coaxial line. The magnetic flux that passes through the loop induces in it a voltage,

$$V_c = -A_c\mu_0 \frac{\partial H_\phi}{\partial t}. \tag{44}$$

In this formula, $A_c$ is the effective area of the loop and $H_\phi$ is the magnetic field at the loop; the area is assumed small and the magnetic field constant over the area. If the disturbance introduced by the presence of the loop is small, the magnetic field at the loop is approximately

$$H_\phi = \frac{\cos kx}{r} h,$$

where $x$ and $r$ are coordinates of the loop. Hence, if Eq. (17) is used,

$$\frac{\partial H_\phi}{\partial t} = \frac{k}{\mu_0 r} \frac{\cos kx}{\sin kl} \frac{1}{\ln b/a} V, \tag{45}$$

and the voltage induced in the loop is simply related to the gap voltage as follows:

$$V_c = -\frac{A_c k}{r} \frac{\cos kx}{\sin kl} \frac{1}{\ln b/a} V. \tag{46}$$

If the admittance looking into the line is a pure conductance $G_c$ and the self-inductance of the loop is neglected, or regarded as part of the line admittance, the power delivered to the line is $G_c\overline{V_c^2}$; since it is also $G_L\overline{V^2}$,

$$G_L = \left(\frac{A_c k}{r} \frac{\cos kx}{\sin kl} \frac{1}{\ln b/a}\right)^2 G_c. \tag{47}$$

This expression gives the output conductance as measured at gap in terms of the conductance as measured at the loop for a coaxial-line cavity and the conditions stated. If the output is not a pure conductance, as is almost always the case unless very careful design requirements are met and the load is matched to the tube, it is clear that the load contributes a susceptance in addition to a conductance at the gap. The prime significance of the above formula lies in the factor $A_c^2$; this

---

[1] For extensive treatments of microwave circuits, the reader is referred to other books in the Radiation Laboratory Series, in particular: "Waveguide Handbook," Vol. 10, edited by N. Marcuwitz; "Principles of Microwave Circuits," Vol. 8, by C. G. Montgomery, R. H. Dicke, and E. C. Purcell; "Microwave Magnetrons," Vol. 6, edited by G. B. Collins.

factor indicates that, as the loop is turned, the gap conductance due to the load changes with the square of the cosine of the angle which it makes with the plane through the position of the loop and the axis. It is, of course, obvious that if the loop is placed in a part of the cavity where the magnetic field is small, the output coupling is weak.

The presence of an output lead on the side of a circular cylindrical resonator destroys the axial symmetry that the fields have in the principal mode in the absence of the coupl ng device. Modes not having that symmetry are excited and contribute to the stored energy, the losses, and other general properties of the resonator. A discussion of these modes is essential to the description of the effect of the output and they are the basis of the exact calculation of the output characteristics.

The effects of external connections on cavity excitation are important in the discussion of tube operation. Reference is made to the detailed treatment of load effects on the performance of reflex klystrons that is to be found in Chap. 15.

**PART II**

# PLANAR SPACE CHARGE TUBES

# CHAPTER 5

## THEORY OF H-F SPACE-CHARGE DEVICES

### By J. K. Knipp

A microwave tube of planar grid structure contains a succession of regions separated by parallel plane grids. The first of these regions has a cathode that emits electrons, and these electrons form a beam that passes through the other regions. In the absence of r-f fields, the motion of the electrons of the beam is controlled by the d-c voltages on the grids and the anode. If within a region of the tube the voltage relative to the cathode is zero or negative, some or all of the electrons are reflected; when such is the case, the beam contains a stream of oncoming electrons and a stream of reflected electrons. If the cathode emits uniformly, if the regions are shallow, and if the grids are of fine mesh, the beam and the fields are fairly uniform and for most purposes can be described without considering variations parallel to the grid planes.

The assumption of uniformity is made in this chapter. Hence the general relations of Sec. 3·4 apply to each of the several regions of the tube. It is also assumed that there is negligible penetration of electric fields through the grids. Thus the discussion is restricted to high-mu tubes. Since the grids are usually far from perfect transmitters of electrons, it is assumed that only a fraction of the electrons incident on a grid is transmitted by it. Although secondaries produced by the impact of electrons on the grids and the anode can produce many complicating effects, such effects are not discussed in this chapter. Finally, only low-level operation is considered; the small-signal approximation is made. All r-f amplitudes are assumed to be so small that quantities containing quadratic and higher-order factors can be neglected. The theory is linear in the r-f amplitudes.

The electrons from the cathode have a spread in velocity corresponding to the temperature of the cathode. Because of velocity differences, electron trajectories are not identical. If there is a potential minimum outside the cathode, slow electrons are reflected and only those with sufficiently high initial velocities pass the minimum. Moreover the transit times of electrons traversing similar paths are different for electrons in different velocity groups. Therefore it is necessary to include the spread in velocity in a general theory of space-charge devices. The velocity spread is particularly important in a space-charge-limited

97

cathode-grid region in which the distance from the cathode to the potential minimum is not a negligible fraction of the cathode-grid spacing. In most output regions, however, the velocity spread can be neglected because of the high voltages that are usually used. It can also be neglected in the grid-screen region of most tetrodes, except when that region contains a virtual cathode. Also, an input region with a temperature-limited cathode can be treated by the single-velocity theory with a fair degree of accuracy. In fact the single-velocity theory has considerable validity with a space-charge-limited cathode if the cathode emission is such that the potential minimum lies near the cathode surface.

The different regions of a tube interact through the beam and through outside coupling devices that affect the gap voltages. The properties of the beam as it leaves one region, together with the nature of the separating grid, determine the properties of the beam as it enters the next region. The number of electrons can be reduced by capture by the grid, but the velocities of the electrons that get through the grid are essentially unchanged. The initial conditions in each region are determined by the final conditions in the preceding region. Hence the characteristics of the tube as a whole result from a synthesis of the characteristics of the individual regions.

What is usually required is the driving current in the output region. This current contains contributions proportional to the input gap-voltage, the negative of the coefficient being the electronic transadmittance, and noise contributions arising from fluctuations in the cathode emission and fluctuations due to the random nature of the process of capture of electrons by the grids. If the velocity spread in the output region is negligible, the driving current is a linear function of the r-f output voltage and the density and velocity modulations at injection. The latter two quantities are related to the density and velocity modulations at the plane of exit of the preceding region. A simple assumption is that the density modulation at injection into the output region that is not due to the action of the grid is a definite fraction of the density modulation at the plane of exit of the preceding region and that the two velocity modulations are the same. This assumption is certainly valid as long as the velocity spread of the incident electrons is a small fraction of the average velocity. When such is not the case, the velocity dependence of the capture mechanism can affect the relationship. In the input region the density and velocity modulations at the exit (grid) plane are the sums of contributions from the input gap voltage and from fluctuations in the cathode emission. If the tube is a tetrode, the grid-screen region is usually not a part of a resonant circuit and no r-f voltage develops in this region. The density and velocity modulations at the exit (screen) plane of this region are linear functions of the density and velocity modulations at the entrance (grid) plane.    The latter are simply related to the modulations at the exit plane of the input region, which in turn are sums of contributions from the input gap voltage and from fluctuations in the cathode emission.

The characteristics of a single region are expressed in terms of quantities that contain the frequency and depend only on the d-c properties of the beam.    Three of these are coefficients of the r-f gap-voltage; they are the beam-loading admittance, the density-modulation admittance, and the velocity-modulation admittance.    In addition there are excitation and modulation functions, which give the effects of the density modulation at injection of infinitesimal velocity groups.    If the velocity spread is negligible, these functions reduce to excitation and modulation matrices.    The elements of these matrices are obtained from the Llewellyn theory, which is developed in Sec. 3·6.    Only a beginning has been made in the solution of the problem of finding the admittances and excitation and modulation functions for a region having a spread in velocity.

In the next section are to be found precise definitions of the quantities just introduced.    In the section following are presented some general relations for the triode and tetrode.    Next are four sections on the application of the single-velocity theory.    In the remaining three sections some of the simpler problems of velocity-distribution phenomena are discussed.

**5·1. Characteristics of a Single Region.**—As a beam passes through a region of a tube, its most important properties are the driving current and the density and velocity modulations at the plane of exit.    These properties can be regarded as produced partly by the gap voltage and partly by the modulations present in the beam at injection.    Thus in the shunt formulation of Sec. 3·4,

$$\left.\begin{aligned}
i_\omega &= -V_\omega Y_B + i_m, \\
i_\omega(d) &= -V_\omega y_m(d) + i_m(d), \\
v_\omega(d) &= -V_\omega \left(\frac{v(d)}{-I_0}\right) f_m(d) + v_m(d).
\end{aligned}\right\} \tag{1}$$

The coefficient $Y_B$ is the beam-loading admittance, the coefficient $y_m(d)$ is the density-modulation admittance at the exit plane, and the factor $f_m(d)$ is the velocity-modulation admittance at the exit plane.    The quantity $i_m$ is the exciting current, and the quantities $i_m(d)$ and $v_m(d)$ are the density modulation and velocity modulation, respectively, at the exit plane arising from modulations present in the beam at injection.

The beam-loading admittance is conveniently combined with the resonator and load admittances (measured at the gap), and the total circuit admittance, $Y = Y_B + Y_R + Y_L$, is introduced. The gap voltage arising from modulations in the beam at injection is then given by the simple relation,

$$i_m = V_\omega Y. \tag{2}$$

In the input there is, in addition, the gap voltage caused by the signal. The signal, of course, has its own noise components.

*Velocity Distribution.*—The velocity spread of the electrons of the beam is described with the use of a current distribution function $i(x,v,t)$. The electron current at the plane $x$ at time $t$ due to electrons with velocities in the range $v$ to $v + dv$ is $i(x,v,t)dv$. The lowest (or most negative) velocity at the plane $x$ at time $t$ is $v^l(x,t)$. The electron current then is

$$i(x,t) = \int_{v^l(x,t)}^{\infty} dv\, i(x,v,t), \tag{3}$$

and, if $v^l(x,t) \geqq 0$, the average velocity of the electrons passing through the plane $x$ at time $t$ is

$$v(x,t) = \frac{\int_{v^l(x,t)}^{\infty} dv\, vi(x,v,t)}{\int_{v^l(x,t)}^{\infty} dv\, i(x,v,t)}. \tag{4}$$

These quantities have their d-c and r-f components, $i(x) = -I_0$, $i_\omega(x)$, $v(x)$, $v_\omega(x)$, which can be expressed in terms of the d-c and r-f components of the distribution function, $i(x,v)$, $i_\omega(x,v)$, and the d-c and r-f components of the lower limit in the velocity, $v^l(x)$, $v_\omega^l(x)$.

*Excitation and Modulation Functions.*—The exciting current and the density and velocity modulations at the plane $x$ due to modulations at injection can be expressed in terms of the modulations in the distribution function at injection. If electrons enter the region only at the first plane, as is assumed, any electrons with negative velocities have been reflected in the region and come originally from the first plane with positive velocities. Hence if the lower limit of the total distribution at the first plane is negative or zero, as is the case when that plane is the cathode, the distribution of the injected electrons extends from zero upwards. The desired expressions are

$$\left.\begin{aligned}
i_m &= \int_0^{\infty} dv'\, i_\omega(0,v')\mu_i(v'), \\
i_m(x) &= \int_0^{\infty} dv'\, i_\omega(0,v')\mu_i(x;v'), \\
v_m(x) &= \frac{v(x)}{-I_0} \int_0^{\infty} dv'\, i_\omega(0,v')\mu_v(x;v').
\end{aligned}\right\} \tag{5}$$

The quantity $\mu_i(v')$ is the excitation function for modulations in the injected current due to electrons in the velocity range $v'$ to $v' + dv'$. The quantities $\mu_i(x;v')$ and $\mu_v(x;v')$ are the corresponding modulation functions for the density and velocity modulations at the plane $x$, respectively. If the lower limit of the total distribution at the first plane is positive, additional terms must be added to the above expressions to provide for the modulation of that lower limit. The excitation and modulation functions contain the frequency but depend only on the d-c properties of the beam. It is clear that $\mu_i(v')$ is the space average of $\mu_i(x;v')$.

*Llewellyn Approximation.*—If all the electrons at a given plane at a given time have the same velocity, which is the basic assumption of the single-velocity theory, $i_\omega(0,v')$ is readily shown to be given by the expression

$$i_\omega(0,v') = i_\omega(0)\delta(v' - v(0)) + I_0 v_\omega(0)\delta'(v' - v(0)) \tag{6}$$

where $\delta(v')$ and $\delta'(v')$ are the Dirac delta function and its derivative. These two functions have the property that for any function $f(v')$

$$\int dv'\, \delta(v')f(v') = f(0),$$

$$\int dv'\, \delta'(v')f(v') = -\left[\frac{\partial f(v')}{\partial v'}\right]_0,$$

provided the integrations include the origin. Substitution of Eq. (6) in Eqs. (5) leads to the expressions

$$\left.\begin{aligned}
i_m &= i_\omega(0)\mu_i(v(0)) - I_0 v_\omega(0)\left[\frac{\partial}{\partial v'}\mu_i(v')\right]_{v(0)}, \\
i_m(x) &= i_\omega(0)\mu_i(x;v(0)) - I_0 v_\omega(0)\left[\frac{\partial}{\partial v'}\mu_i(x;v')\right]_{v(0)}, \\
v_m(x) &= \frac{v(x)}{-I_0}\left\{i_\omega(0)\mu_v(x;v(0)) - I_0 v_\omega(0)\left[\frac{\partial}{\partial v'}\mu_v(x;v')\right]_{v(0)}\right\}
\end{aligned}\right\} \tag{7}$$

It is convenient to rewrite these equations in the form

$$\left.\begin{aligned}
i_m &= i_\omega(0)\mu_{ii} + v_\omega(0)\left(\frac{-I_0}{v(d)}\right)\mu_{iv}, \\
i_m(x) &= i_\omega(0)\mu_{ii}(x) + v_\omega(0)\left(\frac{-I_0}{v(x)}\right)\mu_{iv}(x), \\
v_m(x) &= i_\omega(0)\left(\frac{v(x)}{-I_0}\right)\mu_{vi}(x) + v_\omega(0)\mu_{vv}(x).
\end{aligned}\right\} \tag{8}$$

By comparison of the two sets of equations,

$$
\left.
\begin{aligned}
\mu_{ii} &\equiv \mu_i(v(0)), & \mu_{iv} &\equiv v(d)\left[\frac{\partial}{\partial v'}\,\mu_i(v')\right]_{v(0)}, \\[2mm]
\mu_{ii}(x) &\equiv \mu_i(x;v(0)), & \mu_{iv}(x) &\equiv v(x)\left[\frac{\partial}{\partial v'}\,\mu_i(x;v')\right]_{v(0)}, \\[2mm]
\mu_{vi}(x) &\equiv \mu_v(x;v(0)), & \mu_{vv}(x) &\equiv v(x)\left[\frac{\partial}{\partial v'}\,\mu_v(x;v')\right]_{v(0)}.
\end{aligned}
\right\}
\qquad (9)
$$

It is seen that

$$
\mu_{ii} = \frac{1}{d}\int_0^d dx\,\mu_{ii}(x), \qquad \mu_{iv} = \frac{1}{d}\int_0^d dx\,\frac{v(d)}{v(x)}\,\mu_{iv}(x). \qquad (10)
$$

Since $i_m$, $i_m(x)$, and $v_m(x)$ for the single-velocity theory are given explicitly as functions of $i_\omega(0)$ and $v_\omega(0)$ in Sec. 3·6, the six elements of Eqs. (9) are readily found from the formulas of that section. They can also be calculated from the general theory of the low-velocity gap without reflections, by methods that are described in Sec. 8.

*Excitation and Modulation Matrices.*—The coefficients of Eqs. (8) define two matrices that are useful in the single-velocity theory of space-charge devices. The first of these is the one-row two-column excitation matrix,

$$
\mu_i = (\mu_{ii} \quad \mu_{iv});
$$

and the second is the two-row two-column modulation matrix,

$$
\mu(x) = \begin{pmatrix} \mu_{ii}(x) & \mu_{iv}(x) \\ \mu_{vi}(x) & \mu_{vv}(x) \end{pmatrix}.
$$

The excitation matrix is

$$
\mu_i = \left(\frac{\epsilon_0}{\epsilon}\,M - \frac{a(0)}{a(d)}\,\delta\,\frac{j\theta N}{6} \quad r\,\frac{j\theta}{2}\,He^{-i\eta}\right)\frac{e^{-i\theta/2}}{1 - \left(1 - \dfrac{\epsilon_0}{\epsilon}\right)Ne^{-i\theta/2}}, \qquad (11)
$$

as is seen from Eq. (3.69). The field parameter $\delta$ is not to be confused with the Dirac delta function of Eq. 6. The modulation matrix at the exit plane is

$$
\mu(d) = \begin{cases}
\sigma\left[1 - \left(1 - \dfrac{\epsilon_0}{\epsilon}\right)Ne^{-\frac{j\theta}{2}}\right] + (1-\sigma)He^{-i\eta}\left[\dfrac{\epsilon_0}{\epsilon}\,M - \dfrac{a(0)}{a(d)}\,\delta\,\dfrac{j\theta N}{6}\right] \\[4mm]
- (1-\sigma)\dfrac{2}{j\theta r}\dfrac{\epsilon_0}{\epsilon}\left[1 - \left(1 - \dfrac{\epsilon_0}{\epsilon}\right)Ne^{-\frac{j\theta}{2}}\right] + (1-\sigma)\dfrac{2}{j\theta r}\left(\dfrac{\epsilon_0}{\epsilon}\,M\right. \\[4mm]
\hspace{4cm} \left. + \delta\,\dfrac{j\theta N}{6}\right)\left[\dfrac{\epsilon_0}{\epsilon}\,M - \dfrac{a(0)}{a(d)}\,\delta\,\dfrac{j\theta N}{6}\right]
\end{cases}
$$

$$\left.\begin{array}{l} j\theta\left[1 - \left(1 - \dfrac{\epsilon_0}{\epsilon}\right) Ne^{-\frac{j\theta}{2}}\right] + (1 - \sigma)r\dfrac{j\theta}{2}H^2 e^{-j2\eta} \\[2ex] \left[\dfrac{v(0)}{v(d)} - (1 - \sigma)\right]\left[1 - \left(1 - \dfrac{\epsilon_0}{\epsilon}\right) Ne^{-\frac{j\theta}{2}}\right] \\[2ex] \qquad + (1 - \sigma)\left(\dfrac{\epsilon_0}{\epsilon}M + \delta\dfrac{j\theta N}{6}\right) He^{-j\eta} \end{array}\right\} \dfrac{e^{-j\theta}}{1 - \left(1 - \dfrac{\epsilon_0}{\epsilon}\right) Ne^{-\frac{j\theta}{2}}}. \qquad (12)$$

The elements of this matrix are obtained from Eq. (3.71) and Eq. (3.73) with $x = d$.

*Single-velocity Admittances.*—The beam-loading admittance in the single-velocity theory is given by Eq. (3.68). It is

$$Y_B = \frac{j\omega C \left(1 - \dfrac{\epsilon_0}{\epsilon}\right) Ne^{-\frac{j\theta}{2}}}{1 - \left(1 - \dfrac{\epsilon_0}{\epsilon}\right) Ne^{-\frac{j\theta}{2}}} \qquad (13)$$

The density-modulation admittance at the exit plane is obtained from Eq. (3.70) with $x = d$. It is

$$y_m(d) = \frac{j\omega C(1 - \sigma)He^{-j\left(\eta + \frac{\theta}{2}\right)}}{1 - \left(1 - \dfrac{\epsilon_0}{\epsilon}\right) Ne^{-\frac{j\theta}{2}}}. \qquad (14)$$

The velocity-modulation admittance at the exit plane is obtained from Eq. (3.72) with $x = d$. It is

$$f_m(d) = \frac{j\omega C(1 - \sigma)\dfrac{2}{j\theta r}\left(\dfrac{\epsilon_0}{\epsilon}M + \delta\dfrac{j\theta N}{6}\right)e^{-\frac{j\theta}{2}}}{1 - \left(1 - \dfrac{\epsilon_0}{\epsilon}\right) Ne^{-\frac{j\theta}{2}}} \qquad (15)$$

In these formulas

$$r = \frac{v(d)T}{d}, \qquad \delta = \frac{a(d)T^2}{2d}$$

and

$$\frac{\epsilon_0}{\epsilon} = 1 - \frac{J_0 T^3}{6d}, \qquad \sigma = 1 - \frac{J_0 T^2}{2v(d)}.$$

These parameters are not independent, since

$$1 - \frac{\epsilon_0}{\epsilon} = 1 - r + \delta, \qquad 1 - \sigma = (1 - r + \delta)\frac{3}{r}. \qquad (16)$$

Also it is to be noted that

$$\left.\begin{array}{l} \dfrac{a(0)}{a(d)} = 1 - (1 - \sigma)\,\dfrac{r}{\delta}, \qquad \dfrac{v(0)}{v(d)} = \dfrac{2}{r} + \dfrac{1}{3}\,(1 - \sigma) - 1, \\[3mm] \omega C\left(1 - \dfrac{\epsilon_0}{\epsilon}\right) = \dfrac{G_d r^2}{2}\!\left(\dfrac{\theta}{6}\right) = \dfrac{1}{\rho_0}\left(1 - \dfrac{\epsilon_0}{\epsilon}\right)^2\dfrac{\theta}{2}, \\[3mm] \omega C\,(1 - \sigma) = \dfrac{G_d r}{2}\left(\dfrac{\theta}{2}\right) = \dfrac{1}{\rho_0}\dfrac{3}{r}\left(1 - \dfrac{\epsilon_0}{\epsilon}\right)^2\dfrac{\theta}{2}, \end{array}\right\} \qquad (17)$$

where $G_d = I_0/V_d$, and $\rho_0 = J_0 T^4/12 A \epsilon_0$. For zero direct current, $\epsilon_0/\epsilon$ and $\sigma$ are unity, $\delta = r - 1$, and $a(0) = a(d)$. For maximum direct current, $\epsilon_0/\epsilon$ is zero, $\sigma = -v(0)/v(d)$, $\delta = r = \dfrac{3}{(1 - \sigma)}$, and $a(0)/a(d) = \sigma$.

*Cathode-grid Region.*—Velocity distribution phenomena are usually most important in the input region, because of the low injection velocities, wide thermal spread, and reflected electrons if there is a potential minimum. If the grid has a high positive voltage and the cathode emission is not too great, the current that reaches the grid plane is temperature limited and there is an accelerating field everywhere in the region. A potential minimum can be made to appear at the cathode by increasing the cathode emission or decreasing the grid voltage. As the potential minimum grows, electrons are reflected and the current that reaches the grid plane is space-charge limited. There is a decelerating field between the cathode and the minimum and an accelerating field beyond. If the grid voltage is made sufficiently negative, the minimum reaches the grid and disappears. There is then a decelerating field everywhere within the region and only electrons with high velocities at injection reach the grid plane.

The single-velocity theory can be used to give an approximate treatment of the input region if the grid has a high positive voltage and the current is temperature limited, or space-charge limited with a cathode emission so large that the potential minimum is very near to the cathode. With sufficiently high grid voltage, the spread of the transit angles of the electrons which reach the grid plane is a small fraction of a radian. If there is a potential minimum and it is very near the cathode, the angles of the electrons that are reflected are all much less than one radian. Hence those electrons that are reflected have a negligible effect on the behavior of the gap and those that reach the grid plane can be regarded as having a single velocity.

Temperature-limited cathodes are rarely used because of excessive noise and the tendency of the cathode surface to disintegrate. In microwave tubes the cathode-grid spacing is often so small that the distance from the cathode to the potential minimum is a good fraction of the cathode-grid spacing. In fact with the currents used, the minimum often occurs at the grid or disappears into the grid. A very large fraction of the injected electrons is reflected and a good portion spends a large part of a cycle in the region. These electrons have an appreciable effect on the behavior of the gap.

*Consistent Theory.*—A complete, consistent theory of the r-f behavior of a uniform region must take into account the distribution in velocity of the electrons and include the effects of space charge. The r-f phenomena are completely described in terms of the total r-f current (as determined by the rest of the circuit), the injected r-f electron current distribution (as determined by the cathode or the preceding region), and certain impedance and transfer coefficients. A complete theory must provide these coefficients as functions of frequency.

A starting point in the theory is the defining relation for the total current, Eq. (3·3). Rearranged and with the field replaced by the acceleration $a(x,t)$, it becomes

$$\frac{\partial a(x,t)}{\partial t} = -J(t) + j(x,t). \tag{18}$$

where

$$J(t) = \frac{eI(t)}{mA\epsilon_0}, \qquad j(x,t) = \frac{ei(x,t)}{mA\epsilon_0}.$$

The quantities $J(t)$ and $j(x,t)$ occur frequently in electronic theory and have the dimensions of meter/sec³. If the electron current is one amp/meter², $j(x,t)$ is $2 \times 10^{22}$ meters/sec³.

If the beam is composed of a single stream of electrons, a stream being a single-velocity group, $j(x,t)$ in Eq. (18) can be combined with the partial time derivative to give the total time derivative. The result is Llewellyn's equation, derived in Sec. 3·6,

$$\frac{da(x,t)}{dt} = -J(t).$$

This is the fundamental relation of the single-velocity theory of a uniform region. It serves to determine $a(x,t)$, from which the electron current and other quantities can be derived by the use of Eq. (18).

The problem is much more complex if the beam is composed of more than one stream. To begin with

$$j(x,t) = \int_{v^i(x,t)}^{\infty} dv j(x,v,t), \tag{19}$$

where

$$j(x,v,t) = \frac{ei(x,v,t)}{mA\epsilon_0}.$$

It is to be observed that $J(t)$ is determined by the resonator and load (the circuit) and that $j(x,v,t)$ and $v^i(x\ t)$ are determined by the injected current distribution and the acceleration experienced by the electrons. Hence the acceleration enters on both sides of Eq. (18), which is in reality an integral equation for the acceleration. This integral equation must be satisfied by a consistent theory. In the small-signal approximation, it breaks up into two integral equations, one for the determination of the d-c characteristics and another for the determination of the r-f characteristics. Examples of such equations are given later in the chapter.

**5·2. General Relations for Multi-grid Tubes.**—The exciting current of the output of a multi-grid tube is the sum of a current proportional to the input voltage and a current arising from fluctuations in the cathode emission and fluctuations in the partition of the d-c current to the grids. The exciting current is therefore represented as follows:

$$[i_m]_{\text{out}} = -\lfloor V_\omega \rfloor_{\text{in}} Y_m + \lfloor i_N \rfloor_{\text{out}}. \tag{20}$$

In this expression $Y_m$ is the electronic transadmittance of the tube and $i_N$ is that portion of the exciting current arising from cathode and partition fluctuations except for the noise current arising from the input noise voltage due to cathode fluctuations. The total output noise exciting current arising from cathode and partition fluctuations is

$$- \left[\frac{i_m}{Y}\right]_{\text{in}} Y_m + \lfloor i_N \rfloor_{\text{out}}, \tag{21}$$

where $\lfloor i_m/Y \rfloor_{\text{in}}$ is the input noise voltage due to cathode fluctuations.

The output power is $[\tfrac{1}{2}G_L|V_\omega|^2]_{\text{out}}$ and, neglecting noise,

$$[V_\omega Y]_{\text{out}} = -[V_\omega]_{\text{in}} Y_m.$$

Since the input power is $[\tfrac{1}{2}G_{BR}|V_\omega|^2]_{\text{in}}$, where $G_{BR} = G_B + G_R$ is the beam loading and resonator conductance, the power gain of the tube is

$$G = \left[\frac{1}{G_{BR}}\right]_{\text{in}} |Y_m|^2 \left[\frac{G_L}{|Y|^2}\right]_{\text{out}}. \tag{22}$$

On the other hand, the noise power out due to cathode and partition fluctuations is

$$\frac{1}{2}\left[\frac{G_L}{|Y|^2}\right]_{\text{out}} \left| - \left[\frac{i_m}{Y}\right]_{\text{in}} Y_m + \lfloor i_N \rfloor_{\text{out}} \right|^2,$$

and therefore the noise figure of the tube is

$$NF = 1 + \frac{\dfrac{1}{2}\left[\dfrac{G_L}{|Y|^2}\right]_{\text{out}}\left|-\left[\dfrac{i_m}{Y}\right]_{\text{in}}Y_m + [i_N]_{\text{out}}\right|^2}{GkT_0\,\Delta f} \tag{23}$$

where $k$ is Boltzmann's constant, $T_0$ is the temperature of the room, and $\Delta f$ is the bandwidth of the detecting device. This formula includes the input noise due to cathode fluctuations, which is partially coherent with the remaining noise, but does not contain noise contributions of the circuit. After the gain is substituted from Eq. (22), the formula for the noise figure becomes

$$NF = 1 + \frac{\dfrac{1}{2}\,[G_{BR}]_{\text{in}}\left|-\left[\dfrac{i_m}{Y}\right]_{\text{in}} + \dfrac{[i_N]_{\text{out}}}{Y_m}\right|^2}{kT_0\,\Delta f}. \tag{24}$$

A reduction in the input loading increases the gain and reduces the noise figure.

The net current flowing to a grid, the grid current, is a quantity that is sometimes of interest in circuit analysis. It is the difference in the total currents in the regions immediately preceding and following the grid,

$$I_g = [I_\omega]_{\text{preceding}} - [I_\omega]_{\text{following}}.$$

The grid current is the sum of a current proportional to the input voltage and a current arising from fluctuations in cathode emission and fluctuations in the partition of the d-c current to the grids. Hence it can be represented as follows:

$$I_g = -[V_\omega]_{\text{in}}Y_{mg} + i_{Ng}, \tag{25}$$

where $Y_{mg}$ is a grid transadmittance. The total grid noise current arising from cathode and partition fluctuations is

$$-\left[\frac{i_m}{Y}\right]_{\text{in}}Y_{mg} + i_{Ng}. \tag{26}$$

The electronic transadmittance $Y_m$ and the noise current $[i_N]_{\text{out}}$ are calculated by combining the characteristics of the individual regions of the tube. In general, velocity spread is negligible in all but the input region. The density and velocity modulations at the exit plane of the input region are assumed to be known and the single-velocity theory used for the regions following. At each grid it is assumed that

$$[i_\omega(0)]_{\text{following}} = \alpha_g[i_\omega(d)]_{\text{preceding}} + i_g,$$
$$[v_\omega(0)]_{\text{following}} = [v_\omega(d)]_{\text{preceding}}.$$

In these formulas $\alpha_g$ is the transmission coefficient of the grid and $i_g$ is the grid partition current. The grid partition current has the spectral density,

$$G_{i_g}(f) = 2e\alpha_g(1 - \alpha_g)I_0,$$

where $-I_0$ is the direct current in the region preceding the grid.

*High-mu Triode.*—A triode containing a cathode-grid region $(kg)$ which is completely isolated, except for the unidirectional beam, from the grid-anode region $(ga)$ has an electronic transadmittance and output noise current which are given by the formulas

$$\left. \begin{aligned} Y_m &= \alpha_g \left\{ [y_m(d)]_{kg}[\mu_{ii}]_{ga} + [v(d)f_m(d)]_{kg} \left[ \frac{\mu_{iv}}{v(d)} \right]_{ga} \right\}, \\ [i_N]_{\text{out}} &= \alpha_g \left\{ [i_m(d)]_{kg}[\mu_{i\cdot}]_{ga} + [-I_0 v_m(d)]_{kg} \left[ \frac{\mu_{iv}}{v(d)} \right]_{ga} \right\} + i_g[\mu_{ii}]_{ga}. \end{aligned} \right\} \quad (27)$$

The electronic transadmittance is seen to be the sum of two terms. One term contains the density-modulation admittance at the exit plane of the cathode-grid region and the other contains the velocity-modulation admittance at that plane. Similarly, the output noise current has terms containing the density modulation and velocity modulation at the exit plane of the cathode-grid region; in addition it has a term proportional to the grid partition current.

The grid transadmittance and the grid noise current are given by the formulas,

$$\left. \begin{aligned} Y_{mg} &= [Y_g]_{kg} - Y_m \left[ \frac{-Y_g}{Y} + 1 \right]_{ga}, \\ i_{Ng} &= [i_m]_{kg} - [i_N]_{\text{out}} \left[ \frac{-Y_g}{Y} + 1 \right]_{ga}. \end{aligned} \right\} \quad (28)$$

If the output circuit is tuned, $[-Y_g/Y + 1]_{ga} \approx [-j\omega C/G]_{ga}$ and the displacement current far exceeds the electron current.

The four expressions of Eqs. (27) and (28) are derived by the straightforward application of the relations of the preceding paragraph to the two equations,

$$[i_m]_{\text{out}} = \left[ i_\omega(0)\mu_{ii} + v_\omega(0) \left( \frac{-I_0}{v(d)} \right) \mu_{iv} \right]_{ga},$$

$$I_g = [-V_\omega Y_g + i_m]_{kg} - \left[ i_m \left( \frac{-Y_g}{Y} + 1 \right) \right]_{ga}.$$

and by the comparison of the results with Eqs. (20) and (25).

*Tetrode.*—No appreciable r-f voltage develops in the grid-screen region $(gs)$ of a tetrode if that region is not part of a resonant circuit. The formulas for the electronic transadmittance and output noise current are

$$Y_m = \alpha_s \alpha_g \left\{ [y_m(d)]_{kg}\,[\mu_{ii}(d)]_{gs}[\mu_{ii}]_{sa} + [v(d)f_m(d)]_{kg}\left[\frac{\mu_{iv}(d)}{v(d)}\right]_{gs}[\mu_{ii}]_{sa} \right.$$

$$\left. + [y_m(d)]_{kg}[v(d)\mu_{vi}(d)]_{gs}\left[\frac{\mu_{iv}}{v(d)}\right]_{sa} + [v(d)f_m(d)]_{kg}[\mu_{vv}(d)]_{gs}\left[\frac{\mu_{iv}}{v(d)}\right]_{sa} \right\}$$

$$[i_N]_{\text{out}} = \alpha_s \alpha_g \left\{ [i_m(d)]_{kg}[\mu_{ii}(d)]_{gs}[\mu_{ii}]_{sa} + \lfloor -I_0 v_m(d)]_{kg}\left[\frac{\mu_{iv}(d)}{v(d)}\right]_{gs}[\mu_{ii}]_{sa} \right. \qquad (29)$$

$$+ [i_m(d)]_{kg}[v(d)\mu_{vi}(d)]_{gs}\left[\frac{\mu_{iv}}{v(d)}\right]_{sa} + \lfloor -I_0 v_m(d)]_{kg}[\mu_{vv}(d)]_{gs}\left[\frac{\mu_{iv}}{v(d)}\right]_{sa} \right\}$$

$$+ \alpha_s i_g \left\{ [\mu_{ii}(d)]_{gs}[\mu_{ii}]_{sa} + [v(d)\mu_{vi}(d)]_{gs}\left[\frac{\mu_{iv}}{v(d)}\right]_{sa} \right\} + i_s[\mu_{ii}]_{sa}.$$

In these expressions $\alpha_s$ is the screen transmission coefficient and $i_s$ is the screen partition current. The electronic transadmittance contains twice as many terms as for a triode because both the density modulation and velocity modulation from the input region can, through the action of the grid-screen region, lead to density modulation and velocity modulation at the injection plane of the output region. Similarly, there are twice as many terms from cathode fluctuations in the noise output current; in addition there are both density and velocity modulation contributions from the grid partition current as well as a density contribution from the screen partition current.

The total current for the grid-screen region is just the exciting current. The exciting current is the sum of a current proportional to the input voltage and a current arising from cathode and grid partition fluctuations. Thus

$$[i_m]_{gs} = -[V_\omega]_{\text{in}} Y_m{}' + [i_N]_{gs}, \qquad (30)$$

which is a relation similar to Eq. (20). In this equation

$$Y_m{}' = \alpha_g \left\{ [y_m(d)]_{kg}[\mu_{ii}]_{gs} + [v(d)f_m(d)]_{kg}\left[\frac{\mu_{iv}}{v(d)}\right]_{gs} \right\},$$

$$[i_N]_{gs} = \alpha_g \left\{ [i_m(d)]_{kg}[\mu_{ii}]_{gs} + \lfloor -I_0 v_m(d)]_{kg}\left[\frac{\mu_{iv}}{v(d)}\right]_{gs} \right\} + i_g[\mu_{ii}]_{gs}, \qquad (31)$$

as is seen directly or by the use of Eqs. (27) for the triode.

The grid transadmittance and grid noise current are

$$\begin{aligned} Y_{mg} &= [Y_g]_{kg} - Y_m{}', \\ i_{Ng} &= [i_m]_{kg} - [i_N]_{gs}. \end{aligned} \qquad (32)$$

The screen transadmittance and screen noise current are

$$\begin{aligned} Y_{ms} &= Y_m{}' - Y_m\left[\frac{-Y_g}{Y} + 1\right]_{sa}, \\ i_{Ns} &= [i_N]_{gs} - [i_N]_{\text{out}}\left[\frac{-Y_g}{Y} + 1\right]_{sa}. \end{aligned} \qquad (33)$$

Eqs. (29), (32), and (33) are derived from the three expressions

$$[i_m]_{out} = \left[ i_\omega(0)\mu_{ii} + v_\omega(0) \left(\frac{-I_0}{v(d)}\right) \mu_{iv} \right]_{sa},$$

$$I_g = [- V_\omega Y_g + i_m]_{kg} - [i_m]_{gs},$$

$$I_s = [i_m]_{gs} - \left[ i_m \left(\frac{-Y_g}{Y} + 1\right) \right]_{sa}.$$

Similar relations are readily obtained for tubes containing four and more regions.

**5·3. Positive-grid Space-charge-limited Input with Minimum near Cathode.**—If the rate of emission of electrons by the cathode is such that the potential minimum is very near to the cathode, the electrons that are reflected spend but a small] part of a cycle in the region and their effect on the r-f behavior of the region is small. If in addition the voltage on the grid is high, the transit angles of the electrons that reach the grid are all approximately the same, since the spread in the velocities at injection gives only a small spread in the average velocities during the passage. Under these conditions the space-charge-limited cathode-grid region can be treated approximately by the single-velocity theory.

In the single-velocity theory the maximum direct current occurs when $\epsilon_0/\epsilon = 0$. For this current the smoothing parameter $\sigma$ has the value $-v(0)/v(d)$, which is practically zero since, under the assumption of high grid voltage, $v(d) \gg v(0)$. In addition $r = \delta \approx 3$, and $a(0)/a(d) \approx 0$.

*Gap Impedance and Admittance.*—The beam-loading impedance is obtained from Eqs. (3·65); with $\epsilon_0/\epsilon = 0$, it is

$$Z_B = - \frac{N}{j\omega C} e^{-j\frac{\theta}{2}}.$$

Therefore the gap impedance is

$$Z_g = \frac{1}{j\omega C} [1 - N e^{-j\frac{\theta}{2}}].$$

However from Eq. (17) $1/\omega C = \rho_0 2/\theta$; hence the gap impedance can be written as

$$Z_g = \rho_0 M N + \frac{1}{j\omega C}\left(1 - N \cos \frac{\theta}{2}\right),$$

or alternatively as

$$Z_g = \rho_0 \left[ M N - j \frac{2}{\theta}\left(1 - N \cos \frac{\theta}{2}\right)\right]. \tag{34}$$

The real and imaginary parts of $Z_g/\rho_0$ are shown plotted in Fig. 5·1 as functions of the transit angle. For zero transit angle the gap behaves like a pure resistance. As $\theta$ increases, the resistance becomes zero at $2\pi$ and it oscillates about zero with a period of $2\pi$ and a very small decreasing amplitude. The reactance is everywhere negative, except at the origin where it is zero. For small angles $Z_g \approx \rho_0 \left(1 - j\dfrac{3\theta}{10}\right)$; for very large angles $Z_g \approx \rho_0 \left(-j\dfrac{2}{\theta}\right) = \dfrac{1}{j\omega C}$, which is the impedance of the empty gap.

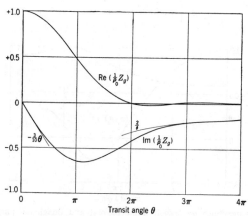

Fig. 5·1.—Dependence on transit angle of real and imaginary parts of diode gap impedance assuming negligible initial electron velocities and complete space charge.

The reciprocal of $Z_g$ is the gap admittance

$$Y_g = \frac{j\omega C}{\left(1 - Ne^{-\frac{j\theta}{2}}\right)}.$$

It is conveniently written as the sum of a conductance and a susceptance as follows:

$$Y_g = \frac{1}{\rho_0}\frac{MN}{\left[(MN)^2 + \left(\dfrac{2}{\theta}\right)^2\left(1 - N\cos\dfrac{\theta}{2}\right)^2\right]} + j\omega C \frac{\left(\dfrac{2}{\theta}\right)^2\left(1 - N\cos\dfrac{\theta}{2}\right)}{\left[(MN)^2 + \left(\dfrac{2}{\theta}\right)^2\left(1 - N\cos\dfrac{\theta}{2}\right)^2\right]}. \quad (35)$$

The dependence on transit angle of the factors multiplying $1/\rho_0$ and $j\omega C$ in $Y_g$ are shown in Fig. 5·2. The conductance has the value $1/\rho_0$ at zero transit angle, drops to zero at $2\pi$, becomes negative, and oscillates about zero with a period of $2\pi$ and decreasing amplitude. The susceptance, on the other hand, has the value $3\omega C/5$ for zero transit angle, is never greater than $\omega C$ for any angle, but attains that value whenever $N = 0$, at which times the conductance is zero. At very large transit angles, $Y_g \approx j\omega C$.

*Excitation Matrix and Input Noise.*—The excitation matrix is obtained from Eq. (11) with $\epsilon_0/\epsilon$ and $a(0)/a(d)$ zero and $r = 3$. It is

$$\mu_i \approx \left( 0 \quad 3\frac{j\theta}{2} He^{-j\eta} \right) \frac{e^{-\frac{j\theta}{2}}}{1 - Ne^{-\frac{j\theta}{2}}}. \tag{36}$$

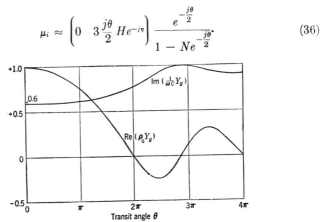

Fig. 5·2.—Dependence on transit angle of real and imaginary parts of diode gap admittance assuming negligible initial electron velocities and complete space charge. Note that the coefficients of the two quantities plotted are not the same.

Hence the noise exciting current of the input is

$$i_m \approx \frac{v_\omega(0) \left( \dfrac{-I_0}{v(d)} \right) 3 \dfrac{j\theta}{2} He^{-j\left(\eta + \frac{\theta}{2}\right)}}{\left(1 - Ne^{-\frac{j\theta}{2}}\right)}.$$

Thus since the coefficient of $i_\omega(0)$ in $i_m$ is practically zero, the input noise is almost entirely due to velocity fluctuations at the potential minimum. For small transit angles

$$\mu_i \approx (0 \quad 3)e^{-j\frac{11\theta}{30}}, \tag{37}$$

and for large transit angles

$$\mu_i \approx (0 \quad -3)e^{-j\theta}. \tag{38}$$

The time average of the square of the current at the cathode plane is related to the spectral density $G_i(f)$ of that current through the formula

$$\overline{i(0,t)^2} = I_0^2 + \int_0^\infty df G_i(f).$$

Similarly

$$\overline{v(0,t)^2} = v(0)^2 + \int_0^\infty df\, G_v(f),$$

where $G_v(f)$ is the spectral density of the average velocity. For the pure shot effect

$$G_i(f) = 2eI_0, \qquad G_v(f) = \frac{2e}{I_0}\,\overline{[v^2 - v(0)^2]}.$$

In the noise exciting current $v_\omega(0)$ is the modulation of the average velocity of the electrons which reach the minimum. At the potential minimum $\overline{[v^2 - v(0)^2]} = \frac{2kT}{m}\left(1 - \frac{\pi}{4}\right)$, where $k$ is Boltzmann's constant and $T$ is the absolute temperature of the cathode. These electrons are emitted by the cathode at random; and since the minimum is at the cathode, the spectral density of the average velocity at the minimum is

$$G_v(f) = \frac{2e}{I_0}\frac{2kT}{m}\left(1 - \frac{\pi}{4}\right).$$

The input noise can be regarded as coming from a voltage source in a series input circuit for which

$$e_s \approx \frac{v_\omega(0)}{j\omega C}\left(\frac{-I_0}{v(d)}\right) 3\frac{j\theta}{2} He^{-j\left(\eta + \frac{\theta}{2}\right)}.$$

Therefore, since

$$|e_s|^2 \approx \frac{|v_\omega(0)|^2}{\omega^2 C^2}\left(\frac{I_0}{v(d)}\right)^2 \frac{9\theta^2}{4} H^2$$

the spectral density of the voltage source is

$$G_{e_s} \approx G_d\rho_0^2 2kT\left(1 - \frac{\pi}{4}\right) 9H^2 = \rho_0 4kT3\left(1 - \frac{\pi}{4}\right) H^2, \qquad (39)$$

where $\rho_0$ is the a-c diode resistance. The quantity $3\left(1 - \frac{\pi}{4}\right) = .644$. Since $H$ is unity for zero transit angle, this formula expresses the familiar effect that at low frequencies a space-charge-limited diode with high positive anode behaves like a series voltage noise source with an equivalent resistance equal to the d-c diode resistance and at approximately $\frac{2}{3}$ the cathode temperature.[1] The spectrum depends on the frequency through the factor $H^2$, which behaves like $4/\theta^2$ for very large values of $\theta$.

[1] Compare E. Spenke, *Wiss. Ver. Siemens*, **16**, 2, 19 (1937); A. J. Rack, *Bell Syst. Tech. J.*, **17**, 592 (1938)· D. O. North, *RCA Rev.*, **4**, 44 (1940).

Since $i_m = e_s Y_g$, the diode noise can also be regarded as coming from a shunt current source the spectral density of which is

$$G_{i_m}(f) = |Y_g|^2 G_{e_s}(f).$$

*Density and Velocity Modulation Admittances.*—With $\sigma \approx 0$ and $\omega C = \theta/2\rho_0$, Eq. (14) gives for the density-modulation admittance (internal transadmittance) at the exit plane (the grid) the expression

$$y_m(d) \approx \frac{1}{\rho_0} \frac{\dfrac{j\theta}{2} H e^{-j\left(\eta + \frac{\theta}{2}\right)}}{1 - N e^{-\frac{j\theta}{2}}}. \tag{40}$$

The magnitude and negative of the phase of $\rho_0 y_m(d)$ are shown plotted in Fig. 5·3 as functions of the transit angle. The magnitude of $y_m(d)$

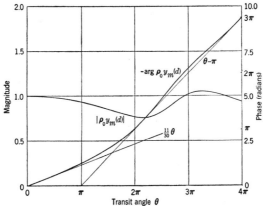

FIG. 5·3.—Dependence on transit angle of magnitude and phase of internal transadmittance at the second plane of diode assuming negligible initial electron velocities and complete space charge.

starts out at zero transit angle as $1/\rho_0$ and oscillates about that value with decreasing amplitude as $\theta$ increases. It never deviates from $1/\rho_0$ by as much as 30 per cent. For small transit angles $y_m(d) \approx \dfrac{1}{\rho_0} e^{-\frac{j 11\theta}{30}}$ and for large transit angles $y_m(d) \approx \dfrac{1}{\rho_0} e^{-j(\theta - \pi)}$.

The velocity-modulation admittance at the exit plane is obtained from Eq. (15), which gives

$$f_m(d) \approx \frac{1}{\rho_0} \frac{\dfrac{j\theta N}{6} e^{-\frac{j\theta}{2}}}{1 - N e^{-\frac{j\theta}{2}}}. \tag{41}$$

For small transit angles $f_m(d) \approx \dfrac{1}{\rho_0} \dfrac{1}{3} e^{-\frac{j\theta}{5}}$ and for large transit angles

$$f_m(d) = \frac{1}{\rho_0} \frac{2}{\theta} \cos \frac{\theta}{2} e^{-j\left(\frac{\theta}{2}+\frac{\pi}{2}\right)}.$$

*Modulation Matrix.*—The modulation matrix at the grid is found by making the proper substitutions in Eq. (12), which then reduces to

$$\mu(d) \approx \begin{bmatrix} 0 & j\theta[1 - Ne^{-\frac{j\theta}{2}} + \frac{3}{2} H^2 e^{-j2\eta}] \\ 0 & -\left[1 - Ne^{-\frac{j\theta}{2}} - 3\frac{j\theta N}{6} He^{-j\eta}\right] \end{bmatrix} \frac{e^{-j\theta}}{1 - Ne^{-\frac{j\theta}{2}}}. \qquad (42)$$

Since the first column of this matrix is approximately zero, the smoothing of the beam as it leaves the space-charge-limited region with respect to density fluctuations at the cathode is practically complete. For small transit angles,

$$\mu(d) \approx \begin{pmatrix} 0 & 3 \\ 0 & \dfrac{j2\theta}{15} \end{pmatrix} e^{-\frac{j7\theta}{10}}, \qquad (43)$$

and for large transit angles

$$\mu(d) \approx \begin{pmatrix} 0 & j\theta \\ 0 & -1 \end{pmatrix} e^{-j\theta}. \qquad (44)$$

**5·4. Grid-screen and Output Regions, Neglecting Velocity Spread.**— The spread in velocity of the electrons is almost always negligible in all regions following the input if there are no reflected electrons in those regions and if the grid and anode voltages are sufficiently high. Two special conditions are of particular interest. If the d-c voltage across the gap is very high, space charge in the gap is negligible and the r-f characteristics of the region are quite simple. On the other hand, if space charge is important, a great simplification is obtained by studying phenomena at large transit angles.

*High-velocity Gap with High Gap-voltage.*—If the d-c gap-voltage is very high, $v(d) \gg v(0)$, and space charge has a negligible effect on the d-c fields. Under these conditions $\epsilon_0/\epsilon \approx 1$, $\sigma \approx 1$, $r \approx 2$, $\delta \approx 1$, and $a(0) \approx a(d)$. The r-f characteristics become

$$\left.\begin{aligned} Y_B &\approx 2G_d \frac{j\theta N}{6} e^{-\frac{j\theta}{2}} \\ y_m(d) &\approx G_d \frac{j\theta}{2} He^{-j\left(\eta+\frac{\theta}{2}\right)}, \qquad f_m(d) \approx G_d \frac{1}{2} He^{-j\left(-\eta+\frac{\theta}{2}\right)}, \\ \mu_i &\approx (1 \quad j\theta)He^{-j\left(\eta+\frac{\theta}{2}\right)}, \\ \mu(d) &\approx \begin{pmatrix} 1 & j\theta \\ 0 & 0 \end{pmatrix} e^{-j\theta}. \end{aligned}\right\} \qquad (45)$$

The velocity modulations at the exit plane arising from both density and velocity modulations at the entrance plane are practically zero.

*Very Large Transit Angle.*—If space charge is not negligible but the transit angle is very large, the r-f characteristics become

$$
\left.
\begin{aligned}
Y_B &\approx 0, \\
y_m(d) &\approx -\frac{G_d}{2} r e^{-j\theta}, \qquad f_m(d) \approx 0, \\
\mu_i &\approx (0 \quad -r) e^{-j\theta}, \\
\mu(d) &\approx \begin{pmatrix} \sigma & j\theta \\ 0 & \dfrac{v(0)}{v(d)} - (1-\sigma) \end{pmatrix} e^{-j\theta}
\end{aligned}
\right\}
\tag{46}
$$

Both the driving current and the velocity modulation at the exit plane are almost entirely due to velocity modulation at injection. Since no special restrictions have been imposed on $\sigma$ and $r$, these relations are readily shown to be consistent with those of the preceding paragraph and also those of Sec. 5·3.

**5·5. Positive-grid High-mu Triode with Minimum near Cathode.**— Both the input and output regions of a positive-grid high-mu triode with large cathode emission can be treated by the single-velocity theory. The formulas of Sec. 5·3 are used for the input and the general formulas of Sec. 5·1, or under special conditions those of Sec. 5·4, are used for the output.

The equation for the electronic transadmittance is

$$
Y_m = \alpha_g \left\{ [y_m(d)]_{kg} [\mu_{ii}]_{ga} + [v(d) f_m(d)]_{kg} \left[ \frac{\mu_{iv}}{v(d)} \right]_{ga} \right\},
$$

which is taken from Eqs. (27). Since the first column is zero in both the excitation and modulation matrices of the input region, density fluctuations in the cathode emission drop out of both the noise figure and the total grid noise current and only velocity and partition fluctuations remain. Eq. (24) for the noise figure becomes

$$
\begin{aligned}
NF = 1 &+ [G_{BR}\rho_0]_{kg} \frac{T}{T_0} \left\{ 3\left(1 - \frac{\pi}{4}\right) \frac{4}{9} \left| -\left[ \frac{\mu_{iv}}{\rho_0 Y} \right]_{kg} \right. \right. \\
&+ \frac{\alpha_g}{\rho_0 Y_m} \left( [\mu_{iv}(d)]_{kg} [\mu_{ii}]_{ga} + [v(d)\mu_{vv}(d)]_{kg} \left[ \frac{\mu_{iv}}{v(d)} \right]_{ag} \right) \bigg|^2 \\
&+ \left. 2\alpha_g(1 - \alpha_g) \left( \frac{eI_0\rho_0}{kT} \right) \frac{1}{|\rho_0 Y_m|^2} |[\mu_{ii}]_{ga}|^2 \right\}.
\end{aligned}
\tag{47}
$$

The total grid noise current due to cathode and partition fluctuations takes the form

$$v_\omega(0) \left(\frac{-I_0}{v(d)}\right) \left\{ [\mu_{iv}]_{kg} \left(\frac{-Y_{mg}}{[Y]_{kg}} + 1\right) - \alpha_g \left([\mu_{iv}(d)]_{kg}[\mu_{ii}]_{ga}\right.\right.$$

$$\left.\left. + [v(d)\mu_{vv}(d)]_{kg} \left[\frac{\mu_{iv}}{v(d)}\right]_{ga}\right)\left[-\frac{Y_g}{Y} + 1\right]_{ga}\right\} - i_g \left[\mu_{ii}\left(\frac{-Y_g}{Y} + 1\right)\right]_{ga}.$$

Using this expression, the total grid noise current is found to have the spectral density

$$G_{I_g}(f) = \frac{4kT}{\rho_0} 3 \left(1 - \frac{\pi}{4}\right) \frac{1}{9} \left[\left| \mu_{\cdot v}\left(\frac{-Y_g}{Y} + 1\right)\right]_{kg}\right.$$

$$- \left(-\left[\frac{\mu_{iv}}{Y}\right]_{kg} Y_m + \alpha_g[\mu_{iv}(d)]_{kg}[\mu_{ii}]_{ga} + \alpha_g[v(d)\mu_{vv}(d)]_{kg} \left[\frac{\mu_{iv}}{v(d)}\right]_{ga}\right)$$

$$\left.\left[\frac{-Y_g}{Y} + 1\right]_{ga}\right|^2 + 2e\alpha_g(1 - \alpha_g)I_0 \left|\left[\mu_{ii}\left(\frac{-Y_g}{Y} + 1\right)\right]_{ga}\right|^2. \quad (48)$$

The noise figure, as given by Eq. (47), contains independent contributions from cathode fluctuations and partition fluctuations. The contribution from cathode fluctuations has input and output terms, which are not independent, however, since they have the common origin in velocity fluctuations of the cathode emission. The same is true of the spectral density of the total noise current. If the circuits are tuned, $G_{I_g}(f)$ is roughly proportional to the square of the frequency, since for each circuit $-Y_g/Y + 1 \approx -j\omega C/G$.

*Output Transit Angle and Electronic Transadmittance.*—It is to be observed that the d-c parameters of the output circuit are determined if the ratio of the output to input gap spacings and the ratio of the output to input transit times are specified, for a simple calculation shows that

$$\left[1 - \frac{\epsilon_0}{\epsilon}\right]_{ga} = \alpha_g \left[\frac{d}{T^3}\right]_{kg} \left[\frac{T^3}{d}\right]_{ga},$$

$$[r]_{ga} = 2 + \alpha_g \left[\frac{d}{T^3}\right]_{kg} \left[\frac{T^3}{d}\right]_{ga} - 3\left[\frac{d}{T}\right]_{kg} \left[\frac{T}{d}\right]_{ga}.$$

and therefore in addition $\delta$, $\sigma$, and also $v(0)/v(d)$ are determined. In theory it is more convenient to vary the output transit time, rather than some other quantity (such as the anode voltage, for example), since otherwise a cubic equation (Eq. 3·45) has to be solved.

The general effect on the electronic transadmittance of an output transit angle that differs from zero is the reduction of its magnitude and the increase of the negative of its phase. These changes are illustrated in Fig. 5·4, which shows the dependence of the magnitude and negative phase on the input transit angle for a tube in which the output spacing is three times the input spacing and the transit angles have the ratios indicated.[1]  In the figure the transmission coefficient is given the value unity.  It is seen that the decrease in the magnitude of the electronic transadmittance can be very large.  An approximate formula, which holds if the output region is a high-velocity gap with high d-c gap voltage, is

$$Y_m \approx \alpha_g \left\{ [y_m(d)]_{kg} + [v(d)f_m(d)]_{kg} \left[ \frac{j\theta}{v(d)} \right]_g \right\} [He^{-j\left(\eta + \frac{\theta}{2}\right)}]_{ga}. \quad (49)$$

Since under these conditions the ratio of grid to anode velocity is small, the term containing the velocity-modulation admittance is small except for very large output transit angles.  For the most part, the dependence

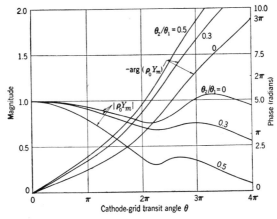

FIG. 5·4.—Dependence on cathode-grid transit angle of magnitude and phase of transadmittance of high-mu triode assuming negligible cathode velocities and complete cathode space charge.   Curves are for grid-plate spacing three times cathode-grid spacing and for three values of ratio of output to input transit angles.

of the electronic transadmittance on the output characteristics is given by the factor $[He^{-j\left(\eta + \frac{\theta}{2}\right)}]_{ga}$.  The functions $H$ and $\eta$ are shown as functions of $\theta$ in Fig. 3·8.  It is significant that since the output noise current has the same factor, this factor drops out in computing the noise figure.  Hence the noise figure is relatively insensitive to the output transit angle as long as that angle is not extremely large.  These effects are independent of the nature of the input region.

*High-velocity Output with Small Transit Angle.*—It is instructive to consider a triode for which space charge and transit angle in the output are both small.  The output excitation matrix, then, is simply (1   0).  The electronic transadmittance reduces to $\alpha_g[y_m(d)]_{kg}$; it is simply propor-

[1] The curves of Fig. 5·4 are based on calculations of J. R. Whinnery, General Electric Data Folder Nos. 46210 and 46218 (1942).

tional to the input internal transadmittance at the grid.   Eqs. (47) and (48) reduce to

$$NF \approx 1 + [G_{BR}\rho_0]_{kg}\, \frac{T}{T_0} \left\{ 3\left(1 - \frac{\pi}{4}\right)\frac{4}{9}\left| \cdot - \left[\frac{\mu_{iv}}{\rho_0 Y}\right]_{kg} + \left[\frac{\mu_{iv}(d)}{\rho_0 y_m(d)}\right]_{kg} \right|^2 \right.$$
$$\left. + \frac{2(1 - \alpha_g)}{\alpha_g}\left(\frac{eI_0\rho_0}{kT}\right)\frac{1}{|[\rho_0 y_m(d)]_{kg}|^2} \right\},$$
$$G_{I_e}(f) \approx \frac{4kT}{\rho_0}\, 3\left(1 - \frac{\pi}{4}\right)\frac{1}{9}\left| \left[\mu_{iv}\left(\frac{-Y_g}{Y} + 1\right)\right]_{kg} - \alpha_g\left[\frac{-\mu_{iv}}{Y}y_m(d)\right.\right.$$
$$\left.\left. + \mu_{iv}(d)\right]_{kg}\left[\frac{-Y_g}{Y} + 1\right]_{ga}\right|^2 + 2e\alpha_g(1 - \alpha_g)I_0\left|\left[\frac{-Y_g}{Y} + 1\right]_{ga}\right|^2. \quad (50)$$

If the input transit angle is small, these equations become

$$NF \approx 1 + G_{BR}\rho_0\, \frac{T}{T_0}\left\{ 3\left(1 - \frac{\pi}{4}\right)4\left| - \frac{1}{\rho_0 Y} + 1\right|^2 \right.$$
$$\left. + \frac{2(1 - \alpha_g)}{\alpha_g}\left(\frac{eI_0\rho_0}{kT}\right)\right\},$$
$$G_{I_e}(f) \approx \frac{4kT}{\rho_0}\, 3\left(1 - \frac{\pi}{4}\right)\left|\left[\frac{-Y_g}{Y} + 1\right]_{kg} - \alpha_g\left[ - \frac{1}{\rho_0 Y}\right.\right.$$
$$\left.\left. + 1\right]_{kg}\left[\frac{-Y_g}{Y} + 1\right]_{ga}\right|^2 + 2e\alpha_g(1 - \alpha_g)I_0\left|\left[\frac{-Y_g}{Y} + 1\right]_{ga}\right|^2. \quad (51)$$

On the other hand, if the input transit angle is large,

$$NF \approx 1 + G_{BR}\rho_0\, \frac{T}{T_0}\left\{ 3\left(1 - \frac{\pi}{4}\right)\frac{4}{9}\theta^2 + \frac{2(1 - \alpha_g)}{\alpha_g}\left(\frac{eI_0\rho_0}{kT}\right)\right\},$$
$$G_{I_e}(f) \approx \left\{\frac{4kT}{\rho_0}\, 3\left(1 - \frac{\pi}{4}\right)\frac{\alpha_g^2}{9}\theta^2 + 2e\alpha_g\,(1 - \alpha_g)I_0\right\}\left|\left[\frac{-Y_g}{Y} + 1\right]_{ga}\right|^2. \quad (52)$$

The noise figure for large input transit angle can be very large because the term due to cathode fluctuations contains the factor $\theta^2$.   For example, if $G_{BR}\rho_0$ and $eI_0\rho_0/kT$ are of the order of magnitude of unity, which is not unreasonable, and if the grid transmission coefficient is 0.8 and the temperature ratio is 3.5,

$$NF \approx 1 + 3.5(\tfrac{8}{27}\theta^2 + \tfrac{1}{2}).$$

With a transit angle of 10 radians, the noise figure is about 100.   It is easily shown that the noise figure as given by Eqs. (52) holds for large input transit angle irrespective of the output condition since the coefficients of the output drop out of the calculation.

**5·6. Positive-grid Tetrode with Minimum near Cathode.**—Just as in a triode, the principal effect of a large output transit angle on the electronic transadmittance of a tetrode is to reduce its magnitude and increase the negative of its phase.   If the output region is a high-velocity gap with high d-c gap voltage, the factor $[He^{-j\left(\eta + \frac{\theta}{2}\right)}]_{sa}$ appears in both the electronic transadmittance and the output noise current. This factor drops out in computing the noise figure, leaving it relatively insensitive to the output transit angle.

If both the grid-screen and the output regions are high-velocity gaps with high gap voltages, the electronic transadmittance is given by the formula

$$Y_m = \alpha_s \alpha_g \left\{ [y_m(d)]_{kg} + [v(d)f_m(d)]_{kg} \left[ \frac{j\theta}{v(d)} \right]_{gs} \right\} [e^{-j\theta}]_{gs} [He^{-j\left(\eta + \frac{\theta}{2}\right)}]_{s_{\text{out}}}. \quad (53)$$

Since the ratio of the grid to screen velocity is small under these conditions, the term containing the velocity-modulation admittance is small except for very large grid-screen transit angles. As expected, the grid-screen region contributes a phase delay equal to its transit angle.

*High-velocity Output with Small Transit Angle.*—In order to simplify matters, both space charge and transit angle in the output are assumed to be small in the remainder of this section. However no restrictions are placed on the grid-screen region, except that there are no reflected electrons. The output excitation matrix becomes (1  0). The electronic transadmittance, as obtained from Eq. (29), is given by

$$Y_m = \alpha_s \alpha_g \left\{ [y_m(d)]_{kg} [\mu_{ii}(d)]_{gs} + [v(d)f_m(d)]_{kg} \left[ \frac{\mu_{iv}(d)}{v(d)} \right]_{gs} \right\}. \quad (54)$$

The cathode contributes only velocity fluctuations to the noise figure, but both grid and screen contribute partition fluctuations. The formula for the noise figure is

$$\begin{aligned}
NF = 1 &+ [G_{BR}\rho_0]_{kg} \frac{T}{T_0} \left\{ 3\left(1 - \frac{\pi}{4}\right)\frac{4}{9} \left| - \left[ \frac{\mu_{iv}}{\rho_0 Y} \right]_{kg} \right. \right. \\
&+ \frac{\alpha_s \alpha_g}{\rho_0 Y_m} \left( [\mu_{iv}(d)]_{kg} [\mu_{ii}(d)]_{gs} + [v(d)\mu_{vv}(d)]_{kg} \left[ \frac{\mu_{iv}(d)}{v(d)} \right]_{gs} \right) \Big|^2 \\
&+ 2\alpha_s^2 \alpha_g (1 - \alpha_g) \left( \frac{eI_0\rho_0}{kT} \right) \frac{1}{|\rho_0 Y_m|^2} |[\mu_{ii}(d)]_{gs}|^2 \\
&+ 2\alpha_g \alpha_s (1 - \alpha_s) \left( \frac{eI_0\rho_0}{kT} \right) \frac{1}{|\rho_0 Y_m|^2} \Big\}. \quad (55)
\end{aligned}$$

The total grid noise current due to cathode and partition fluctuations becomes

$$\begin{aligned}
v_\omega(0) \left( \frac{-I_0}{v(d)} \right) &\left\{ \left[ \mu_{iv}\left( \frac{-Y_g}{Y} + 1 \right) \right]_{kg} + \alpha_g \left[ \frac{\mu_{iv}}{Y} \right]_{kg} \left( [y_m(d)]_{kg}[\mu_{ii}]_{gs} \right. \right. \\
&+ [v(d)f_m(d)]_{kg} \left[ \frac{\mu_{iv}}{v(d)} \right]_{gs} \right) - \alpha_g \left( [\mu_{iv}(d)]_{kg}[\mu_{ii}]_{gs} \right. \\
&+ [v(d)\mu_{vv}(d)]_{kg} \left[ \frac{\mu_{iv}}{v(d)} \right]_{gs} \right) \Big\} - i_g [\mu_{ii}]_{gs}. \quad (56)
\end{aligned}$$

Similarly, the total screen noise current due to cathode and partition fluctuations becomes

$$
v_\omega(0)\left(\frac{-I_0}{v(d)}\right)\left\{-\left[\frac{\mu_{iv}}{Y}\right]_{kg}\left(\alpha_g[y_m(d)]_{kg}[\mu_{ii}]_{gs}+\alpha_g[v(d)f_m(d)]_{kg}\left[\frac{\mu_{iv}}{v(d)}\right]_{gs}\right.\right.
$$
$$
\left.-Y_m\left[\frac{-Y_g}{Y}+1\right]_{sa}\right)+\alpha_g\left([\mu_{iv}(d)]_{kg}[\mu_{ii}]_{gs}+[v(d)\mu_{vv}(d)]_{kg}\left[\frac{\mu_{iv}}{v(d)}\right]_{gs}\right)
$$
$$
-\alpha_s\alpha_g\left([\mu_{iv}(d)]_{kg}[\mu_{ii}(d)]_{gs}+[v(d)\mu_{vv}(d)]_{kg}\left[\frac{\mu_{iv}(d)}{v(d)}\right]_{gs}\right)\left[\frac{-Y_g}{Y}+1\right]_{sa}\right\}
$$
$$
+i_g\left\{[\mu_{ii}]_{gs}-\alpha_s[\mu_{ii}(d)]_{gs}\left[\frac{-Y_g}{Y}+1\right]_{sa}\right\}-i_s\left[\frac{-Y_g}{Y}+1\right]_{sa}.\quad(57)
$$

*Very Large Input and Grid-screen Transit Angles.*—It is of particular interest to study the effect of space charge in the grid-screen region, for the space charge can be used to reduce the noise figure of the tube. The analysis is greatly simplified by assuming that both the input and the grid-screen transit angles are very large, for then limiting forms can be used for the modulation admittances and matrix elements.

If both the input and grid-screen transit angles are very large, Eq. (54) for the electronic transadmittance becomes

$$
Y_m\approx\frac{\alpha_s\alpha_g}{\rho_0}\left\{-[\sigma]_{gs}+\left[\frac{v(d)}{\theta}\right]_{kg}\left[\frac{\theta}{v(d)}\right]_{gs}[1+e^{j\theta}]_{kg}\right\}[e^{-j\theta}]_{kg}[e^{-j\theta}]_{gs}.\quad(58)
$$

It is seen from this formula that the electronic transadmittance can be made larger than $\alpha_s\alpha_g/\rho_0$ by making the product $[v(d)/\theta]_{kg}[\theta/v(d)]_{gs}$ greater than unity and by selecting a suitable value of the input transit angle, for then the velocity modulation produced by the input voltage gives rise to a large output excitation current because of the long drift time in the separation region.

However, for a low noise figure, conditions leading to a greatly enhanced electronic transadmittance are not the most favorable, as has been observed by L. C. Peterson.[1] In fact by properly choosing $[\sigma]_{gs}$ contributions to the output noise current arising from density and velocity modulations at the entrance plane of the grid-screen region can be made to cancel each other. The result is that the principal contribution to the noise figure is eliminated and the noise figure is very substantially reduced.

When both input and grid-screen transit angles are very large, Eq. (55) for the noise figure reduces to

---

[1] L. C. Peterson, Bell Telephone Laboratories MM-42-130-91. Llewellyn and Peterson use a space-charge factor $\zeta$ which is $(1-\sigma)v(d)/[v(0)+v(d)]$.

$$NF \approx 1 + [G_{BR}\rho_0]_{kg} \frac{T}{T_0} \left\{ 3\left(1 - \frac{\pi}{4}\right)\frac{4}{9} \lfloor\theta^2\rfloor_{kg} \right.$$

$$\left| \frac{[\sigma]_{gs} - \left[\dfrac{v(d)}{\theta}\right]_{kg} \left[\dfrac{\theta}{v(d)}\right]_{gs}}{[\sigma]_{gs} - \left[\dfrac{v(d)}{\theta}\right]_{kg} \left[\dfrac{\theta}{v(d)}\right]_{gs} [1 + e^{j\theta}]_{kg}} \right|^2$$

$$+ \frac{2(1-\alpha_g)}{\alpha_g}\left(\frac{eI_0\rho_0}{kT}\right) \left| \frac{[\sigma]_{gs}}{[\sigma]_{gs} - \left[\dfrac{v(d)}{\theta}\right]_{kg} \left[\dfrac{\theta}{v(d)}\right]_{gs} [1 + e^{j\theta}]_{kg}} \right|^2$$

$$\left. + \frac{2(1-\alpha_s)}{\alpha_s\alpha_g}\left(\frac{eI_0\rho_0}{kT}\right) \left| \frac{1}{[\sigma]_{gs} - \left[\dfrac{v(d)}{\theta}\right]_{kg} \left[\dfrac{\theta}{v(d)}\right]_{gs} [1 + e^{j\theta}]_{kg}} \right|^2 \right\}. \quad (59)$$

Examination of this expression shows that the contribution arising from cathode fluctuations, which is usually the largest term because of the factor $\lfloor\theta^2\rfloor_{kg}$, can be made zero by putting

$$[\sigma]_{gs} = \left[\frac{v(d)}{\theta}\right]_{kg}\left[\frac{\theta}{v(d)}\right]_{gs}. \quad (60)$$

For this value of the grid-screen smoothing parameter,

$$Y_m = \frac{\alpha_s\alpha_g}{\rho_0}[\sigma e^{-j\theta}]_{gs}. \quad (61)$$

Since this parameter is never greater than unity, the condition of Eq. (60) gives a reduction of the electronic transadmittance from its low-frequency value $\alpha_s\alpha_g/\rho_0$, which is accompanied by a decrease in the gain of the tube. It is to be noted that the contribution to the noise figure arising from grid partition fluctuations is zero if $[\sigma]_{gs}$ is zero but that the contribution arising from screen fluctuations cannot be made zero. The three contributions all vary inversely with the square of the magnitude of the electronic transadmittance. There is an optimum condition, which is not greatly different from Eq. (60), for which the noise figure is a minimum. It is to be expected that such a condition exists under much more general conditions than have been here assumed.

**5·7. General Relations for Velocity Distribution Phenomena.**—The general properties of the beam are described in terms of the distribution in velocity of the electrons of which it is composed. Such a description can be made using a charge distribution function or a current distribution function. The two are proportional, with the velocity as the factor of proportionality. In this discussion the current distribution function $i(x,v,t)$ is used. Its definition is that $i(x,v,t)dv$ is the current at the plane $x$ at time $t$ due to electrons having velocities in the range $v$ to $v + dv$.

If $v^l(x,t)$ is the lowest (or most negative) velocity at the plane $x$ at time $t$, the integrated current is

$$i(x,t) = \int_{v^l(x,t)}^{\infty} dv\, i(x,v,t).$$

Similarly, the charge density is

$$\rho(x,t) = \int_{v^l(x,t)}^{\infty} dv\, \frac{i(x,v,t)}{Av}.$$

The current distribution function can be used to calculate current averages in the beam. For example, if $v^l(x,t) \geqq 0$, the instantaneous average velocity of the electrons passing through the plane $x$ at time $t$ is

$$v(x,t) = \frac{\displaystyle\int_{v^l(x,t)}^{\infty} dv\, vi(x,v,t)}{\displaystyle\int_{v^l(x,t)}^{\infty} dv\, i(x,v,t)},$$

and the instantaneous mean square deviation from the instantaneous average velocity is

$$\Delta(x,t) = \frac{\displaystyle\int_{v^l(x,t)}^{\infty} dv[v^2 - v(x,t)^2]i(x,v,t)}{\displaystyle\int_{v^l(x,t)}^{\infty} dv\, i(x,v,t)}.$$

*Liouville's Theorem.*—If the electrons with the velocity $v$ at the plane $x$ at time $t$ were injected at $x = 0$ with velocity $v'$ at time $t'$, because of the conservation of particles

$$i(x,v,t)dv\, dt = i(0,v',t')dv'\, dt'.$$

However in addition there is a relation between $i(x,v,t)$ and $i(0,v',t')$ which does not involve differentials. This is

$$\frac{i(x,v,t)}{v} = \frac{i(0,v',t')}{v'}, \tag{62}$$

and is a form of Liouville's theorem.

The proof of the theorem is obtained by considering the two-dimensional phase space in which $x$ is the abscissa and $v$ is the ordinate. Each electron is assigned a point in this space according to its position and velocity. The point will move about in time. The area $\Delta x\, \Delta v$ occupied by the points for a cluster of neighboring electrons having about the same velocity has the property that it does not change in time; for

$$\frac{d}{dt}(\Delta x\, \Delta v) = \left[\frac{\partial}{\partial v}\left(\frac{dv}{dt}\right) + \frac{\partial}{\partial x}\left(\frac{dx}{dt}\right)\right]\Delta x\, \Delta v;$$

but $\dfrac{dv}{dt} = a(x,t)$ and $\dfrac{dx}{dt} = v$ are to be regarded as functions of $x$ and $v$; hence

$$\frac{d}{dt}\,(\Delta x\,\Delta v)\,=\,0.$$

This is one statement of Liouville's theorem. In terms of $x,v,t$ and $0,v',t'$

$$v\,dt\,dv\,=\,v'\,dt'\,dv'.$$

Therefore Eq. (62) follows from the preceding equation for particle conservation.

According to Liouville's theorem the density of electrons in phase space does not change with time provided one keeps moving with the electrons. Thus the total derivative of $i(x,v,t)/v$ is zero if taken along with the electrons. This derivative is

$$\left[\frac{\partial}{\partial t}\,+\,v\,\frac{\partial}{\partial x}\,+\,a(x,t)\,\frac{\partial}{\partial v}\right]\left[\frac{i(x,v,t)}{v}\right]\,=\,0.$$

The direct proof of this relation gives an alternative derivation of the theorem.

Liouville's theorem has an important bearing on the theory of space-charge devices. The distribution function is used to calculate the properties of the beam. The theorem gives this function at any plane in terms of the function at the plane of injection once the motion of the electrons is known.

*Thermal Distribution of Velocities.*—The electrons emitted by a cathode have very nearly a Maxwell-Boltzmann velocity distribution. If there is a positive electric field at the surface, electrons are prevented from returning to the cathode. The distribution function at the cathode is then zero for all negative velocities and is given by the expression

$$i(0,v')\,=\,-I_c\frac{mv'}{kT}\,e^{-\frac{mv'^2}{2kT}},$$

for $0 \leqq v'$. In this expression $-I_c$ is the total cathode emission current, $T$ is the absolute temperature of the cathode, and $k$ is Boltzmann's constant. This constant has the value $1.38 \times 10^{-23}$ joule/degree; for a temperature of 1160 degrees Kelvin, $kT = \frac{1}{10}$ electron volt. $I_c$ is determined by the emissive properties of the cathode and by its temperature. Since in the presence of an accelerating field the current is not changed appreciably by changing the field but is changed by changing the temperature, such a cathode is said to be temperature-limited.

The average velocity of emission and the mean square deviation from the average are given by the formulas,

$$v(0) = \frac{\int_0^\infty dv' \, v' i(0,v')}{\int_0^\infty dv' \, i(0,v')},$$

$$\Delta(0) = \frac{\int_0^\infty dv'[v'^2 - v(0)^2]i(0,v')}{\int_0^\infty dv' \, i(0,v')}.$$

For a Maxwell-Boltzmann distribution, they have the values,

$$v(0) = \sqrt{\frac{\pi k T}{2m}} \equiv v_{\text{th}}, \qquad \Delta(0) = \frac{2kT}{m}\left(1 - \frac{\pi}{4}\right).$$

If the d-c potential measured from the cathode is $V(x)$ at the plane $x$, the velocity of the slowest electron, in the absence of an r-f field, is $\sqrt{2eV(x)/m}$. The velocity of an electron emitted with velocity $v'$ is given by

$$v(x;v') = \left[v'^2 + \frac{2eV(x)}{m}\right]^{\frac{1}{2}}.$$

The semicolon is used to emphasize the fact that $v'$ is not the velocity at $x$ but rather the velocity at $x = 0$. The d-c distribution function is easily obtained by using Liouville's theorem. It is zero for all velocities less than $\sqrt{2eV(x)/m}$; for velocities greater than this value,

$$i(x,v) = \frac{v}{v'} i(0,v') = -I_c \frac{mv}{kT} e^{-\left[\frac{mv^2}{2} - eV(x)\right]\big/kT}.$$

If the field at the cathode is negative and the d-c potential has a minimum a distance $c$ from the cathode, all electrons with energy insufficient to get them past the minimum are reflected. The distribution function at the cathode is

$$i(0,v') = -I_c \frac{mv'}{kT} e^{-\frac{mv'^2}{2kT}}, \qquad -u(c) \leq v';$$

$$i(0,v') = 0, \qquad\qquad v' < -u(c),$$

where $u(c)$ is the speed of injection of an electron which has energy enough to just reach the minimum

$$u(c) = \sqrt{\frac{-2eV(c)}{m}}.$$

The integrated current is

$$i(0) = \int_{-u(c)}^\infty dv' \, i(0,v') = -I_c e^{-\frac{mu(c)^2}{2kT}} = -I_c e^{eV(c)/kT} = -I_0.$$

The distribution function anywhere in the gap is again easily obtained from charge conservation or from Liouville's theorem. For example, at a plane beyond the minimum $(x > c)$,

$$i(x,v) = -I_c \frac{mv}{kT} e^{-\left[\frac{\frac{mv^2}{2} - eV(x)}{kT}\right]}, \qquad v^l(x) \leqq v;$$

$$i(x,v) = 0, \qquad v < v^l(x);$$

where

$$v^l(x) = \left[ u(c)^2 + \frac{2eV(x)}{m} \right]^{1/2} = \left[ -\frac{2eV(c)}{m} + \frac{2eV(x)}{m} \right]^{1/2}.$$

The integrated current is, of course, the same as $i(0)$,

$$i(x) = -I_c e^{eV(c)/kT} = -I_0.$$

In terms of $I_0$,

$$i(x,v) = -I_0 \frac{mv}{kT} e^{-\left[\frac{\frac{mv^2}{2} - eV(x) + eV(c)}{kT}\right]}, \qquad v^l(x) \leqq v;$$

$$i(x,v) = 0, \qquad v < v^l(x).$$

The average velocity and mean square deviation are

$$v(x) = \sqrt{\frac{2kT}{m}} \left( \sqrt{\eta} + e^{\eta} \int_{\sqrt{\eta}}^{\infty} dz \, e^{-z^2} \right),$$

$$\Delta(x) = \frac{2kT}{m} \left[ 1 + \eta - \left( \sqrt{\eta} + e^{\eta} \int_{\sqrt{\eta}}^{\infty} dz \, e^{-z^2} \right)^2 \right]$$

where $\eta = e[V(x) - V(c)]/kT$. At the minimum

$$v(c) = \sqrt{\frac{\pi kT}{2m}} \equiv v_{th}, \qquad \Delta(c) = \frac{2kT}{m} \left( 1 - \frac{\pi}{4} \right).$$

In the limit $\eta \to \infty$,

$$v(x) \to \sqrt{\frac{2kT\eta}{m}} = \left[ \frac{2eV(x)}{m} - \frac{2eV(c)}{m} \right]^{1/2}, \qquad \Delta(x) \to 0.$$

At the minimum the velocity spread, or root mean square deviation, is of the same order of magnitude as the average velocity. On the other hand, in the limit $\eta \to \infty$ the velocity spread becomes a negligible fraction of the average velocity.

*Series Formulation.*—It is seen in Chapter 3 that the results of the Llewellyn theory are given directly in terms of the series formulation

$$V_\omega = -I_\omega Z_g + e_s$$
$$i_\omega(x) = -I_\omega \alpha(x) + i_s(x),$$
$$v_\omega(x) = -I_\omega \left(\frac{v(x)}{-I_0}\right) \beta(x) + v_s(x). \tag{63}$$

The theory of velocity-distribution phenomena also leads directly to the series formulation. The three quantities, $e_s$, $i_s(x)$, and $v_s(x)$ can be written in terms of modulations in the distribution function at injection. If the lower limit at injection is negative or zero, the expressions have the form

$$e_s = \int_0^\infty dv'\, i_\omega(0,v')z_g(v'),$$
$$i_s(x) = \int_0^\infty dv'\, i_\omega(0,v')\alpha(x;v'),$$
$$v_s(x) = \frac{v(x)}{-I_0} \int_0^\infty dv'\, i_\omega(0,v')\beta(x;v'). \tag{64}$$

where $z_g(v')$ is the *excitation impedance* for injected electrons in the velocity range $v'$ to $v' + dv'$, and $\alpha(x;v')$ and $\beta(x;v')$ are the corresponding series density and velocity modulation functions. From Eq. (3·11) it follows that

$$z_g(v') = \frac{1}{j\omega C}\frac{1}{d}\int_0^d dx\, \alpha(x;v') \tag{65}$$

The shunt excitation and modulation functions of Eqs. (5) are related to the series functions as follows:

$$\mu_i(v') = z_g(v')Y_g,$$
$$\mu_i(x;v') = z_g(v')y_m(x) + \alpha(x;v'),$$
$$\mu_v(x;v') = z_g(v')f_m(x) + \beta(x;v'). \tag{66}$$

*Integral Equation for the R-f Field.*—The determining relation which is encountered in the small-signal approximation is an integral equation of the form

$$a_\omega(x) = b_\omega(x) + \int_0^d d\zeta a_\omega(\zeta)K(\zeta,x),$$

where $a_\omega(x)$ is the Fourier integral transform of the acceleration $a(x,t)$. The quantity $b_\omega(x)$ is a known combination of d-c and r-f quantities. The kernel $K(\zeta,x)$ is calculated from the d-c characteristics of the gap, namely the d-c distribution function of the injected current and certain phase factors containing d-c transit times.

The solution of this equation is given by Fredholm's theory[1] in terms of a *resolving kernel* $L(x,y)$ which is itself a solution of the integral equation

[1] E. T. Whittaker and G. N. Watson, *Modern Analysis*, Chap. 11.

$$L(x,y) = K(x,y) + \int_0^d d\zeta L(x,\zeta)K(\zeta,y).$$

This equation is free of r-f amplitudes but contains the frequency in the phase factors of the kernel. It has been found possible to find the resolving kernel in closed form in only a few relatively simple limiting cases, such as the limit of low frequencies or negligible velocity spread. However the theory gives formal expression to the fundamental concepts of the r-f behavior of a gap containing space charge and is a starting point for detailed calculations of the characteristics of the region.

The solution in terms of the resolving kernel is

$$a_\omega(x) = b_\omega(x) + \int_0^d d\zeta b_\omega(\zeta)L(\zeta,x).$$

The function $b_\omega(x)$ is linear in the amplitudes $J_\omega$ and $j_\omega(0,v')$, which are the Fourier integral transforms of $J(t)$ and $j(0,v',t')$, respectively. By using this equation, the r-f characteristics are obtained explicitly in terms of the resolving kernel.

**5·8. Low-velocity Gap without Reflections.**—The discussion of velocity-distribution phenomena in a uniform region is greatly simplified if all the electrons traverse the gap in the same direction without reflections. Since there are no electrons with negative velocities in the gap, the lower limit $v^i(x,t)$ is everywhere positive at all times.

It is shown in this section that the resolving kernel for such a region is determined by the equation

$$L(x,y) = K(x,y) + \int_x^y d\zeta L(x,\zeta)K(\zeta,y).$$

This is a Fredholm integral equation with *variable upper and lower limits*. The kernel is

$$K(x,y) = \int_{v^i(0)}^\infty dv' \frac{j(0,v')}{j\omega v'} \frac{\partial}{\partial v'} e^{-i\omega[T(y;v')-T(x;v')]}, \tag{67}$$

where $j(0,v') = ei(0,v')/mA\epsilon_0$ and $T(y;v')$ is the time required for an electron to go from the injection plane to the plane $y$ in the absence of the r-f field.

In the limit of zero frequency, the kernel is shown to be

$$K(x,y) = \int_x^y d\zeta \frac{1}{a(\zeta)} \frac{d^2a(\zeta)}{d\zeta^2},$$

where $a(\zeta)$ is the acceleration experienced by the electron at the plane $\zeta$ in the absence of the r-f field. The resolving kernel is found to be

$$L(x,y) = -\frac{\partial^2}{\partial x\,\partial y}\left[a(x)a(y)\int_x^y \frac{d\zeta}{a(\zeta)^2}\right].$$

If all the electrons at any moment are injected with the same velocity (Llewellyn approximation), the kernel is

$$K(x,y) = \frac{-J_0}{j\omega v(0)} \frac{\partial}{\partial v(0)} e^{-j\omega[T(y;v(0))-T(x;v(0))]},$$

and the corresponding resolving kernel is found to be

$$L(x,y) = \frac{-J_0}{v(x)v(y)} [T(y;v(0)) - T(x;v(0))]e^{-j\omega[T(y;v(0))-T(x;v(0))]}.$$

*D-c Conditions.*—The acceleration in the absence of the r-f field is calculated from the equation

$$\frac{da(x)}{dx} = - \int_{v^i(x)}^{\infty} dv \frac{j(x,v)}{v} = - \int_{v^i(0)}^{\infty} dv' \frac{j(0,v')}{v(x;v')},$$

where

$$j(x,v) = \frac{ei(x,v)}{mA\epsilon_0}, \qquad v(x;v') = \left[v'^2 + 2\int_0^x d\zeta a(\zeta)\right]^{\frac{1}{2}}.$$

Since

$$T(x;v') = \int_0^x \frac{d\zeta}{v(\zeta;v')},$$

the equation for the acceleration can be integrated directly,

$$a(x) - a(0) = - \int_{v^i(0)}^{\infty} dv' j(0,v') T(x;v').$$

However, another and more useful expression is obtained by multiplying by $a(x)$ before integrating, thus obtaining

$$a(x)^2 - a(0)^2 = -2 \int_{v^i(0)}^{\infty} dv' j(0,v')[v(x;v') - v'].$$

The introduction of the d-c potential

$$V(x) = \frac{m}{e} \int_0^x d\zeta a(\zeta)$$

as the independent variable makes it possible to solve this equation by separation of variables. The function $a(x)$ becomes a function of $V$ alone:

$$a(x) = \left\{a(0)^2 - 2 \int_{v^i(0)}^{\infty} dv' j(0,v') \left[\left(v'^2 + \frac{2eV}{m}\right)^{\frac{1}{2}} - v'\right]\right\}^{\frac{1}{2}}.$$

Hence

$$x = \frac{e}{m} \int_0^{V(x)} \frac{dV}{a(x)}. \tag{68}$$

This is a form that lends itself to numerical integration.

The a-c resistance of such a region, of which a temperature-limited diode is an example, is infinite, since a small change in the d-c voltage produces no change in the current. If, however, the field at the injection plane is zero and is kept zero during the change, a change in current is required to satisfy the conditions. On putting $x = d$ in the last equation and differentiating with respect to $I_0$, there is found for the a-c resistance under such conditions

$$\rho = \frac{dV(d)}{dI_0} = \frac{ma(d)}{e} \int_0^d dx \frac{d}{dI_0} \ln a(x).$$

Usually $j(0,v')$ is simply proportional to $I_0$ and $\frac{d}{dI_0} \ln a(x) = \frac{1}{2I_0}$. Then

$$\rho = \frac{a(d)d}{2J_0 A \epsilon_0}.$$

This expression is readily checked for Childs' law, since

$$V(d) = \frac{m J_0^{2/3}(6d)^{4/3}}{e8},$$

and

$$a(d) = J_0^{2/3}(6d)^{1/3}.$$

Hence by differentiation or by substitution in the above,

$$\rho = \frac{(6d)^{4/3}}{12 J_0^{1/3} A \epsilon_0}.$$

*Derivation of Integral Equation.*—Because of the presence of noise, which has a continuous spectrum, it is convenient to represent all time-dependent quantities with Fourier integrals. To this end, there is introduced a time interval much longer than all periods under consideration and all time-dependent functions are put equal to their average values outside of this interval. It is then possible to carry out the Fourier analysis without difficulty in terms of Fourier integrals in the usual way. For example,

$$j(x,t) = j(x) + \int_{-\infty}^{\infty} \frac{d\omega}{2\pi} j_\omega(x) e^{j\omega t},$$

where $j(x)$ is the average value of $j(x,t)$ and $j_\omega(x)$ is its Fourier transform,

$$j_\omega(x) = \int_{-\infty}^{\infty} dt j(x,t) e^{-j\omega t}, \tag{69}$$

and it is understood that the integration is actually limited to the time interval mentioned.

When written in terms of Fourier transforms, Eq. (18) takes the form

$$j\omega a_\omega(x) = -J_\omega + j_\omega(x). \tag{70}$$

The procedure in the development of a general consistent theory is to find an expression for $j_\omega(x)$ in terms of $a_\omega(x)$. The transform of the time $T(x,t;v')$ required for an electron which is injected with velocity $v'$ to reach the plane $x$ at time $t$ appears at an intermediate step but is eliminated by a direct calculation from the field.

On introducing the velocity distribution into Eq. (69),

$$j_\omega(x) = \int_{-\infty}^{\infty} dt \int_{v^l(x,t)}^{\infty} dv j(x,v,t) e^{-j\omega t}.$$

If an electron at the plane $x$ with velocity $v$ at time $t$ was injected at $x = 0$ with velocity $v'$ at time $t'$, then by particle conservation

$$j(x,v,t)dv\, dt = j(0,v',t')dv'\, dt'.$$

Hence it follows that

$$j_\omega(x) = \int_{-\infty}^{\infty} dt' e^{-j\omega t'} \int_{v^l(0,t')}^{\infty} dv' j(0,v',t') e^{-j\omega T(x,t;v')}.$$

In this equation Fourier integral expressions are substituted for the three time-dependent quantities, $j(0,v',t')$, $v^l(0,t')$, $T(x,t;v')$, and only terms linear in the amplitudes are retained. The result is

$$j_\omega(x) = \int_{v^l(0)}^{\infty} dv' j_\omega(0,v') e^{-j\omega T(x;v')} - v_\omega^l(0) j(0,v^l(0)) e^{-j\omega T(x;v^l(0))}$$

$$- \int_{v^l(0)}^{\infty} dv' j(0,v') j\omega T_\omega(x;v'). \tag{71}$$

In the single-velocity theory the corresponding expression is Eq. 3·18.

The next step is to use

$$T(x,t;v') = \int_0^x d\eta \left[ v'^2 + 2 \int_0^\eta d\zeta'' a(\zeta'',t'') \right]^{-\frac{1}{2}}$$

to find an equation for $T_\omega(x;v')$. Now

$$a(\zeta'',t'') = a(\zeta'') + \int_{-\infty}^{\infty} \frac{d\omega}{2\pi} a_\omega(\zeta'') e^{j\omega t''},$$

$$v(\eta;v') = \left[ v'^2 + 2 \int_0^\eta d\zeta a(\zeta) \right]^{\frac{1}{2}}.$$

These expressions are substituted in $T(x,t;v')$, the denominator is expanded, and quadratic and higher terms are dropped:

$$T(x,t;v') = T(x;v') - \int_{-\infty}^{\infty} \frac{d\omega}{2\pi} e^{j\omega t'} \int_0^x d\eta \frac{1}{v(\eta;v')^3} \int_0^\eta d\zeta a_\omega(\zeta) e^{j\omega T(\zeta;v')}.$$

Hence, after rearrangement,

$$T_\omega(x;v') = \int_0^x d\zeta a_\omega(\zeta)e^{j\omega[T(\zeta;v')-T(x;v')]} \frac{\partial}{v'\partial v'}[T(x;v') - T(\zeta;v')]. \quad (72)$$

The desired integral equation is obtained by using Eq. (70) with Eq. (71) for $j_\omega(x)$ into which Eq. (72) has been substituted. The result is an integral equation with a variable upper limit,

$$a_\omega(x) = b_\omega(x) + \int_0^x d\zeta a_\omega(\zeta)K(\zeta,x), \quad (73)$$

where $b_\omega(x)$ is defined by

$$j\omega b_\omega(x) = -J_\omega + \int_{v^i(0)}^\infty dv'j_\omega(0,v')e^{-j\omega T(x;v')} - v_\omega^i(0)j(0,v^i(0))e^{-j\omega T(x;v^i(0))}, \quad (74)$$

and the kernel is given by Eq. 67.

*Density Modulation.*—By Fredholm's theory, Eq. (73) has the solution

$$a_\omega(x) = b_\omega(x) + \int_0^x d\zeta b_\omega(\zeta)L(\zeta,x), \quad (75)$$

where $L(\zeta,x)$ is the resolving kernel. The resolving kernel is, in turn, the solution of

$$L(x,y) = K(x,y) + \int_x^y d\zeta L(x,\zeta)K(\zeta,y), \quad (76)$$

which is the fundamental integral equation of the uniform low-velocity gap without reflections. The r-f characteristics can be written explicitly in terms of the resolving kernel.

In order to find the density modulation, Eq. (75) is substituted in Eq. (70). The result is found in the series form,

$$i_\omega(x) = -I_\omega\alpha(x) + i_s(x),$$

with

$$\left.\begin{aligned}
\alpha(x) &= \int_0^x d\zeta L(\zeta,x) \\
i_s(x) &= \int_{v^i(0)}^\infty dv'i_\omega(0,v')\alpha(x;v') - v_\omega^i(0)i(0,v^i(0)\alpha(x;v^i(0)),
\end{aligned}\right\} \quad (77)$$

where in the latter expression

$$\alpha(x;v') = e^{-j\omega T(x;v')} + \int_0^x d\zeta e^{-j\omega T(\zeta;v')}L(\zeta,x), \quad (78)$$

which is the series density-modulation function.

*Gap Voltage.*—The elements of the series formula for the gap voltage,

$$V_\omega = -I_\omega Z_g + e_s,$$

are calculated from the integrals of Eq. (3·11). The results are

$$Z_g = \frac{1}{j\omega C} \frac{1}{d} \int_0^d dx \left[ 1 + \int_x^d d\zeta L(x,\zeta) \right], \\ e_s = \int_{v^i(0)}^\infty dv' i_\omega(0,v') z_g(v') - v_\omega^i(0) i(0,v^i(0)) z_g(v^i(0)), \quad \biggr\} \quad (79)$$

with the excitation impedance given by

$$z_g(v') = \frac{1}{j\omega C} \frac{1}{d} \int_0^d dx e^{-i\omega T(x;v')} \left[ 1 + \int_x^d d\zeta L(x,\zeta) \right]. \quad (80)$$

It is interesting to note that, since the transit angle tends towards zero with increasing electron velocity, as $v' \to \infty$,

$$\alpha(x;v') \to 1 + \alpha(x), \qquad z_g(v') \to Z_g.$$

Therefore from Eq. (66) it is seen that the excitation function $\mu_i(v')$ and the density-modulation function $\mu_i(x;v')$ both have the limiting value unity for very high velocities of injection. This is as expected since very fast electrons are practically unaffected by the field.

*Velocity Modulation.*—It follows from the definition of the instantaneous average velocity at the exit plane $v(d,t)$, that the velocity modulation at the exit plane is given by the relation,

$$v_\omega(d) = \frac{v(d)}{-I_0} \left\{ \int_{v(d)}^\infty dv \left[ \frac{v - v(d)}{v(d)} \right] i_\omega(d,v) \right. \\ \left. - v_\omega^i(d) \left[ \frac{v^i(d) - v(d)}{v(d)} \right] i(d,v^i(d)) \right\}. \quad (81)$$

In order to convert this into the series form

$$v_\omega(d) = -I_\omega \left( \frac{v(d)}{-I_0} \right) \beta(d) + v_s(d),$$

where, as it turns out,

$$v_s(d) = \frac{v(d)}{-I_0} \left\{ \int_{v^i(0)}^\infty dv' i_\omega(0,v') \beta(d;v') - v_\omega^i(0) i(0,v^i(0)) \beta(d;v^i(0)) \right\} \quad (82)$$

the two quantities, $i_\omega(d,v)$ and $v_\omega^i(d)$, must be expressed in terms of $I_\omega$, $i_\omega(0,v')$, and $v_\omega^i(0)$.

The first step is to find formulas involving $a_\omega(x)$. From Liouville's theorem,

$$\frac{i_\omega(d,v)}{v} = \frac{i_\omega(0,v')}{v'} e^{-i\omega T(d;v')} - \frac{\partial}{v'\partial v'} \left( \frac{i(0,v')}{v'} \right) \int_0^d dx a_\omega(x) e^{-i\omega[T(d;v')-T(x;v')]}. \quad (83)$$

From the energy integral,

$$v^l(d)v^l_\omega(d) = v^l(0)v^l_\omega(0)e^{-i\omega T(d;v^l(0))} + \int_0^d dx a_\omega(x)e^{-i\omega[T(d;v^l(0))-T(x;v^l(0))]}. \quad (84)$$

Eq. (75) is used to eliminate $a_\omega(x)$. There enters the quantity,

$$\alpha(v',v'') = \frac{1}{d}\int_0^d dx \alpha(x;v')e^{-i\omega[T(d;v'')-T(x;v'')]}. \quad (85)$$

The substitution of the results in Eq. (81) leads to the expected form with

$$\left.\begin{aligned}
\beta(d) &= -\frac{d}{j\omega}\int_{v^l(0)}^\infty dv'' \left[\frac{v(d;v'')-v(d)}{v(d)}\right]\frac{\partial}{\partial v''}\left(\frac{j(0,v'')}{v''}\right)\alpha(\infty,v'') \\
&\quad -\frac{d}{j\omega}\left[\frac{v^l(d)-v(d)}{v(d)}\right]\frac{j(0,v^l(0))}{v^l(0)}\alpha(\infty,v^l(0), \\
\beta(d;v') &= \left[\frac{v(d;v')-v(d)}{v(d)}\right]e^{-i\omega T(d;v')} -\frac{d}{j\omega}\int_{l(0)}^\infty dv''\left[\frac{v(d;v'')-v(d)}{v(d)}\right] \\
&\quad \frac{\partial}{\partial v''}\left(\frac{j(0,v'')}{v''}\right)\alpha(v',v'') -\frac{d}{j\omega}\left[\frac{v^l(d)-v(d)}{v(d)}\right]\frac{j(0,v^l(0))}{v^l(0)}\alpha(v',v^l(0)),
\end{aligned}\right\} \quad (86)$$

where $v(d)$ is the d-c average velocity at the exit plane and $v(d;v'')$ is the velocity at the exit plane of an electron injected with the velocity $v''$, computed in the absence of the r-f field.

*Low-frequency Approximation.*—A power series expansion in $\omega$ can be expected to converge rapidly at low frequencies. The first terms are readily calculated. Such an expansion gives for the kernel

$$K(x,y) = \int_{l(0)}^\infty dv'\frac{j(0,v')}{v'}\frac{\partial}{\partial v'}\left\{-\int_x^y\frac{d\eta}{v(\eta;v')} + \frac{j\omega}{2}\left[\int_x^y\frac{d\eta}{v(\eta;v')}\right]^2 - \cdots\right\} \quad (87)$$

The first term is

$$\int_x^y d\eta\frac{1}{a(\eta)}\frac{d^2a(\eta)}{d\eta^2},$$

as is seen by referring to the d-c conditions. The corresponding term in the resolving kernel is

$$-\frac{\partial^2}{\partial x\,\partial y}\left[a(x)a(y)\int_x^y\frac{d\eta}{a(\eta)^2}\right],$$

as a direct substitution in the integral equation shows. The second term in the resolving kernel is

$$\frac{j\omega}{2}\frac{\partial^2}{\partial x\,\partial y}\left(a(x)a(y)\int_{v^l(0)}^\infty dv'\frac{j(0,v')}{v'}\frac{\partial}{\partial v'}\left\{\left[\int_x^y d\eta\frac{v(\eta;v')}{a(\eta)^2}\right]^2 - \left[\int_x^y d\eta\frac{v'}{a(\eta)^2}\right]^2\right\}\right).$$

This term is obtained by deriving from the integral equation an equation containing only terms proportional to $j\omega$. This is an integral equation the kernel of which is the first term of $K(x,y)$.

The resolving kernel is, therefore,

$$L(x,y) = -\frac{\partial^2}{\partial x\,\partial y}\left[a(x)a(y)\left(\int_x^y \frac{d\eta}{a(\eta)^2} - \frac{j\omega}{2}\int_{v^i(0)}^\infty dv'\,\frac{j(0,v')}{v'}\,\frac{\partial}{\partial v'}\cdot\right.\right.$$
$$\left.\left.\left\{\left[\int_x^y d\eta\,\frac{v(\eta;v')}{a(\eta)^2}\right]^2 - \left[\int_x^y d\eta\,\frac{v'}{a(\eta)^2}\right]^2\right\}\right)\right] + \cdots. \quad (88)$$

By using this expression it is found that

$$\left.\begin{aligned}
\alpha(x) &= -1 + \frac{\partial}{\partial x}\left[a(0)a(x)\left(\int_0^x \frac{d\eta}{a(\eta)^2} - \frac{j\omega}{2}\int_{v^i(0)}^\infty dv'\,\frac{j(0,v')}{v'}\,\frac{\partial}{\partial v'}\right.\right. \\
&\qquad\left.\left.\cdot\left\{\left[\int_0^x d\eta\,\frac{v(\eta;v')}{a(\eta)^2}\right]^2 - \left[\int_0^x d\eta\,\frac{v'}{a(\eta)^2}\right]^2\right\}\right)\right] + \cdots, \\
Z_g &= \frac{1}{j\omega C}\frac{a(0)a(d)}{d}\left(\int_0^d \frac{d\eta}{a(\eta)^2} - \frac{j\omega}{2}\int_{v^i(0)}^\infty dv'\,\frac{j(0,v')}{v'}\,\frac{\partial}{\partial v'}\right. \\
&\qquad\left.\cdot\left\{\left[\int_0^d d\eta\,\frac{v(\eta;v')}{a(\eta)^2}\right]^2 - \left[\int_0^d d\eta\,\frac{v'}{a(\eta)^2}\right]^2\right\}\right) + \cdots,
\end{aligned}\right\} \quad (89)$$

and in addition

$$\left.\begin{aligned}
\alpha(x;v') &- \alpha(x) - 1 \\
&= -j\omega\frac{\partial}{\partial x}\left\{a(x)\int_0^x d\eta\,\frac{1}{a(\eta)^2}\,[v(\eta;v') - v']\right\} + \cdots, \\
z_g(v') &- Z_g = -\frac{1}{j\omega C}\frac{a(d)}{d}\,j\omega\int_0^d d\eta\,\frac{1}{a(\eta)^2}\,[v(\eta;v') - v'] + \cdots.
\end{aligned}\right\} \quad (90)$$

Similar expressions can be derived for $\beta(d)$ and $\beta(d;v')$.

*Llewellyn Approximation.*—In the Llewellyn approximation all electrons at a given plane at a given moment are assumed to have the same velocity. Thus

$$i(x,v,t) = i(x,t)\delta(v - v(x,t)),$$

where $\delta(v)$ is the Dirac delta function. This problem is discussed in Chap. 3 by using the Llewellyn equation, which is based on the fact that current and charge density are proportional in this approximation. Such a treatment has no simple extension to multistream phenomena. For this reason it is of interest to see how the Llewellyn electronic equations are derived from the more general theory of this chapter.

In the small-signal approximation

$$\left.\begin{aligned}
i(x,v) &= i(x)\delta(v - v(x)) = -I_0\delta(v - v(x)), \\
i_\omega(x,v) &= i_\omega(x)\delta(v - v(x)) + I_0 v_\omega(x)\delta'(v - v(x)),
\end{aligned}\right\} \quad (91)$$

where $\delta'(v)$ is the derivative of the Dirac delta function.

The kernel becomes

$$K(x,y) = -\frac{J_0}{j\omega v(0)}\frac{\partial}{\partial v(0)}e^{-i\omega[T(y;v(0))-T(x;v(0))]}. \tag{92}$$

In order to find the resolving kernel, the following two functions are introduced:

$$k(x,y) = K(x,y)e^{j\omega[T(y;v(0))-T(x;v(0))]},$$
$$l(x,y) = L(x,y)e^{j\omega[T(y;v(0))-T(x;v(0))]}.$$

The integral equation becomes

$$l(x,y) = k(x,y) + \int_x^y d\zeta\, l(x,\zeta)k(\zeta,y),$$

with

$$k(\zeta,y) = -J_0\int_\zeta^y d\eta\,\frac{1}{v(\eta)^3}.$$

The integral equation can be converted into the differential equation

$$v(x)\frac{\partial}{\partial x}\left(v(x)\frac{\partial}{\partial x}\left\{v(x)[l(x,y)-k(x,y)]\right\}\right) = -J_0 k(x,y),$$

which is to be solved with the conditions

$$l(y,y) = k(y,y) = 0, \qquad \left\{\frac{\partial}{\partial x}[l(x,y)-k(x,y)]\right\}_y = 0.$$

The solution is

$$l(x,y) = \frac{-J_0}{v(x)v(y)}\int_x^y d\eta\,\frac{1}{v(\eta)},$$

and hence the resolving kernel is

$$L(x,y) = \frac{-J_0}{v(x)v(y)}[T(y;v(0))-T(x;v(0))]e^{-i\omega[T(y;v(0))-T(x;v(0))]}. \tag{93}$$

With the distribution function as defined by Eq. (91), the series formulation as given by Eqs. (63) and (64) becomes

$$\left.\begin{aligned}
V_\omega &= -I_\omega Z_\varrho + i_\omega(0)z_\varrho(v(0)) - I_0 v_\omega(0)\left(\frac{\partial z_\varrho(v')}{\partial v'}\right)_{v(0)},\\
i_\omega(d) &= -I_\omega\alpha(d) + i_\omega(0)\alpha(d;v(0)) - I_0 v_\omega(0)\left(\frac{\partial}{\partial v'}\alpha(d;v')\right)_{v(0)},\\
v_\omega(d) &= -I_\omega\left(\frac{v(d)}{-I_0}\right)\beta(d) + \frac{v(d)}{-I_0}\left\{i_\omega(0)\beta(d;v(0))\right.\\
&\qquad\qquad\qquad\qquad \left.- I_0 v_\omega(0)\left(\frac{\partial}{\partial v'}\beta(d;v')\right)_{v(0)}\right\}.
\end{aligned}\right\} \tag{94}$$

The nine coefficients are known functions of the resolving kernel, which is also known. They can be calculated in detail.[1] The results are identical with those of the Llewellyn calculation.

*Narrow Velocity Spread.*—The integral equation treatment of the electronic behavior of a uniform gap makes possible a formal extension of the Llewellyn theory to include a narrow spread in the velocity of the electrons of the beam. Since no convenient representation of the resolving kernel has been found, only a brief indication of the method will be presented.

The distribution function can be used to calculate the current and a set of moments, the first two of which are the average velocity and the mean square deviation. Thus

$$i(x,t) = \int dv\, i(x,v,t),$$

$$i(x,t)v(x,t) = \int dv\, v\, i(x,v,t),$$

$$i(x,t)\,\Delta(x,t) = \int dv[v^2 - v(x,t)^2]i(x,v,t),$$

and so forth. If the velocity spread is small, it is possible to show that for the purpose of calculating average values the distribution function can be represented as follows:

$$i(x,v,t) = i(x,t)\{\delta(v - v(x,t)) + \tfrac{1}{2}\Delta(x,t)\delta''(v - v(x,t)) + \cdots\}. \quad (95)$$

Using this expression, it is found that

$$\left.\begin{aligned}
i(x,v) &= -I_0\{\delta(v - v(x)) + \tfrac{1}{2}\Delta(x)\delta''(v - v(x)) + \cdots\}, \\
i_\omega(x,v) &= i_\omega(x)\{\delta(v - v(x)) + \tfrac{1}{2}\Delta(x)\delta''(v - v(x)) + \cdots\} \\
&\quad + v_\omega(x)I_0\{\delta'(v - v(x)) + \tfrac{1}{2}\Delta(x)\delta'''(v - v(x)) + \cdots\} \\
&\quad - \Delta_\omega(x)I_0\{\delta''(v - v(x)) + \cdots\} + \cdots.
\end{aligned}\right\} \quad (96)$$

where

$$-I_0 v(x) = \int dv\, v\, i(x,v),$$

$$-I_0 \Delta(x) = \int dv[v^2 - v(x)^2]i(x,v).$$

The electronic equations take the form of relations giving $V_\omega$, $i_\omega(d)$, $v_\omega(d)$, $\Delta_\omega(d)$, etc., as linear functions of $I_\omega$, $i_\omega(0)$, $v_\omega(0)$, $\Delta_\omega(0)$, etc., the coefficients of which contain $I_0$ and the d-c moments. The Llewellyn theory gives an exact solution under the assumption that the second and all higher moments are zero.

---

[1] See "Temperature-limited Diode," J. K. Knipp, RL Report No. 761, 1946.

The kernel is

$$K(x,y) = \left\{ 1 + \frac{1}{2} \Delta(0) \frac{\partial^2}{\partial v(0)^2} + \cdots \right\} K_L(x,y), \qquad (97)$$

where

$$K_L(x,y) = \frac{-J_0}{j\omega v(0)} \frac{\partial}{\partial v(0)} e^{-j\omega[T(y;v(0))-T(x;v(0))]}$$

is the kernel for the Llewellyn approximation.

**5·9. Retarding Field with Reflections.**—The presence of electrons with negative velocities is a complication which is difficult to handle. Since the theory in its present state leads to very few results, only a brief discussion will be presented. For reflection of electrons to take place the field must be positive. It can either be positive all the way across the gap or start out positive at the first plane and end up negative at the second plane. In the latter case the potential has a minimum within the region. This minimum is itself a complication. It has been treated successfully at low frequencies and affords an explanation of the space-charge reduction of shot noise. The discussion of this section is restricted to conditions in which the field is positive everywhere in the region. The d-c voltage of the second plane is negative with respect to the first. Electrons which are injected with high energies are able to overcome the retarding field and reach the second plane. However, the low-energy electrons are stopped in the region and sent back to the first plane. If these reflected electrons spend an appreciable fraction of a cycle in the region, they affect the r-f behavior of the region in many ways. They load the circuit through a contribution to the beam loading; they excite the gap voltage through a contribution to the exciting current; and through their own modulations they affect the modulations of the electrons that reach the second plane.

*Space-constant Field.*—A relatively simple and very instructive example of reflection phenomena is afforded by a region in which the reflecting d-c field is very strong and the current densities are small. Space-charge is negligible and the electric field can be treated as space-constant. It is represented by

$$E(x,t) = -\frac{ma(t)}{e} = -\frac{m}{e}(a + a_\omega e^{j\omega t}),$$

where $a$ is a negative quantity. The r-f voltage is $V_\omega = ma_\omega d/e$.

Since, under these assumptions, the electrons affect each other only indirectly, only a single velocity group need be considered. The effect of a distribution in velocity is the average over the velocity groups of the effects of the separate groups.

In the region penetrated by the electrons, the electron current is the sum of contributions from the oncoming and reflected streams,

$$i(x,t) = i^+(x,t) + i^-(x,t).$$

If an electron at the plane $x$ at time $t$ with a positive velocity was injected at $x = 0$ at time $t'$, the time of passage is $t - t' = T(x,t)$. Similarly, if an electron at the plane $x$ at time $t$ with negative velocity was injected at $x = 0$ at time $t''$, the time of passage is $t - t'' = T^-(x,t)$. They are represented by

$$T(x,t) = T' + T_\omega(x)e^{j\omega t},$$
$$T^-(x,t) = T - T' + T_\omega^-(x)e^{j\omega t}.$$

where $T$ is the total time spent in the region and $T'$ is the time required to go from the first plane to the plane $x$ without reflection, both in the absence of the r-f field. By particle conservation,

$$i^+(x,t) = i^+(0,t') \frac{dt'}{dt}, \qquad i^-(x,t) = -i^+(0,t'') \frac{dt''}{dt},$$

and therefore

$$i_\omega(x) = i_\omega^+(0)[e^{-j\theta'} - e^{-j(\theta-\theta')}] + I_0[j\omega T_\omega(x) - j\omega T_\omega^-(x)]. \tag{98}$$

This expression is to be compared to Eq. (3·18) of the single-velocity theory.

The quantities $T_\omega(x)$ and $T_\omega^-(x)$ are readily found by direct integration of Newton's law. If $v(x)$ is the speed of the electrons at the plane $x$, in the absence of the r-f field ($v(x)$ is always positive), the result is

$$\left. \begin{aligned} T_\omega(x) &= -\frac{v_\omega^+(0)}{v(x)} T' e^{-j\theta'} - \frac{a_\omega}{v(x)(j\omega)^2}[1 - e^{-j\theta'} - j\theta' e^{-j\theta'}], \\ T_\omega^-(x) &= \frac{v_\omega^+(0)}{v(x)}(T - T')e^{-j(\theta-\theta')} \\ &\quad + \frac{a_\omega}{v(x)(j\omega)^2}[1 - e^{-j(\theta-\theta')} - j(\theta - \theta')e^{-j(\theta-\theta')}]. \end{aligned} \right\} \tag{99}$$

The quantity of interest is the driving current,

$$i_\omega = \frac{1}{d} \int_0^{T/2} dT' v(x) i_\omega(x).$$

The integration is carried out using $v(x) = v(0) + aT'$ and the result expressed in the familiar form,

$$i_\omega = -V_\omega Y_B + i_m,$$

The expression which is found for the beam-loading admittance is

$$Y_B = \frac{G_0}{2}\left(\frac{v(0)T}{d}\right)^2 \frac{j\theta N}{6} e^{-\frac{j\theta}{2}}, \tag{100}$$

where $G_0 = I_0/V_0$. The dependence of its real and imaginary parts on $\theta$ are shown plotted in Fig. 3.4. The expression for the exciting current is

$$i_m = i_\omega^+(0) \left(\frac{aT^2}{2d}\right) \left(\frac{-j\theta N}{6}\right) e^{-\frac{j\theta}{2}} + v_\omega^+(0) \left(\frac{-I_0}{v(0)}\right) \left(\frac{v(0)T}{d}\right) \frac{j\theta}{2}$$
$$\left(M - \frac{j\theta}{6} \frac{N}{}\right) e^{-\frac{j\theta}{2}}. \quad (101)$$

Because of cancellation, the exciting current is zero for zero $\theta$. Except for a term $i^\omega(0) M e^{\frac{-j\theta}{2}}$ which is not present in Eq. (101), the above expressions for $Y_B$ and $i_n$ are very similar to those for the high-velocity gap (see Eq. 3.37).

*D-c Conditions.*—The acceleration in the absence of the r-f field is calculated from the equation

$$\frac{da(x)}{dx} = -\int_{v^i(x)}^{\infty} dv \frac{j(x,v)}{v},$$

where

$$v^i(x) = -\left[-2\int_x^d d\zeta a(\zeta)\right]^{\frac{1}{2}},$$

since the velocity distribution contains reflected electrons. All the electrons in the region are injected at the first plane and therefore the above integral can be expressed in terms of $j(0,v')$,

$$\frac{da(x)}{dx} = -2\int_{u(x)}^{u(d)} dv' \frac{j(0,v')}{v(x;v')} - \int_{u(d)}^{\infty} dv' \frac{j(0,v')}{v(x;v')},$$

where

$$v(x;v') = \left[v'^2 + 2\int_0^x d\zeta a(\zeta)\right]^{\frac{1}{2}},$$
$$u(x) = \left[-2\int_0^x d\zeta a(\zeta)\right]^{\frac{1}{2}}.$$

Direct integration gives

$$a(x) - a(0) = -2\int_0^{u(x)} dv' j(0,v') T(r',v') - 2\int_{u(x)}^{u(d)} dv' j(0,v') T(x;v')$$
$$- \int_{u(d)}^{\infty} dv' j(0,v') T(x;v'),$$

where $r'$ is the plane of reflection of an electron injected with velocity $v'$. On the other hand, integration after multiplying by $a(x)$ gives

$$a(x)^2 - a(0)^2 = 4 \int_0^{u(x)} dv' j(0,v')v' - 4 \int_{u(x)}^{u(d)} dv' j(0,v')[v(x;v') - v']$$
$$-2 \int_{u(d)}^{\infty} dv' j(0,v')[v(x;v') - v'].$$

The introduction of $a(d)$ yields the simpler relation,

$$a(x)^2 - a(d)^2 = -4 \int_{u(x)}^{u(d)} dv' j(0,v')v(x;v') - 2 \int_{u(d)}^{\infty} dv' j(0,v')[v(x;v')$$
$$- v(d;v')].$$

By introducing the d-c potential, a form is obtained which is useful in numerical integration.

The d-c voltage at the second plane is

$$V(d) = -\frac{mu(d)^2}{2e}.$$

The a-c resistance is $\rho = dV(d)/dI_0$; but

$$I_0 = -\int_{u(d)}^{\infty} dv' i(0,v');$$

hence

$$\frac{1}{\rho} = \frac{-ei(0,u(d))}{mu(d)}. \tag{102}$$

For a Maxwell-Boltzmann distribution, this expression yields the familiar

$$\rho I_0 = \frac{kT}{e}.$$

At $1160°$ K, $kT/e$ is $\frac{1}{10}$ volt.

*Integral Equation.*—The Fourier transform of $j(x,t)$ is

$$j_\omega(x) = \int_{-\infty}^{\infty} dt \int_{v^i(x,t)}^{\infty} dv j(0,v,t)e^{-i\omega t}$$

It can be written in terms of $j(0, v', t')$:

$$j_\omega(x) = \int_{-\infty}^{\infty} dt' \left\{ -\int_{u(x;t')}^{u(d;t')} dv' j(0,v',t')e^{-i\omega t} + \int_{u(x;t')}^{\infty} dv' j(0,v',t')e^{-i\omega t} \right\},$$

where $u(x;t')$ is the speed of injection of an electron which is injected at $t'$ and reaches $x$ with zero velocity.

The two time intervals $T(x,t;v')$ and $T^-(x,t;v')$ are introduced; they are the times required for an electron injected with velocity $v'$ to reach $x$ at time $t$ directly and by reflection, respectively. In terms of these quantities,

$$j_\omega(x) = \int_{-\infty}^{\infty} dt' e^{-i\omega t'} \left\{ \int_{u(x;t')}^{u(d;t')} dv' j(0,v',t')[e^{-i\omega T(x,t;v')} - e^{-i\omega T^-(x,t;v')}] \right.$$
$$\left. + \int_{u(d;t')}^{\infty} dv' j(0,v',t') e^{-i\omega T(x,t;v')} \right\}.$$

On introducing Fourier integral expressions for all time-dependent quantities and keeping only terms linear in the amplitudes, there results

$$j_\omega(x) = \int_{u(x)}^{u(d)} dv' j_\omega(0,v') \left[ e^{-i\omega T(x;v')} - e^{-i\omega T^-(x;v')} \right]$$
$$+ \int_{u(d)}^{\infty} dv' j_\omega(0,v') e^{-i\omega T(x;v')} - \int_{u(x)}^{u(d)} dv' j(0,v') [j\omega T_\omega(x;v')$$
$$- j\omega T_\omega^-(x;v')] - \int_{u(d)}^{\infty} dv' j(0,v') j\omega T_\omega(x;v')$$
$$- u_\omega(d) j(0,u(d)) e^{-i\omega T^-(x;u(d))}. \quad (103)$$

A simple calculation yields [compare with Eq. (84)]

$$u_\omega(d) = -\frac{1}{u(d)} \int_0^d d\zeta\, a_\omega(\zeta) e^{i\omega T(\zeta;u(d))}. \quad (104)$$

Eq. 72 is valid for $T_\omega(x;v')$, which is written in the form

$$T_\omega(x;v') = -\int_0^x d\zeta\, a_\omega(\zeta) \frac{\partial}{j\omega v'\partial v'} e^{-i\omega[T(x;v')-T(\zeta;v')]}. \quad (105)$$

The derivation of an expression for $T_\omega^-(x;v')$ follows along similar lines but is somewhat more tedious since care must be exercised to avoid integrals which diverge at the point of reflection. It is found that

$$T_\omega^-(x;v') = -\int_0^x d\zeta\, a_\omega(\zeta) \frac{\partial}{j\omega v'\partial v'} e^{i\omega[T(x;v')-T(\zeta;v')]}$$
$$- \int_0^{r'} d\zeta\, a_\omega(\zeta) \frac{\partial}{j\omega v'\partial v'} [e^{-i\omega[T^-(x;v')-T(\zeta;v')]} - e^{i\omega[T(x;v')-T(\zeta;v')]}]. \quad (106)$$

It is of interest to note that if $a(\zeta)$ and $a_\omega(\zeta)$ are constants, these expressions give the Eqs. (99) with $v_\omega^+(0) = 0$, as direct integrations show.

The integral equation for $a_\omega(x)$ is obtained by using Eq. (70) with Eq. (103) for $j_\omega(x)$ into which Eqs. (104), (105), and (106) have been substituted. The result is

$$a_\omega(x) = b_\omega(x) - \frac{c_\omega}{j\omega C\rho} e^{-i\omega T^-(x;u(d))} + \int_0^d d\zeta\, a_\omega(\zeta) K(\zeta,x), \quad (107)$$

where $b_\omega(x)$ is defined by

$$j\omega b_\omega(x) = -J_\omega + \int_{u(x)}^{u(d)} dv' j_\omega(0,v') \left[ e^{-j\omega T(x;v')} - e^{-j\omega T^-(x;v')} \right]$$

$$+ \int_{u(d)}^{\infty} dv' j_\omega(0,v') e^{-j\omega T(x;v')}, \quad (108)$$

and $c_\omega$ is the constant

$$c_\omega = \frac{1}{d} \int_0^d d\zeta a_\omega(\zeta) e^{j\omega T(\zeta;u(d))}, \quad (109)$$

and the kernel is defined as follows:

$$\begin{aligned} K(\zeta,x) &= F(\zeta,x) + G(\zeta,x), & \zeta < x, \\ K(\zeta,x) &= F(x,\zeta), & x < \zeta; \end{aligned} \Bigg\} \quad (110)$$

$$\begin{aligned} F(\zeta,x) &= \int_{u(x)}^{u(d)} dv' \frac{j(0,v')}{j\omega v'} \frac{\partial}{\partial v'} \left[ e^{-j\omega[T(x;v')-T(\zeta;v')]} - e^{-j\omega[T^-(x;v)-T(\zeta;v')]} \right], \\ G(\zeta,x) &= \int_{u(d)}^{\infty} dv' \frac{j(0,v')}{j\omega v'} \frac{\partial}{\partial v'} e^{-j\omega[T(x;v')-T(\zeta;v')]}. \end{aligned} \Bigg\} \quad (111)$$

*Density Modulation.*—The solution of Eq. (107) is

$$a_\omega(x) = b_\omega(x) + \int_0^d d\zeta b_\omega(\zeta) L(\zeta,x) - \frac{c_\omega}{j\omega C\rho} \left[ e^{-j\omega T^-(x;u(d))} \right.$$

$$\left. + \int_0^d d\zeta e^{-j\omega T^-(\zeta;u(d))} L(\zeta,x) \right],$$

where $c_\omega$ is a constant that remains to be evaluated. After substituting from Eq. (108), the solution can be written in the form,

$$j\omega a_\omega(x) = -J_\omega[1 + \phi(x)] + \int_0^{\infty} dv' j_\omega(0,v') \phi(x;v') - \frac{c_\omega}{C\rho} \phi^-(x), \quad (112)$$

where

$$\phi(x) = \int_0^d d\zeta L(\zeta,x), \qquad \phi^-(x) = e^{-j\omega T^-(x;u(d))} + \int_0^d d\zeta e^{-j\omega T^-(\zeta;u(d))} L(\zeta,x),$$

$$\phi(x;v') = \begin{cases} \int_0^{r'} d\zeta [e^{-j\omega T(\zeta;v')} - e^{-j\omega T^-(\zeta;v')}] L(\zeta,x), & 0 < v' < u(x), \\[2mm] [e^{-j\omega T(x;v')} - e^{-j\omega T^-(x;v')}] + \int_0^{r'} d\zeta [e^{-j\omega T(\zeta;v')} - e^{-j\omega T^-(\zeta;v')}] L(\zeta,x), \\ & u(x) < v' < u(d), \\[2mm] e^{-j\omega T(x;v')} + \int_0^d d\zeta e^{-j\omega T(\zeta;v')} L(\zeta,x), & u(d) < v'. \end{cases}$$

The constant $c_\omega$ is found by using Eq. (112) in Eq. (109). The result is

$$\frac{c_\omega}{C\rho} = \frac{-J_\omega \chi + \int_0^{\infty} dv' j_\omega(0,v') \chi(v')}{j\omega C\rho + \chi^-}, \quad (113)$$

where

$$\chi = \frac{1}{d} \int_0^d dx[1 + \phi(x)]e^{j\omega T(x;u(d))},$$

$$\chi(v') = \frac{1}{d} \int_0^d dx\phi(x;v')e^{j\omega T(x;u(d))},$$

$$\chi^- = \frac{1}{d} \int_0^d dx\phi^-(x)e^{j\omega T(x;u(d))}.$$

Hence

$$j\omega a_\omega(x) = -J_\omega \left\{1 + \phi(x) - \frac{\phi^-(x)\chi}{j\omega C\rho + \chi^-}\right\}$$
$$+ \int_0^\infty dv'j\omega(0,v') \left\{\phi(x;v') - \frac{\phi^-(x)\chi(v')}{j\omega C\rho + \chi^-}\right\}. \quad (114)$$

Eq. (70) gives the density modulation, which is written in the series form

$$i_\omega(x) = -I_\omega\alpha(x) + i_s(x),$$

with

$$i_s(x) = \int_0^\infty dv'i_\omega(0,v')\alpha(x;v').$$

The coefficients are

$$\alpha(x) = \phi(x) - \frac{\phi^-(x)\chi}{j\omega C\rho + \chi^-}, \quad (115)$$

$$\alpha(x;v') = \phi(x;v') - \frac{\phi^-(x)\chi(v')}{j\omega C\rho + \chi^-}.$$

In the limit of zero transit angles, $\phi^-(x)$ becomes $1 + \phi(x)$, $\chi^-$ becomes $\chi$, and it is found that

$$1 + \alpha(x) \rightarrow \frac{j\omega C}{\chi} \left(\frac{1 + \phi(x)}{\frac{j\omega C}{\chi} + \frac{1}{\rho}}\right)$$

For the gap admittance is found

$$Y_g \rightarrow \frac{1}{\rho} + \frac{j\omega C}{\chi},$$

which is just the sum of the a-c conductance and the susceptance due to a capacity modified by the presence of space charge. In addition

$$y_m(d) \rightarrow \frac{1}{\rho} - \frac{j\omega C}{\chi} \phi(d).$$

As expected, the internal transadmittance at the exit plane becomes the sum of the a-c conductance and a low-frequency space-charge contribution. In the limit of zero transit angles, $\phi(x,v')$ and $x(v')$ both become zero for velocities of injection too small to reach the second plane, $v' < u(d)$; while for $v' > u(d)$, $\phi(x;v')$ becomes $1 + \phi(x)$ and $\chi(v')$ becomes $\chi$. Thus it follows that both $\alpha(x;v')$ and $z_g(v')$ are zero for $v' < u(d)$; and for $v' > u(d)$

$$\alpha(x,v') \rightarrow 1 + \alpha(x), \qquad z_g(v') \rightarrow Z_g,$$

and both the excitation function $\mu_i(v')$ and the density-modulation function $\mu_i(d;v')$ become unity.

# CHAPTER 6

## SPACE-CHARGE DEVICES AS MICROWAVE AMPLIFIERS

### By J. B. H. Kuper

**6·1. Introduction.**—The importance of microwave amplifiers has been discussed in Chap. 2, where it was pointed out that the commercially available triodes, the "lighthouse" family, are not satisfactory amplifiers when operated much above 1000 Mc/sec. The best experimental triodes and tetrodes perform well at 3000 Mc/sec, but at still higher frequencies the amplifier field will probably be left to the klystrons and other "high-velocity" types such as the traveling-wave tube.

In this chapter an attempt is made to justify the above conclusions on the basis of the rather meager experimental data at hand. Unfortunately it is not possible to correlate the experiments with the theory developed in the preceding three chapters, except in a most general fashion. This difficulty results from the fact that real tubes depart widely from the ideal geometry and simple conditions postulated in the theoretical treatment. Also in most experimental amplifiers a negative grid is used while most cases considered in Chap. 5 used a positive grid. Under wartime conditions the rather disappointing experimental results precluded the expenditure of time needed for a check of the theory.

The experiments can be discussed in elementary terms with the introduction of an "effective transconductance," which is the magnitude of the complex transadmittance multiplied by the beam coupling coefficient of the input gap. This simplification is permissible only because microwave amplifiers are usually operated in class A (indeed it is somewhat doubtful if class C operation has been attained above 3000 Mc/sec) and the phase shift resulting from transit time in the amplifier tube is rarely measured.

**6·2. Elementary Discussion of Grid-separation Amplifiers.**—A tube intended for microwave use must possess either an integral cavity resonator or a structure to which a cavity may readily be attached; any other circuit would be impractically small or would have excessive radiation losses. When this need is understood, it is a matter of topology that the grounded-grid circuit—sometimes called the "grid-separation" circuit—is the natural one to use. Fortunately, a circuit of this type is usually stable without neutralization. The designation "grid-separation" seems more appropriate than the more usual term "grounded-grid"; the grid actually separates the input and output circuits physically, and it is meaningless to speak of "grounding" one part of a cavity resonator.

For a planar triode the input resonator would be a coaxial line whose outer conductor would make contact with the grid and whose inner conductor would end at the cathode. Such a line would normally have an adjustable short-circuiting plunger, set to give the line an electrical length of 1, 3, 5, . . . quarter-wavelengths. The output circuit would be a similar coaxial line between the grid and plate. Each cavity would have suitable coupling loops or probes and provisions for applying the necessary d-c voltages.

*Gain of a Low-level Grid-separation Amplifier.*—When such an amplifier has its input and output circuits tuned to resonance, so that they appear as pure resistances, and when the input circuit is matched to the generator impedance the equivalent circuit is as shown in Fig. 6·1. The tube is drawn as a tetrode merely to emphasize the separation of input and output circuits, here assumed to be completely isolated except for the unidirectional electron stream. In a low-level amplifier the r-f voltages developed across the input and output gaps are always small compared with the d-c beam voltage. The input line is assumed to be matched so that any power sent down the

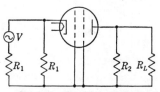

Fig. 6·1.—Equivalent circuit of a grid-separation amplifier with complete isolation between input and output circuits except for the unidirectional electron stream. Direct-current connections omitted.

line is dissipated in the input losses $R_1$. These losses may be defined by noting that, if the r-f power $P_1$ is applied to the line, an rms voltage $V_1$ is developed between cathode and grid where

$$V_1^2 = P_1 R_1. \qquad (1)$$

This voltage produces an r-f current $i$ passing through the first grid having a value

$$|i| = |g_m| V_1, \qquad (2)$$

where $|g_m|$ is the absolute value of the transadmittance of the electron stream or the "effective transconductance." This value may, under the proper circumstances, be only a little less than that of the familiar low-frequency $g_m$ (see Figs. 5.3 and 5.4). If $V_2$ is the r-f voltage developed across the output circuit, the total power delivered by the beam is

$$P_2 = V_2^2 \left( \frac{1}{R_2} + \frac{1}{R_L} \right), \qquad (3)$$

and the useful power $P_L$ is $V_2^2/R_L$. If the full r-f current $|i|$ arrives in the output circuit, $V_2$ is given by

$$V_2 = i \left( \frac{R_2 R_L}{R_L + R_2} \right),\tag{4}$$

and therefore

$$P_L = \frac{i^2}{R_L} \left( \frac{R_2 R_L}{R_L + R_2} \right)^2 = i^2 \frac{R_2^2 R_L}{(R_L + R_2)^2}.\tag{5}$$

By combining Eqs. (1) and (2) and substituting for $i$ in Eq. (5), the following relation for the power gain is obtained:

$$G = \frac{P_L}{P_1} = \frac{g_m^2 R_1 R_2^2 R_L}{(R_L + R_2)^2}.\tag{6}$$

For a constant-current generator such as this amplifier, the maximum value of $P_L$ is obtained when $R_L = R_2$, in which case

$$G_{\max} = \frac{g_m^2 R_1 R_2}{4}.\tag{7}$$

In this simplified derivation the effects of transit time, represented by the beam-coupling coefficient, are assumed to have been included in the effective transconductance. The details of the calculation of the interaction between the electron beam and the gap are discussed in Chaps. 3 and 5. From Eq. (7) it is clear that the maximum gain obtainable is dependent not only on the transconductance but also on the shunt resistances of the input and output circuits, which are partly functions of the tube and partly of the rest of the resonator.

*High-efficiency Amplifiers.*—Equations (6) and (7) lose their meaning when applied to a power amplifier operated in Class B or C in the interests of efficiency because there the tube is not operating as a constant current device. The concept of the transconductance must therefore be revised. In the first place, the loading is adjusted to let the r-f voltage in the output circuit rise to the point where it almost stops the beam, thus giving the best possible "electronic efficiency." Beyond this point any increase in current calls for a heavier load. Because the circuit losses remain the same if the r-f voltage is kept at its optimum value while the output power is increasing, the "circuit efficiency" may also become high. High-efficiency operation of this sort, it appears, has not yet been achieved at microwave frequencies. In the second place, in discussing high-efficiency operation it seems simplest to follow the terminology that is usual in klystron work and to speak of "bunches" of charge traversing the output r-f gap (the grid-plate region) with the distinction that here the bunches are formed by "gating" action at the potential minimum and not by velocity modulation and a drift space. In fact, a power tube must have a negligible drift space or separation between input and output circuits, otherwise the velocity variations accompanying the gating action may lead to "debunching." No detailed treatment of power amplifiers is given here in view of the lack of experimental data, and the balance of this chapter is concerned mostly with low-level amplifiers.[1]

*Resonator parameters.*—Provided the resonator geometry is such that there is a well-defined region—the r-f gap—across which most of the capacitance is found, the $Q$ is given approximately by the familiar low-frequency expression $Q = \omega CR$, where $C$ is the effective capacitance, ordinarily fixed by the tube geometry, and $R$ is the circuit shunt resistance. The values of $C$ and $R$ are by no means independent, however, because for many common resonator shapes that portion of $R$ contributed by circuit losses is directly proportional to the length of the r-f gap, whereas $C$ varies inversely with this length (see Chap. 4). In most tube designs, beam loading on the cathode side insures that $R_1$ is enough smaller than $R_2$ to outweigh differences in effective capacitance in the input and output circuits, and thus makes the bandwidth of the input circuit greater than that of the output circuit, usually by a factor of 2 or more.

The shunt impedances $R_1$ and $R_2$ may be estimated in several ways. Where the geometry is simple, the factor relating shunt impedance and unloaded $Q$ is known. Standing-wave measurements in the input line will then permit calculation of $R$. On the other hand, it may be possible to vary a bias until electron flow is just cut off; this method measures the peak r-f voltage, from which the shunt impedance may readily be computed if the driving power is known. A correction for transit-time effects, using the beam coupling coefficient, may be advisable.

*High-frequency $g_m$.*—Before proceeding to the experimental data it may be well to examine further the statement about high-frequency $g_m$ that was made in connection with Eq. (2).[2] The calculations of Llewellyn and Peterson[3] show that the magnitude of the transconductance for small signals does not greatly deteriorate even at very high frequencies. Their curves predict a minimum of slightly less than 0.8 of the d-c value for a transit angle of $2\pi$, after which the $g_m$ oscillates but never departs from the d-c value by more than 10 per cent. For small angles ($\pi$ or less)

---

[1] For a résumé of experiments on several types of power amplifiers and a discussion of the failure to achieve Class C operation, see H. W. Jamieson and J. R. Whinnery, "Power Amplifiers with Disk-Seal Tubes," *Proc. I.R.E.*, **34**, 483 (1946).

[2] The treatment here follows that in H. V. Neher, "Some Notes on Space-charge-limited Oscillators and Amplifiers at Microwave Frequencies," RL Report No. 822, Nov. 15, 1945.

[3] F. B. Llewellyn and L. C. Peterson, "Vacuum Tube Networks," *Proc. I.R.E.*, **32**, 144, (1944). See also Fig. 5·3.

the phase lag of the current passing the grid is $\frac{11}{30}$ of the transit angle, and at larger angles the lag is approximately equal to the angle less $\pi$. In computing transit angles in a space-charge-limited region it must be remembered that an electron requires 50 per cent more time to traverse the distance than it does in a space-charge-free region.

*Spread in Transit Angles.*—It should not be assumed that the results reached by Llewellyn and Peterson predict satisfactory operation at higher and higher frequencies without the necessity for decreasing the cathode-grid spacing. Where the lag in transconductance is large it becomes very necessary to keep the *spread* in transit angles to a low value. For, if the phase of some of the electrons passing the grid differs by $\pi$ from that of other electrons which ideally would have the same phase, then these two groups of electrons will cancel each other, electron for electron, and the resultant transconductance will suffer accordingly. A criterion that the spread in transit angles for all electrons must not exceed $\pm\pi/4$ may be set arbitrarily. Any variation in cathode-grid spacing from point to point results in the same percentage variation in transit angle, and any variation in potential causes roughly half that variation in transit angle.

The factors that affect the phases of the electrons may be listed in two main categories, as follows:

1. Irregularities in the electric field between cathode and grid.
    a. Edge effects or fringing. These result in a different distance of travel as well as in a variation in field strength (most important for small cathodes).
    b. Nonuniform spacing between cathode and grid—for example, lack of parallelism in a planar structure.
    c. Coarse grid mesh. For a parallel-wire grid the spacing between wires should not exceed the cathode-grid spacing. A limit is thus set on the wire size also because, for good transparency, the wire diameter should be less than one-third the spacing. For a woven-mesh grid the requirement on wire size is still more stringent because of the irregularities introduced by the weave.
    d. Irregularities on the surface of the cathode are just as important as irregularities in grid surface.
    e. Variation in contact potential over the grid. It is known that such a potential may amount to several volts and there is no *a priori* reason to assume it is constant over the whole grid surface.
2. Irregularities in emission over the cathode surface. These may be a serious factor not only in causing variations in transit angles but also in causing excessive loading. If the cathode does not emit uniformly over its surface but has some temperature-limited

regions and some regions that emit several times more copiously than is necessary, the transit angle may vary by at least 50 per cent. There is a transconductance from a temperature-limited region that is due to transit-angle "bunching" (see Eq. 3.28) and this transconductance may be completely out of phase with that from the space-charge-limited regions.

The difficulties of making a high-frequency amplifier are apparent when it is pointed out that even for very close spacings (of the order of 0.001 in.) the cathode-grid transit angle for an electron with thermal energy is about $2\pi$ at 3000 Mc/sec—which, with the limits on spread of $\pm\pi/4$, means an allowable variation of $\pm 12$ per cent in spacing. Nevertheless, the factors listed under Category 1 can be made to approach the ideal simply by refinements in construction. On the other hand, the production of a satisfactory cathode that emits uniformly over its surface is presumably the major problem to be solved.

*Maximum Value of Low-frequency Transconductance.*—As the grid is brought closer and closer to the cathode the low-frequency transconductance per unit current tends to approach a limit set by the thermal energy distribution of the electrons. If the grid is at the potential minimum, the electrons reaching it are those with energies greater than a certain minimum value. From kinetic theory it may be shown that the limiting conductance per unit current is given by

$$\frac{g_m}{I_0} = \frac{e}{kT} \text{ volts}^{-1},\qquad(8)$$

where $e$ is the electron charge, $k$ is Boltzmann's constant, and $T$ is the absolute temperature of the cathode. For a cathode at 1050°K the limiting conductance is about 11 mhos/amp or 11000 $\mu$mhos/ma. The best cathode in the series of experimental tubes built at the Radiation Laboratory was less than half as good as this ideal; it had a static $g_m$ of 5000 $\mu$mhos at 1 ma plate current and 8000 $\mu$mhos at 2 ma. The spacings were such that the potential minimum was put in the plane of the grid at about 1 ma. This experimental result is taken to mean that only a fraction of the cathode surface was emitting copiously.

The high-frequency $g_m$ can be computed from Eq. (7) provided the shunt impedances and the gain are known. Where the geometry permits a good estimate of the shunt impedances, the values obtained for the best tubes (from the standpoint of the factors listed under Category 1) are in fair agreement with the low-frequency results, as is shown in Sec. 6·3.

*Bandwidth.*—Measurements of gain are of little value unless the bandwidth is specified. In almost all grid-separation amplifiers the loading on the input circuit is so heavy that the bandwidth of the output circuit is the determining factor. Writing $C_2$ for the effective capacitance across the output circuit, the bandwidth $\Delta f$ between the half-power points is given by

$$\Delta f = \frac{f}{Q} = \frac{R_2 + R_L}{2\pi C_2 R_2 R_L}.$$  (9)

Combining this result with Eq. (7) gives an equation for a figure of merit, power gain multiplied by bandwidth,

$$G \cdot \Delta f = \frac{g_m^2 R_1}{2\pi C_2} \cdot \frac{R_2}{(R_L + R_2)}.$$  (10)

If the amplifier is loaded for maximum gain, $R_L = R_2$, the figure of merit is

$$[G \cdot \Delta f]_{\text{at max} G} = \frac{g_m^2 R_1}{4\pi C_2};$$  (11)

this figure is a property of the tube alone, if it is granted that most of the input loading is in the tube rather than in circuit losses. If the loading is adjusted for the highest possible figure of merit, the latter approaches, as a limit for very heavy loads, a value just twice that given by Eq. (11)—that is,

$$\lim_{R_L \to 0} (G \cdot \Delta f) = \frac{g_m^2 R_1}{2\pi C_2}.$$  (12)

At this limit the gain would fall to zero, but long before this condition was reached the bandwidth of the input circuit would have become the limiting factor.

*Effect of Feedback.*—In practice, the assumption of negligible feedback is unjustified; there is considerable coupling through the plate-cathode capacitance. If the resultant voltages across the input and output gaps are denoted by $V_1'$ and $V_2'$ where the primes indicate that feedback is included, and if $m$ is the feedback voltage ratio, then for the special case of 180° transit angle

$$V_1' = V_1 + mV_2' = V_1 + mi' \frac{R_2 R_L}{R_L + R_2} = \frac{V_1}{1 - mg_m \dfrac{R_2 R_L}{R_L + R_2}},$$  (13)

and it can readily be shown that the power output is

$$P_0' = \frac{g_m^2 R_2^2 R_L}{(R_L + R_2)^2} \left[ \frac{V_1}{1 - mg_m \dfrac{R_2 R_L}{R_L + R_2}} \right]^2.$$  (14)

The gain with feedback, $G'$, is given, in terms of the gain $G$ predicted by Eq. (6), by the expression

$$G' = G \left( 1 - \frac{\gamma}{1 + x} \right)^{-2}$$  (15)

where $\gamma$ is written for $m g_m R_2$ and $x = R_2/R_L$. The effect of the kind of positive feedback considered here is to increase the gain markedly, especially at light loads (small $x$), and to shift the maximum output point to lighter loads than the value $R_L = R_2$ which was predicted by Eq. (7).

Another effect of positive feedback is the narrowing of the input circuit bandwidth, which may become severe enough to reduce drastically the figure of merit. The existence of a positive feedback means that from the point of view of the generator in the input circuit a negative conductance has been inserted parallel with the positive conductance already present to represent the losses. Since the input power $P_1$ [in Eq. (1)] remains constant while the developed voltage $V_1$ is increased by the factor

$$\frac{1}{1 - m g_m \dfrac{R_2 R_L}{R_L + R_2}} = \frac{1}{1 - \dfrac{\gamma}{1 + x}}$$

[see Eq. (13)], the input resistance with feedback $R_1'$ is enhanced by the same factor as the gain [in Eq. (15)]. The input circuit bandwidth is inversely proportional to $R_1$, and so must decrease as the gain is increased by regeneration. With even moderate amounts of regeneration the input circuit bandwidth may become less than that of the output circuit, and the generator may no longer be matched to the input; Eq. (1) therefore is no longer valid. For this reason an exact expression for the figure of merit is too complicated to be useful. Qualitatively the figure of merit may increase slightly with very small amounts of regeneration, provided the input circuit without feedback is much broader than the output circuit. After the regeneration has been increased to the point where the input circuit is the narrower one, the figure of merit decreases rapidly.

**6·3. Experimental Amplifier Tubes for the 3000-Mc/sec Region.—** H. V. Neher at the Radiation Laboratory[1] improved the space-charge-controlled amplifier tubes for the 3000-Mc/sec region and this work resulted in some experimental triodes and tetrodes that gave remarkably good performance. These tubes were difficult to produce consistently, however, and so far have not been produced commercially. Their construction is illustrated in Fig. 6·2.

The tube is mounted in a standard metal envelope containing both input and output resonators, which are tuned by distorting the envelope slightly. The input circuit comprises the cathode assembly 1, mounted in a copper sleeve 2, which forms the inner conductor, a flexible diaphragm

[1] H. V. Neher, "A Preliminary Report on the Radiation Laboratory S-band Amplifier," RL Report No. 306, July 10, 1943, and "Some Notes on Space-charge-limited Oscillators and Amplifiers at Microwave Frequencies," RL Report No. 822, Nov. 15, 1945.

6, and an outer conductor 5, closed by the first grid 7.   This grid is wound with 0.0003-in. tungsten wire stretched across a $\frac{1}{8}$-in. hole in a 0.005-in. molybdenum disk, and is insulated (for direct current) from the outer conductor 5 and the screen grid 8 by mica disks.   The input circuit is fed by a coaxial line 22, tapped on to the center conductor by a flexible sleeve 4.   The circuit is tuned by applying pressure with the screws in

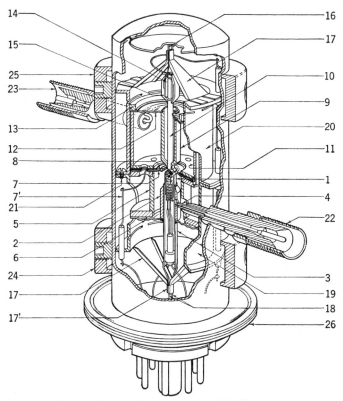

Fig. 6·2.—Cutaway drawing of an experimental 3000-Mc/sec amplifier tube.

the heavy ring 24.   Pressure applied in line with the bent strut 17 moves the cathode away from the grid and increases the resonant frequency; pressure along the diameter at right angles moves the cathode closer to the first grid and lowers frequency.   The output circuit consists of the copper anode 9, the diaphragm 12, the outer conductor 11, and a grid 8. The latter is similar to the grid 7 except for wire spacing.   The actuating rod 10 for the output-circuit tuning is made of Invar and forms part of the temperature-compensation system.   The entire output circuit is at anode potential, being insulated by mica from the grid 8, mounting sleeve 20, and retaining ring 13, and from the tuning mechanism with a ceramic bead 14. The output-coupling loop mounted on the coaxial fitting 23 enters the cavity through an oversized hole in 11.

This construction is unconventional but has several important characteristics.

1. Resonators are "built in" and are of simple geometry.
2. Cathode and anode spacings are adjustable (at the price of a shift in frequency).
3. The cathode can be flattened in place both before and after coating.
4. A high degree of parallelism between cathode and grid can be maintained.
5. Cathode-grid spacing can be calibrated in terms of resonant frequency by measurements on the cold circuit before assembly.
6. Fine, taut grids with wires as small as 0.0003 in. and spacings down to 0.001 in. can be used.
7. By stacking grids with mica insulators it is possible to make a pentode almost as easily as a triode.

The performance of the best of these experimental tubes was very satisfactory. Gains up to 20 db at 6 Mc/sec bandwidth and noise figures in the order of magnitude of 9 db were obtained in the 3000-Mc/sec region. One triode that was operated as an oscillator gave an output of 1 watt at 25 per cent efficiency. In general, it was necessary to use a tetrode structure to avoid instability. A few tubes of similar structure, designed for the 10,000-Mc/sec region, were built by G. A. Hobart III. The best of these had a gain of 10 db and a noise figure of 18 db, and oscillated at 1 per cent efficiency. The bandwidth was not recorded.

Because the simple geometry permits the estimation of the shunt resistances, the effective $g_m$ for radio frequencies can be calculated from Eq. (6). Typical values for one tube are: $R_1 = 300$ ohms, $R_2 = 70,000$ ohms, gain = 100, r-f $g_m = 4400$ $\mu$mhos [computed from Eq. (6)], and low-frequency $g_m = 6000$ $\mu$mhos (measured at direct current). These measurements appear to confirm the predictions of Llewellyn and Peterson, referred to in Sec. 6·2, that transconductances closely approaching the d-c values may be obtained at microwave frequencies, provided the spread in transit angles is kept low.

*Input Loading.*—At low frequencies, because the signal is injected between the cathode and grid, $R_1$ would be expected to be simple diode loading—that is, $R_1 = \dfrac{1}{g_m}$. The modifications introduced by transit-time effects have been worked out by Benham,[1] and Llewellyn and

---

[1] W. E. Benham, "Theory of the Internal Action of Thermionic Systems at Moderately High Frequencies," *Phil. Mag.* **5**, 641, (1928), also **11**, 457 (1931).

Peterson.[1]  In general, as the frequency is raised the conductance decreases slowly at first, drops to zero at a transit angle of $2\pi$, then goes negative, and passes through zero again at $3\pi$.  At frequencies of about 1000 to 1500 Mc/sec with comparatively large grid-cathode spacings, it is possible to follow this behavior experimentally.  In the negative conductance region, oscillation at low efficiency (the so-called "monotron" mentioned in Chap. 2) has been obtained.[2]  In the 3000-Mc/sec region it becomes very difficult to follow this ideal diode behavior; the reason for the difficulty must be discovered.  One possible reason is the variation in transit angles introduced by the spread in initial velocities (the thermal-energy distribution).  A simple calculation shows that this effect is small even for a diode voltage of 2 with spacings of a few thousandths of an inch.  Experimentally, it has been found that the

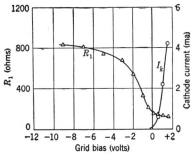

FIG. 6·3.—Variation of input shunt resistance of an experimental 3000-Mc/sec amplifier with grid bias. The corresponding cathode current is also shown.

input circuit resistance is sensitive to grid bias, as is shown in Fig. 6·3.  This experiment was made on a tube with a cathode area of 0.08 cm², a grid wire diameter of 0.0003 in., and a spacing of 0.002 in. between centers, at a grid-cathode spacing of 0.0036 in. and a frequency of 3000 Mc/sec.  At sufficiently high negative biases the shunt resistance $R_1$ approaches the values found for a cold tube, but as the bias is decreased the resistance drops rapidly.  When current flow begins, the resistance has already fallen almost to its minimum; the actual flow of current has little effect on the loading.  Similar variations in shunt resistance are found if the grid bias is held constant and the heater power is varied; under these conditions the cathode current will also change widely. This change is caused in part by the shift of the potential minimum (virtual cathode) from the cathode toward the grid as the emission becomes more plentiful, and in part by nonuniformity in activity over the cathode surface, which means that some regions are temperature-limited.

The foregoing results can be understood with reference to the classical theories of cathode behavior.  Electrons are emitted from the cathode, the number per unit time depending on the nature and temperature of the surface.  How far these electrons travel from the cathode will

[1] F. B. Llewellyn and L. C. Peterson, "Vacuum Tube Networks," *Proc. I.R.E.*, **32**, 144 (1944) Fig. 4.

[2] F. B. Llewellyn and A. E. Bowen, "Ultra-High-Frequency Oscillations by Means of Diodes," *Bell System Tech. J.*, **18**, 280 (1939).

depend on their initial velocities and on the field in which they find themselves. Ordinarily, there is a large excess of emission that results in the turning back of many electrons to the cathode by the negative field built up by their own charges. Only a few have sufficient initial energy to pass the resulting potential minimum that constitutes the "virtual cathode."[1] A simple calculation shows that, for ordinary current densities and cathode temperatures, the transit angle for an electron that almost reaches the potential minimum and is then turned back to the cathode is between $\pi$ and $2\pi$ at a frequency of 3000 Mc/sec. Under these conditions the exchange of energy between the electrons and the r-f field is close to its maximum value. In the first order this energy exchange should cancel out over a cycle because of the random emission from the cathode, but second-order effects are important and result in a net transfer of energy from the field to the electrons. For example, this hypothesis predicts that some electrons will strike the cathode with extra energy (back bombardment); this energy reappears as cathode-heating. Energy is conserved, but back bombardment is an unduly expensive method of heating a cathode. The loading that results from this process ordinarily appears to be heaviest at frequencies around 3000 Mc/sec, and it is expected that it would decrease somewhat at higher frequencies; however, this decrease has apparently not yet been observed.

The conclusion is that an ideal cathode would be one that emits uniformly over its whole surface, with the result that the potential minimum would be plane and the spread in transit angles would be minimized. For a low-level amplifier the cathode temperature should be adjusted so that the emission is only a little greater than the standing current—enough to supply the demands of the signal without reaching saturation. Under these conditions there would be the least possible loading by low-energy electrons shuttling between the cathode and potential minimum, without sacrificing gain. As a practical working rule the input-circuit loading at frequencies in the 3000-Mc/sec region is given by $R_1 A = 25$ ohms-cm², where $A$ is the cathode area in square centimeters.

**6·4. Noise in Microwave Amplifiers.** *Input Circuit Noise.*—The noise generated in the input and output circuits of an amplifier of this sort may be measured separately, provided the circuit not being measured is detuned to avoid feedback effects. If the current is not temperature-limited, the noise power originating in the input circuit can be remarkably low. This fact is shown in Fig. 6·4, where the 3000 Mc/sec noise power $N_1$ in units of $kT(\Delta f)$—$4 \times 10^{-15}$ watts for 1 Mc/sec

---

[1] The distance from the cathode to the potential minimum may be calculated from data published by B. J. Thompson, D. O. North, and W. A. Harris, "Fluctuations in Space-charge-limited Currents at Moderately High Frequencies," *RCA Rev.*, **4**, 443, (1940).

at room temperature—is plotted against grid bias for a tube with a grid-cathode spacing of 0.001 in.  The plate current is also shown.  The noise

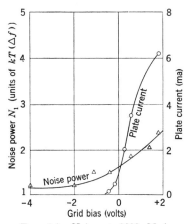

FIG. 6·4.—Noise at 3000 Mc/sec generated in input circuit of an experimental amplifier with grid-cathode spacing of 0.001 in. as a function of grid bias  The corresponding plate current is also shown.

becomes very low at high negative biases because the transit angle between cathode and potential minimum becomes very small.  At the normal operating current of 2 ma the noise power is still less than twice $kT(\Delta f)$ and the actual flow of current makes comparatively little difference.  As long as electrons come near the grid it does not matter whether they continue through it.

If the heater power is reduced so that a temperature-limited current is obtained, the situation is very different, as shown in Fig. 6·5.  The circuit is quiet as long as the current is space-charge-limited, but the noise rises rapidly as the current becomes more and more temperature-limited.  At still higher positive biases the noise curve should level off at a value corresponding to the familiar temperature-limited diode.

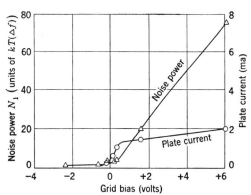

FIG. 6·5.—Noise generated in the input circuit of the amplifier shown in Fig. 6·4 with the heater power decreased to give temperature-limited emission.

At low frequencies the noise from a temperature-limited diode or from a closely spaced space-charge-limited diode may readily be calculated.  Considering the cathode-grid region as a space-charge-limited diode, if the potential minimum is at the grid, as it will be to a fair approximation, the number of electrons reaching the grid will be governed by the laws of probability. A perfectly random current, therefore, may be assumed. Furthermore, at low frequencies the electrons that are turned back before reaching the potential minimum will not exchange energy with the field because of the averaging-out over the cycle; the averaging is effective at small transit angles. Under these conditions the mean-square noise current is given by the equation

$$\overline{I_n^2} = 2eI_0(\Delta f), \tag{16}$$

where $e$ is the electron charge, $I_0$ the average current, and $\Delta f$ the bandwidth of the detecting device. These currents will cause a voltage $V_n$ to be built up across the circuit given by

$$\overline{V_n^2} = 2eI_0(\Delta f)R_1^2, \tag{17}$$

where $R_1$ is the shunt resistance of the input circuit. Expressing the noise power in terms of the Johnson noise, $4kT_0R(\Delta f)$, developed across any resistance $R$ at the temperature $T_0$ gives

$$N_1 = \frac{e}{2KT_0} I_0R_1. \tag{18}$$

At low frequencies, $R_1 = 1/g$, where $g$ is the diode conductance and $g/I_0$ is given in the ideal case by Eq. (8). Substituting these values in Eq. (18) there is obtained

$$N_1 = \frac{1}{2} \frac{T}{T_0}, \tag{19}$$

where $T$ and $T_0$ are cathode and room temperatures respectively, for the noise power in terms of Johnson noise in an ideal closely spaced diode at low frequencies. $N_1$ is often referred to as the "noise ratio" of the input circuit.

At high frequencies the low-energy electrons (those which shuttle between the cathode and the virtual cathode) discussed in connection with input loading also contribute noise. Both experimental and theoretical considerations indicate that the extra noise current is very nearly offset by the attendant decrease in $R_1$. Thus Eq. (19) may be used for microwave frequencies, and in fact it agrees well with the results of Fig. 6·4 at zero bias.

*Output Circuit Noise.*—The output circuit noise may be measured either by detuning the input or by reflecting a short circuit in the input line to the gap. The effectiveness of this procedure (and the absence of feedback) may be tested by measuring the gain, which should be down by about 30 db. In a widely spaced tube at low frequencies the reduction of noise by space-charge smoothing is well known.[1]  For a closely spaced diode where the anode is at or near the potential minimum, there is no smoothing effect since the minimum is essentially tied to the anode and is not free to vary.  As the cathode-grid spacing is increased, the potential minimum becomes free to perform its gating action.  The factor relating the noise with space-charge smoothing to that from a perfectly random current is usually called $\Gamma^2$, and theoretical values for this factor have been checked experimentally.

The smoothing factor $\Gamma^2$ may be measured conveniently by replacing the hypothetical diode plate with a grid and measuring the noise in the output circuit.  A series of measurements at 3000 Mc/sec with various cathode-grid spacings is shown in Fig. 6·6.  Noise power in units of $kT(\Delta f)$ is plotted against plate current.  For Curve 1 the cathode-grid spacing is 0.036 cm, and the cathode is operated at a temperature low enough to make the emission temperature-limited.  As is to be expected, the noise power is linear with the current.  For the rest of the curves the current was space-charge-limited.  For Curve 2 the spacing is 0.009 cm, and for Curve 3 it is 0.013 cm.  The reduction of noise is appreciable.  In Curves 4 and 5, taken at spacings of 0.028 cm and 0.036 cm respectively, a positive grid bias is required to obtain the higher currents.  These portions of the curves are indicated by broken lines and the experimental points have been corrected (arrows) for the extra noise due to grid interception.  The smallest value of $\Gamma^2$ (Curve 5) is found to be 0.20, in contrast to the low-frequency theoretical value of 0.02 for the same spacing and current.  Thus, space-charge smoothing appears to exist at 3000 Mc/sec but is much less effective than at low frequencies.  This decrease in effectiveness is to be expected because the interaction between slow electrons that gives rise to the smoothing takes appreciable time.  Also, the smoothing can be obtained only with cathode-grid

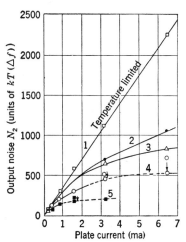

Fig. 6·6.—Output-circuit noise showing effects of space-charge smoothing. In curve 1 the emission is temperature-limited; in curves 2 to 5 the current is space-charge-limited and the cathode-grid spacings are 0.009, 0.013, 0.028 and 0.036 cm respectively. Broken lines corrected for interception noise.

---

[1] A good discussion of this is given in B. J. Thompson, D. O. North, and W. A. Harris, "Fluctuations in Space-Charge-Limited Currents at Moderately High Frequencies," *RCA Rev.*, **4**, 441, (1940).

spacings that are far too large to give a satisfactory high-frequency transconductance. The result is that the current in the output circuit must be considered to have the full shot noise.

*Over-all Noise.*—The over-all noise in these experimental tubes was found to be equal to the sum of the input- and output-circuit contributions. This relation does not necessarily hold, especially at low frequencies, where feedback effects may reduce the noise originating between cathode and grid when the input and output circuits are in resonance. When the input circuit is as quiet as it was in these experiments, no appreciable feedback effect is to be expected.

The output-circuit noise voltage is given by Eq. (17), with $R_1$ replaced by $R_2$. In terms of Johnson noise, the output noise ratio is

$$N_2 = \frac{e}{2kT_0} I_0 R_2,\tag{20}$$

analogous to Eq. (18). In order to calculate the noise figure for the amplifier as a whole, this noise ratio may be referred to the input circuit by dividing by the gain and adding it to the input contribution, Eq. (19), plus one to insure the correct reduction to a passive network; thus

$$\overline{NF} = 1 + N_1 + \frac{N_2}{G}.\tag{21}$$

By taking the gain at matched load as given by Eq. (7), and substituting from Eqs. (19) and (20), there is obtained

$$\overline{NF} = 1 + \frac{1}{2}\frac{T}{T_0} + \frac{2e}{kT_0}\cdot\frac{I_0}{g_m^2 R_1}.\tag{22}$$

This expression has been checked for various amplifiers in the 3000-Mc/sec region and has almost always predicted the noise figure within a factor of 2. It is interesting to note that the properties of the output circuit do not enter into the noise figure.

The factor $\dfrac{I_0}{g_m^2 R_1}$ in the last term of Eq. (22) may be written in the following way:

$$\frac{I_0}{g_m^2 R_1} = \frac{1}{\left(\dfrac{g_m}{I_0}\right)^2 \left(\dfrac{I_0}{A}\right) R_1 A}.\tag{23}$$

The maximum practical current density $I_0/A$ for an oxide-coated cathode is about 0.2 amp/cm²; $R_1 A$ has an experimental value of about 25 ohms/cm²; and the theoretical limit for $g_m/I_0$ is 11 per volt [Eq. (8)]. When these values are substituted in Eq. (22), an optimum noise figure of 4·2 is obtained. The best of Neher's experimental tubes has a noise figure of about 7, but has a value of $g_m/I_0$ that is only about 0.4 the possible maximum.

The conclusion is that satisfactory low-level amplifiers of more or less conventional design can be developed for the frequency range up to at least 3000 Mc/sec. All that is needed is the application of refinements in construction and the development of more dependable and uniform cathodes. Interesting possibilities for future research include the replacement of the actual cathode as a part of the input circuit by a virtual cathode formed by injecting the beam at low velocity into an r-f gap between two grids. Preliminary studies indicate that such a virtual cathode may be "quiet" and at the same time show a high mutual conductance. Another possibility is raised by a suggestion of Peterson[1] that at high frequencies there should be a reduction in noise if a space charge is built up between the input and output circuits of a tetrode. This can be done if the first grid is run a few volts positive with respect to the cathode and the second grid at a lower positive potential. As the injected current is raised, there will be sudden discontinuity in current to the second grid and a simultaneous formation of a virtual cathode between the grids. This point is known as the "Kipp" point,[2] and Peterson predicted that some interesting effects would be observed just below this point (see Sec. 5.6). The general features of his theory have been confirmed by Neher. Depending on the various currents and voltages, the signal power and noise power coming out of the tube are drastically affected and to different degrees; for example, the signal could be enhanced as much as 10 db or could be diminished 20 db with less than 50 per cent change in plate current. The effect is most marked with comparatively large grid-cathode spacings, and so far the best that has been done is to give a tube with rather wide spacings a noise figure about as low as that obtained with close spacings. There seems to be no easy way of getting a mental picture of the process, except that transit angles of the order of $2\pi$ are involved. Further research seems necessary.

**6·5. High-efficiency Amplifiers.**—The question of high-efficiency Class B and Class C amplifiers has received relatively little attention. So far no successful tubes have been built for frequencies of 3000 Mc/sec and above, but some measurements on the behavior of the experimental amplifiers designed for Class A operation described in Secs. 6·3 and 6·4 have indicated that Class B or Class C operation can be attained, given sufficient driving power. These small experimental tubes have insufficient power-handling capacity to make a useful device.

---

[1] L. C. Peterson, "Receiver Noise Figures," BTL Memorandum MM-42-130-91, Sept. 30, 1942.

[2] J. K. Knipp, "Space Charge Between Parallel Planes," RL Report No. 534, Mar. 22, 1944.

In order to get high efficiency it seems necessary to use a tetrode structure with a negligible drift distance between the input and output circuits so as to avoid ordinary drift-space bunching that would have a "debunching" effect in this case. Since for a high electronic efficiency the electrons should reach the plate with a very low velocity, triodes would have poor output circuit efficiency. It would be necessary to use close spacings because the electrons would start across the output gap with a comparatively low velocity; these close spacings would cause relatively high circuit losses.

The output circuit would have to be designed so that loading by secondaries ejected from the plate could be avoided. Probably such a design would necessitate a slat or honeycomb construction of the plate that would act as an electron trap or Faraday cage. The mechanical difficulties of maintaining constant close spacings between cathode and grid become increasingly serious, and the problems of producing a uniformly effective cathode become more difficult, as the cathode area is increased.

**6·6. Practical Triode Amplifiers.**—The commercially available space-charge-control tubes best suited to amplifier applications are the lighthouse family of disk-seal planar triodes. The graduated disk-seal construction of the lighthouse tubes was chosen with the intention of facilitating their insertion in a grid-separation circuit with concentric coaxial-line cavities, the cylinder in contact with the grid disk serving simultaneously as outer conductor for the output (plate) circuit and inner conductor for the input (cathode) circuit. This arrangement is shown schematically in Fig. 6·7; the d-c connections and necessary blocking condensers are omitted. It should be noted that, if the over-all diameter of the circuit is kept small and if the anode lead is made massive for good heat conduction, the output lead must be small in diameter.

In order to improve cooling of the anode and to reduce losses in the output circuit, some tubes have been designed with an inverted structure, the cathode being at the small end with a concentric heater lead. An example of this construction was the CV90, developed in England.[1] The 2C38, 2C39, and 2C41 are samples of the inverted lighthouse construction developed in the United States; they are sometimes referred to as "oilcan" tubes. Although they are certainly superior to ordinary lighthouse tubes in respect to power handling capabilities it is not at all clear that the inverted lighthouse tubes make better low-level amplifiers.

Only a few studies of the performance obtainable from lighthouse tube amplifiers over the frequency range 1000 to 3000 Mc/sec were undertaken during the war because the work was time-consuming and

---

[1] A smaller version of this tube, the 2C36, was put into limited production in this country toward the end of the war.

the results disappointing. Furthermore in view of the wide variations in performance from tube to tube the samples studied were usually too small to give a trustworthy picture.

In the region from 500 to 1000 Mc/sec, amplifiers using apparatus similar to that shown in Fig. 6·7 have been widely used. The d-c insulation between cathode and grid is provided by the mica condenser

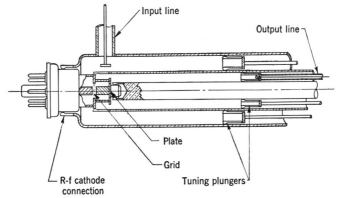

Fig. 6·7.—Sketch of a typical grid-separation circuit for a lighthouse tube. Direct-current connections and insulation omitted.

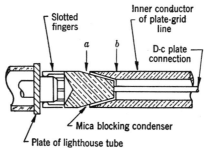

Fig. 6·8.—Sketch of a plate blocking condenser for lighthouse-tube circuits.

built into the lighthouse tube between the cathode proper and the base shell which forms the r-f cathode connection. Plate voltage is applied by means of a d-c lead within a hollow plate connector provided with a blocking condenser as indicated roughly in Fig. 6·8. A condenser of this type introduces the minimum losses in the cavity if placed with point $a$ near a current node. At the higher frequencies it is advisable to make the electrical length of the dielectric-filled line $a - b$ a quarter wavelength.[1] A choke plunger might be used instead of one with

---

[1] At this wavelength the coaxial line formed with the d-c lead as the center conductor should have a high impedance, and r-f chokes (quarter-wavelength cups) on the center conductor may be advisable to reduce leakage.

contact fingers.  The use of such a plunger, however, would require an increase in the diameter of the grid line to obtain reasonable clearances, and this in turn would require an increase in size of the cathode-grid cavity.  This enlargement may give trouble with a higher mode (than the principal *TEM*-mode), which becomes possible when the arithmetic-mean circumference of the two conductors is approximately equal to the wavelength.

Typical noise figures for an amplifier of this sort, using a 446B or 2C40 lighthouse tube, are 7 db at 500 Mc/sec and 10 db at 1000 Mc/sec. Above 1000 Mc/sec the noise figures deteriorate rapidly;[1] average values are 16 db at 2000 Mc/sec and about 21 db at 3000 Mc/sec, when the tube is operated at a plate voltage of 300 and a current of 20 ma.[2]  At frequencies below about 1500 Mc/sec the noise figure is improved by operating at lower plate currents.  Along with the rapid increase in noise figure at the higher frequencies there is a marked decline in the gain. For a typical tube and circuit the gain might drop from 10 or 11 db at 1500 Mc/sec to about 1 db at 3000 Mc/sec.

A characteristic of the noise figure is that it fluctuates much less from tube to tube than does the gain.  Doubling the shunt resistance of the output circuit doubles the power gain (and halves the bandwidth), but it also doubles the shot noise from the output circuit.  As was pointed out in the discussion of Eq. (22), the properties of the output circuit do not enter in the computation of the noise figure, and as the contribution of the output circuit usually makes up by far the larger proportion of the noise figure, the over-all noise figure varies little from tube to tube.  As a result, measurements of noise figures made in various laboratories may be expected to agree within 2 db, if obviously defective tubes are excluded.

At frequencies greater than about 2000 Mc/sec it is usually impossible to use coaxial-line resonators with lighthouse tubes in their fundamental mode.  Because of the capacitive loading contributed by the tube the quarter-wavelength line must be shortened so much that the plunger would strike the glass envelope of the tube.  In these circumstances an integral number of half-wavelengths is added to the line; the line is then said to be operating in the $\frac{3}{4}\lambda$, $\frac{5}{4}\lambda$, etc., mode.  In comparison with the fundamental ($\frac{1}{4}\lambda$) mode, these higher modes have somewhat greater Q's and therefore smaller bandwidths.  The higher Q results from the

---

[1] See measurements reported by W. M. Breazeale and M. Waltz, "Performance of the GL446 Lighthouse Tube as an R-f Amplifier in the 10–20 cm Region," RL Report No. 291, Oct. 5, 1942.

[2] Measurements in general agreement with these but running 2 or 3 db higher have been reported by P. M. Garratt in "Lighthouse Tubes as R-f Amplifiers in the 10-cm Range," General Electric Data Folder 46231, and in "Performance Characteristics of GL446 Amplifiers," General Electric Data Folder 46240.

fact that the volume available for storing electromagnetic energy has been increased more than has the dissipation. The factor by which the Q is increased in going from one mode to another depends to some extent on the capacitive loading provided by the tube but more on the distribution of the dissipation between losses in the resonator and the external load. If the circuit efficiency is high and the capacitive loading light, the bandwidth in the $\frac{3}{4}\lambda$ mode may be only a little more than one third of that in the fundamental mode. Allowance for this effect should be made in applying the results of Sec. 6·2 by suitably increasing the value of $C_2$ used in Eqs. (9) to (12).

*Experimental Results with Lighthouse Tubes.*—The validity of the conclusions of Sec. 6·2 has been tested with some simple experiments.[1] The circuit was basically that of Fig. 6·7 except that the cathode and grid lines were of larger diameter in order to facilitate coupling out of the grid-plate cavity. The outer and inner diameters of the cathode-grid circuit were 5.5 and 3.48 cm, and the corresponding dimensions for the grid-plate circuit were 3.32 and 1.1 cm. Choke plungers were used to avoid variable contact resistances, and although efforts were made to reduce resonance effects in the lines behind the plungers, these effects could not be completely eliminated. The input line was lossy and was matched to the cathode grid cavity with an adjustable probe. A constant power of the order of magnitude of a milliwatt from a swept frequency oscillator was available at the input. The output loop could be rotated to vary the coupling.

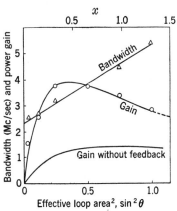

FIG. 6·9.—Gain and bandwidth of a typical 2C40 amplifier at 9.9 cm, with varying load. Plate voltage 250, current 30 ma.

Figure 6·9 shows the variation of gain and bandwidth with rotation of the loop for a typical 2C40 operated at 250 volts on the plate with a current of 30 ma.[2] Results are plotted against $\sin^2\theta$, where $\theta$ is the angle between the plane of the loop and the magnetic field in the cavity. This gives a scale proportional to $1/R_L$ or to $x$. The bandwidth varies linearly as expected, and the scale of $x$ may be established by use of the fact that $\Delta f$ doubles in going from $x = 0$ to $x = 1$. The gain curve is computed from Eq. (15), using $\gamma = 0.75$ and $g_m^2 R_1 R_2 = 5.72$ to fit at the

[1] Unpublished work of M. C. Waltz at Radiation Laboratory.

[2] The recommended plate dissipation was exceeded in order to facilitate measurement of output powers.

peak. For comparison, a theoretical curve of gain without feedback, normalized to the same value of $g_m^2 R_1 R_2$, is also shown. The value chosen for $\gamma$ may seem unduly large but it must be remembered that $g_m R_2$ is greater than 4, probably by a factor of at least 2; therefore, $m$ is much less than unity, probably not greater than 0.1. In these experiments the cavity geometry was not favorable for estimating $C_2$ or the losses $R_1$ and $R_2$. If it is assumed that $R_1 = 150$ ohms (a normal value for a cathode area of $\frac{1}{6}$ cm$^2$ spaced a few thousandths of an inch from the grid) and the assumption that $C_2 = 6$ $\mu\mu f$ is made (allowing for the $\frac{3}{4}$-mode in the cavity), $g_m$, $R_2$, and $m$ may be esti-

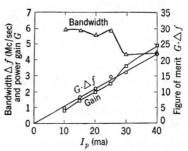

FIG. 6·10.—Gain, bandwidth, and figure of merit of a typical 2C40 light-house tube as functions of plate current, plate voltage held constant at 250 volts. Frequency is 3030 Mc/sec.

mated from the experimental bandwidth at zero load, 2.3 Mc/sec, and the value of $g_m^2 R_1 R_2$ obtained from the gain curve. The quantities $g_m$, $R_2$, and $m$ so obtained are respectively 1900 $\mu$mhos, 11,000 ohms, and 0.035. The assumptions regarding phase of feedback, etc., involved in deriving Eqs. (14) and (15), are much too drastic for these numerical results to have any real significance, but at any rate they form a plausible set.

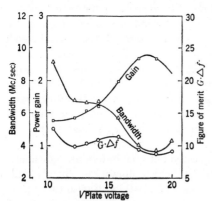

FIG. 6·11.—Gain, bandwidth, and figure of merit of the typical 2C40 lighthouse tube shown in Fig. 6·10 as functions of plate voltage, plate current held constant at 20 ma.

In Fig. 6·10 the gain, bandwidth, and figure of merit for the same tube are shown as functions of the plate current, varied by changing grid bias, with the plate voltage held constant at 250 volts. The coupling was occasionally readjusted during the experiment for optimum output. As a result the bandwidth appears to vary erratically; this variation is presumably due to the difficulty in locating the maximum of the gain curve, especially when little or no regeneration is present. Since the points for the gain tend to fluctuate in a compensating direction, the figure of merit follows a smooth curve reasonably well.

In Fig. 6·11 the gain, bandwidth, and figure of merit are shown as in Fig. 6·10, except that in this experiment the plate current was constantly readjusted to 20 ma while the voltage was varied over a range from 110 volts (the minimum at which 20 ma could be obtained without using positive grid bias) to 400 volts. For convenience, the data are plotted against the square root of the voltage. The tendency for the gain and bandwidth to vary inversely while the figure of merit remains relatively constant is striking. The cyclical variation of the gain is readily understood provided there is feedback by the plate-cathode capacitance. In the absence of feedback the gain and bandwidth at optimum load would be expected to remain relatively independent of voltage, provided the r-f voltages are small compared with the corresponding d-c voltages and that the beam-coupling coefficient for the output circuit is not appreciably affected. If there is feedback, however, the phase of the transconductance becomes important. Because this phase is varied by changing the electron velocity while the phase of the feedback is constant, a cyclical variation of the gain is to be expected. As the feedback swings from positive to negative, the loading required for optimum output becomes heavier.

Measurement of amplifier performance over a frequency band requires more careful cavity construction than was used in the experiments detailed above. The bandwidth of choke plungers must be taken into account, and it is important to eliminate any leakage past the plungers that can give rise to resonances and possibly to coupling between cavities. Failure to suppress completely such extra feedback or fluctuations in $R_1$ and $R_2$ results in a curve of gain vs. frequency in which the general trend is hard to see because of numerous peaks and valleys. Because of the decrease in effective $g_m$ resulting from spread in transit angles, the general trend of the gain curve may be expected to fall slowly at first and then rapidly as the frequency is increased. Superimposed on this downward trend there may be an oscillation that is due to feedback through the plate-cathode capacitance when the phase of the $g_m$ is shifted by the change in frequency.

An idea of the variations to be expected between individual lighthouse tubes may be obtained from Table 6·1, which shows gain, bandwidth, and figure of merit for a group of 446B and 2C40 lighthouse tubes produced over a period of years by various companies. In tube 2C40 No. 2, which has the highest gain of the lot, the amplifier is on the verge of oscillating when lightly loaded. Under these conditions the bandwidth is very small, not so much because of the light loading of the output circuit as because of the reduction in bandwidth of the input, and the figure of merit decreases markedly, as is usual when there is regeneration. Since tube variations are so pronounced, any practical application of an amplifier of this type is difficult. The chief value of amplifier measure-

Table 6·1.—Properties of Representative Lighthouse Tubes as Amplifiers
at 10 cm.

Plate voltage 250, current 32 ma.    Load adjusted for maximum gain

| Tube type | Tube number | Power gain | Bandwidth, Mc/sec | Figure of merit, power gain × bandwidth, Mc/sec |
|-----------|-------------|-----------|-------------------|-------------------------------------------------|
| 2C40 | 4′ | 2.56 | 9.3 | 23.8 |
| 446B | 1 | 3.25 | 6.9 | 22.4 |
| 2C40 | 2* | 13.7 | 0.85 | 11.6 |
| 2C40 | 2* | 9.6 | 2.9 | 27.8 |
| 2C40 | 2* | 4.4 | 7.8 | 34.3 |
| 2C40 | y | 1.96 | 7.2 | 14.1 |
| 446B | 3 | 4.83 | 4.7 | 22.7 |
| 2C40 | 4 | 3.6 | 5.0 | 18 |
| 2C40 | 5 | 9.0 | 3.9 | 35 |
| 2C40 | 6 | 5.8 | 4.7 | 27.3 |
| 446B | 7 | 3.25 | 4.6 | 15 |
| 2C40 | 8 | 7.3 | 3.2 | 23.4 |
| 2C40 | 10 | 5.3 | 4.7 | 25 |
| 2C40 | 11 | 4.85 | 3.9 | 19 |
| 2C40 | 12 | 7.3 | 3.1 | 22.6 |
| 2C40 | 13 | 1.69 | 6.5 | 11 |
| 2C40 | 14 | 5.3 | 4.3 | 22.8 |
| 2C40 | 8′ | 3.25 | 5.6 | 18.2 |
| 2C40 | x | 9.0 | 2.9 | 26 |

* Various settings of coupling loop.

ments on lighthouse tubes in the 3000-Mc/sec region is to increase understanding of the behavior of such tubes as oscillators.

In view of the importance of feedback effects it is natural to inquire whether neutralization can be accomplished. Over a small frequency range good neutralization can be obtained with a slot or other coupling device properly placed in the partition between input and output cavities. Because of the dimensions of the envelope this coupling has to be located at an appreciable fraction of a wavelength from the capacitive coupling being neutralized—a distance that makes the adjustment frequency sensitive. Very little experimental work, it appears, has been done on this problem. Neutralization, however, has sometimes been obtained accidentally in the course of attempting to make oscillators. Care must be taken to insure good contact to the grid disk of the tube. If one or more of the spring fingers does not make contact, or if the slots between the fingers are resonant, there may be considerable extra feedback in addition to that caused by direct capacitive coupling through the grid.

# CHAPTER 7

## MICROWAVE TRIODE OSCILLATORS

### By J. B. H. Kuper

**7·1. Introduction.**—Space-charge-control tubes capable of functioning as amplifiers in the microwave region can, of course, be made to oscillate if provided with the proper feedback. The only triodes commercially available during the war that were suitable for use at frequencies much higher than 1000 Mc/sec were the lighthouse family of tubes. As a result there is a considerable amount of information on how to make a lighthouse tube oscillate at a given frequency, but comparatively little work has been done on the fundamentals of triode operation.[1]

When operated in a grid-separation circuit of the type described in Sec. 6·6 or in the "reentrant" oscillator circuit that is discussed in Sec. 5 of this chapter, a typical 2C40 lighthouse tube might furnish 1 watt at 20 per cent efficiency in the 1000-Mc/sec region and perhaps 0.1 watt at 2 per cent efficiency in the 3000-Mc/sec region. The upper frequency limit of most lighthouse tubes is in the neighborhood of 3500 to 4000 Mc/sec. Despite their poor efficiency, lighthouse tube oscillators are often used as superheterodyne local oscillators or as signal generators because they do not require complicated regulated power supplies. In comparison with the more common form of reflex klystron, the integral-cavity type, triode oscillators have the advantages of flexibility and cheapness, but these are offset to a considerable degree by the fact that the external cavity resonator is expensive.

In microwave oscillators it is scarcely possible to consider the tube apart from the circuit; cavity problems loom large in any application. A satisfactory cavity design must not only accommodate a large range of electrical properties from tube to tube, but must also solve the mechanical problem of making good contact to the tube without subjecting it to mechanical stresses. Cooling of the plate of the tube is also an important consideration in cavity design.

When a resonator is suitably modified to withstand high voltages, lighthouse oscillators may be operated under pulse conditions with voltages up to 3 or 4 kv and the same (or lower) average input powers as are

---

[1] For an extensive discussion of oscillator circuits for the lighthouse tubes see A. M. Gurewitsch and J. R. Whinnery, "Microwave Oscillators Using Disk-Seal Tubes," *Proc. I.R.E.*, **35**, 462 (1947).

used under c-w conditions.   As a result of the decreased time of transit from cathode to plate under higher plate voltages, slight additional modifications to the cavity will be needed to secure the correct phase of feedback.   Where 2- to 3-kv pulses are applied to the plate of a 2C43 tube, r-f pulse powers of the order of magnitude of a kilowatt may be obtained in the 3000 Mc/sec region, and somewhat more at lower frequencies. Oscillators of this kind have been used as medium-power beacon transmitters and for special-purpose short-range radar sets.   Pulse operation is discussed in the next chapter; the remainder of this chapter is devoted to a consideration of the fundamental circuit types and c-w operation.

The very large number of oscillator designs that have been used in practical applications is in itself an indication that a thoroughly practical general-purpose cavity has not yet been developed.   The compromises that must be made in the interests of simplicity generally result in a serious loss in flexibility; the more limited the application (particularly in respect to frequency band), the greater the chance of achieving a satisfactory design.   It would be unprofitable to describe a number of these devices in detail; rather it seems best to emphasize the fundamental principles involved.

One of the chief factors involved in these compromises is the fact that at the higher frequencies it is necessary to adjust not only the magnitude of the voltage that is fed back to the input but also the phase.   When the phase of the transadmittance becomes much greater than $\pi$ radians, the phase adjustment may be critical in comparison with the adjustment of magnitude.   Ordinary oscillator cavities do not permit continuous adjustment of feedback phase.   This fact is responsible for many interesting points of behavior, some of which are mentioned in succeeding sections.

Most statements in the remainder of this chapter refer specifically to lighthouse tubes, but it is felt that the conclusions would be applicable in general to other forms of close-spaced triodes.   Physically the lighthouse tubes depart so widely from the ideal structures postulated in Chaps. 3 and 5 that there is little use in attempting a rigorous analysis. For example, the spacing between grid wires in a 2C40 tube is greater than the separation between grid and cathode.   The "plane" of the grid is far from being flat, and there are serious differences in transit angle between those electrons that pass close to the wires and those that go through near the centers of the holes.

**7·2. Principal Types of Oscillator Circuits Applicable to Triodes.**—In the frequency region from about 50 to 200 or 300 Mc/sec, the standard triode oscillator is one in which the resonant tank circuit is connected between the grid and the plate, and the cathode lead is (usually) provided with an r-f choke.   Although various forms of this arrangement have received special names, basically it is a Colpitts oscillator in which the tube interelectrode capacitances and strays provide the capacitance potential divider for the cathode.   When the frequency becomes high enough to make the use of coaxial-line resonators advisable, this arrangement requires modification.   Stray capacitance between the plate and cathode is cut out by the shielding action of the grid connection, leaving only a very small internal plate-cathode capacitance.   The latter is so much smaller than the grid-cathode capacitance that the resulting grid-cathode voltage is insufficient to sustain oscillations.   One remedy is to increase artifically the plate-cathode capacitance by means of one or more conducting strips fastened to the cathode lead, passing through holes in the grid connector and presenting a surface to the plate or plate lead.   This form of Colpitts circuit will give satisfactory results provided the phase angle of the tube transadmittance is small.   At considerably higher frequencies (around 1000 Mc/sec) an analogous arrangement, in which the grid and cathode are exchanged, is sometimes used; the resonator is connected between the plate and the cathode, and the grid is capacitively coupled to or tapped onto a suitable point on the inside of the resonator.   This circuit operates well when the phase lag in the tube is about $\pi$ radians because it provides a reversed feedback voltage. This circuit resembles the "grid tickler" or "reverse feedback" circuit except for a reversal of the tickler connections to provide the $\pi$ radians phase shift.   With a given set of interelectrode spacings and voltages, there is an intermediate frequency range in which neither of these circuits works—that is, where the phase lag is about $\pi/2$ radians.

The other types of circuits generally bear less resemblance to familiar low-frequency forms.   The grid-separation amplifier, discussed in the previous chapter, is well adapted mechanically to the lighthouse tubes, and functions as an oscillator if the right amount and phase of feedback are provided.   A circuit of this type is the most flexible because it permits enough adjustments to take care of any phase shifts that may be encountered.   In fact, the multiplicity of adjustments is the greatest drawback to the general use of grid-separation oscillators.   If one is willing to make the adjustments, this oscillator will give the best performance of which the tube is capable.

Since lighthouse tubes require relatively large driving voltages at the higher frequencies, various attempts have been made to build oscillators consisting essentially of a transmission line, radial or coaxial, running between the grid-plate gap and the cathode-grid gap.   Such a line generally is not uniform; rather there are one or more discontinuities that permit designation of a portion of the line as the principal "tank" circuit—that is, the region in which most of the energy is stored.   This portion plays the major role in determining the frequency of oscillations.

For obvious mechanical reasons this transmission line must be folded. One of the designs for realizing an oscillator of this type is the ambiguously named "reentrant" oscillator[1] illustrated in Fig. 7·1. In this oscillator there is a cylindrical conductor connected to the cathode, a concentric rod or tube connected to the plate cap, and a short open-ended cylinder connected to the grid disk. The cathode and plate cylinders are connected (as far as radio frequency is concerned) by a short-circuiting plunger that may be either of the choke or of the contact type. The choke type is preferred, particularly when high plate voltages are used, because it simplifies the d-c insulation problem. The necessary d-c connection to the grid is made by a wire or a spring located at or near a

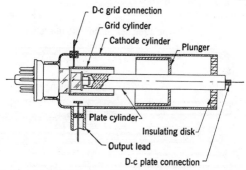

FIG. 7·1.—Section of a typical "reentrant" cavity oscillator for a lighthouse tube. All three cylinders have spring fingers to make contact to the tube.

voltage node, and r-f power is coupled out by a loop or probe inserted usually in the space between the grid and cathode cylinders. Although the construction of this oscillator is simple and it has the great merit of readily accommodating the inevitable mechanical imperfections of the tubes, its electrical behavior is complicated. For the present it will suffice to remark that, because the region between the grid and plate cylinders usually contains the major part of the stored energy, it is the most important region in determining the frequency, whereas the position of the plate-cathode plunger chiefly affects the feedback.

Numerous hybrid oscillator designs are possible—for example, the combination of a radial transmission-line cavity for the input circuit and a coaxial-line cavity for the output circuit. Most of the hybrid designs that have been found useful at frequencies above 2000 Mc/sec may be considered as variants of either the basic grid-separation circuit or the folded-transmission-line circuit typified by the reentrant oscillator. At somewhat lower frequencies, up to perhaps 1500 Mc/sec, many other

[1] Several variants are described by A. M. Gurewitsch, "Cavity Oscillator Circuits," *Electronics*, **19**, 2, 135 (1946).

schemes have been used. Among these are the so-called "coaxial butter-fly" circuits and the "cylinder" circuits, which have been described by Karplus.[1] Most of these may be analyzed as combinations of coaxial lines loaded by concentrated (if not "lumped") reactances. Because of their limited applications, no detailed discussion of the hybrid circuits is given here.

The coaxial-line grid-separation oscillator and the reentrant oscillator are the only types used extensively in the microwave region—the former mostly in cases where wide tuning ranges are required, and the latter where tuning ranges of about 10 per cent are sufficient and the utmost

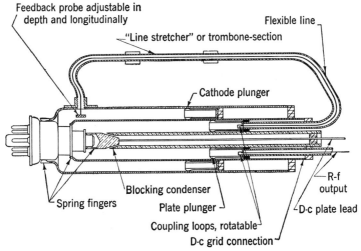

Feedback probe adjustable in depth and longitudinally

"Line stretcher" or trombone-section

Flexible line

Cathode plunger

Spring fingers

Blocking condenser

Plate plunger

Coupling loops, rotatable

D-c grid connection

R-f output

D-c plate lead

Fig. 7·2.—Sketch of lighthouse-tube grid-separation oscillator with enough adjustments to permit obtaining optimum conditions for any tube when frequency and voltages are specified.

simplicity in construction is desired. From the standpoint of the tube, however, the ideal oscillator would be something like that shown schematically in Fig. 7·2. This is an oscillator of the coaxial-line type providing enough adjustments to permit achievement of optimum conditions of feedback. The two coaxial cavities are tuned with plungers of either the choke or the quarter-wavelength spring-finger type. The space behind the plungers is made nonresonant by the use of high-loss insulating material on the heels of the plungers and for the supporting rings. In general, the two cavities should be operating in different modes—for example, $\frac{3}{4}$ and $\frac{5}{4}$ wavelengths (effective)—so as to avoid troubles

[1] E. Karplus, "Wide-Range Tuned Circuits and Oscillators for High Frequencies," *Proc. I.R.E.*, **33**, 426 (1945).

with undesired low frequencies that might arise if they were both tuned to the same wavelength.

The probe that injects feedback voltage into the cathode-grid cavity should be adjustable radially and longitudinally (by a slot) so that the feedback line is always terminated by the tube input losses, transformed to the line impedance by the cavity. When the feedback line is so terminated, the use of a telescoping section (a "line stretcher") provides any phase of feedback voltage that may be required by the transit angle in the tube. The two rotatable coupling loops mounted in the plate plunger permit adjustment of the magnitude of the feedback voltage and of the load. There is unavoidable interaction between these last two adjustments, but otherwise the adjustments are nearly independent and can be made in a systematic manner. Nevertheless, it is clear that such a multiplicity of adjustments can never be tolerated in a practical oscillator. This device could be used only under laboratory conditions for special purposes.

Because equipment designers usually want a single-control oscillator, although they can sometimes be persuaded to accept a subsidiary "trimming" adjustment, considerable sacrifices in performance are to be expected. The alternative of ganging the necessary adjustments is almost certainly too complicated mechanically. In the practical forms of the coaxial-line grid-separation oscillator, or of the reentrant oscillator, the phase and magnitude of the feedback cannot be adjusted independently; a fixed adjustment or a crude tracking scheme is satisfactory over a narrow frequency range. Unfortunately, redesigning an oscillator for a moderate shift in frequency may require considerable experiment; it is not often possible to use simple scaling methods.

The remainder of this chapter and the succeeding one are devoted to a discussion of the operation of these two circuit types. The discussion is general and nonmathematical, chiefly because the necessary tube parameters are very seldom known with sufficient accuracy to justify anything more than a qualitative treatment.

**7·3. Power Supply and Bias Considerations.**—Because of the very low efficiency of even the best triode oscillators at frequencies above 1500 Mc/sec, slightly different bias and supply arrangements from those used at low frequencies are advisable. Particularly with an oscillator that requires more than one adjustment, so that there is a good chance of setting the circuit in a nonoscillating condition, the use of grid-leak bias may be dangerous. This situation is in contrast to that occurring at low frequencies, where the use of a grid leak assists starting of oscillations and automatically adjusts the bias as required by changing load conditions, etc.

To protect the tube against overheating when it is not oscillating, it is often advisable to use some cathode bias. This bias needs only to be sufficient to prevent overload at the plate voltage used and the remainder of the bias voltage may be furnished by a grid leak. Bypass condensers are ordinarily not required for the bias resistors. The cathode condenser that is built into the tube structure is usually sufficient to prevent r-f voltage from appearing on the d-c cathode connection. The reentrant oscillator is an exception if the d-c lead to the grid cyclinder is not at a voltage node; in this case a small condenser formed by a mica washer, or a quarter-wavelength choke may be necessary. With a well-designed cavity there should be no troublesome leakage of r-f power from the d-c plate lead.[1]

At moderately high frequencies (200 Mc/sec or less) a reentrant cavity, especially if provided with a choke plunger between the cathode and plate cylinders, may appear merely as some extra capacitance in parallel with the tube interelectrode capacitances. Because of the high transconductance of the lighthouse tubes at these frequencies, parasitic oscillations in the circuits formed by the power-supply leads are sometimes encountered. These lower-frequency oscillations are found most often in bench setups and are cured by the insertion of appropriate r-f chokes in the leads. They are often encountered also when attempting to measure the usual parameters, mutual conductance, plate resistance, and $\mu$ with a vacuum-tube bridge of standard design. The subject is mentioned here mainly to warn the experimenter to suspect parasitics in cases of erratic behavior.

Another common difficulty is intermittent or interrupted oscillation, which may be "self-quenched" superregeneration ("squegging") at a moderately high audio frequency or lower frequency "motorboating." The latter is usually a fault of the power supply itself and is remedied by proper bypassing, but the former is more difficult to overcome. Because the operator generally lacks adequate control over the feedback, it not infrequently happens that the feedback is excessive, and super-regeneration occurs with a quench frequency that depends mainly on the time constant of the grid leak and the stray grid-ground capacitances. Reduction of this time constant generally stops the superregeneration, but the proper cure is to reduce the feedback.

Unless a high degree of frequency stability is required, it is not necessary to regulate the power supply. When stability is important, however, it is usually necessary to regulate the heater voltage as well as the plate supply. Voltage regulation is more important with the reentrant oscillator than with the two-cavity coaxial grid-separation circuit. When the taut-grid 2C40 and 2C43 tubes are used, the frequency shifts

---

[1] If present, the leakage can readily be detected by running a finger or screwdriver along the lead and noting the reaction on the oscillator.

resulting from an unregulated supply should not exceed 0.5 Mc/sec (at 3000 Mc/sec) for a 1 per cent change in line voltage.

The provision of adequate cooling of the anode is important enough to deserve mention here, although it is more a question of cavity design than of power supply.   Because of the low efficiency, plate input power is practically synonomous with plate dissipation.   Most oscillator designs bury the plate connection within a pair of concentric cylinders.   Since these are usually silver-plated, they practically eliminate radiation cooling.   It is necessary to provide adequate conduction along the plate cylinder or to blow air on the plate cap itself.   A surprisingly large number of small ventilation holes may be bored in the cylindrical conductors forming the oscillator cavity with no apparent detriment to performance.

**7·4. Two-cavity Grid-separation Oscillators.**—Many of the important points in the construction of two-cavity coaxial-line grid-separation oscillators are obvious and need only be listed here.   These are: (1) the importance of designing contact fingers to provide good electrical (and thermal) contact without stressing the tube mechanically; (2) the necessity for dependable action of the short-circuiting plungers (which means the use of choke plungers, unless too wide a frequency range is required); (3) the avoidance of resonances in the supposedly "dead" region behind the plungers; and (4) the possibility of higher modes in the outer coaxial line at high frequencies.

In most applications it is desirable to gang the two plungers so that a single tuning control will suffice.   Such a procedure is complicated because the graph of wavelength against plunger position is not a straight line.   The departure from a straight line is due to the loading effect of the tube on the open end of the coaxial line.

The r-f gap in the tube may be represented to a first approximation by a lumped capacitance, provided the radius of the plate or cathode is very much less than one-quarter wavelength (this condition always being satisfied in lighthouse tubes).   This lumped capacitance loads a radial transmission line at the center, and this radial line in turn loads the coaxial line.   This resonator is evidently somewhat more complicated than the simple klystron resonator discussed in Chap. 4.   The transition region between the radial and the coaxial transmission lines makes calculations of resonant frequency unsatisfactory.   The lack of a simple method of calculating the dimensions of this resonator is not serious since the actual tubes depart widely from the simple geometry considered here.

If the mode in which the resonator is operating is designated as the $(n/4)$-mode, where $n$ is any odd integer, $n = 1, 3, 5, \cdots$ ; then as $n$ increases, the effect of the loading becomes less important and the tuning curve (wavelength vs. plunger position) approaches a straight line of slope $4/n$. When $n$ is not very large, however, as the line length is decreased the points depart more and more from the predicted line, always lying above it. It is this curvature, which depends on the loading and therefore is different for the two cavities, that makes ganging difficult. In taking experimental data for the design of a tracking mechanism, it is worth remembering that the complete curve for only one mode needs to be determined accurately for each cavity; the rest of the curves in the family are readily constructed by adding or subtracting the proper number of half wavelengths. If carried over a sufficiently large wave-

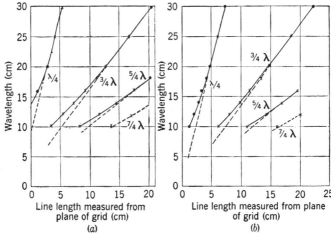

Fig. 7·3.—Tuning curves for a type 446 tube in a two-cavity grid-separation oscillator. Crosses, experimental points, and dots obtained by extrapolation.

(a)  Cathode line
$\frac{7}{8}$-in. inner conductor
$1\frac{1}{2}$-in. outer conductor

(b)  Plate line.
$\frac{3}{8}$-in. inner conductor
$\frac{3}{4}$-in. outer conductor

length range, a family of curves of this sort will show whether or not it is necessary to use different modes for the two cavities to avoid operation in the fundamental. The physical line lengths required for a given wavelength depend on the diameters of the conductors and the configuration of the contact fingers, but the data of Fig. 7·3 give an idea of the orders of magnitude. The resonant wavelengths for the various modes are plotted as functions of distances (in centimeters) from the plane of the grid disk to the short circuit. The data were taken on a 446 tube in an oscillator in which the inner and outer conductors of the plate cavity were $\frac{3}{8}$ in. and $\frac{3}{4}$ in. in diameter, and of the cathode cavity $\frac{7}{8}$ in. and $1\frac{1}{2}$ in., respectively. It should be noted that for this particular tube a radial cavity $1\frac{1}{2}$ in. in diameter between the cathode shell and the grid disk would resonate near 14 cm, and a similar cavity between the grid and the plate disks ¾ in. in diameter would resonate a little below 10 cm. Figure 7·3 also indicates that, unless precautions are taken, it is not safe to use the ¼λ-mode in both cavities at 10 cm because in that case the lengths of the lines would be too close to those required for oscillation in the fundamental mode between 22 and 25 cm.

Feedback arrangements for oscillators of this type are numerous, and in general not very satisfactory. Various types of coupling loops or loop-and-probe combinations inserted through the grid conductor are often used; these function well over a 10 to 20 per cent frequency band. When wider bands are required, several different feedback devices may be employed simultaneously. Another common scheme is to cut a longitudinal slot in the grid cylinder and to mount a small probe on one of the shorting plungers so that it picks up some energy from the other cavity. If the same mode is used in both cavities, the feedback tracks roughly at least over a considerable range.

Ordinarily, the coupling between the two circuits will be much tighter than critical coupling, so the response curve will have two peaks. Therefore, if both cavities are tuned to the same frequency, all of these schemes can produce only zero or $\pi$ radians phase shift in the feedback. Detuning of the cathode circuit allows some adjustment of the angle, but at a sacrifice in driving voltage. Furthermore, a phase shift of $\pi/2$ or $3\pi/2$ radians is impractical.

Unless very strong coupling is used, the frequency stability of these oscillators with respect to power supply or thermal variations is noticeably better than that of the reentrant oscillator. Not only is the cathode-grid capacitance less tightly coupled to the frequency determining circuit, but the common practice of using ¾λ- or ⁵⁄₄λ-modes in the grid-plate cavity reduces the importance of changes in plate spacing. The higher $Q$ in the frequency-determining circuit proportionately reduces the sensitivity to changes in any of the tube parameters, whereas the loose coupling further reduces the importance of heater voltage.

Despite this advantage of the two-cavity circuit, it has been used relatively little on account of the mechanical difficulties in producing the oscillators and the evident complexity of the adjustments. The main uses have been for laboratory measurements on the tubes and for special signal generators. In most of the large-scale applications the reentrant oscillator has been preferred in spite of its inferior stability and the fact that it is less flexible and harder to understand.

**7·5. Reentrant Oscillators.**—In order to analyze the behavior of the reentrant oscillator in terms of an equivalent circuit,[1] a somewhat simplified picture will be introduced first. In Fig. 7·4 the d-c grid lead is

---

[1] The treatment follows that of J. R. Whinnery, "A Preliminary Report on Re-entrant Oscillator Theory," General Electric Data Folder, 46256, Aug. 2, 1943.

omitted, numerous discontinuities are ignored, and the load is represented by a lumped admittance $Y_L$.

The most common method of tuning a reentrant oscillator over a 5 to 10 per cent tuning range is to slide the plate connector partly off the plate cap of the tube in such a way as to leave a discontinuity, which may be treated as a variable lumped inductance $L_t$ in series with the coaxial line 3. A motion of $\frac{1}{16}$ in. will shift the frequency about 100

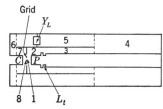

FIG. 7·4.—Idealized reentrant cavity, d-c grid connection omitted.

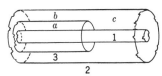

FIG. 7·5.—Coaxial line configuration similar to that at the end of a grid cylinder.

Mc/sec in the 3000-Mc/sec region. The grid cylinder, which is usually made to snap on to the grid disk, has a short "overhang" extending toward the cathode. Tuning is sometimes done by varying the length of the grid cylinder with a telescoping section.

Before proceeding to the equivalent circuit a few remarks on the fields in the neighborhood of one of the ends of the grid cylinder may be

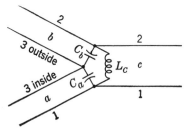

FIG. 7·6.—Equivalent circuit for the configuration of Fig. 7·5, $L_c$ is resonant with the series combination of $C_a$ and $C_b$.

helpful. In the configuration shown in Fig. 7·5 a coaxial line $c$ is connected to two concentric lines $a$ and $b$, which are formed by inserting the cylinder 3 into line $c$. Provided cylinder 3 has negligible thickness, the analysis is simple. A wave in line $c$ proceeding to the left is split into two waves with amplitudes proportional to the characteristic impedances of $a$ and $b$, and there is no reflection. However, a wave sent down line $a$ to the right will, in general, be partly reflected and partly transmitted into $b$ and $c$. This wave will "see" a discontinuity capacitance arising from the fringing field at the end of 3; and a wave sent to the right in $b$ will behave qualitatively like one in $a$. The characteristic impedance of line $c$ will be the sum of the impedances of lines $a$ and $b$.

These considerations lead to an equivalent circuit for Fig. 7·5 as shown in Fig. 7·6. The two discontinuity capacitances $C_a$ and $C_b$ may be calculated from the geometry. The discontinuity appearing across line $c$ is an inductance $L_c$, which is resonant with the series combination of $C_a$ and $C_b$.  When line $c$ is closed with a short-circuiting plunger, as in the reentrant oscillator, its effect may be merged with $L$ as a variable reactance.  Thus line $a$ is terminated by line $b$ in series with a variable reactance, adjustable by moving the short-circuiting plunger in $c$.  If line $b$ has a dissipative load, variation of the length of $c$ will produce a variable phase shift of the wave in $b$ with respect to that in $a$, but the phase shift will be accompanied by a change in magnitude and it will not be possible to reach all angles.

After this digression, it is now possible to draw an equivalent circuit for the complete oscillator, provided some simplifying assumptions are made.  In addition to neglecting the effects of the d-c grid connection, the reflections from the output probe, and the losses at the r-f contacts, it is convenient to assume small-signal conditions, so that the tube charac-

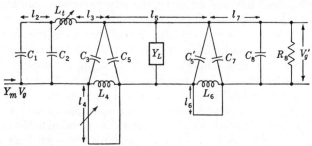

FIG. 7·7.—Equivalent circuit for oscillator of Fig. 7·4, assuming small-signal theory.

teristics may be expressed by input and transfer admittances.  Also, the tube is assumed to have infinite plate resistance and the plate-cathode capacitance is neglected.  The assumption of small signals limits the analysis to conditions at the start of oscillation.  Given sufficient knowledge of the tube parameters, it is possible to predict whether oscillations will occur and at what frequency, but no conclusions can be drawn about the equilibrium amplitude of oscillations.  Experimentally, the most serious assumption is the neglect of the reflections from the d-c grid connection and the output probe.

Referring to Fig. 7·4, the input region 8 may be considered as a capacitance $C_8$ shunted by a loading resistance $R_8$, across which the voltage $V_g$ is developed.  As a result of this voltage, there will be a current generator $Y_m V_g$ in the output circuit, where $Y_m$ is the trans-admittance.  The grid-plate capacitance is designated as $C_1$ and the discontinuity capacitance at the plate disk of the tube is $C_2$.  The circuit then will be as shown in Fig. 7·7.  The various pieces of coaxial line appearing in Fig. 7·4 are indicated here by small $l$'s with a subscript to correspond to the numbers already used.  It should be noted that there is a mechanical requirement that the length of line 5 be the sum of the lengths of lines 2, 3, and 7.

For oscillations to persist, it is necessary that a current $Y_m V_g$, fed in at the left-hand end, give a voltage $V'_g$ in the correct phase at the right-hand end. For the oscillations to build up, $V'_g$ must be at least infinitesimally greater than $V_g$. The frequency of oscillation will adjust itself until the phase shift produced by the circuit plus that produced by transit time is just $2\pi$ or a multiple thereof. Calculations performed by Whinnery and others, for cases in which the tube transadmittance was known, have shown that the circuit of Fig. 7·7 will predict correctly the range of lengths of $l_4$ over which oscillation will be obtained.[1]

Obviously, there will be successive positions, differing by a half wavelength, for the short-circuiting plunger on $l_4$. Unfortunately, the agreement between experiment and theory is mainly reassurance that the analysis has been followed correctly; the tube parameters are known too rarely for calculations to be of much practical use.

Before this analysis was available, it was known empirically that the region from $C_1$ to the junction of lines 3, 4, and 5 (the end of the grid cylinder) was the most important in determining frequency. Because the reflection at the end of the grid cylinder is large in all normal reentrant oscillator construction,[2] it is to be expected that the greater part of the stored energy will be found here. To a rough approximation, the line as far as the end of the grid cylinder behaves like a loaded half-wavelength line, which is physically about one quarter-wavelength long at 3000 Mc/sec, but the other circuit parameters cannot entirely be neglected.

The load can be connected almost anywhere in the circuit and about the same amount of power can be obtained, but it has been found best experimentally, from the standpoint of smooth operation over a range of frequencies, to connect the load as shown in line 5. Fortunately, this connection is also convenient mechanically. This optimum location could have been predicted from Whinnery's analysis, since placing a load on line 5 assists in obtaining a wider range of phase shifts by adjustment of the plunger in line 4.

It was known early that different dimensions were required to reach the same frequency under c-w and pulse conditions. Clearly, the applied voltage will affect the phase of $Y_m$ and the line lengths must be altered to correspond.

---

[1] Most of these comparisons between theory and experiment were made in the 1000-Mc/sec region with selected tubes for which the spacings were known.

[2] In some experimental oscillators, which were constructed by J. B. H. Kuper and P. A. Cole at the Radiation Laboratory and which had a very low characteristic impedance for line 5, the position of the short circuit in line 4, or rather the length $l_2 + l_3 + l_4$, was the main frequency-determining element.

In spite of its limitations it appears that Whinnery's equivalent circuit is invaluable in understanding the behavior of reentrant oscillators. Perhaps the most important result is the fact that only a limited range of feedback phase angles can be obtained by adjustment of the plunger, and then only with a corresponding variation in amplitude.

**7·6. Behavior of Practical Reentrant Oscillators.**—In most reentrant oscillators the arrangement of the cathode cylinder and its contact to the cathode shell of the tube departs widely from the simple scheme shown in Fig. 7·4. Since no attempt is ordinarily made to use the equivalent circuit quantitatively, this variation is not very important, but it must be remembered that any change in dimensions in the oscillator cavity will affect the feedback and probably the frequency also. The location of the d-c grid connection is sometimes very important in obtaining oscillations at a particular frequency. A 3000-Mc/sec oscillator may operate at some frequency in the 1000-Mc/sec region if the arrangement of contact springs for the d-c grid connection is wrong.

The operating wavelength, length of the grid cylinder, and location of the short-circuiting plunger are given in Table 7·1 for a typical 2C40 tube. The measurements were made under c-w conditions with 200 volts on the plate and under pulse conditions with 1200 volts in an

TABLE 7·1.—RELATION OF WAVELENGTH, GRID CYLINDER LENGTH, AND PLUNGER
POSITION FOR A 2C40 IN A REENTRANT OSCILLATOR
RL Dwg. D-11089-A. Continuous-wave measurements at 200 volts, pulse measurements at 1200 volts

| Wavelength, cm | Continuous wave | | Pulse | |
|---|---|---|---|---|
| | Grid cylinder $l_2 + l_3$, cm | Plunger distance $l_4$, wavelengths | Grid cylinder $l_2 + l_3$, cm | Plunger distance $l_4$, wavelengths |
| 8.8 | 1.84 | 0.40 | 1.58 | 0.36 |
| 9.2 | 2.08 | 0.41 | 1.75 | 0.37 |
| 9.6 | 2.32 | 0.41 | 1.90 | 0.37 |
| 10.0 | 2.60 | 0.405 | 2.07 | 0.40 |

oscillator shown in the Radiation Laboratory drawing D-11089-A. The position of the plunger determining $l_4$ (see preceding section) is given in wavelengths from the end of the grid cylinder.

The wavelength varies almost linearly with the length of the grid cylinder, but the optimum electrical length of $l_4$ remains more or less constant. The physical position of the plunger is changed considerably. The small variations in plunger distance are within the experimental error in locating the optimum position. There is a striking difference between the optimum dimensions for c-w and pulse operation. This difference is a result of the decreased transit time at the higher plate voltage. The full effect of the change in voltage is not seen because the tube spacings decrease with increasing temperature and the average input power is usually higher under c-w conditions. An oscillator designed for pulse operation will operate under c-w conditions if the grid-cylinder length and plunger distance are both increased. Naturally, the insulation of the plate lead need not be so good for c-w operation.

In many practical oscillators there is no convenient independent adjustment of $l_4$. Instead, the plunger is fastened to the plate rod, and the length of line 4 is increased slightly as the rod is pulled off the plate cap of the tube, increasing $L_t$ and with it the wavelength. For small changes in wavelength, approximately the same electrical length of $l_4$ will be necessary, as indicated in Table 7·1. These measurements indicate merely that it is plausible to move the two adjustments in the same

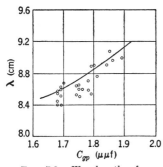

FIG. 7·8.—Wavelength of oscillation in a fixed-tuned reentrant oscillator vs. grid-plate capacitance of various 464A tubes. The curve is calculated by Whinnery. Circles represent measured points with different tubes.

direction but they give no information about the relative rates required. In many oscillators where this sort of "ganging" is used, it is possible when changing tubes to shift the position of the short-circuiting plunger on the plate rod.

The power output to be expected from a 2C40 in a reentrant oscillator varies widely with frequency and from tube to tube. The tuning range may be comparatively wide if the length of the grid cylinder is varied, but if the tuning is done by sliding the plate rod part way off the cap, a range between 5 and 10 per cent is to be expected in the 3000-Mc/sec region. The range is partly a question of how far the plate rod may be withdrawn without interfering with the cooling of the plate. Because even the best contact fingers loosen in time, it is well not to push the tuning range to its limit.

In most applications of lighthouse tubes it is necessary to design the cavity to tune over a specified range with any tube. Because of manufacturing variations from tube to tube, or rather from batch to batch, it sometimes happens that a large part of the available tuning range is used up in compensating for tube changes. As might be expected, the grid-plate capacitance, appearing as $C_1$ in Fig. 7·7, has a large influence on the wavelength of oscillation with all other dimensions fixed. With normal cavity proportions the effect of variations in grid-cathode capacitance might be only a fifth as great as that of the grid-plate capacitance. Experimentally, there is no correlation between operating wavelength and grid-cathode capacitance but, as is shown in Fig. 7·8, there is a good correlation between wavelength in a fixed-tuned oscillator and grid-plate capacitance. These data (from Whinnery's report) were taken on 464A tubes. A theoretical curve calculated from the equivalent circuit is also shown. The calculations were made using the capacitances measured on the cold tubes; a correction for the thermal change in capacitances would improve the agreement.

Several anomalous points of behavior have been observed in oscillators operating with very long pulses (about 40 μsec) or with c-w with high plate voltages (300 volts or more). This behavior, for want of a better term, has been called "drooping." Some measurements by R. Kyhl indicate that "drooping" is encountered when the transit angle is slightly greater than $\pi/2$ radians. In general, the behavior consists in a decrease in power output, or an increase in pulse-buildup time, under conditions which would ordinarily be expected to be more favorable. Examples are: a decrease in output power as the cathode gradually reaches its full temperature with recovery if the heater voltage is dropped, a decrease in output power as the wavelength is increased, and a decrease in output power when the plate voltage is raised beyond a certain value. Not all tubes show this behavior; it is commonest in tubes with the smaller grid-cathode spacings. Increasing the plate voltage or decreasing the frequency will decrease the transit angle; increasing the heater voltage will have the same effect because the cathode post expands toward the grid and at the same time the virtual cathode moves farther out. If the transit angle is not much greater than $\pi/2$ radians, a moderate decrease in the angle may put it beyond the range afforded by the adjustment of $l_4$. Thus, it is generally not possible to pass continuously from c-w operation at 200 or 300 volts to pulse operation in the 1 to 2 kv volt range. At intermediate voltages there is a region in which no oscillation is found, and sometimes there is a narrow range in which oscillation at some frequency far removed from the normal range of the cavity is observed.

The question of frequency stability with respect to heater- and plate-voltage changes may be considered in a general way on the basis of the equivalent circuit. Increasing either voltage decreases the transit angle, which affects $Y_m$. Expansion of the cathode post increases $C_{gk}$ with some effect on the frequency, but with a larger effect on the feedback. An increase in plate dissipation expands the plate post and increases $C_{gp}$, thus lowering the frequency. The frequency shifts depend on the proportions of the cavity used; some data obtained on a common form of oscillator under pulse conditions are given in the next chapter.

**7·7. Modulation of Triode Oscillators.**—Because of the importance of transit time in the operation of triode oscillators in the microwave region, attempts to modulate them are less satisfactory than attempts to modulate self-excited oscillators at lower frequencies. Mechanical frequency variation over a range of 10 to 20 Mc/sec can readily be obtained by rotating a paddle of metal, or a low-loss dielectric such as polystyrene, in the oscillator cavity. Frequency modulation by this means is useful in special signal generators for amplifier alignment and similar purposes, and can also be used as the basis for an electro-mechanical automatic frequency control. However, it is not modulation in the sense that it can be used for conveying complicated information such as speech or video signals. Modulation of this sort must be electrical, and preferably should be applied to a high-impedance control electrode.

Little has been done on the problem of obtaining frequency modulation that is substantially free from incidental amplitude modulation, or vice versa. In principle, at least, a lighthouse triode or diode could be used with an eighth-wavelength line to function as a variable reactance. A few attempts have been unsuccessful because of the difficulties in obtaining a sufficiently high r-f conductance with available tubes. A reactance tube using electrons injected parallel to a magnetic field, like those used for electronic tuning of magnetrons, could certainly be used to frequency modulate a lighthouse tube.

Slight frequency deviations, up to perhaps 100 kc/sec, can be obtained simply by applying a small voltage in series with the grid bias of a lighthouse tube. Unless the deviation is kept small, however, there is an objectionable amount of amplitude modulation. With a proper adjustment of modulating voltages simultaneously applied to the grid and plate of a lighthouse tube, it should be possible to vary the phase of the transadmittance without affecting the amplitude appreciably. Although such a system would be difficult to adjust, it should permit fairly large deviations.

Amplitude modulation (as distinct from pulse modulation) appears more difficult to achieve than satisfactory frequency modulation. The use of a two-cavity grid-separation oscillator seems to be indicated, and even then it may be advisable to apply the modulation to both grid and plate. Doubtless various schemes involving variable conductances supplied by an auxiliary tube can be made to work.

The whole subject of modulation of triodes at microwave frequencies is another illustration of the narrowness of wartime research where attention is focused sharply on the immediate application. Although the problems are not simple, there is little reason to doubt that solutions will be forthcoming soon. The question of pulse modulation of lighthouse tubes, together with a detailed discussion of cavity designs and performance, is taken up in the next chapter.

# CHAPTER 8

## PULSE OPERATION OF MICROWAVE TRIODES

### By J. B. H. Kuper[1]

**8·1. Factors Important in Pulse Operation.**—Lighthouse-tube oscillators designed for pulse operation have been used extensively as transmitters in low power radar sets and lightweight beacons, and as signal generators. It is almost axiomatic that any radar or beacon application in which 1-$\mu$sec pulses of 1 to 3 kw r-f pulse power are useful is also an application demanding extreme compactness, light weight, and low power consumption. Hence, in addition to the requirements on tuning range, frequency stability, and mechanical simplicity of the oscillator cavity that were discussed in the preceding chapter in connection with low-level c-w applications, the question of efficiency becomes of great importance in pulse operation.

The designer of an efficient pulser must take into consideration the pulser load impedance presented by the lighthouse-tube oscillator. This impedance varies somewhat from tube to tube, but is affected markedly by the adjustment of the oscillator circuit and the applied voltages. The impedance often is not constant over the duration of the pulse.

The preferred method of obtaining pulse operation is to apply a positive voltage pulse to the plate of the lighthouse tube. This method is dependable and will give satisfactory tube life, but many designers prefer not to build a pulser capable of furnishing the plate power. Instead, the plate voltage is applied continuously with the tube biased beyond cutoff, and the hold-off bias is overcome by a pulse applied to the grid or cathode. With this method of operation (referred to as "grid" or "cathode pulsing"), the adjustment of the oscillator is somewhat more difficult, and the lighthouse tubes often fail prematurely. "Grid" or "cathode pulsing" is generally not recommended by the tube manufacturers, and its use is largely confined to low power applications, such as signal generators.

The question of starting time, the interval between application of a voltage pulse and the buildup of the r-f oscillations, is often critical in pulse operation. Attainment of a short (less than $\frac{1}{4}$ $\mu$sec) and reproduci-

[1] Most of the material for this chapter, including all of the illustrations, was compiled by M. E. Gardner, who was in charge of research on pulse operation of lighthouse tubes at the Radiation Laboratory. His cooperation is gratefully acknowledged.

ble starting time requires that the oscillator have strong feedback. Largely for this reason the "reentrant" oscillator is used almost universally in pulse operation of lighthouse tubes. When feedback conditions are wrong, as in severe "drooping" (Sec. 7·6), the starting time may be as much as 40 μsec or more.

Standardization on the use of the reentrant oscillator and adoption of a normal pulse length of 1 μsec with a recurrence frequency of 1000 pps for experimental investigations has resulted in making available much more controlled data on pulse operation than has so far been obtained on c-w performance. With the one type of cavity and a constant duty ratio, the important parameters to be studied are feedback control (choke plunger position), pulse voltage, bias, and load adjustment. Load adjustment and feedback are unfortunately not independent.

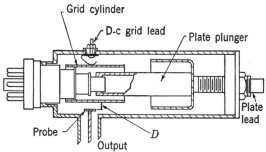

Fig. 8·1.—Cross section of a reentrant cavity for pulse operation. Distance $D$ is measured from probe to grid cylinder.

**8·2. Typical Cavity Design.**—A schematic drawing of a typical reentrant oscillator designed for pulse operation in the 3000-Mc/sec region is shown in Fig. 8·1. This cavity differs from that of Fig. 7·1 mainly in the spacing between the plate choke plunger and the cathode cylinder, which has been increased to withstand high plate voltages. Figure 8·2 is a photograph of an experimental cavity that has been cut open to show the arrangement of the parts. The grid cylinder snaps on to the grid disk of the 2C43 lighthouse tube. The d-c connection to the grid is made by springs that are mounted on the cathode cylinder with small screws passing through bakelite bushings. Mica washers provide bypassing to prevent leakage of r-f energy on the grid leads. Three contact springs are provided in this cavity, of which two appear in the photograph. The quarter-wavelength cup forming the plate choke plunger is fixed on the plate rod. To tune the oscillator the entire assembly can be moved on or off the plate cap of the tube by means of the tuning knob and screw in the end cap. The output probe is located in the region between the grid and cathode cylinders; the depth of penetration is adjusted by means of a threaded collar.

In order to obtain a good voltage-pulse shape, without making the internal impedance of the pulser inconveniently low, it is necessary to keep the stray capacitance of the lead from the pulser to the tube as low as possible.  This, together with the problem of breakdown under high voltages, makes the use of plate blocking condensers undesirable.  Use of a choke type of plate plunger avoids the necessity of a blocking condenser.

Fig. 8·2.—Photograph of an experimental reentrant oscillator, cut open to show arrangement of parts.

A typical reentrant oscillator might have a cathode cylinder $1\frac{1}{2}$ in. in diameter (inside) with a $\frac{1}{8}$-in. air gap between cathode cylinder and plate choke, giving a quarter wavelength line with a characteristic impedance of about 10 ohms.  If the end space beyond the plate plunger is resonant an appreciable amount of energy may leak into the end space and cause "dead spots" or irregularities in tuning.  This difficulty can be avoided by inserting lossy material in the end space.

The grid cylinder must make good mechanical and electrical contact to the grid disk of the tube.  This requires the use of a springy material (phosphor bronze or beryllium copper), carefully machined.  The usual dimensions for the grid cylinder are a $\frac{7}{8}$-in. outside diameter, with the length as given in Table 7·1. It is customary to extend the grid cylinder past the grid toward the cathode shell to produce an "overhang" or "skirt," as shown in Fig. 8·3, which illustrates a design for operation around 3300 Mc/sec. For pulse operation in the 3000-Mc/sec region, a typical skirt would leave about $\frac{1}{16}$ in. spacing between the end of the grid cylinder and the cathode shell of the lighthouse tube. The length of the skirt has comparatively little effect on power output or frequency

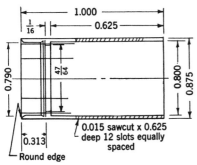

FIG. 8·3.—Grid cylinder for a reentrant oscillator operating in the 3000 Mc/sec region.

of oscillations but does appear to affect the stability of the oscillator.[1] With longer grid cylinders and a corresponding lengthening of the distance to the r-f short circuit produced by the plate plunger, reentrant oscillators operate satisfactorily down to about 1000 Mc/sec.

The choke plunger may be located as indicated in Table 7·1 or it can, of course, be moved out a half-wavelength. This is sometimes done if the cup forming the plate choke overlaps the end of the grid cylinder and so leaves insufficient clearance for high pulse voltages. In any event the cup can be turned either to face the tube (as in the illustrations) or in the opposite direction; the location of the "short-circuit" at the bottom of the cup is the important dimension.

The tuning range of this type of reentrant oscillator is about 10 per cent for any one tube, as in the case of the oscillators discussed in the preceding chapter. This range is set by the length of the plate cap, and may be extended by the use of a telescoping grid cylinder or similar means. For ranges much greater than about 10 per cent, however, it will probably be necessary to provide an independent adjustment of the choke-plunger position. For this reason the simple tuning scheme illustrated here has been used most widely.

Since the efficiency of a lighthouse oscillator operated under pulse conditions in the 3000-Mc/sec region is only about 20 per cent or so, it is important to provide good cooling for the plate seal of the tube unless the duty ratio is small. The cathode cylinder may be provided with several small holes for ventilation without appreciably affecting the operation of the oscillator. At frequencies in the 1000-Mc/sec range,

[1] M. E. Gardner and S. C. Peek, "Preliminary Data on the GL 464 High Frequency Triode When Used as a Pulse Oscillator," RL Internal Report 52-8/5/43.

the efficiency is considerably higher, but the difference between operation at 1000 and at 3000 Mc/sec is not nearly as great in pulse operation as it is under c-w conditions.

**8·3. Tube-design Requirements.**—In general, the requirements to be met by a tube intended for pulse applications in the microwave region are the same as those previously discussed in connection with c-w operation. The chief exception is the cathode emission that is required. The cathode should be capable of emitting at least 10 amp/cm² under pulse conditions, and preferably much more. This is not a stringent requirement since emissions approaching 100 amp/cm² appear to be possible with the best commercial cathodes. Furthermore, the cathode area should be as large as convenient, with due regard to the importance of maintaining a reasonably constant r-f field and transit angle for all parts of the electron beam. In the 2C43 lighthouse tube, which is intended primarily for pulse operation in the 2000- to 3000-Mc/sec region, the cathode area is about 0.3 cm². Most of the data available on the behavior of lighthouse tubes under pulse conditions were taken with pulse durations of 1 or 2 $\mu$sec. Relatively little is known about the effects of very long pulses on oscillator efficiency and cathode life.

The interelectrode spacings can be considerably larger in a tube designed for pulse operation than in its c-w counterpart. For the same transit angles the spacings increase as the square root of the voltage, but it is customary to increase the spacings only enough to prevent flashover, and to take advantage of a reduction in transit angle. This procedure accounts in large measure for the difference in efficiency between the 2C43 operating under pulse conditions and the 2C40 operating continuously at the same frequency.

The frequency stability of an oscillator with respect to changes in ambient temperature or in applied voltages is dependent to a great degree on details of construction of the tube. In most pulse applications where the duty ratio is constant, the problems are just the same as those encountered in c-w operation, but in other cases, notably beacon transmitters, the duty ratio may fluctuate wildly. The maintenance of a stable frequency in this application requires exceptionally good compensation for thermal effects.

For identical cavity adjustments the impedance presented to the pulser is affected strongly by the fineness of the grid structure and its spacing from the other electrodes, particularly the cathode. Opening up the grid mesh or moving it closer to the cathode results in a lower impedance, and increasing the cathode emission likewise decreases the impedance.

The anode of the tube is relatively unimportant. The spacing between anode and grid should be held constant because the grid-plate capacitance is a major factor in determining the frequency of oscillations, as was shown in Fig. 7·8. The particular spacing chosen is a minor matter; a compromise must be made between extremely short spacings, which are hard to maintain accurately in production and may give trouble with breakdown under high pulse voltages, and longer spacings, which involve excessive transit angles.

The material used for the anode post naturally has a large influence on the frequency stability because expansion of the plate changes the grid-plate capacitance. There is not, however, much point in attempting to achieve perfect compensation within the tube as the cavity will have a temperature coefficient of frequency of its own.

**8·4. Effect of Plate-plunger Position.**—As the analysis of the reentrant oscillator (Sec. 7·5) showed, the location of the plate choke plunger (or the length of line $l_4$) is important in determining the feedback phase and magnitude. In addition, there is a change in frequency accompanying a motion of the plunger. This tuning effect is a minor one, however, in comparison to the tuning ranges made available by altering the length of the grid cylinder or inserting a discontinuity in the plate lead. The output coupling also affects the feedback, particularly if the probe is placed as usual in the region between the cathode line and grid cylinder. As a result the location of the plunger and the depth of penetration of the output probe are interdependent.

The curves of Fig. 8·4 illustrate these effects in a general way. The curves are the averaged values for several 2C43 tubes, with different interelectrode capacitances, operated at a pulse voltage of 3.0 kv. For each setting of the choke plunger the output probe was adjusted for maximum output, and the distance between the probe and the grid cylinder, dimension $D$ of Fig. 8·1, is plotted. The operating wavelength, r-f power output, and pulse plate current for this load adjustment are plotted. As the short-circuiting plunger is moved away from the tube, no oscillations are found until the plunger is almost 4.5 cm away from the plane of the grid. As the plunger is withdrawn further, the r-f power builds up rapidly to a broad maximum and then falls off rather slowly. Further motion of the plunger causes the oscillations to stop and nothing happens until the length of $l_4$ is increased to about 8.9 cm (a half-wavelength longer), when the cycle starts to repeat.

As the plunger is moved away from the tube the output probe must also be withdrawn from the cavity, otherwise the oscillator soon overloads and the range of plunger positions over which oscillations are obtained would be shortened markedly. The wavelength increases almost linearly with increase of $l_4$, and the plate current increases rapidly from a minimum value obtained when oscillations are just starting. The best efficiency is obtained when the power output is noticeably less than its maximum, and the plunger adjustment for optimum efficiency is critical.

Since the curves of Fig. 8·4 were taken at a constant plate voltage, the plate-current curve shows the variation of pulser load conductance with plunger position for a given grid-bias resistor.

The position of the plunger also has an effect on the starting time because the time required for oscillations to build up to an appreciable amplitude from the noise level, or an initial transient, is dependent on the feedback. Thus it may be found that the starting time will be relatively long, perhaps 0.5 μsec or more, near the ends of the range of

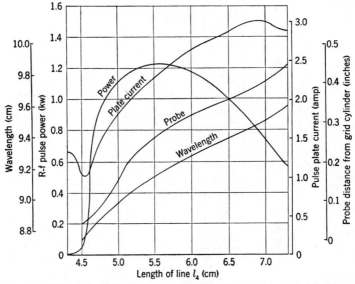

Fig. 8·4.—Effect of choke position on wavelength, output-power, and plate current.

plunger positions over which oscillation is obtained. At some point within this range, where the feedback is optimum at low levels, the starting time will have a minimum value of 0.1 μsec or less.

**8·5. Grid Bias.**—In oscillators in which a positive voltage pulse is applied to the plate, it is most convenient to supply the grid bias by means of a grid-leak resistance. Once the r-f adjustments of the cavity, tuning, plunger position, and load coupling have been fixed, the choice of the grid-biasing resistor affects the output power and efficiency, and possibly the starting time also. The optimum bias resistor depends on the pulse voltage applied to the plate.

A convenient means of illustrating the effects of changing grid-bias resistance is a performance chart constructed as follows.[1]  With a fixed adjustment of the cavity the pulse plate current is plotted against the pulse plate voltage with grid-bias resistor as a parameter, and the loci of constant r-f output power are drawn.  Figure 8·5 is a sample chart presenting averaged results for ten tubes in a cavity operating at 2600 Mc/sec with all adjustments locked.  As the bias resistor is increased the r-f power decreases, but so does the input power.  Also, as the bias resistor is increased the starting time for the lower plate voltages is

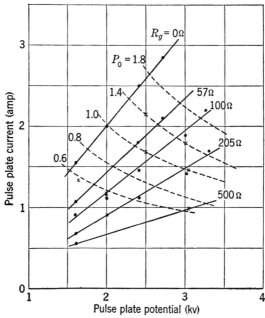

Fig. 8·5.—Average performance chart of ten 2C43 tubes in a fixed oscillator operating at about 2600 Mc/sec as a function of grid-bias resistance.  Pulse-power output (kw) shown by broken lines.

increased, and unstable operation may result.  Tubes that have poor cathode emission will have bias-resistor curves that lie close together and have low current values and small slopes.

The load impedance presented to the pulse generator can readily be calculated from the data of the performance chart.  The impedance increases with increasing bias resistance and decreases slightly with increasing plate voltage.

It is not possible to draw general conclusions about the effects of changes in cavity proportions on the impedance.  In most cases, tuning

[1] M. E. Gardner, "Performance of Lighthouse Tubes as Pulsed Oscillators in a Re-entrant Cavity," RL Internal Report 52-5/4/44.

a given oscillator to lower frequencies decreases the impedance, and so does moving the plate plunger away from the tube (see Fig. 8·4). However, in a particular case an oscillator designed for operation around 3400 Mc/sec showed an impedance only two-thirds that of a 2600-Mc/sec oscillator.

The efficiency obtained from a lighthouse tube operating under pulse conditions is very sensitive to the r-f adjustments of the cavity. For fixed cavity adjustments it is possible to draw some general conclusions about the variation of efficiency with grid-bias resistance and plate voltage. At low plate voltages the highest efficiency is obtained with very low bias resistances, but for these low resistances the efficiency falls off as the plate voltage is increased. For higher resistances the efficiency increases with plate voltage, and for some intermediate value of bias the efficiency is almost constant and near the maximum determined by the r-f conditions.

**8·6. Plate and Heater Voltages.**—Many of the effects of varying plate voltages have already been mentioned in the preceding sections. The variation of output power with plate voltage is visible in the sample performance chart (Fig. 8·5) but is shown more clearly in the curves of Fig. 8·6, which are average results for five 2C43 tubes. The 2C43 tube has a maximum voltage rating of 3.5 kv, but appears to give satisfactory life at 4.0 kv, provided the duty ratio is such that the plate dissipation is well below 12 watts. In the 3000-Mc/sec region the 2C43 does not operate satisfactorily with pulse voltages less than about 1.5 kv.

Where it is necessary to operate at low pulse voltages, and low r-f power is sufficient, the 2C40 tube is often used, despite the fact that this tube is not designed or recommended for pulse operation. Although occasional tubes fail prematurely, most 2C40's can be operated at pulse voltages ranging from 0.8 to 1.2 kv, and give pulse-power outputs in the 3000-Mc/sec region of about 100 watts.

At low plate voltages the starting time may be undesirably long; failure to achieve optimum adjustment of the cavity greatly magnifies this difficulty. In a typical experiment a 2C40 that starts satisfactorily with a pulse voltage of 1000 shows a delay of $\frac{1}{4}$ μsec at 900 volts. At 800 volts the starting time is variable (commonly referred to as "jittering") and about $\frac{1}{2}$ μsec; at 750 volts the delay exceeds $\frac{3}{4}$ μsec and is very unsteady (about half the time the oscillator fails to start at all). Similar difficulties with starting are found with 2C43's at somewhat higher voltages.

The frequency of oscillation is affected by changes in pulse plate voltage in at least two ways. An increase in input power causes the plate rod to expand and increase the grid-plate capacitance, while a decrease in transit time necessitates an increase in frequency. The resultant of these opposing effects depends on the details of construction of the cavity and on the duty ratio. Typical curves of frequency shift with pulse plate voltage for various grid-bias resistors are shown in Fig. 8·7. These were taken on 2C43 tubes at about 3400 Mc/sec with a pulse

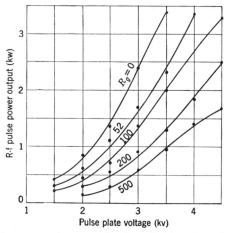

Fig. 8·6.—R-f pulse power output as a function of plate voltage for various grid-bias resistors, $f_0 \approx 2550$ Mc/sec (average of five 2C43 tubes).

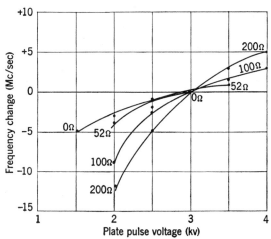

Fig. 8·7.—Frequency shift with changes in plate pulse voltage and grid-bias resistor, $f_0 \approx 3400$ Mc/sec.

duration of 1 μsec and a recurrence frequency of 1000 pps. In this case the transit time effect is more important than the heating.

The heater voltage also affects the frequency in several ways. Expansion of the cathode increases the grid-cathode capacitance (tending to lower the frequency) and decreases the transit time from the virtual cathode to the grid; furthermore, an increase in emission tends to decrease the transit time.    Changes in grid-cathode capacitance are only about one fifth as effective in shifting frequency as changes in grid-plate capacitance.    For the 2C43 under pulse conditions the opposing effects are about balanced, and both positive and negative frequency shifts with

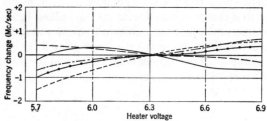

FIG. 8·8.—Frequency variation of five 2C43 tubes with changes in heater voltage, $f_0$ = 2500 Mc/sec.

heater voltage are observed.    This effect is illustrated in Fig. 8·8, which shows the frequency variation for heater voltages from 5.7 to 6.9 for five 2C43 tubes measured at 2500 Mc/sec.

**8·7. Load Coupling.**—By the adjustment of the position of the output probe it is possible to transfer an optimum amount of power to a resistive load terminating the output line.    The same amount of power could, of course, be obtained with a fixed probe position by using an adjustable

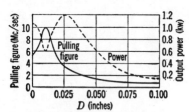

FIG. 8·9.—Power output and pulling figure for a typical oscillator as functions of output-probe depth.

transformer (such as a double-stub tuner), provided the transformer losses are not excessive.    Because the adjustment is easier, variation of the probe depth is the method usually adopted.

In some applications where the load may vary with time, the effect of the load on the frequency must be taken into account.    Following the usage adopted for magnetrons, it is customary to express the frequency shifts with load changes in terms of the "pulling figure."    The pulling figure is defined as the difference between the highest and lowest frequencies obtained when a load with a standing-wave voltage ratio of

1.5 is moved a half wavelength along the line to produce all phases of reflection.

A sample of the variation of power output and pulling figure as a function of the distance between the end of the output probe and the grid cylinder (dimension $D$ in Fig. 8·1) is shown in Fig. 8·9.   Here the power output (broken line) goes through a minimum and then a maximum as the probe distance is increased.   The minimum in power output is evidently due to a severe overload because the pulling figure is a maximum at the same probe position.   Where frequency stability is important, it is good practice to decrease the loading until the power output has dropped to about 0.8 of the maximum value, and so to secure a much lower pulling figure.

# PART III

# KLYSTRONS

# CHAPTER 9

# VELOCITY MODULATION AND KLYSTRON BUNCHING

## By D. R. Hamilton

**9·1. Introduction.**—It is pointed out in Chap. 1 that the conventional multielectrode tube encounters serious limitations at microwave frequencies, and that some of these limitations may be minimized by new techniques of vacuum-tube construction. Regardless of circuit improvements thus made possible, however, there remains the basic electronic necessity for transit of the electrons through the control (i.e., cathode-grid) region in a time considerably smaller than a cycle of the microwave oscillation in question. Since it is an essential feature of such tubes that the electron velocity in the cathode-grid region never exceeds a value corresponding to a small fraction of the plate voltage, the requirement of short transit time becomes a very stringent requirement on interelectrode spacing.

The basic electronic problem in these tubes and in any oscillator or amplifier is, in general, the problem of utilizing an r-f voltage (derived from feedback or input) to produce at some other point a conduction current with an r-f component—that is, it is the problem of producing an electronic transfer admittance, or transadmittance.

The klystron[1] is the product of an approach to the transadmittance problem that differs radically from previously described (and historically antecedent) approaches, and was stimulated by the difficulties encountered in the latter. Electronically there are two marked innovations in the klystron. The most important of these is the combined process of velocity modulation and bunching, by which the finite transit time of electrons becomes the basic means of producing (rather than a limitation upon) the transadmittance. This process of velocity modulation and bunching is the element common to all klystrons, and it is therefore discussed in some detail in this chapter before the various types of klystron are described.

The second radical departure in the klystron is made possible by the first and is not discussed further in itself—it is the application of the velocity-modulating r-f control voltages to the electrons after, rather than before, the acceleration of the electrons by the full applied plate voltage. Although the electrons must preferably have a transit time

[1] R. H. Varian and S. F. Varian, *Jour. App. Phys.*, **10,** 321 (1939).

through the control region of less than one cycle, the electron velocity is much higher for a given plate voltage and the geometrical limitations on the control region are therefore greatly relaxed.

The present chapter is intended to be a reference compendium of the basic information about velocity modulation and bunching that will be required for subsequent discussion of the various forms of klystrons. Thus, the choice of material has been governed primarily by the topics covered in the later chapters rather than by any desire to summarize completely all the features of bunching that would be necessary to form a complete discussion of this very interesting field. For the same reason, all discussion of the way in which klystron behavior is affected by the details of the bunching process is left for the later chapters. It is therefore suggested that the reader may profitably confine a first reading to Section 9·2 of the present chapter, returning to the other sections as they are referred to in later chapters.

**9·2. Simple Velocity Modulation and Bunching.**—The schematic diagram in Fig. 9·1 represents, in an idealized form, that part of a klystron

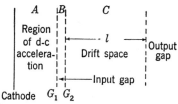

in which the processes of velocity modulation and bunching take place. This region corresponds to the input or cathode-grid space of a triode, in the sense that from this region there emerges an intensity-modulated conduction current that serves to drive the output cavity resonator. The nature of microwave cavity resonators and the way in which they are driven

Fig. 9·1.—Schematic representation of velocity modulation and bunching region in klystron.

by an r-f component of the conduction current is discussed in Chaps. 3 and 4; this chapter is concerned only with the genesis of the electronic transadmittance to which this r-f conduction current corresponds.

The space shown in Fig. 9·1 comprises three separate regions. The processes that occur in these regions are first qualitatively summarized, temporarily making simplifications in order to emphasize the fundamental points.

In region $A$—the space between the cathode $K$ and the grid $G_1$— there exists only a d-c field that corresponds to the application of full beam voltage between $K$ and $G_1$. The influence of the d-c field results in the injection into region $B$, through $G_1$, of a stream of electrons all having the same velocity $v_0$ (given by $mv_0^2/2 = eV_0$) and with current density constant in time.

In region $B$—the control region (or "input gap") between grids $G_1$ and $G_2$—there is an externally impressed alternating r-f voltage the instantaneous value of which is written as $V \sin \omega t$. This instantaneous voltage is the real part of the complex voltage $V_1 e^{j\omega t}$; the complex voltage amplitude $V_1$ is thus given by

$$V_1 = -jV. \tag{1}$$

Throughout the present section it is assumed, for simplicity, that $V/2V_0 \ll 1$, and that the time of transit through region $B$ is very small compared with one cycle of the r-f oscillation. (This transit-time condition is easier to meet here than in the analogous cathode-grid region of a triode because the electrons have already received full d-c acceleration in region $A$.) No electrons are turned back between $G_1$ and $G_2$, and the current density of the stream of electrons leaving $G_2$ is closely constant in time, just as it was at $G_1$. Individual electrons are speeded up or slowed down in passage through the input gap, depending on the phase of the r-f field at the time of the electron's transit. Adopting the convention that the r-f voltage is positive when electrons are accelerated, it follows that each electron in passage from $G_1$ to $G_2$ has gained an energy $eMV \sin \omega t$. Here $M$ is the beam-coupling coefficient discussed in Chap. 3; $M \leqq 1$. Hence when the electron passes through $G_2$ it has a velocity $v$ given by the relation $mv^2/2 = eV_0 + eMV \sin \omega t$. Since $mv_0^2/2 = eV_0$, it follows that

$$v = v_0 \sqrt{1 + \left(\frac{MV}{V_0}\right) \sin \omega t} \approx v_0 \left[1 + \left(\frac{MV}{2V_0}\right) \sin \omega t + \cdots \right], \tag{2}$$

to a good degree of approximation when $MV/2V_0 \ll 1$.

It is this periodic variation of electron velocity that is expressed by saying that the beam is velocity-modulated[1] as it leaves the input gap between $G_1$ and $G_2$; the quantity $V/V_0$ is known as the "depth of modulation."

Region $C$—which extends from $G_2$ to the first grid $G_3$ of the output gap —is called the "drift space." It is assumed, again for simplicity, that in region $C$ there are no d-c fields and no r-f fields, and that any space-charge effects are negligible. The only effects are kinematic; the electrons that were speeded up in $B$ begin to catch up with the slower electrons that are ahead of them, and eventually result in a breaking up of the beam into groups or bunches. This process, known as "bunching,"[2] is illustrated in Fig. 9·2; here the relation between distance and time is

---

[1] It should be noted that "modulation," as used here, does not have the common connotation of superposition of further time variation on an already sinusoidally varying quantity; rather, the time variation is superimposed on a previously time-constant quantity, the electron velocity. These two senses of "modulation" make possible somewhat awkward expressions such as "the frequency modulation of velocity-modulation tubes." The nomenclature is, however, well established by usage.

[2] D. L. Webster, *Jour. App. Phys.*, **10**, 501 (1939).

shown for each of a series of typical electrons in what is known as an "Applegate diagram." The velocity modulation appears as a periodic change in the slope of the electron trajectories at the input gap; bunching corresponds to the convergence and eventual crossing of these trajectories. It may be noted that at $G_3$ the current is not uniform in time; instead, it has r-f components. It may be noted also that the larger $V/V_0$ is, the less drift length is required to produce a given degree of bunching, and that with an excessive amount of r-f voltage or of drift length the

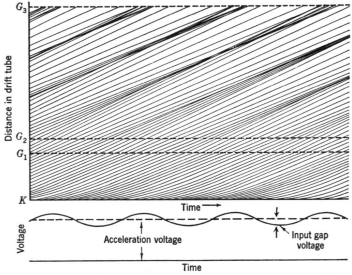

Fig. 9·2.—Applegate diagram of electron trajectories in velocity modulation and bunching.

trajectories diverge from their crossover points and the r-f component of current diminishes.

The main point is that the low-velocity cathode-grid control region of the triode is replaced in the klystron by a composite region in which external r-f control is exerted only on high-velocity electrons, and in which differences of finite electron transit times have been used to produce an intensity-modulated conduction current.

The simplifications assumed in the preceding description of velocity modulation and bunching are continued in the following quantitative discussion.

In considering the relation between time of departure from the input gap, $t_1$, and time of arrival at the output gap, $t_2$, the time of transit through the gaps is ignored. Then, by Eq. (2),

$$\omega t_2 = \omega t_1 + \frac{\omega l}{v} \approx \omega t_1 + \left(\frac{\omega l}{v_0}\right)\left[1 - \left(\frac{MV}{2V_0}\right)\sin \omega t_1\right].$$

The quantity $\omega l/v_0$ is the d-c transit time through the drift space, measured in radians of the input frequency; it is represented by $\theta_0$:

$$\theta_0 \equiv \frac{\omega l}{v_0}. \tag{3a}$$

It is also convenient to define

$$X_0 \equiv \frac{MV\theta_0}{2V_0}; \tag{3b}$$

$X_0$ as given here is a particular example of a dimensionless quantity known as the "bunching parameter"; the definition of the bunching parameter is generalized in succeeding sections. In terms of the transit angle $\theta_0$ and the bunching parameter $X_0$, the above transit-time relation becomes

$$\omega t_2 = \omega t_1 + \theta_0 - X_0 \sin \omega t_1. \tag{3c}$$

Many of the more general situations discussed later in this chapter are described by a transit-time relation given in the above form, but with a more general definition of bunching parameter than that given in Eq. (3b). In order to emphasize this fact, and in order to put the results of the discussion that now follows into a form that will be readily applicable later, the subscript is omitted from the bunching parameter in the discussion of the consequences of Eq. (3c).

This relation embodied in Eq. (3c) is shown in Fig. 9·3 for $X =$ 0.5, 1, 1.84, and 3.83. The quantitative relations in the bunching process are more clearly indicated here than in Fig. 9·2, and the illustration suggests a simple means of finding the actual waveform of the bunched current by application of the principle of conservation of charge. Thus, the electrons arriving at the output gap in the time

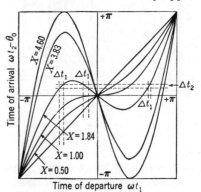

FIG. 9·3.—Relation between time of departure from input gap, $t_1$, and time of arrival at output gap, $t_2$, for several values of bunching parameter $X$.

interval $\Delta t_2$ are made up of one or more groups of electrons (three for the case indicated in Fig. 9·3) that have left the input gap during intervals $\Delta t_1 = |dt_1/dt_2| \, \Delta t_2$. If the d-c beam current is $I_0$, the total charge carried by the electrons arriving in $\Delta t_2$ is

$$I_0 \sum_{t_1(t_2)} \Delta t_1 = I_0 \, \Delta t_2 \sum_{t_1(t_2)} \left| \frac{dt_1}{dt_2} \right|,$$

when the summation encompasses all times of departure $t_1$ that correspond to the same time of arrival $t_2$. The total charge is also $i \, \Delta t_2$ where $i$ is the instantaneous current through the output gap; hence

$$i(t_2) = I_0 \sum_{t_1(t_2)} \left| \frac{dt_1}{dt_2} \right|. \tag{4}$$

This equation simply states that the output gap current at any instant $t_2$ is obtained from Fig. 9·3 by adding the absolute values of all the inverse derivatives $dt_1/dt_2$ corresponding to the given time of arrival $t_2$. This process has been carried out in obtaining Fig. 9·4, which therefore shows the dependence on time of the instantaneous output-gap current for the four previously used values of the bunching parameter, $X = 0.5, 1, 1.84$, and $3.83$.

The infinite-current peaks are a striking feature of Fig. 9·4 and arise in an obvious manner.   For $X < 1$, the electrons that arrive at the output

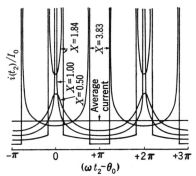

gap at any given instant are those that left the input gap at a single previous instant; for $X > 1$, on the other hand, it has already been noted that for a portion of a cycle the electrons that left the input gap at several different times arrive simultaneously at the output gap. As indicated in Fig. 9·3, this portion of the cycle begins and ends at the values of $t_2$ for which $dt_2/dt_1 = 0$; $dt_2/dt_1 = 0$ means that electrons leaving the input gap in an increment of time $dt_1$ arrive at the output gap in an infinitely shorter increment of time $dt_2$ and therefore constitute an instantaneously infinite current, carrying only a finite charge.

FIG. 9·4.—Dependence of relative current at output gap $i(t_2)/I_0$ on time $t_2$ for various values of bunching parameter $X$.

The component of the waveforms of Fig. 9·4 at the fundamental frequency depends not so much on the presence of infinite peaks as on the general concentration of current in one particular half cycle.   It is obvious from Fig. 9·4 that this concentration increases as $X$ initially increases.   As $X$ increases past unity the two infinite-current peaks, which contain a considerable concentration of current, become more and more separated in time.   At $X = 1.84$ the concentration of current is still rather high; as may be seen shortly, this value of $X$ corresponds approximately to the maximum value of the fundamental component. At $X = 3.83$, however, the peaks are somewhat more than a half cycle apart and in their effect (for example, in driving a circuit) they oppose each other in phase; although the current is hardly constant in time, the fundamental component is exactly zero at this value of $X$.

For high harmonics the infinite-current peaks become very important because any one of such peaks provides an appreciable concentration of current in a half cycle of a high harmonic. Since infinite peaks occur only for $X \geq 1$, not much harmonic content should be expected for $X < 1$. Whenever the two peaks that are present when $X > 1$ are separated by an integral number of half cycles of the harmonic in question, their resulting opposition in phase brings the content of this harmonic nearly to zero. The amplitude of higher harmonics is thus expected to be a maximum near $X = 1$, and to oscillate about zero as $X$ increases past this point.

The above description is an intuitive Fourier analysis of the bunched beam current; for more exact information an exact Fourier analysis is needed and this will now be made.

Since the output-gap current $i(t_2)$ is periodic with the angular frequency $\omega$, this current may be expressed as the sum of a series of harmonics of $\omega$:

$$i(t_2) = \text{Re} \sum_{m=0}^{\infty} i_m e^{jm\omega t_2}. \tag{5}$$

The values of $i_m$ are thus the complex current amplitudes at the various harmonics, just as $V_1$ is the complex r-f gap-voltage amplitude. By the usual theory of Fourier series, the values of $i_m$ are given by

$$\pi i_m = \int_{-\pi}^{\pi} i(t_2) e^{-jm\omega t_2} d(\omega t_2). \tag{6}$$

If the relation for $i(t_2)$ given by Eq. (4) is recalled, it is apparent that

$$\pi i_m = I_0 \int_{-\pi}^{\pi} d(\omega t_2) e^{-jm\omega t_2} \sum_{t_1(t_2)} \left| \frac{dt_1}{dt_2} \right|. \tag{7}$$

This expression is made analytically inconvenient by the occurrence of the absolute value and discrete summation in the integrand. These features, arising from the multiple-valued dependence of $t_1$ on $t_2$ shown in Fig. 9·4, are necessary only for $X > 1$. For $X \leq 1$, $|dt_1/dt_2|$ may be replaced by $dt_1/dt_2$, in which case the above equation becomes

$$\pi i_m = I_0 \int_{-\pi}^{\pi} e^{-jm\omega t_2} d(\omega t_1).$$

This equation has sometimes been derived for $X \leq 1$ in this manner, and the results then applied to instances where $X > 1$. This procedure has given rise to some confusion, not because the equation is incorrect (it is not), but because its validity for $X > 1$ is not immediately obvious. The demonstration of this validity may be based explicitly on Eq. (7), but it may also be demonstrated in a more general manner as follows.

Since $i(t_2)\,dt_2$ is an element of charge, Eq. (6) is a summation of the phase factor $e^{-jm\omega t_2}$ over all electrons that pass through the output gap in one cycle. The order in which the contributions of the various electrons are summed up is immaterial; for example, a summation index not necessarily assigned in the order of arrival of electrons at the output gap may be associated with each individual electron. In this case,

$$i_m = \frac{\omega}{\pi}\,e \sum_n e^{-jm\omega t_{2n}},$$

where $e$ is the charge on the electron. Here $t_{2n}$ is the arrival time for the $n$th electron, and the summation is over all electrons passing through the output gap in one cycle. As a particular illustration, since $t_2$ is a single-valued function of $t_1$, $n$ may be identified with the time of departure $t_1$; since the electrons in the element of charge $I_0\,dt_1$ arrive (to first order) at the same time $t_2(t_1)$, the summation may be written as an integral, giving

$$i_m = \frac{1}{\pi}\,I_0 \int_{\omega t_2 = -\pi}^{\pi} e^{-jm\omega t_2(t_1)}d(\omega t_1).$$

Here the specific limits of integration indicate that the integral is extended only over those values of $t_1$ that, although they may not in themselves lie within a single period, correspond to arrival times $t_2$ lying within one period. But since $t_2 - t_1$ is a periodic function of $t_2$, the limits of integration may be further changed to correspond to an arbitrary addition or subtraction of an integral number of periods to the $t_1$ corresponding to any $dt_2$. In particular, this arbitrary change can be carried out in such a way as to make the integration over $t_1$ correspond to integration over a single consecutive period of $t_1$. This process is easily visualized with the aid of an extension of Fig. 9·3 to cover several periods of $t_1$ and $t_2$. Thus finally

$$\pi i_m = I_0 \int_{-\pi}^{\pi} e^{-jm\omega t_2}d(\omega t_1). \tag{8}$$

By Eq. (3), Eq. (8) may be written

$$i_m = \frac{I_0}{\pi}\,e^{-jm\theta_0} \int_{-\pi}^{\pi} e^{-jm(\omega t_1 - X\sin\omega t_1)}d(\omega t_1).$$

Using the Bessel function expansion of the integrand,

$$\int_{-\pi}^{\pi} e^{-jm(Z - X\sin Z)}\,dZ = 2\pi J_m(mX),$$

the equation for $i_m$ becomes

$$i_m = 2I_0 e^{-im\theta_0} J_m(mX). \tag{9}$$

In Fig. 9·5 are shown, for the fundamental and several harmonics, the absolute values of the current components divided by beam current, $|i_m|/I_0 = 2J_m(mX)$. These curves show in more detail the dependence of current component on bunching parameter that has already been qualitatively discussed.

Since the leading term in $J_m(mX)$, and hence the predominant term for $X \ll 1$, is proportional to $X^m$, only the fundamental component is linear in $X$ for small bunching voltages. The maximum value of $|i_1|/I_0$, 1.16, occurs for $X = 1.84$ and, as the harmonic order increases, the value of $X$ for maximum harmonic content approaches unity. For $m \gg 1$ the maximum value of $J_m(mX)$ approaches the value $0.65/m^{\frac{1}{3}}$; this remarkably slow diminution of harmonic amplitude with harmonic order is a charac-

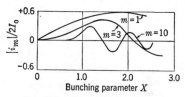

FIG. 9·5.—Dependence of harmonic components $i_m$ of bunched beam current on bunching parameter X for several values of harmonic order.

teristic feature of klystron bunching arising from the infinite peak of Fig. 9·4, as has already been noted qualitatively.

**9·3. Debunching in a Klystron.**—The preceding section has dealt with bunching as a process involving simply the kinematics of electrons in a field-free drift space. It is clear, however, that with sufficiently high current density, space-charge forces may influence the electron motion more than the electrode or gap voltages. If this is true, it might be better to begin by considering bunching as a phenomenon involving waves in a traveling space charge.[1] The present discussion is concerned only with those effects of space charge that are easily considered as modifications of bunching, or as "debunching."[2] This distinction is not a sharp one and lies primarily in the degree of approximation.

*Space-charge Spreading of an Unneutralized D-c Beam.*—As an introduction to debunching, the orders of magnitude involved in space-charge

[1] D. L. Webster, *Jour. App. Phys.*, **10**, 15 (1939).

W. C. Hahn, *G. E. Review*, **42**, 258 (1939).

W. C. Hahn and G. F. Metcalf, *Proc. I.R.E.* **27**, 106 (1939).

S. Ramo, *Proc. I.R.E.*, **27**, 757 (1939).

E. Feenberg, "Theory of Small Signal Bunching in a Beam of Finite Cross Section," Sperry Gyroscope Co. Report 5221–1043, Sept. 17, 1945.

E. Feenberg and D. Feldman, *Jour. App. Phys.*, **17**, 1025 (1946).

[2] E. Feenberg, "Theory of Bunching," Sperry Gyroscope Co. Report 5221–105, Nov. 24, 1942.

W. W. Hansen, unpublished notes.

effects may be seen by considering a simpler question: How much does a cylindrical beam of initially parallel electrons, located in empty space, spread out as a result of mutual repulsion of the electrons?    Figure 9·6 is a schematic representation of such a beam.    In the usual case that is of interest to this discussion, electron velocity ≪ velocity of light, and drift-tube diameter ≪ waveguide-cutoff diameter—that is,

$$\beta \equiv \frac{v_0}{c} \ll 1, \qquad \lambda \gg 3.4a..$$

The first inequality ensures that the magnetic interaction between electrons can be neglected; the second inequality means that the drift tube is unable to act as a transmission line for electromagnetic waves of the fundamental frequency.    Hence, when the discussion returns to debunching the potential at any point can be taken as a time-varying electrostatic potential rather than as a rigorous solution of Maxwell's equations.

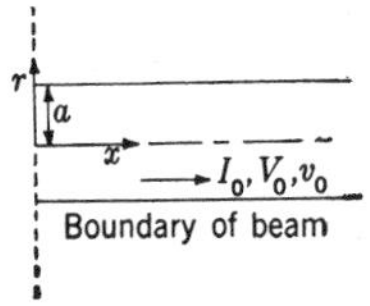

FIG. 9·6.—Beam geometry.

A simple and approximate way of determining the spread of the d-c beam is to find the radial electric field at the edge of the beam assuming there is no spreading, and then to calculate the displacement of an edge-of-the-beam electron under the influence of this force.    For beam current, voltage, diameter, and electron velocity, given by $I_0$, $V_0$, $2a$, and $v_0$, respectively, the charge density in the beam has the value

$$\rho = \frac{I_0}{\pi a^2 v_0}.$$

By Gauss's theorem, the flux of the electric field strength **E** through any closed surface is given by $\int \mathbf{E} \cdot d\mathbf{S} = q/\epsilon_0$, where $q$ is the total charge enclosed by the surface; applying this relation to a cylinder coaxial with and enclosing the beam, it is found that the radial field $E_r$ at the edge of the beam is given by

$$E_r = \frac{I_0}{2\pi a v_0 \epsilon_0} \qquad \text{volts/meter.}$$

Here $\epsilon_0 = 8.85 \times 10^{-12}$ farad/meter; $I_0$ is in amperes, $a$ in meters, $v_0$ in meters/sec.    An electron with initial radial velocity of zero, traveling a distance $x = v_0 t$ under the influence of this force, is radially deflected a distance $\Delta a$ given by

$$\Delta a = \frac{1}{2} \frac{e}{m} E_r \left(\frac{x}{v_0}\right)^2, \tag{10}$$

where $e$ = the charge on the electron = $1.6 \times 10^{-19}$ coulombs; $m$ = the mass of the electron = $9.0 \times 10^{-31}$ kg.    Equation (10) can be written

$$\frac{\Delta a}{a} = \frac{1}{4}(hx)^2. \tag{11a}$$

Here $h$ is a parameter given by

$$(ha)^2 = \frac{1}{\pi \epsilon_0} \frac{e}{m} \frac{I_0}{v_0^3} = \frac{60 I_0}{\beta V_0}, \tag{11b}$$

with $I_0$ and $V_0$ in amperes and volts.

*The Debunching Wave Number.*—This simple example is interesting both in itself (for purposes of later comparison) and for the way in which it introduces an important characteristic of space-charge flow—the occurrence of the parameter $h$, which describes the combined effects of the parameters $a$, $I_0$, and $V_0$ on the relative spreading in a given distance. This parameter has the dimension of inverse length; because of its repeated occurrence in space-charge calculations, $h/2\pi$ is called in klystron theory the "debunching wave number"; the reciprocal, $2\pi/h$, is called the "debunching wavelength." Generally speaking, space-charge effects become appreciable as soon as the distances involved become comparable to the characteristic length $1/h$; thus in the example above, the beam diameter has increased by roughly 25 per cent when $z = 1/h$.

The relation between the debunching wave number and the primary tube parameters is much simpler than it appears at first sight. The quantities $I_0/v_0^3$ and $I_0/\beta V_0$ are both proportional to the perveance of the electron gun, $I_0/V_0^{3/2}$; this perveance is independent of beam voltage. More specifically, it is a constant in any space-charge limited multi-electrode gun with all auxiliary voltages proportional to $V_0$. The perveance depends only on gun geometry; if the gun is represented by a plane parallel diode of electrode diameter $2a$ and electrode spacing $s$, to which it usually bears a close resemblance, then

$$\frac{I_0}{V_0^{3/2}} = 2.33 \times \frac{10^{-6} \pi a^2}{s^2},$$

where $I_0$ and $V_0$ are in amperes and volts, respectively. Comparing this relation with Eq. (11) and utilizing the relation $10\beta = \sqrt{V_0/2550}$, it is seen that

$$hs = 0.47; \qquad \frac{1}{h} = 2.1s. \tag{12}$$

Thus the debunching wavelength $2\pi/h$ is roughly thirteen times the cathode-anode spacing in the equivalent electron gun.

*Space-charge Debunching of a Bunched Beam.*—With this introductory exploration of a simple d-c problem, the discussion may now be brought back to the bunching of a velocity-modulated beam. Several important differences from the foregoing simple example immediately become apparent. Perhaps the most marked difference occurs in the reflex klystron, in which the axial velocity of the electrons is reduced to zero and reversed. Space-charge effects are very pronounced in this region of low velocity. They are also difficult to analyze partly because of the positive and negative velocities that occur at every point in the reflection region, partly because different electrons penetrate to different depths in the field, and partly because in the region of low velocity the r-f component of electron velocity exceeds the d-c component. This latter point makes perturbation calculations difficult. The question of space-charge effects in reflex klystrons is discussed in more detail in Chap. 13. The present section is limited to debunching in a drift space that is free of d-c fields, such as is described in the first section of this chapter; many of the simplifying assumptions found necessary in that section are also used here.

In a practical field-free drift space the physical circumstances differ in one basic respect from those assumed above, and in a manner not dependent on the presence of r-f modulation of velocity or density. Residual gas is present, and is ionized by the electron beam. The slowly moving and continuously produced gaseous ions build up a positive ion cloud in the beam, which more than neutralizes the negative space charge of the electrons; this process goes on until the center of the beam becomes positive enough (by a few volts) to cause the ions to diffuse out of the beam as fast as they are formed. This slight positive potential at the center of the beam is not enough to affect the electron beam in a well-evacuated tube; in a "gassy" tube it produces the phenomenon of "gas focusing." Since the positive ion cloud is made up of particles too massive to respond appreciably to the r-f fluctuations in the electron stream, the net effect is the approximate disappearance of the time-average value of the charge density in the electron beam.

Under these circumstances of zero average charge density the d-c beam of Fig. 9·6 will not spread at all. In a bunched beam, however, the bunches and the space between the bunches (or "antibunches") are regions of instantaneous negative and positive space charge respectively; thus debunching effects are present, although in some respects they are diminished by the positive ions. It is convenient to separate these effects into transverse and longitudinal debunching, corresponding to expansion of the bunch by space-charge forces transverse to and parallel to the beam.

*Transverse Debunching.*—Transverse debunching is similar to the simple spreading of a d-c beam. The bunches spread out and the anti-bunches narrow down; excessive spreading causes loss of the bunch on the walls of the drift tube. This spreading is easily estimated (ignoring drift-tube-wall effects) when the bunch is long and flat, for then the maximum radial electric field is approximately that existing in a long beam of uniform charge density equal in magnitude to the charge density at the center of the bunch. This assumption corresponds to the assumption $X \ll 1$ (degree of bunching small) and $\beta\lambda \gg a$ (separation between centers of bunches large compared with the drift-tube radius).

The r-f component of the current at the center of the bunch is then $2I_0J_1(X) \approx I_0X$ and the r-f charge density is given by $\rho = I_0X/\pi a^2 v_0$. The corresponding radial field, $E_r$, at the edge of the beam is given by

$$\epsilon_0 E_r = \frac{\rho a}{2} = \frac{I_0 X}{2\pi a v_0}.$$

This differs by the factor $X$ from the field obtained with direct current; since the radial force on a given electron is increasing with distance from the input gap, or time, the radial spreading will be proportional to the cube of distance, in comparison with the square in the d-c case. Specifically, since $X = \dfrac{\omega x}{v_0} \dfrac{V}{2V_0} = \omega t \dfrac{V}{2V_0}$, the field is given by

$$\epsilon_0 E_r = I_0 \left( \frac{\omega t}{2\pi a v_0} \right) \left( \frac{V}{2V_0} \right);$$

integration of the equation of motion, $m\, d^2r/dt^2 = eE_r$, gives for the deflection of an edge-of-the-beam electron

$$\frac{\Delta a}{a} = \frac{X}{12} (hx)^2.$$

Comparison with Eq. (11a) shows that the effect of the absence of d-c space charge and of the presence of r-f space charge is to decrease the unneutralized d-c spreading by the factor $X/3$. If circumstances are such that the part of the bunch that expands beyond the original beam diameter is wasted, then debunching diminishes the r-f current by a factor

$$1 - \frac{\Delta i}{i} = 1 - \frac{\Delta a}{a} = 1 - \frac{X}{12} (hx)^2. \tag{13}$$

This factor is not $(1 - 2\Delta a/a)$ because only the bunch, not the antibunch, is changed.

Transverse debunching is very small in small-signal amplifiers where $X \ll 1$, but, if the results are extrapolated to a power tube in which $X \approx 2$, transverse debunching is appreciable when $hx \geqq 1$.

The effect of a metal tube surrounding the beam, which is neglected in the foregoing discussion, is to increase the spreading because of the positive image charges induced by the electrons in the wall of the drift tube.[1]

[1] E. Feenberg, "Small Signal Theory of Longitudinal and Transverse Debunching," Sperry Gyroscope Co. Report 5221-114, Apr. 12, 1944.

*Longitudinal Debunching.*—Consider now the case of longitudinal debunching. It is again convenient to assume a drift-tube wall distant from the beam; a metallic wall that is adjacent to the beam allows no longitudinal forces to exist at the outer edge of the beam. Otherwise, the physical conditions that are assumed in order to simplify the analysis of longitudinal debunching are just the opposite of those assumed for transverse debunching; it is assumed that the beam diameter is much greater than the separation of the bunches, i.e., that $2a \gg \beta\lambda$.

This assumption makes the problem one-dimensional; consequently, it allows a method of solution that is more complete and exact, within the limitation of this initial assumption, than the perturbation procedure used for transverse debunching. The method consists basically of assuming an unknown functional relation between bunching parameter and distance, and then finding out what this functional relation must be in order to satisfy the physical laws governing space-charge flow.

As seen in Chap. 3, these laws are three: (1) Poisson's equation relating space charge and potential or field, (2) the continuity equation relating current and time rate of change of charge density, and (3) Newton's law of motion relating force and acceleration. Conservation of charge, which is implicit in the continuity equation, is also used as in Sec. 9·2. In applying these laws it is convenient to deal only with the r-f component of charge density and current. The d-c current has only a magnetic effect, the neglect of which has already been noted; in an "infinitely wide" beam (with end effects neglected) the d-c component of charge has no physical effect and in the presence of the positive ion cloud the total d-c charge density is physically approximately zero.

Poisson's equation and the equation of continuity are commonly combined to deduce the fact that the divergence of the total current density (displacement current plus convection current) vanishes; this means, in the present case, that

$$\frac{\partial}{\partial x}\left[\frac{i(x,t)}{\pi a^2} + \epsilon_0 \frac{\partial}{\partial t} E(x,t)\right] = 0 \tag{14}$$

where the electric field, $E(x,t)$, is now parallel to the axis of the beam. With the assumption of an infinitely wide beam, and the consequent absence of any return path for the r-f component of current, the total current (quantity in brackets) must vanish; hence

$$\frac{\partial}{\partial t} E(x,t) = -\frac{1}{\pi a^2 \epsilon_0} i(x,t). \tag{15}$$

Without the assumption of an infinitely wide beam, the space-constant but time-dependent total current would have to be added to the right-hand side of Eq. (15); together with the added edge effects, this would considerably complicate the subsequent treatment, eventually limit its validity to infinitesimal bunching parameter, and probably not add a compensating amount of physical insight into the problem. Hence the development continues on the basis of Eq. (15).

This equation may now be integrated with respect to time to give the following relation between the current and the electric field:

$$E(x,t) = -\frac{1}{\pi a^2 \epsilon_0} \int_{x/v_0}^{t} i(x,t')\, dt'. \tag{16}$$

Mathematically speaking, it will be noted that any constant lower limit for this integral is as good as any other one, if an arbitrary constant of integration is added. Actually, the lower limit has been chosen so that this constant of integration vanishes. The corresponding physical picture is simple. The end result of this choice of limits is consistent with a fact that is to be suspected from what has already been discovered about the electron trajectories—namely, that an electron at the center of a bunch experiences no longitudinal space-charge fields. A center-of-the-bunch electron passes through the input gap at time $t = 0$ and passes the point $x$ at $t = x/v_0$. Hence the lower limit has been so chosen as to make $E(x,x/v_0) = 0$. Physically speaking, the above equation then shows that the field at any point is that which is produced by the charge lying between the point in question and the center of the nearest bunch; for the indicated integration of current with respect to time is identical with an integration of charge density with respect to distance, carried out from the point $x$ to the center of the nearest bunch.

It is now convenient to assume, subject to more exact determination shortly, an unspecified functional relation between the position of an electron and time. By analogy with Eq. (3) this relation is written

$$\omega t = \omega t_1 + \frac{\omega x}{v_0} - X(x) \sin \omega t_1, \tag{17}$$

where $t$ is the time of arrival at point $x$. This is an assumption that is intuitively appealing, but it is justified only by the subsequent deduction of a definite differential equation for the function $X(x)$. In order to take the next step it is also necessary to require that $X(x) \leqq 1$; this requirement means that when the differential equation for $X(x)$ has a solution for which $X(x) > 1$, this solution probably does not represent the facts in that region of $x$ for which $X(x) > 1$.

The r-f current $i(x,t)$ is obtained by subtracting the d-c current $I_0$ from the total conduction current. Conservation of charge says that the latter is given, for $X(x) \leqq 1$ (see Sec. 9·2), by $I_0(dt_1/dt)$; hence

$$i(x,t) = I_0 \left[ \left( \frac{dt_1}{dt} \right)_x - 1 \right].$$

This current may in turn be used to find the electric field as given by Eq. (16), with the following result:

$$E(x,t) = \frac{I_0}{\epsilon_0 \pi a^2}\left[ t_1(t) - t_1\left(\frac{x}{v_0}\right) - t + \frac{x}{v_0}\right]$$

$$= \frac{-I_0}{\epsilon_0 \omega \pi a^2} X(x) \sin \omega t_1.$$

Here use is made of the fact that the time of passage of the center of the bunch through the input gap, $t_1(x/v_0)$, is zero.

Since $t_1$ is constant for a given electron, this value of field may be used in the equation of motion to give the acceleration of an electron as a function solely of its position. Thus, by use of the assumption of Eq. (17), the equation of motion becomes

$$\frac{d^2x}{dt^2} = \frac{eE(x,t)}{m} = \frac{-eI_0}{\epsilon_0 m \omega \pi a^2} X(x) \sin \omega t_1. \tag{18}$$

But Eq. (17) implicitly contains, independently of any physical laws, a relation between $x$ and $t$ from which a value of $d^2x/dt^2$ may be obtained by differentiation; thus

$$\frac{d^2x}{dt^2} = \frac{\dfrac{v_0^3}{\omega}\dfrac{d^2X(x)}{dx^2}(\sin \omega t_1)\left(\dfrac{dx/dt}{v_0}\right)^2}{1 - \dfrac{v_0}{\omega}\dfrac{dX(x)}{dx}\sin \omega t_1}. \tag{19}$$

If a solution for $X(x)$ may be found that makes Eqs. (18) and (19) consistent, then this solution and Eq. (17) accurately represent the physical situation.

It is consistent with the final result, and with the assumption $V/2V_0 \ll 1$, which has already been made, to set $(1/v_0)\, dx/dt \approx 1$ and $(v_0/\omega)\, dX/dx \ll 1$. (Note that, in the absence of space charge,

$$\left(\frac{v_0}{\omega}\right)\frac{dX}{dx} = \frac{V}{2V_0}.\Big)$$

Making this simplification, and recalling the definition of the debunching wave number $h$, Eqs. (18) and (19) give

$$\frac{d^2X}{dx^2} + h^2 X = 0. \tag{20}$$

From Eq. (17) it is apparent that $X(0) = 0$, and, by comparing $dx/dt$ as given by Eq. (2) and by differentiating Eq. (17), it may be found that $dX(0)/dx = V\omega/2V_0 v_0$. These boundary conditions serve to specify the solution of Eq. (20) as

$$X(x) = X_0(x) \frac{\sin hx}{hx}$$

$$X_0(x) = \frac{\omega x}{v_0} \cdot \frac{V}{2V_0}. \tag{21}$$

Here $X_0(x)$ is the value that $X$ would have in the absence of space charge; it corresponds exactly to the $X_0$ of Eq. (3b).

The amplitudes of the fundamental and various harmonic components of the beam current, as given in Sec. 9·2, are unaltered in their dependence on $X$ by this altered dependence of $X$ on $x$. Thus Eq. (9) still holds true with $X$ given by Eq. (21), the only new restriction being that $X(x) \leqq 1$. Harmonic components of the beam are appreciable, however, only for $X > 1$. Hence perhaps the only way in which Eq. (21) should be applied to questions of higher harmonic content is to note that if $X(x)$ is such that the condition for the validity of Eq. (21), $X \leqq 1$, is satisfied at all values of $x$, then the harmonic content will be very much less than without debunching. The condition for $X \leqq 1$ at all values of $x$ may be written $(V/2V_0)(\omega/hv_0) \leqq 1$; this relation is equivalent to

$$h\beta\lambda \geqq \frac{\pi V}{V_0}, \quad \text{or} \quad \frac{\beta\lambda}{s} \geqq \frac{6.6V}{V_0}, \tag{22}$$

as the condition for drastic diminution in high harmonic content. This condition is referred to later in the discussion of frequency multiplier klystrons.

*Summary.*—The foregoing discussion of debunching may be summed up as follows. The approximations involve small velocity modulation ($V/2V_0 \ll 1$), small bunching ($X \leqq 1$ in one case, $X \ll 1$ in the other), and neglect of the effects of the conducting walls of the drift tube. Transverse debunching has been estimated by a perturbation procedure with the additional condition $\beta\lambda \gg 2a$, which incidentally tends to reduce the longitudinal debunching; the net result, as given by Eq. (13), is a reduction by the factor $1 - X(hx)^2/12$ of that part of the r-f component of the beam that lies within the original beam diameter. Longitudinal debunching has been calculated by a more exact space-charge-wave procedure which, however, is accurate for $\beta\lambda \ll 2a$; and the result, as given by Eq. (21), is a reduction factor in the r-f current of

$$\frac{(\sin hx)}{hx} \approx 1 - \frac{(hx)^2}{6} + \cdots.$$

Thus if these results are extrapolated to the usual operating region of $X = 1$ or 2, the two effects appear comparable in magnitude and become appreciable when $hx \geqq 1$.

**9·4. Bunching with Finite Gap-voltage and Arbitrary Drift-space Characteristics.**—In order to emphasize the basic features of bunching and debunching, the foregoing discussion has made use of certain simplifying assumptions that are not always justified.   The rejection of all these assumptions at one and the same time, and the subsequent deduction of a complete and rigorous solution to the bunching problem in all generality, appears desirable at first sight.   It will become apparent that this procedure would be very difficult, and second thought suggests that it might not be too profitable.   It would certainly have a tendency to obscure, under the weight of a large number of parameters, the physical significance of some of the effects involved.

The actual procedure of the present chapter is to utilize the simple bunching theory of Sec. 9·2 as a starting point from which to branch out in various directions.   The various sections of the chapter consider one or two effects at a time, and each section is based on a prior knowledge only of Sec. 9·2.

As the various simplifications made in Sec. 9·2 are eliminated, the bunching process is affected.   In the simplest case, where the r-f voltage is small, the electron velocity as well as the electron energy is sinusoidally modulated; when the gap voltage is large, and $M \approx 1$, the electron energy is still sinusoidally modulated, but, since

$$\sqrt{1 + \left(\frac{MV}{V_0}\right)} \sin \omega t_1 \neq 1 + \left(\frac{MV}{2V_0}\right) \sin \omega t_1$$

except when $MV/2V_0 \ll 1$, the velocity is no longer sinusoidally modulated.   When the conditions $V/2V_0 \ll 1$ and $M \approx 1$ are both violated, not even the electron energy is sinusoidally modulated.   An arbitrary d-c field in the drift space affects the electron transit times in such a way that even a sinusoidal velocity modulation does not result in a sinusoidal modulation of the time of arrival of electrons at the output gap.   All of these effects thus change the waveform of the bunched beam current from that discussed in Sec. 9·2.

The present section is concerned with eliminating the two following assumptions:

1. That the r-f gap voltage is small, i.e., $V/2V_0 \ll 1$.
2. That the drift space is free of d-c fields.

In order to emphasize the main features of what happens, the assumption that $M \approx 1$ is made; this assumption means that the electron energy is sinusoidally modulated.   Some of the consequences of removing this assumption are discussed in Sec. 9·5.   Space-charge effects are neglected in the present and subsequent sections.

The reader who is familiar with the various types of klystrons will note that the second assumption noted above does not hold for reflex klystrons, for there the electron spends most of its time in a d-c retarding electric field that is strong enough to slow the electron down to a stop and reverse its direction of motion.   Very conveniently, as will be shown in detail, this reflecting action makes only minor changes in the simple bunching theory of Sec. 9·2; more generally, the results of Sec. 9·2 are valid to a large extent for a drift space with arbitrary d-c fields.   The debunching theory of Sec. 9·3, however, is another story.   Whereas bunching is a purely kinematical matter relating only to questions of total time spent in the drift space, debunching on the other hand involves the details of the mutual interaction of electrons at every point in the drift space; as a result, practically nothing is known about debunching in any but the field-free drift space, and it has not so far been found possible to combine the results of Sec. 9·3 with those of the present section.

The general properties of the drift space may be described by expressing the electron transit angle through the drift space as an analytic function, $\theta(V_e)$, of the electron energy $V_e$.   The time of arrival at the output gap, $t_2$, is then given by the relation

$$\omega t_2 = \omega t_1 + \theta_0 + \left(\frac{d\theta}{dV_e}\right)_0 (V_e - V_0) + \frac{1}{2}\left(\frac{d^2\theta}{dV_e^2}\right)_0 (V_e - V_0)^2 + \cdots , \quad (23)$$

in which the subscript zero signifies evaluation for $V_e = V_0$.

The assumption $M \approx 1$ is necessary in order that the electron energy may still be considered to be sinusoidally modulated; the electron energy $V_e$ is then given by the relation

$$V_e = V_0\left[1 + \left(\frac{MV}{V_0}\right)\sin \omega t_1\right]. \quad (24)$$

It is to be noted that this does not necessarily correspond to a sinusoidal velocity modulation [cf. Eq. (2)].   Thus the expression for $\omega t_2$ may be written

$$\omega t_2 = \omega t_1 + \theta_0 - X \sin \omega t_1 + a_2 X^2 \sin^2 \omega t_1 + a_3 X^3 \sin^3 \omega t_1 + \cdots , \quad (25)$$

where

$$X = -MV\left(\frac{d\theta}{dV_e}\right)_0 = a_1 X_0, \qquad X_0 = +\frac{MV}{2V_0}\theta_0, \quad (26a)$$

$$a_1 = -\frac{2V_0}{\theta_0}\left(\frac{d\theta}{dV_e}\right)_0, \quad (26b)$$

$$a_2 = \frac{1}{2}\frac{\left(\dfrac{d^2\theta}{dV_e^2}\right)_0}{\left(\dfrac{d\theta}{dV_e}\right)_0^2}, \quad (26c)$$

$$a_3 = -\frac{1}{6} \frac{\left(\dfrac{d^3\theta}{dV_e^3}\right)_0}{\left(\dfrac{d\theta}{dV_e}\right)_0^3}. \tag{26d}$$

In Eq. (26a), $X_0$ is the value of the bunching parameter deduced under the simplified assumption of Sec. 9·2; see Eq. (3b).

The quantities $a_1$, $a_2$, $a_3$, etc. thus constitute a set of coefficients that specify the properties of the drift space in a form relevant to and convenient for considerations of bunching. The significance of these coefficients will become more apparent as the development proceeds.

To return to Eq. (25), this generalized relation between time of departure and time of arrival may be used in Eq. (8) to give the r-f components of the beam current because the latter equation is a very general one. Thus Eq. (8) becomes

$$i_m = \frac{I_0}{\pi} e^{-jm\theta_0} \int_{-\pi}^{\pi} e^{-jm(\omega t_1 - X \sin \omega t_1)} e^{-jm(a_2 X^2 \sin^2 \omega t_2 + \cdots)} d(\omega t_1).$$

In the simplest practical cases, as will be seen shortly, the coefficients $a_n$ are small compared with unity (in fact, $|a_n| \ll |a_{n-1}|$) and the second exponential in this equation may therefore be expanded as a power series. Only the two leading terms are carried through the next three equations to indicate the method. Expanding the exponential, the current components are thus

$$i_m = \frac{I_0}{\pi} e^{-jm\theta_0} \int_{-\pi}^{\pi} (1 - jma_2 X^2 \sin^2 \omega t_1 + \cdots) e^{-jm(\omega t_1 - X \sin \omega t_1)} d(\omega t_1).$$

It is to be noted, however, that

$$\frac{d}{dX} e^{jmX \sin \omega t_1} = jm \sin \omega t_1 e^{jmX \sin \omega t_1}, \tag{27}$$

and that differentiation with respect to $X$ may be taken outside the integral;[1] thus

$$i_m = \frac{I_0}{\pi} e^{-jm\theta_0} \left(1 + j\frac{a_2 X^2}{m} \frac{d^2}{dX^2} + \cdots\right) \int_{-\pi}^{\pi} e^{-jm(\omega t_1 - X \sin \omega t_1)} d(\omega t_1).$$

It has already been shown, however, that

$$\int_{-\pi}^{\pi} e^{-jm(\omega t_1 - X \sin \omega t_1)} d(\omega t_1) = 2\pi J_m(mX).$$

---

[1] E. Feenberg, "Theory of Bunching," Sperry Gyroscope Co. Report 5221-105, Nov. 24, 1942.

Hence, the current components, including the terms of next higher order that were left out of the foregoing equation for sake of conciseness, are given by

$$i_m = 2I_0 e^{-im\theta_0}\left(1 + j\frac{a_2X^2}{m}\frac{d^2}{dX^2} + \frac{a_3X^3}{m^2}\frac{d^3}{dX^3} - \frac{a_2^2X^4}{2m^2}\frac{d^4}{dX^4} + \cdots\right)$$
$$J_m(mX). \quad (28)$$

This is the final expression for the current components in the general kinematic situation specified by Eqs. (23) and (24).

Comparison of Eq. (28) and Eq. (9) indicates that the leading term in $i_m$ is unaffected in functional form by finite gap voltage and arbitrary d-c fields in the drift space; the only change is in the generalization in the definition of the bunching parameter in Eq. (26a). One way of expressing this generalization is to say that, in the calculation of the bunching parameter, the transit angle $\theta_0$ has been replaced by another angle $a_1\theta_0$; this latter quantity is sometimes called the "bunching angle" for convenience of reference. At later points in this book, where bunching theory is applied with a degree of generality somewhat less than is used here, the bunching angle is considered to be intrinsically positive and is denoted by $\theta_e$.

In the simple cases already mentioned, for which $a_3 \ll a_2 \ll a_1$, the second term in Eq. (28) is the first order and next most important term. Since it is small and in quadrature to the first term, it may be considered as producing simply a phase shift. The third and fourth terms, which are normally still smaller than the second, are in phase with the leading term and therefore describe a change in amplitude.

These deviations from simple theory have important consequences in free-running oscillators, where they give rise to hysteresis and associated phenomena (see Chap. 14). Limiting discussion to the case where $m = 1$, which is useful in oscillators, it is seen that Eq. (28) may be rewritten

$$i_1 = 2I_0 e^{-j(\theta_0+\Delta_v\theta)}\left(1 + \frac{\Delta_v i_1}{i_1}\right)J_1(X), \quad (29)$$

where $\Delta_v\theta$ and $\Delta_v i_1/i_1$ are defined as[1]

$$\Delta_v\theta = -a_2X^2\frac{J_1''(X)}{J_1(X)}$$
$$\frac{\Delta_v i_1}{i_1} = \frac{[a_3X^3J_1'''(X) - \frac{1}{2}a_c^2X^4J_1^{iv}(X)]}{J_1(X)}. \quad (30)$$

The functions $J_1(X)$ and $X^2J_1''(X)/J_1(X)$ are shown in Fig. 9·7; the functions $X^3J_1'''(X)/J_1(X)$ and $X^4J_1^{iv}(X)/J_1(X)$ are shown in Fig. 9·8.

---

[1] The subscript $v$ distinguishes the quantities in Eq. (29) from similar quantities arising from finite-gap-transit effects that are discussed in the next section and are labelled with a subscript $G$.

To obtain any numerical values of $\Delta_v\theta$ and $\Delta_v i_1/i_1$, the data in Figs. 9·7 and 9·8 must be supplemented by a knowledge of the coefficients $a_n$, which are discussed shortly. Numerical values for $\Delta_v\theta$ and $\Delta_v i_1/i_1$ for typical situations in a reflex klystron with a linear reflecting field are given in Table 9·2 at the end of Sec. 9·5, where a comparison is made with the phase shifts and amplitude changes arising from finite gap-transit angles.

Aside from such numerical values, some additional conclusions may be drawn from Figs. 9·7 and 9·8. It is apparent that $\Delta_v\theta$ and $\Delta_v i_1/i_1$ are small for $X < 1$ because they are proportional to $X^2$. At $X = 2$ (the vicinity of normal oscillator operating conditions), the functions in Figs. 9·7 and 9·8 are not too much greater than unity, but for larger values of $X$ (overbunching) some of the terms become very large. This corresponds in part, but not completely, to the fact that the leading term in

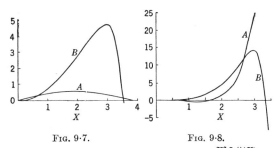

Fig. 9·7.                    Fig. 9·8.

Fig. 9·7.—Functional dependence of $J_1(X)$ (curve $A$) and $\dfrac{-X^2 J_1''(X)}{J_1(X)}$ (curve $B$) on $X$.

Fig. 9·8.—Dependence of $X^3 J_1'''(X)/J_1(X)$ (curve $A$) and $X^4 J_1^{iv}(X)/2J_1(X)$ (curve $B$) on $X$.

$i_1$, $J_1(X)$, is approaching zero; therefore the "correction" terms in $i_1$ become predominant. These correction terms prevent the current $i_1$ from having the zeros indicated in Fig. 9·5. A more physical picture of this phenomenon results from the treatment in Sec. 9·6; experimental data on the point appear in Fig. 10·8 (Chap. 10).

*The Drift-space Coefficients.*—The discussion needs now to be turned to a general consideration of the drift-space coefficients $a_1$, $a_2$, and $a_3$. These coefficients are readily obtained for the two simple drift spaces already mentioned, the field-free drift space and the uniform reflecting field, because of the simple dependence of $\theta$ on $V_e$ in these two cases. For a field-free drift space of constant length, $\theta$ is inversely proportional to electron velocity, hence $\theta = \text{constant} \times V_e^{-\frac{1}{2}}$. In a uniform reflecting field, the depth of penetration into the field is proportional to $V_e$, whereas the average velocity of the electron is still proportional to $V_e^{\frac{1}{2}}$; the transit angle $\theta$ is proportional to the ratio of these two factors, hence $\theta = \text{constant} \times V_e^{\frac{1}{2}}$. Because the faster electrons penetrate more deeply, they spend more time in the reflecting field.    Consequences of this fact are noted several times in the further development of this subject.

These two simple drift spaces are thus special instances of a somewhat more general case, $\theta = \text{constant} \times V_e^n$.  For $\theta = \text{constant} \times V_e^n$ it is easy to show that

$$a_1 = 2n,$$
$$a_2 = \frac{1}{2\theta_0} \cdot \frac{n-1}{n},$$

and

$$a_3 = -\frac{1}{6\theta_0^2} \cdot \frac{(n-1)(n-2)}{n^2}.$$

From these general relations, Table 9·1 may be deduced.

TABLE 9·1.—DRIFT-SPACE COEFFICIENTS

|  | Field-free drift space ($n = -\frac{1}{2}$) | Uniform reflecting field ($n = \frac{1}{2}$) |
|---|---|---|
| $a_1$ | $+1$ | $-1$ |
| $a_2$ | $\dfrac{3}{2\theta_0}$ | $-\dfrac{1}{2\theta_0}$ |
| $a_3$ | $-\dfrac{5}{2\theta_0^2}$ | $-\dfrac{1}{2\theta_0^2}$ |

The first point to be noted here is the difference in the sign of $a_1$ in the two cases.    From Eq. (26a), it is seen that this difference in signs corresponds to a negative bunching parameter in a uniform reflecting field and a positive bunching parameter in a field-free drift space.    This convention deviates from the customary one of making $X$ an inherently positive quantity and altering the sign of the term $X \sin \omega t_1$ in Eq. (25) to fit the circumstances.    Perhaps unfortunately, the latter convention has become firmly entrenched in common usage for the simple theory of the reflex klystron with linear drift space; hence, with the exception of Chap. 13, it is followed in all subsequent discussions involving reflex bunching. For more generalized discussions of bunching such as those of Chap. 13, however, the convention that the sign for $a$ is the sign of $X$ seems much preferable and is therefore used.

Since $J_1(-X) = -J_1(X)$, a reversal of sign of $X$ corresponds to a phase shift of 180° in $i_1$; physically speaking, this means a phase shift of 180° in time of arrival of the bunch.    Thus in a field-free drift space $(X > 0)$, the electrons that pass through the input gap at $\omega t_1 = 0$ and $2\pi$ are at the centers of successive bunches, whereas, in a uniform reflecting field $(X < 0)$, the centers of the bunches are the electrons for which

$\omega t_1 = \pi$ and $3\pi$.  Physically, this phenomenon is easily traced back to the fact, already mentioned, that in the uniform reflecting field the faster electrons have the longer transit time.  This phenomenon has an exact analogy in a ball thrown up into the air; the harder it is thrown, the longer it takes to return.  Thus the center of the bunch is the electron that passes through the input gap at the instant when the r-f field is zero and changing from accelerating to decelerating.  Just the reverse is true in field-free bunching.  The questions of sign and phase discussed in this paragraph are simple physical matters for which the foregoing general treatment is not at all necessary.

It may also easily be seen that, in a drift space that is composed of one field-free section and one section with a uniform reflecting field,

$$-1 < a_1 < 1$$

depending on the relative proportions of the two regions.

The next interesting point to be noted in Table 9·1 is the dependence of the $a$'s on $\theta_0$.  Since, in most practical cases, $\theta_0 \geqq 10$ radians, the fact that $a_2\theta_0$, $a_3\theta_0^2$, . . . are approximately unity is important because it means that each coefficient $a_n$ is smaller than the preceding one by at least an order of magnitude, and this in turn makes the expansion in Eq. (28) well-behaved.

It should be noted, however, that this simple relation between $\theta_0$ and the $a$'s holds only when $\theta = \text{constant} \times V_e^n$, a simple relation that fortunately includes the two simplest practical examples.  A more complicated arrangement of d-c fields in the drift space might at some value of $V_0$, for example, correspond to a large $(d^2\theta/dV_e^2)_0$ and a small $(d\theta/dV_e)_0$; if this were true, the second term in Eq. (28) would outweigh the first and the functional dependence of $i_m$ on $X$ would be completely altered.  Some specific examples of such behavior are discussed in Chap. 13 in connection with reflection-field effects.

**9·5. Influence of Finite Gap-transit Angle on Bunching.**—In the previous section the effect of the passage of electrons through the input gap was described as a simple energy modulation, expressed in electron volts by Eq. (24):

$$V_e = V_0 \left( 1 + \frac{MV}{V_0} \sin \omega t_1 \right).$$

The effects of the drift-space characteristics and the finite size of $V/V_0$ were then investigated.  In actual practice, gap-transit times of a half cycle or more are often encountered.  In such cases, effects arise that make a discussion of velocity modulation and bunching incomplete without an investigation of at least the general anatomy and orders of magnitude of these effects.[1]

One phenomenon arising from finite gap transit angles is beam loading; another is the existence of the beam-coupling coefficient $M$. These phenomena have already been discussed in Chap. 3. Although the subject of beam loading does not lie within the scope of the present chapter, it is intimately related to some of the effects discussed herein.

It becomes apparent from the preceding discussions that any analysis of klystron electronics begins with an investigation of electron kinematics. This investigation has as its result an expression for time of arrival of an electron at a given point in terms of time of departure from a reference point where the initial conditions are known—that is, the entrance to the input gap. The effect of a finite gap-transit angle on such a kinematical analysis is two-fold. In the first place, the time of electron arrival at any point is directly affected by any finite gap-transit angle, and this gap-transit angle varies with the phase of the r-f field at which an electron enters the gap. In the second place, the change in electron energy in passing through a gap, $V_e - V_0$, is no longer a simple sinusoidal function of time such as that referred to above.

Such considerations are, of course, just as relevant to the passage through the output gap as through the input gap. Although the output gap may appear not to be involved, per se, in the question of velocity modulation and bunching with which this chapter is concerned, nevertheless this is the appropriate place to discuss any questions of finite output-gap-transit angle that need to be discussed. Since these questions will be passed over lightly, a brief discussion of the relation between input-gap- and output-gap-transit-angle effects, and the reason for the brevity of the treatment of the latter, is in order.

The effect of the output-gap-transit angle may be described as follows. The bunched current effective in driving the output circuit is (for plane-parallel geometry) the value of the instantaneous r-f conduction current averaged over all points in the output gap. If the transit time through the output gap is finite, however, the r-f field in this gap has time to modify the electron motions; hence the instantaneous r-f current at any point in the gap is also modified by the r-f field, and the over-all driving current for the output circuit may not be calculated rigorously without including the reaction of the output circuit (r-f voltage in the output gap) back upon the driving current. This factor becomes particularly important when the r-f voltage in the output gap is comparable to or greater

---

[1] For a general discussion of finite gap-transit angles from a viewpoint somewhat different from that of this section, see E. Feenberg, "Theory of Bunching," Sperry Gyroscope Co., Report 5221-105, Nov. 24, 1942; also compare Chap. 12 and:

J. K. Knipp, 'Notes on the Reflex Oscillator," RL Report 709, May 3, 1945.

than the beam voltage; in this instance electrons may actually be turned back at the output gap.

However, the main emphasis of the book is upon reflex klystrons; here the r-f voltage in the single (input and output) gap is usually considerably less than beam voltage. In this situation the input-gap effects are the more important, especially because these effects influence the whole course of bunching in the drift space. Furthermore, any general discussion of output-gap effects adds a great deal of complication to the analysis and probably could not be justified without going into the effect of the input gap in considerably more detail than is intended.

For these reasons output-gap effects are not to be discussed further, beyond noting in the discussion of input-gap effects some obvious generalization of results to output-gap effects. In discussing input-gap effects the aim of the present section is to indicate the nature and magnitude of these effects rather than to cover the subject with complete generality. After these general comments, the discussion may now be centered on the details of what happens in the input gap.

The basic equations for phenomena occurring in gaps are discussed in Chap. 3. Thus the manner in which the presence of an r-f field modifies the gap transit time is indicated in Eqs. (3·15) and (3·25). These equations may be applied to give the transit time through the complete gap for the case when the beam is unmodulated upon entrance into the gap; in the notation of Chap. 3, this corresponds to taking $v_\omega(0) = 0$, $x = d$, $T' = T$, $M' = M$, $N' = N$, $\theta' = \theta = \omega T$. Writing $\theta = \theta_1$ to correspond to the notation of the present chapter, and noting by a comparison of Eqs. (1) and (3·13) that $V_\omega = -jV$, one finds for the actual gap transit angle (which will be denoted by $\theta_g$), the following expression (accurate to first order in $V/2V_0$):

$$\theta_g = \theta_1 + \frac{\theta_1}{2} \frac{V}{2V_0} \left[ -M \sin \omega t_1 + \frac{N\theta_1}{6} \cos \omega t_1 \right]$$

$$= \theta_1 - \frac{\theta_1}{2} \frac{V}{2V_0} \sqrt{M^2 + \frac{N^2\theta_1^2}{36}} \sin \left( \omega t_1 - \tan^{-1} \frac{N\theta_1}{6M} \right) \qquad (31a)$$

In this equation $\omega t_1$ is defined, as a matter of convenience, as "(phase angle at entrance into the gap) + $\theta_1/2$"; that is, $t_1$ is the time at which an electron would pass the center of the gap in the absence of the r-f field. The functions $M(\theta_1)$ and $N(\theta_1)$, both of which approach unity as $\theta_1$ approaches zero, are defined in Chap. 3 as follows:

$$M = \frac{(\sin \theta_1/2)}{(\theta_1/2)}$$

$$N = \frac{24}{\theta_1^3} \left( \sin \frac{\theta_1}{2} - \frac{\theta_1}{2} \cos \frac{\theta_1}{2} \right)$$

In Fig. 3·8 are shown, as functions of $\theta_1$, the functions

$$H = \sqrt{M^2 + N^2\theta_1^2/36}$$

and $\eta = \tan^{-1}(N\theta_1/6M)$ which occur in Eq. (31a).

The above expression for the gap transit angle may now be used to determine the velocity with which the electrons leave the gap; this is a matter of prime importance since it determines the subsequent bunching action. The exact change in the electron's velocity which occurs in the gap is given by Eq. (3·19); utilizing the value of the gap transit angle given in Eq. (31a), bearing in mind the changes in notation mentioned above, and discarding terms of higher order than $(V/2V_0)^2$, the following relation is obtained for $V_e$, the energy of the electron on leaving the gap:

$$V_e - V_0 = MV \sin \omega t_1 + \left(\frac{V^2\theta_1}{24V_0}\right)\left[-P \sin 2\omega t_1 + \frac{MN\theta_1}{2}\right] \quad (31b)$$

In this equation the function $P$ is defined as

$$P(\theta_1) = \left(\frac{6}{\theta_1^3}\right)(\theta_1 - \sin \theta_1).$$

This function approaches unity as $\theta_1$ approaches zero, but has no zeros for $\theta_1 > 0$. In Fig. 3·3, $M$, $N$, and $P$ are shown as functions of $\theta_1$.

A general treatment of input-gap effects could now be carried out in the framework of the previous section by adding to the right-hand side of Eq. (23) the term $\theta_g$, and using in Eq. (23) the expression for $V_e - V_0$ given by Eq. (31b) alone rather than that of Eq. (24). In carrying out such a treatment the method of Sec. 9·4 could be used intact if the sin $2\omega t_1$ and cos $\omega t_1$ terms in Eq. (31) were expanded as a power series in sin $\omega t_1$; however, this particular method has faults that make it not very practicable.

The salient features of any such general analysis are emphasized when only the linear term in $(V_e - V_0)$ is used, that is, if Eq. (23) is replaced by

$$\omega t_2 = \left(\omega t_1 - \frac{\theta_1}{2}\right) + \theta_g + \theta_0 + \left(\frac{d\theta}{dV_e}\right)_0 (V_e - V_0) + \cdots. \quad (32)$$

With the values for $\theta_g$ and $(V_e - V_0)$ given by Eq. (31), Eq. (32) becomes

$$\omega t_2 \approx \omega t_1 + \frac{\theta_1}{2} + \theta_0 - \frac{V\theta_1}{4V_0}\left(M \sin \omega t_1 - \frac{N\theta_1}{6} \cos \omega t_1\right)$$
$$- X \sin \omega t_1 + \frac{V\theta_1 X}{24V_0}\left(\frac{P}{M} \sin 2 \omega t_1 - \frac{N\theta_1}{2}\right). \quad (33)$$

This equation has been written explicitly to make the origin of the various terms of the next equation more obvious. Rearranging Eq. (33) and keeping only first-order terms in $V/2V_0$,

$$\omega t_2 \approx \omega t_1 + \frac{\theta_1}{2} + \theta_0 - \frac{\beta X^2}{2} - \left( X + \frac{MV\theta_1}{4V_0} \right)$$
$$[\sin (\omega t_1 - \beta) - \gamma \sin 2(\omega t_1 - \beta)] \quad (34)$$

where

$$\beta = \frac{VN\theta_1^2}{24V_0X} = -\frac{N\theta_1^2}{12Ma_1\theta_0}$$
$$\gamma = \frac{VP\theta_1}{24V_0M} = -\frac{PX\theta_1}{12M^2a_1\theta_0}. \quad (35)$$

It is to be noted that $\beta$ is independent of r-f gap voltage.

This equation describes several effects of the finite gap-transit angle on both the amplitude and phase of the r-f components of the bunched current. If the amplitude effects are considered first, it may be noted that the coefficient of $-\sin (\omega t_1 - \beta)$ (which would be the argument of the Bessel functions giving the current components if $\gamma$ were zero) is $X + MV\theta_1/4V_0$. This fact is not surprising, since $MV\theta_1/4V_0$ is just the contribution to the bunching parameter that would be made by a (d-c) field-free drift space with transit angle $\theta_1/2$; thus the "effective" bunching parameter is obtained by extending the drift space back to the middle of the gap and considering the r-f field as concentrated at the middle of the gap. It is to be noted that in the other places where $X$ occurs in Eq. (34), the term $(X + MV\theta_1/4V_0)$ could be substituted at will since the resulting changes would be of order $(V/2V_0)^2$.

A much less trivial effect is the existence of the second-harmonic term, $\sin 2(\omega t_1 - \beta)$. It may be seen by comparing Eqs. (33) and (34) that the term arises from the modification of $V_e - V_0$ in the presence of a finite input gap. One might say that velocity modulation by a sinusoidal voltage in a finite gap is like velocity modulation in an infinitesimal gap by a fundamental and second-harmonic voltage. Since the second-harmonic term has the same symmetry about $\omega t_1 - \beta = 0$ as does the first-harmonic term, the presence of the second harmonic does not change the phase of the bunch, but it does change the shape of the bunch and the magnitude of the r-f component.

This may be seen graphically in Fig. 9.9. Here then is shown the relation between $t_2$ and $t_1$ for the simplified relations

$$\omega t_2 = \omega t_1 - X(\sin \omega t_1 - \gamma \sin 2\omega t_1) \quad (36)$$

with $X = 2$ and $\gamma = 0, 0.5$.

In Fig. 9.10 are shown the resulting dependences on time of bunched beam current. It is apparent from these figures that the presence of the second-harmonic term, with a coefficient negative with respect to the first, tends to concentrate more current at the center of the bunch. This phenomenon has been analyzed in considerable detail in connection

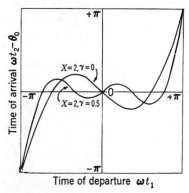

FIG. 9·9.—Transit-time phase relations in the presence of second harmonic velocity modulation or equivalent. Relation between time of arrival $t_2$ and time of departure $t_1$: $\omega t_2 = \omega t_1 - X (\sin \omega t_1 - \gamma \sin 2 \omega t_1)$.

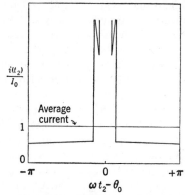

FIG. 9·10.—Waveform of bunched beam current as modified by presence of second-harmonic velocity modulation or equivalent; compare with Fig. 9·9.

with cascade bunching,[1] where it also occurs. (See the discussion of cascade bunching in Sec. 9·8.) The behavior of the fundamental component of the bunched beam $i_1$ is indicated in Fig. 9·11. It is apparent from the figure that this maximum current component occurs in the vicinity of $X = 2$, $\gamma = 0.4$ and that at this point the maximum current component has been increased by 28 per cent over the value at $\gamma = 0$. This result should really be stated for $|X| = 2$, since the sign of $X$ is irrelevant to the results, and it is to be noted from Eq. (35) that $\gamma$ is positive for $0 \leqq \theta_1 < 2\pi$. Defining this frac-

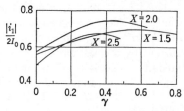

FIG. 9·11.—Dependence of $i_1$, fundamental component of bunched beam current, on bunching parameter $X$ and on the parameter $\gamma$ giving the relative amplitude of second harmonic in simplified bunching equation for a finite gap [see Eq. (35)].

tional increase of $i_1$ as $\Delta_G i_1/i_1$, it is seen from the figure that, for $|X| = 2$, the following equation may be written:

$$\frac{\Delta_G i_1}{i_1} \approx 0.28 \left[ 1 - \left( 1 - \frac{\gamma}{0.44} \right)^2 \right]. \tag{37}$$

[1] E. Feenberg, "Theory of Cascade Bunching," Sperry Gyroscope Co. Report 5221-143, Aug. 22, 1945.

For most values of $\theta_1$ (i.e., $\theta_1 \leqq 5$), $P/M \approx 1$; for $V/V_0 = 0.4$ and $\theta_1 = \pi$, $\gamma = .05$. This gives only some 6 per cent increase in fundamental component of the bunched beam. But it may be observed from Fig. 3 that as $\theta_1 \rightarrow 2\pi$, $M \rightarrow 0$ and $P/M \rightarrow \infty$. Thus $\gamma$ may be brought into the optimum vicinity of $\frac{1}{2}$ by letting $\theta_1$ approach $2\pi$, provided that by some means, such as a large drift space, the value of $X$ is enabled to remain in the vicinity of 2.

Phase effects shown in Eq. (34) are likewise quite striking and are of two types, as represented by the presence of the term $\beta X^2/2$ and by the change from $\omega t_1$ to $(\omega t_1 - \beta)$.

The term $\beta X^2/2$ comes from the constant term $V^2MN\theta_1^2/48V_0$ in $(V_e - V_0)$, which represents the beam loading at the input gap; that is, the beam-loading term in $(V_e - V_0)$ is the average amount of energy abstracted from the gap by each electron. Since the mean velocity of a beam passing through a finite gap is thus increased by an amount proportional to $(V/V_0)^2$, or $X^2$, the time of transit of the bunch is changed by a corresponding amount—an increase for a normal reflex klystron $(d\theta/dV_e < 0)$ and a decrease for a field-free drift space. It may be noted by comparison with Eq. (26) and Table 9·1 that the sign of $\beta$ is determined by the sign of $a_1$.

The presence of $\beta$ in the argument of $\sin(\omega t_1 - \beta)$ also represents a phase shift of the bunched beam, which may be traced back to its source in the phase difference between the transit time $\theta_g$ and the r-f voltage $V \sin \omega t_1$. It might be said that because of this phase difference the bunching that occurs in the gap is out of phase with that which occurs in the drift space, and so manages to shift the phase of the final bunched current by a small amount. But, although this phase shift varies from mode to mode, it is independent of r-f voltage; hence it has little significance. As a numerical example, suppose that $\theta_0 = 10$, $X = -2$, $\theta_1 = \pi$, $M = 0.67$, and $V/V_0 = \frac{2}{3}$; then $\beta = -0.11$ radians or $-0.02$ cycles.

Since the only phase shift of much interest is therefore $-\beta X^2/2$, a phase shift $\Delta_G\theta$, which is due to the finite gap-transit time, may be written as

$$\Delta_G\theta = -\frac{\beta X^2}{2}.$$

Of these two phase shifts, the second may be expected to have an analogue in the output gap; but the first shift—the only one that is relevant—is a drift-space effect pure and simple. Of the two amplitude effects, the obvious addition of $MV\theta_1/4V_0$ to the bunching parameter has an analogue in the output gap. The much more interesting effect of the finite input-gap angle in producing more efficient bunching is again something that requires a drift space for its unfolding and hence has no output-gap analogue. It is clear that the principal output-gap effects are the usual beam-coupling-coefficient effect and the normal beam loading.

As already noted, these summarizing comments hold true where the output-gap voltages and dimensions are such as not to approach the condition of turning back electrons. It should also be realized that the use of only the leading terms in Eq. (32) implies that the coefficients $a_n$ of the previous section are small, or that in normal cases the d-c drift angle $\theta_0$ is large. This assumption that $\theta_0 \gg 1$ is equivalent to the assumption used through this section that $V/2V_0 \ll 1$, so the whole scheme is consistent.

As a final comparison of the results of the last two sections, it is interesting to compare the quantities $\Delta_v\theta$, $\Delta_v i_1/i_1$, $\Delta_G\theta$, and $\Delta_G i_1/i_1$ of a simpler case in which the values of $a_n$ are known—the reflex klystron with a linear reflection field. The condition for approximately optimum operation, $|X| = 2$, will be used, and in calculating $\Delta_G\theta$ and $\Delta_G i_1/i_1$ gap-transit angles of $\pi$ and $1.8\pi$ will be used. The results are shown in Table 9·2.

TABLE 9·2.—PHASE AND AMPLITUDE CHANGES IN BUNCHING IN THE PRESENCE OF
FINITE GAP-VOLTAGES AND TRANSIT TIMES

$$|X| = 2$$

|  | $\theta_0 = 5$ | | $\theta_0 = 50$ | |
|---|---|---|---|---|
| $\Delta_v\theta$ | −0.28 | | −0.028 | |
| $\Delta_v i_1/i_1$ | −0.046 | | −0.0005 | |
|  | $\theta_1 = \pi$ | $\theta_1 = 1.8\pi$ | $\theta_1 = \pi$ | $\theta_1 = 1.8\pi$ |
| $\Delta_G\theta$ | −0.41 | −3.7 | −0.041 | −0.37 |
| $\gamma$ | 0.16 | 3.6 | 0.016 | 0.36 |
| $\Delta_G i_1/i_1$ | 0.15 | ? ! | 0.015 | 0.28 |

The combination $\theta_1 = 1.8\pi = 5.7$ and $\theta_0 = 5$ is extreme. The fact that this gives $\gamma = 3.6$ means that the bunching is almost complete second-harmonic bunching, and badly overbunched at that. This combination is included as a matter of curiosity.

The effects of a gap-transit angle in the vicinity of $2\pi$ are apparent; and they persist even at $\theta_0 = 50$. It is to be noted, however, that for $\theta_1 = 1.8\pi$ the beam-coupling coefficient $M$ is about 0.11 and it is therefore necessary to have $V/V_0 \approx 0.7$ in order to make $|X| = 2$. In addition to reducing the accuracy of the approximation, this high gap voltage may also involve high power loss in the resonator. It is true, in general, that for $\theta_1 = \pi$ the phase and amplitude effects arising from the two different sources are comparable, the finite-transit-angle effects being somewhat the larger.

**9·6. Bunching by a Gap Voltage Comparable to Beam Voltage.**—The treatment of finite-gap-voltage effects in Sec. 9·4 provides an analytical description that is convenient for many applications. If the effective r-f voltage becomes comparable to or greater than the beam voltage, however,[1] the treatment of Sec. 9·4 loses its usefulness or breaks down entirely. For, with $M \approx 1$ and $V/V_0 \gtrsim 1$, some of the electrons of the beam are turned back at the input gap, and even before this condition is reached, the bunching process is markedly changed.

Such situations, although seldom occurring in oscillators or amplifiers, are not uncommon in frequency multipliers. The input frequency of a frequency multiplier is low, often below the microwave region; therefore, a drift space of convenient physical dimensions corresponds to a drift-space transit angle $\theta_0$ that is smaller than that common in oscillators. To obtain satisfactory bunching ($MV\theta_0/V_0 \approx 2$) it is therefore necessary to increase $MV/V_0$. Furthermore, the bunching produced when $V/V_0 \gtrsim 1$ has characteristics that are desirable for frequency multipliers in certain situations, as is discussed in the next chapter. The analysis of these effects given here is limited to bunching in a field-free drift space such as is found in frequency multipliers; the general procedure, but not all the detailed results, may be applied to any type of klystron bunching. Aside from detailed results, the method of dealing with this very high input-gap voltage is interesting also for the light it sheds on the nature of the bunching process.

As in the previous section, the assumed conditions are simplified so as to emphasize the salient features of the phenomenon under discussion. Space-charge debunching effects are ignored. Gap-transit-time effects, except the existence of the beam-coupling coefficient $M$, are also ignored. It is assumed that $M \approx 1$; when $M$ is small compared with unity, the situation is very much more complicated—for example, with a small $M$ there may be no electrons turned back at the gap even with $V/V_0$ considerably larger than unity. Finally, as already noted, a field-free drift space is assumed. All told, the assumed conditions are identical with those of Sec. 9·2 except for the assumptions $MV/V_0 \approx 1$ and $M \approx 1$, which replace the assumption $MV/V_0 \approx 0$. It may frequently be convenient to compare the results of these two assumptions; for this purpose,

---

[1] The treatment of this section follows, in large part, E. Feenberg, "Bunching Theory for Two-resonator Klystron Multipliers," Sperry Gyroscope Co. Report 5221-117, May 23, 1944.

$MV/V_0 \approx 1$ is referred to in the remainder of this section as the "large-signal case," as compared with the "small-signal case" of Sec. 9·2.

An example of the type of velocity modulation produced for $V/V_0 > 1$ is shown in Fig. 9·12, which shows the velocity modulation resulting when $V/V_0 = \frac{4}{3}$, $M = 1$. The deviation of the velocity from an even approximately sinusoidal dependence on time is obvious; furthermore, during nearly a quarter of a cycle electrons are turned back at the input gap and so do not reach the drift space at all. The term "velocity modulation," therefore, is no longer completely descriptive of the input-gap process.

The corresponding effect on transit time is shown in Fig. 9·13. Here $t_2$, the time of arrival at some point (for example, the output gap) is shown as a function of time of departure from the input gap for a field-free drift space with a d-c transit angle of $\theta_0 = 6$ radians. The values of $X = MV\theta_0/2V_0$ with which the curves are labeled, namely 0.5, 1, 2, and 4, are similar to the values of $X$ for the analogous curves of Fig. 9·3; the curve for $X = 4$ corresponds to the $(V/V_0 = \frac{4}{3})$ velocity modulation shown in Fig. 9·12, and both figures show the period during which no electrons penetrate the gap.

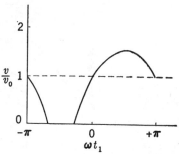

FIG. 9·12.—Dependence of relative electron velocity $v/v_0$ on time of passage $t_1$ through an r-f gap with gap voltage $\frac{4}{3}V_0 \sin \omega t_1$; $M = 1$.

The bunched-beam-current waveform is readily obtained from Fig. 9·13 as discussed in Sec. 9·2, and is shown in Fig. 9·14. The curves of Fig. 9·14 should be compared with those of Fig. 9·4, which correspond to similar values of $X$ in the small-signal case.

It is apparent that in Fig. 9·14 the most marked effects of a large $MV/V_0$ occur for $X = 2$ and $X = 4$. At $X = 2$, the intensity in the earliest-arriving peak has been somewhat enhanced, whereas the latter one has been greatly diminished. This effect corresponds to the difference in the breadth of the corresponding maxima and minima ("points of stationary phase") in Fig. 9·13; the smaller the value of $d^2t_2/dt_1^2$ at a point of stationary phase, the more intense is the corresponding infinite peak of $i$. The trend shown for $X = 2$ in Fig. 9·14 has its logical conclusion for $X = 4$; here, with $V/V_0 > 1$, there is only one current peak per cycle.

It may be recalled that, in the discussion of small-signal bunching in Sec. 9·2, it is pointed out that the alternating behavior of any given r-f component of $i$ as a function of $X$ (shown in Fig. 9·5) is caused by the interference of the two infinite peaks, which separate in time as $X$

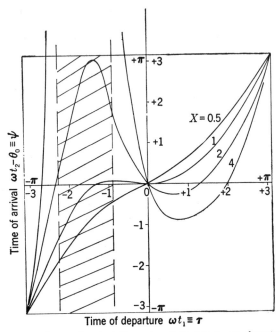

FIG. 9·13.—Dependence of arrival time at output gap, $t_2$, on departure time from input gap, $t_1$. Cross-hatched area represents interval of $t_1$ during which no electrons pass through input gap; $\theta_0 = 6$ radians.

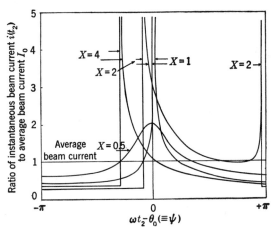

FIG. 9·14.—Time dependence of instantaneous bunched beam current for various values of bunching parameter $X$; field-free drift space, $\theta_0 = 6$ radians, hence large bunching voltage. Derived from Fig. 9·13.

increases and alternately reinforce and cancel each other as their phase difference increases at the harmonic in question. It is apparent from Fig. 9·14 that in the present large-signal case these peaks are no longer equal in amplitude, with the result that this interference between peaks cannot give rise to zeros in the absolute value of $i_m$; furthermore, when $V/V_0 > 1$ and $M \approx 1$, there is no interference at all because there is only a single peak, and $|i_m|$ is then a very smooth function of $X$ determined principally by the relation between $t_1$ and $t_2$ near the point of stationary phase in Fig. 9·13.

It turns out that the $t_2$ − vs − $t_1$ diagrams for $X > 1$ in Figs. 9·14 and 9·3 may, for purposes of calculating current waveforms and r-f components

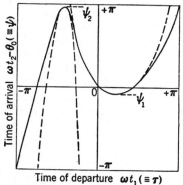

FIG. 9·15.—Representation of the $(X = 2)t_2$ − vs − $t_1$ diagram of Fig. 9·13 by two equivalent parabolas (indicated by broken curves); $\theta_0 = 6$ radians.

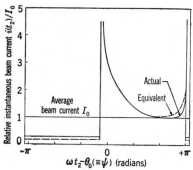

FIG. 9·16.—Waveform of bunched beam current as produced by "actual" (solid curve) and "equivalent" (broken curve) $t_2$ − vs − $t_1$ diagrams of Fig. 9·15.

of bunched beam current, be represented by two parabolas that coincide with the $t_2$ − vs − $t_1$ curves at the points of stationary phase. The "actual" and the "equivalent" $t_2$ − vs − $t_1$ diagrams for the large-signal $(X = 2)$ case are shown in Fig. 9·15; the "actual" diagram is the same as that shown in Fig. 9·13. In Fig. 9·16 are shown the corresponding current wave-forms. It is seen that the correspondence of the time dependence of $i(t)$ is close; the principal difference between the two curves, the addition of a d-c component, is irrelevant for the present purposes.

**9·7. Analytical Discussion of Bunching by a Gap Voltage Comparable to Beam Voltage.**—Thus it seems, from the results shown in Fig. 9.16, that an analytical deduction of the properties of the bunched beam current from the behavior in the immediate vicinity of the points of stationary phase holds some promise. Such a process has the advantage that, for the determination of $i_m$, only the points of stationary phase in Fig. 9·15 and the second derivatives (shape of the equivalent parabolas) at these points need be known. This analysis will now be carried out, and the degree of validity of the results will be checked by application to the small-signal case for which the values of $i_m$ are already known from Sec. 9·2.

To avoid cumbersome expression, the following notation is introduced:

$$\omega t_1 \equiv \tau \qquad \omega t_2 - \theta_0 \equiv \psi. \tag{39}$$

The points of stationary phase ($d\psi/d\tau = 0$) will be labeled $\psi_1$, $\psi_2$; the corresponding values of the second derivative $\psi'' = d^2\psi/d\tau^2$ are $\psi_1''$ and $\psi_2''$; $\psi_1$ and $\psi_2'' < 0$, $\psi_2$ and $\psi_1'' > 0$. Then the two parabolas in the equivalent $t_2 - \text{vs} - t_1$ (or $\psi - \text{vs} - \tau$) diagram are given by

$$\psi = \psi_1 + \left(\frac{\psi_1''}{2}\right)(\tau - \tau_1)^2$$

$$\psi = \psi_2 + \left(\frac{\psi_2''}{2}\right)(\tau - \tau_2)^2,$$

and for $M \approx 1$ and $V > V_0$ there will be only one parabola, the first of the two above.

By Eq. (8), the $m^{\text{th}}$ harmonic of the bunched beam current is, in this notation,

$$
\begin{aligned}
i_m &= \frac{I_0}{\pi} \int_{-\pi}^{\pi} e^{-jm(\psi+\theta_0)} \, d\tau \\
&= \frac{I_0}{\pi} e^{-jm\theta_0} \left[ e^{-jm\psi_1} \int_{-\pi}^{\pi} e^{-j\frac{m\psi_1''}{2}(\tau-\tau_1)^2} \, d\tau + e^{-jm\psi_2} \int_{-\pi}^{\pi} e^{-jm\frac{\psi_2''}{2}(\tau-\tau_2)^2} \, d\tau \right].
\end{aligned}
$$

The largest part of these integrals comes from the regions $\tau - \tau_1 \approx 0$ and $\tau - \tau_2 \approx 0$; hence when $|m\psi''| \gg 1$, the limits of integration may be changed to $\pm \infty$ without much error. When the limits are changed, and the variable altered to simplify the exponentials, and remembering that $\psi_1'' > 0$, $\psi_2'' < 0$, the above integrals become

$$
\begin{aligned}
i_m &= \frac{I_0}{\pi} e^{-jm\theta_0} \left[ e^{-jm\psi_1} \sqrt{\frac{2}{m\psi_1''}} \int_{-\infty}^{\infty} e^{-jx^2} \, dx + e^{-jm\psi_2} \sqrt{\frac{2}{-m\psi_2''}} \int_{-\infty}^{\infty} e^{jx^2} \, dx \right] \\
&= I_0 e^{-jm\theta_0} \sqrt{\frac{2}{\pi m}} \left[ \frac{1}{\sqrt{\psi_1''}} e^{-j\left(m\psi_1 + \frac{\pi}{4}\right)} + \frac{1}{\sqrt{-\psi_2''}} e^{-j\left(m\psi_2 - \frac{\pi}{4}\right)} \right]. \tag{40}
\end{aligned}
$$

In obtaining this equation, use is made of the definite integral

$$\int_{-\infty}^{\infty} e^{jx^2} \, dx = \sqrt{\pi} \, e^{j\pi/4}.$$

There is an additional limitation on Eq. (40) in the assumption that $X$ is large enough so that the $t_2 - \text{vs} - t_1$ diagram may be represented by the two-parabola equivalent. In the small-signal case for $X = 1$ (and in the large-signal case, for some value of $X$ slightly less than unity) there is only one point of stationary phase, and at this point $\psi' = \psi'' = 0$; the dependence of $\psi$ on $\tau$ is essentially cubic and the basis of Eq. (40) is invalid, as witness the fact that, when $\psi'' = 0$, Eq. (40) has $i_m = \infty$. This fact, as well as the $|m\psi''| \gg 1$ condition, will increase the validity of Eq. (40) as $X$ exceeds unity. The point at which Eq. (40) becomes valid is best found by applying this equation to the small-signal case, for which the exact value of $i_m$ is already known by Sec. 9·2.

In the small-signal case, $\psi_2 = -\psi_1$ and $\psi_2'' = -\psi_1''$, and Eq. (40) reduces to

$$i_m = I_0 e^{-jm\theta_0} \frac{2^{3/2}}{\sqrt{\pi m \psi_1''}} \cos\left(m\psi_1 + \frac{\pi}{4}\right). \tag{41}$$

This equation may be compared with the exact small-signal result,

$$i_m = 2I_0 J_m(mX) e^{-jm\theta_0}. \tag{Eq. (9)}$$

In order to carry out the comparison, the small-signal dependence of $\psi_1$ and $\psi_1''$ on $X$ must be known. By Eqs. (3) and (39), here

$$\psi = \tau - X \sin\tau,$$
$$\psi_1 = \cos^{-1}\left(\frac{1}{X}\right) - \sqrt{X^2 - 1}, \tag{42}$$
$$\psi_1'' = \sqrt{X^2 - 1}.$$

It is apparent from Eqs. (41) and (42) that, at the first maximum of the approximate $i_m$ given by Eq. (41), $m\psi_1 + \pi/4 \approx 0$. This is an approximate relation because the increase of $\psi_1''$ with $X$ has been ignored; a more closely figured maximum would have a value of $m\psi_1 + \pi/4$ somewhat less than zero. From Eq. (42) the values of $X$ and $\psi_2''$ corresponding to $m\psi_1 + \pi/4 = 0$ may be determined. The results of this process are given in Table 9·3 below. In this table $X_m$ represents the value of $X$ that maximizes $i_m$. The values of $X_m$ corresponding to the exact and approximate Eqs. (9) and (41) are given, as are also the

TABLE 9·3.—COMPARISON OF VALUES OF MAXIMUM $i_m$ AND CORRESPONDING VALUE OF BUNCHING PARAMETER, $X_m$, AS GIVEN FOR THE SMALL-SIGNAL CASE BY THE EXACT AND APPROXIMATE EQS. (9) AND (41)

| $m$ | $m\psi_1''$ | $X_m$ approx. | $X_m$ exact | Approx. max. $\|i_m\|/2I_0$ | Exact max. $\|i_m\|/2I_0$ |
|---|---|---|---|---|---|
| 1 | 1.6 | 2.15 | 1.84 | 0.58 | 0.58 |
| 3 | 3.0 | 1.47 | 1.40 | 0.44 | 0.43 |
| 10 | 6.5 | 1.19 | 1.18 | 0.31 | 0.30 |

corresponding maximum values of $i_m$. Also, for reference, $m\psi_1''$ is shown.

It appears from this table that, by the time the first maximum of $i_m$ has been reached, Eq. (41) is a very good approximation, regardless of whether $m\psi''$ is much larger than unity. The error in the approximate value of $X_m$ is due in large part to the roughness of the location of the maximum in Eq. (41), as already noted. A procedure similar to the above, carried out for the small-signal case with $X = 1$ and with

$$\psi = \frac{\psi_1''' \tau^3}{6},$$

gives results that are as valid at $X = 1$ as are the above results for $X \geqq X_m$.

The only results that are usually desired, however, are the value of the first maximum of $|i_m|$ and the general functional dependence of $|i_m|$ thereafter; for this, Eq. (40) thus seems to be satisfactory. By Eq. (40),

$$\sqrt{2\pi m} \frac{|i_m|}{2I_0} = \sqrt{\frac{1}{\psi_1''} - \frac{1}{\psi_2''} - \frac{2 \sin m(\psi_1 - \psi_2)}{\sqrt{-\psi_1'' \psi_2''}}}. \tag{43}$$

Thus as $X$ and $\psi_2 - \psi_1$ increase, $|i_m|/I_0$ oscillates between two limits:

$$\left( \frac{1}{\sqrt{\psi_1''}} - \frac{1}{\sqrt{-\psi_2''}} \right) \leqq \sqrt{2\pi m} \frac{|i_m|}{2I_0} \leqq \left( \frac{1}{\sqrt{\psi_1''}} + \frac{1}{\sqrt{-\psi_2''}} \right). \tag{44}$$

By Eq. (43), $|i_m|$ is equal to its upper limit when

$$\sin m(\psi_2 - \psi_1) = 1. \tag{45}$$

The corresponding maximum of $|i_m|$ is about the same as this upper limit but occurs at a slightly smaller value of $X$, just as for the small-signal case discussed in the preceding paragraph.

The extension to the case $M \approx 1$ and $V > V_0$, when there is only one point of stationary phase, is simple. Thus,

$$\frac{|i_m|}{I_0} = \sqrt{\frac{2}{\pi m \psi_1''}}, \qquad V > V_0. \tag{46}$$

Evaluation of $|i_m|$ as given by Eqs. (44), (45), and (46) follows the same procedure as with the small-signal case. In the present large-signal case, the relation between $\psi$ and $\tau$ for a field-free drift space is

$$\psi = \tau + \theta_0 \left[ \frac{1}{\sqrt{1 + (MV/V_0) \sin \tau}} - 1 \right]. \tag{47}$$

For the case of a reflex klystron with a linear reflecting field,

$$\psi = \tau + \theta_0 \left[ \sqrt{1 + \left( \frac{MV}{V_0} \right) \sin \tau} - 1 \right]; \tag{48}$$

this latter case, which is not discussed here, may be handled just as the field-free case. Equation (47) and similar equations for $\psi'$, $\psi''$ may be treated graphically to give, as functions of $X$ for various values of $\theta_0$, the values of $\psi_1''$ and $\psi_2''$ and the corresponding limits to $|i_m|$. Similarly, a graphical determination of the dependence of $\psi_1$ and $\psi_2$ on $X$ and $\theta_0$ allows the determination from Eq. (45) of the values of $X$ at which $|i_m|$ is equal to its upper limit, as well as the corresponding approximately maximum values of $|i_m|$.

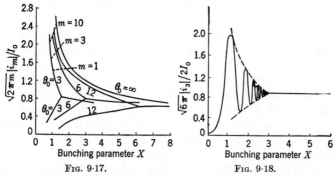

FIG. 9·17.

FIG. 9·18.

FIG. 9·17.—Upper and lower limits of $|i_m|$, $m$th harmonic of bunched beam current, as function of bunching parameter $X$ for various values of $\theta_0$. For $MV/V_0 = 2X/\theta_0 > 1$, upper and lower limits coalesce to a single value. Dotted lines are loci of the first maxima of $|i_m|$ for various values of harmonic order $m$.

FIG. 9·18.—Dependence of third harmonic of bunched beam current, $i_3$, on bunching parameter $X$ when $\theta_0 = 6$ radians.

The details of this procedure are not given here, but Fig. 9·17 shows, for $\theta_0 = 3$, 6, 12, and $\infty$, the dependence on $X$ of the upper and lower limits to $\sqrt{2\pi m}\, |i_m|/2I_0$ for $MV/V_0 < 1$ and the single value of

$$\sqrt{2\pi m}\, \frac{|i_m|}{I_0}$$

for $V/V_0 > 1$. The case $\theta_0 = \infty$ corresponds to the small-signal case discussed earlier; for $\theta_0 = \infty$ the lower limit to $|i_m|$ is zero, as already noted. The light dotted lines represent, for different values of $m$, the locus of points at which the value of $|i_m|$ first equals the upper limiting value; these points therefore indicate the approximate locations and heights of the first maximum.

It is apparent that many of the combinations of $X$ and $\theta_0$ shown in Fig. 9·17 correspond to values of $MV/V_0$ for which the procedures of Secs. 9·2 and 9·4 are applicable; this correspondence provides a convenient connecting link between the two treatments.

In Fig. 9·18 is sketched, from Fig. 9·17, the approximate dependence of $|i_m|/2I_0$ on $X$ for $\theta_0 = 6$, $m = 3$. The increasing rapidity of the variation of $|i_m|$ as the point ($X = 1·5$, $MV/V_0 = 1$) is approached is caused by the corresponding rapid upward motion of the first point of stationary phase in Fig. 9·13.

Some interesting points of general structure are apparent in Fig. 9·17. For example, in reducing $\theta_0$ from $\infty$ to 3 radians, the value of the bunching parameter required to produce "optimum bunching" (in the sense of making the graph of $|i_m|$ tangent to its upper limit) is reduced by approximately 50 per cent for $m = 1$ and 30 per cent for $m = 10$. In later applications it may be seen that this reduction is no great advantage because the diminished value of $X$ for optimum bunching is bought at the expense of an increase in $MV/V_0$. As a matter of fact, in reflex oscillators (in which phenomena of the same type occur, although Fig. 9·17 refers to a field-free drift space) this effect is very detrimental to oscillator efficiency.

On the other hand, Fig. 9·17 shows that the maximum amplitude of the various harmonics decreases only slightly as $\theta_0$ decreases from the small-signal value of infinity; the decrease in the actual maxima is probably even less, as these maxima lie above and to the left of the points of tangency whose locus is graphed in Fig. 9·17.

Probably the most important feature of Figs. 9·17 and 9·18 is the practically complete lack of dependence of $|i_m|$ on $X$, once $V > V_0$. This independence has important applications in frequency multipliers, since it has the effect that in an overdriven multiplier with small $\theta_0$ the output is practically independent of r-f input over wide ranges of the latter; this point is discussed in detail in Chap. 11.

**9·8. Cascade Bunching.**—The preceding sections have been concerned with the bunching action that follows passage of an electron beam through a single velocity-modulating r-f gap. Two successive transits of a beam through an r-f gap or gaps produce velocity modulation and bunching of the type known as "cascade bunching."[1] One example of cascade bunching is provided by the cascade amplifier (see Chap. 10), in which the beam passes through three resonators in succession; the input signal is applied to the first gap and the output taken from the last gap. Another example occurs in the reflex klystron (see Chap. 14). Here the beam passes once through a gap and is reflected for a second passage; part of the beam is often reflected from the cathode region for a third passage. In the first of these examples the cascade action is intentional and beneficial; in the second it is unintentional and usually detrimental. The basic processes are identical, however, and it is these basic processes with which this section is concerned.

All the complications of Secs. 9·3 through 9·7 apply as much to

---

[1] E. Feenberg, "Small Signal Theory for Multiple Resonator Klystron Amplifier," Sperry Gyroscope Co. Report 5221-106, July 14, 1943; see also "Theory of Cascade Bunching," Sperry Gyroscope Co. Report 5221-143, Aug. 22, 1945.

cascade bunching as to single-gap bunching, but the most profitable procedure for this section is to omit discussion of these higher-order effects and to emphasize those features that are characteristic of the cascade process per se.   The general assumptions of Sec. 9·2 are therefore retained—that is, no space-charge debunching, no gap-transit effects (except for the usual beam-coupling coefficient, $M$), no higher-order terms in $V/V_0$.  The generalized form of the bunching parameter $X$ (Sec. 9·4) may be retained at no cost; therefore, the results of the present section are applicable to any drift space, as long as the drift-space coefficients $a_n$ are not sufficiently abnormal to emphasize higher-order terms in $V/V_0$.

Given the above premises, the notation to be used is a simple generalization of that of Sec. 9·2.   For the complex r-f voltages,

$$V_1 = -jV \equiv -j\alpha_1 V_0 \qquad (49a)$$
$$V_2 \equiv -\alpha_2 V_0 e^{j(-\theta_{01}+\beta)} \qquad (49b)$$

Thus the voltage notation has been generalized so that the first- and second-gap real r-f voltage amplitudes are $\alpha_1 V_0$ and $\alpha_2 V_0$.  In the real (as opposed to complex) notation, the first-gap and second-gap time-dependent r-f voltages are thus $\mathrm{Re}\ (V_1 e^{j\omega t_1}) = \alpha_1 V_0\ \sin \omega t_1$ and $\mathrm{Re}\ (V_2 e^{j\omega t_2}) = -\alpha_2 V_0 \cos (\omega t_2 - \theta_{01} + \beta)$ respectively.   The phase of the second-gap r-f voltage with respect to the first, as specified by the phase factor $\beta$, is kept arbitrary in this section; in the later applications of the results, $\beta$ is determined by the operating conditions.   The somewhat awkward appearance of the phase of the second-gap r-f voltage is chosen for convenience in these later applications.   It may be noted that the center of a bunch (for example, the electron for which $\omega t_1 = 0$) arrives at the second gap when the r-f voltage at the latter has the value $-\alpha_2 V_0 \cos \beta$; thus $\beta = 0$ is the condition for maximum extraction of energy from the beam by the second resonator.   But this is simply a quick look behind the scenes.   As already noted, this section is concerned not with the origin of the second-gap r-f voltage (that is, with the dependence of $\alpha_2$ on $\beta$), but only with the results of its existence; and these results may be deduced without reference to the origin of the second-gap voltage.

The remainder of the new notation to be used in this section is as follows:

$X_{13}$: value that bunching parameter would have at the third gap if there were only first-gap modulation.

$i_{12}$, $i_{13}$: fundamental r-f component of the bunched-beam current at the second and third gaps.  (Note that the subscript 1 refers not to the first gap but to the fundamental component.)

$\theta_{0n}$, $(d\theta/dV_e)_{0n}$, $M_n$ with $n = 1$, $2$: the values of $\theta_0$, $(d\theta/dV_e)_0$, and $M$ for the first and second gap or the drift space following the first and second gaps, as the case may be.

$X_{12}$: bunching parameter at the second gap, which is due to velocity modulation at the first gap; $X_{12} \equiv -M_1\alpha_1 V_0(d\theta/dV_e)_{01}$.

$X_{23}$: bunching parameter at the third gap in the presence of only second-gap modulation; $X_{23} \equiv -M_2\alpha_2 V_0(d\theta/dV_c)_{02}$.

The first step in the development is now the usual one of investigating the electron kinematics. The time of arrival at the second gap, $t_2$, is given by

$$\omega t_2 = \omega t_1 + \theta_{01} - X_{12} \sin \omega t_1. \tag{50}$$

On leaving the second gap the energy of the electron in electron volts, $V_e$, is the energy on entering the gap, $V_0(1 + M_1\alpha_1 \sin \omega t_1)$, plus the modification of $V_e$ in the second-gap passage; thus

$$V_e = V_0[1 + M_1\alpha_1 \sin \omega t_1 - M_2\alpha_2 \cos (\omega t_2 - \theta_{01} + \beta)]. \tag{51}$$

The time of arrival, $t_3$, at the point where the r-f current is to be evaluated —hereafter referred to as the third gap—is then given by

$$\omega t_3 = \omega t_2 + \theta_{02} + V_0\left(\frac{d\theta}{dV_e}\right)_{02} [M_1\alpha_1 \sin \omega t_1 - M_2\alpha_2 \cos (\omega t_2 - \theta_{01} + \beta)]$$
$$= \omega t_1 + \theta_{01} + \theta_{02} - X_{13} \sin \omega t_1 + X_{23} \cos (\omega t_2 - \theta_{01} + \beta). \tag{52}$$

So far this discussion has involved only the usual restrictions of zero-order theory that allow the bunching parameter to have any value as long as the $\alpha$'s are small compared with unity. To be useful in evaluating the final r-f current, however, Eq. (52) must be altered so that $\omega t_1$ appears explicitly throughout, instead of implicitly in the $\omega t_2$ term. If the additional restriction

$$X_{12} < 0.4 \tag{53}$$

is made, the alteration in Eq. (52) is much simplified. The change causes little inconvenience in discussing later applications of cascade bunching, and since it makes $X_{12}^2/2 < 0.1$ it makes quite accurate the approximation

$$\cos (\omega t_2 - \theta_{01} + \beta) \approx \cos (\omega t_1 + \beta) + X_{12} \sin \omega t_1 \sin (\omega t_1 + \beta).$$

Thus Eq. (52) becomes

$$\omega t_3 = \omega t_1 + \theta_{01} + \theta_{02} - X_{13} \sin \omega t_1 + X_{23} \cos (\omega t_1 + \beta)$$
$$+ X_{23}X_{12} \sin \omega t_1 \sin (\omega t_1 + \beta). \tag{54}$$

Equation (54) is the final kinematical equation that is used in the remainder of this section to evaluate the r-f current under various circumstances.

In many practical cases the last term in Eq. (54) may be neglected, for example, where $X_{12}$ is much smaller than $X_{13}$ or $X_{23}$, both of which may be of the same order and greater than unity; this happens when $\theta_{01} \ll \theta_{02}$ as with multiple transits in the usual reflex klystron. The last term in Eq. (54) may also be neglected when $X_{12}$ and $X_{13}$ are of the same order but are no greater than $X_{23}$, with $|X_{23}| \ll 1$ in turn; this corresponds to the situation in any cascade amplifier operating at low signal level.

In any such situation where the approximation of neglecting $X_{12}X_{23}$ in Eq. (54) may be made, the equation may be written in an easily handled form by combining the two remaining sinusoidal terms into one. A little trigonometric manipulation shows that

$$-X_{13} \sin \omega t_1 + X_{23} \cos (\omega t_1 + \beta) = -X' \sin (\omega t_1 + \theta') \qquad (55)$$

where

$$X' e^{j\theta'} \equiv X_{13} - jX_{23}e^{j\beta}; \qquad X' \text{ real.} \qquad (56)$$

Thus Eq. (54) becomes

$$\omega t_3 = (\omega t_1 + \theta') + \theta_{01} + \theta_{02} - \theta' - X' \sin (\omega t_1 + \theta'). \qquad (57)$$

By comparison with Eqs. (3c) and (9) it is apparent that the fundamental r-f component of the bunched beam current is given by

$$i_1 = 2I_0 e^{-j(\theta_{01}+\theta_{02}-\theta')} J_1(X'). \qquad (58)$$

Thus, to the degree of approximation with which these last two paragraphs have been concerned, the bunching is represented by an "effective bunching parameter" $X'$; the current waveform and the maximum value of the various r-f components of the bunched beam current are the same as in simple bunching. The significance of the effective bunching parameter may be realized more readily by noting that the respective r-f voltages momentarily glimpsed at the two gaps by an electron traveling at beam velocity are the real parts of the complex expressions,

$$-je^{j\omega t}(V_1 \text{ and } - jV_2 e^{j\beta}).$$

Thus, in using Eq. (56) to find $X'$ as a geometrical sum of the bunching parameters $X_{13}$ and $X_{23}$, the phases associated with $X_{13}$ and $X_{23}$ are simply the corresponding phases of bunching produced by the first and second gaps. As would be expected, it appears from Eq. (58) that the phase of the bunching differs by the term $-\theta'$ from that which would obtain in the presence of first-gap velocity modulation alone.

Because $V_2$, and hence $X_{23}$, are found to be functions of $\beta$ in the practical cases to be discussed later, it is clear that $X'$ and $\theta'$ cannot be further specified without the knowledge of this functional relation which must wait for the specific situations in later chapters. There are, of course, cases in which the $X_{12}X_{23}$ term in Eq. (54) must not be neglected. One of the most prominent of such instances is the cascade amplifier operated with sufficient drive to produce optimum bunching at the third gap; here $X_{23} \approx 2$, and $X_{12}$ and $X_{13}$ are comparable to each other. The $X_{12}X_{23}$ term describes the fact that the second gap has an intensity-modulated electron beam to work on; as a result of this fact, some parts of the bunch are more heavily weighted than others. The results of this effect are rather surprising, and arise from the fact that $\sin \omega t_1$ $\sin (\omega t_1 + \beta)$ is an essentially second-harmonic term. Thus, making use of the definition of $X'$ and $\theta'$ in Eqs. (55) and (56), Eq. (54) may be rewritten

$$\omega t_3 = \omega t_1 + \theta_{01} + \theta_{02} + \frac{X_{12}X_{23}}{2} \cos \beta - X' \sin (\omega t_1 + \theta')$$

$$+ \frac{X_{12}X_{23}}{2} \sin \left( 2\omega t_1 + \beta - \frac{\pi}{2} \right). \quad (59)$$

If, by analogy with Eq. (36), a new quantity $\gamma$ is defined by the equation

$$\gamma \equiv \frac{X_{12}X_{23}}{2X'}, \quad (60)$$

then Eq. (59) becomes

$$\omega t_3 = \omega t_1 + \theta_{01} + \theta_{02} + \frac{X_{12}X_{23}}{2} \cos \beta - X' \left[ \sin (\omega t_1 + \theta') \right.$$

$$\left. - \gamma \sin \left( 2\omega t_1 + \beta - \frac{\pi}{2} \right) \right]. \quad (61)$$

This equation is very similar to Eq. (36); the only important difference is the inequality in Eq. (61) of the phases of the first- and second-harmonic terms.

In the discussion of Eq. (36) in the section on finite gap-transit times it was shown that the presence of a second-harmonic term in the kinematical equation may result in as much as a 28 per cent increase in $i_1$; in the notation of Eq. (61) this would occur when $X' = 2$, $\gamma = 0.4$, $\theta' = \beta - \frac{\pi}{2}$. In discussing Eq. (36) there was no occasion to consider what might happen if the first- and second-harmonic terms were out of phase, as they are in Eq. (61). By substituting the arrival time of Eq. (61) in the basic Eq. (8), and carrying out some manipulation, it may be shown that for a given $X'$ and $\gamma$, $|i_1|$ is always a maximum when $\theta' = \beta - \frac{\pi}{2}$; the condition $X' = 2$, $\gamma = 0.4$, $\theta' = \beta - \frac{\pi}{2}$, therefore, determines an absolute maximum of $|i_1|$ for a kinematical situation described by Eq. (61). The same calculation just referred to shows that, in the neighborhood of this absolute maximum, $|i_1|$ is proportional to

$$\cos \frac{1}{2}\left(\theta' - \beta + \frac{\pi}{2}\right).$$

It is interesting to note that the origins of the second-harmonic terms in Eqs. (36) and (61) are rather different—the former case represents the effect of a finite gap-transit angle in distorting velocity modulation, and the present case represents the cooperative effect of the two separated gaps, but the end result is the same.

As a second point, it should be noted that if either or both of the drift spaces are reflector-like (negative bunching parameter) in cascade bunching, then the value of $\gamma$ given by Eq. (60) may be negative. A parabolic extrapolation of the curves in Fig. 9·5 (analytically justified) shows that a negative $\gamma$ may make a very sizable reduction in $i_1$.

The general theory of cascade bunching has been developed in the second item of the reference at the beginning of the section; in this work the effects of harmonic voltages in the second gap have been considered, and the harmonic content of the bunched beam has been evaluated in detail.

**9·9. Bunching in the Presence of Harmonic Phase and Amplitude Modulation.**—In the discussion of reflex-klystron modulation in Chap. 16, the question is considered of what happens when the beam current or the reflection time is subjected to a small degree of modulation at a frequency near one of the harmonics of the fundamental frequency of velocity modulation. It is shown in that chapter that this question may be reduced to the simpler one of what happens when this additional modulation is at an exact harmonic of the fundamental frequency.

Such a modulation is exactly like the type that is discussed in Secs. 9·5 and 9·8; in these sections it is noted that when velocity modulation is produced by passage through a single r-f gap with a finite transit angle, or when it is produced by passage through two r-f gaps in succession, then the resultant velocity modulation possesses harmonic components.

In Secs. 9·5 and 9·8, this fact is of interest because with large r-f voltage this "equivalent harmonic modulation" is able to cause an increase in the maximum value of $|i_1|/I_0$ from 1.16 to 1.48. A detailed proof of this last statement is not given in Secs. 9·5 and 9·8, nor will it be given here, for, in the small-signal modulation theory to which the results of the present section will be applied, it is not necessary to go into the lengthy details required to prove the relations that were used for the large-signal case. Nevertheless, the procedure used here indicates the method that would be followed in the large-signal case.

The basic relation to be used is the general bunching relation given in Eq. (8). This relation will be specialized to give the fundamental component of the bunched beam current, the only component to be investigated here; it will be generalized to include the possibility of time variation of the initial beam current. This equation then becomes

$$\pi i_1 = \int_{-\pi}^{\pi} I_0(t_1)e^{-j\omega t_2}d(\omega t_1). \qquad (62)$$

The simple transit-time relation, Eq. (3c), will be rewritten to conform to the customary, rather than the consistent, sign convention for the bunching parameter in a reflex klystron—that is, $X$ will be considered inherently positive; this question of sign is discussed in Sec. 9·4. Thus

$$\omega t_2 = \omega t_1 + \theta + X \sin \omega t_1. \qquad (63)$$

*Transit-time Modulation at a Harmonic Frequency.*—Suppose that the drift-space transit angle, written now as $\theta$, is given a slight modulation at the frequency $n\omega$. Denoting by $m$ the amplitude of the modulation (as distinct from the previous use of $m$ to indicate harmonic order), and denoting by $\gamma$ an arbitrary phase angle (as distinct from the usage of Secs. 9·5 and 9·8), the modulation of $\theta$ may be expressed as follows:

$$\theta = \theta_0 [1 + m \cos (n\omega t_1 + \gamma)]. \qquad (64)$$

Since only small-signal modulation theory is in question, $m$ is assumed to be small compared with unity. Equation (64) is in itself somewhat of an idealization because it assumes a modulation such that the value of $\theta$ for a given electron depends only on its time of passage through the input r-f gap. This assumption is strictly valid only for a phase modulation produced simply by an additional velocity modulation at the frequency $n\omega$.

Substituting Eqs. (63) and (64) into Eq. (62) and carrying out the Bessel-function expansion of the exponential terms, there results a complicated expression that may be greatly simplified by use of the assumption $m \ll 1$; the final result is

$$i_1 = -2I_0 e^{-j\theta_0}\left\{J_1(X) + \left(\frac{jm\theta_0}{2}\right)[e^{j\gamma}(-1)^{n+1}J_{n+1}(X) + e^{-j\gamma}J_{n-1}(X)]\right\}. \qquad (65)$$

*Current Modulation.*—Let the time dependence of the beam current $I_0(t_1)$ in Eq. (62) be represented by

$$I_0(t_1) = I_{00}[1 + m \cos (n\omega t_1 + \gamma)], \qquad (66)$$

corresponding to a modulation of $I_0$ at the harmonic $n\omega$. Since the Bessel-function expansion of the integral in Eq. (62) is simpler than in the previously discussed case, it is not necessary to assume $m \ll 1$ for simplification, and so the final result holds true for any degree of current modulation, that is,

$$i_1 = -2I_{00}e^{-i\theta_0} \left\{ J_1(X) - \frac{m}{2} \left[ e^{i\gamma}J_{n-1}(X) + e^{-i\gamma}(-1)^{n+1}J_{n+1}(X) \right] \right\}. \quad (67)$$

It is to be recalled that this equation has been derived for future use in connection with reflex klystrons; because the conventional, rather than the consistent, sign convention for $X$ has been used in its derivation, the sign of $X$ in Eqs. (65) and (67) must be reversed if these equations are applied to klystrons with field-free drift space.

# CHAPTER 10

## AMPLIFIER KLYSTRONS

### By D. R. Hamilton

**10·1. Multiresonator Klystron Types.**—The preceding chapter has been concerned solely with the way in which velocity modulation and bunching produce beam current intensity modulation by the time the electron beam is ready to pass through the r-f interaction gap of the output resonator. The effects of the resultant driving of the output circuit in a number of klystron types that may be classified as "multiresonator" klystrons are considered in the present chapter and in the following chapter. The principal feature that these tubes have in common is a drift space that is usually field-free. This characteristic distinguishes them from the reflex klystrons that are discussed in the remaining chapters of the book. The proportionate number of chapters devoted to the discussion of multiresonator klystrons and of reflex klystrons is a rough indication of the relative utilization of these klystron types at the present time.

The multiresonator klystrons are discussed first because they are naturally associated with the basic form of klystron—the amplifier. The klystron amplifier is operated simply by supplying r-f power to the input resonator and abstracting a larger amount of r-f power from the bunched beam at the output resonator; normally no regenerative feedback is used. The frequency multiplier is an analogous device except that the output circuit is tuned to a harmonic of the input frequency, and therefore is driven by the beam at this harmonic frequency. An obvious adaptation of the amplifier is the two-resonator klystron oscillator in which power from the output circuit is returned to the input circuit in the proper phase for maintaining self-sustaining oscillations.

Although d-c fields may appear in the drift space of multiresonator klystrons without reflecting electrons, they are usually mechanically inconvenient; hence, for all further discussion in this chapter, an entirely field-free drift space is assumed. Klystron amplifiers may be conveniently divided into three categories. The simplest form of amplifier is the two-resonator single-stage type, the characteristics of which depend somewhat on its use. In general, when it is used to amplify small signals there is high-gain small-signal operation ($X \ll 1$), and noise considerations are important; when used to generate large power outputs it operates at optimum bunching ($X \approx 2$), and both gain and noise are comparatively irrelevant. These two categories of amplifier, which are termed "voltage amplifiers" and "power amplifiers" respectively, overlap to a considerable extent and the division is somewhat arbitrary. A third convenient category is the "cascade amplifier," so-called because it has three or more resonators and thus (as will shortly be seen in more detail) two or more stages of amplification. Such a klystron may be designed or used primarily as a "cascade voltage amplifier" or as a "cascade power amplifier"; in either case new operating characteristics are introduced by the cascade feature.

The properties of klystron amplifiers are discussed in the present chapter. Chapter 11 deals with frequency multipliers and two-resonator oscillators.

**10·2. General Voltage-amplifier Relations.**—A schematic diagram of the type 410R, a common two-resonator klystron amplifier, is shown in Fig. 10·1. An electron beam passes through the r-f gaps of two cavity-resonators in sequence; across the gap of the first cavity there is an r-f voltage, the "input signal," whose r-f power is supplied by an external source. The input-cavity gap voltage velocity-modulates the electron beam, which is thus, to some degree, bunched when it reaches the output gap. This intensity-modulated beam current acts as a driving current for the output cavity and delivers r-f power to the latter, just as in the microwave triode amplifier.

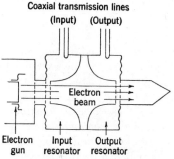

Fig. 10·1.—Schematic diagram of a typical (type 410R) two-resonator klystron amplifier.

*General Amplifier Gap-voltage Relations.*—The way in which an intensity-modulated electron beam drives the output cavity, whether in a klystron or in some other device, is discussed in detail in Chap. 3. There it is shown that if the shunt admittance of the output cavity plus load is $Y_2$, as measured at the gap at a frequency $\omega$, and if the component of the intensity-modulated beam at the frequency $\omega$ is $i(\omega)$, then the complex r-f voltage $V_2$ that is developed across the output gap at the frequency $\omega$ is given by the expression

$$V_2(\omega) = -M_2 \frac{i(\omega)}{Y_2(\omega)}. \tag{1}$$

Thus the driving current for the output circuit is simply $M_2 i(\omega)$. When Eq. (1) gives a value of $V_2$ large enough to turn electrons back at the second gap, Eq. (1) is no longer valid; this point is discussed in more detail in Sec. 10·6. In any case, this limitation on Eq. (1) does not arise in a voltage amplifier.

It is convenient to use an explicit form for the shunt admittance $Y_2$ in dealing with Eq. (1). For a loaded cavity resonator with resonant frequency, shunt conductance, and $Q$ of the cavity-plus-load combination given respectively by $\omega_2$, $G_2$, and $Q_2$, and with no other resonances near $\omega_2$, the shunt admittance is given by the expression

$$Y_2 = G_2\left[1 + jQ_2\left(\frac{\omega}{\omega_2} - \frac{\omega_2}{\omega}\right)\right] \approx G_2(1 + 2jQ_2\delta_2), \tag{2}$$

where

$$\delta_2 \equiv \frac{\omega}{\omega_2} - 1. \tag{3}$$

Here the shunt conductance $G_2$ may be written as

$$G_2 \equiv G_L + G_B + G_R; \qquad G_{BR} \equiv G_B + G_R, \tag{4}$$

where $G_L$, $G_B$, and $G_R$ represent, respectively, the contribution to the shunt conductance by the external load, by beam loading arising from the passage of the beam through the resonator, and by ohmic losses in the resonator. Equation (4) simply provides a notation for use in discussing these various contributions.

It is also convenient in applications of Eq. (1) to define an "electronic transfer admittance" or "electronic transadmittance" $Y_e$ as the ratio of output-gap driving current to input-gap voltage:

$$Y_e \equiv M_2\frac{i(\omega)}{V_1(\omega)}. \tag{5}$$

In terms of the electronic transfer admittance and the output-cavity shunt admittance, the "gap-voltage gain" or ratio of output- to input-gap voltages is given by

$$\frac{V_2}{V_1} = -\frac{Y_e}{Y_2} = -\frac{Y_e}{G_2(1 + 2jQ_2\delta_2)}. \tag{6}$$

(Note the change, in Eqs. (1) and (5), from the sign convention of Chap. 3.)

*General Amplifier Power Relations.*—The power $P_2$ delivered from the electron stream to the output resonator may be found either from the power required to sustain $V_2$ across $G_2$, $\frac{1}{2}|V_2|^2G_2$, or directly from the power delivered to $V_2$ by the driving current $M_2i$,

$$-\tfrac{1}{2}\mathrm{Re}(M_2i^*V_2) = -\tfrac{1}{2}\mathrm{Re}(Y_e^*V_1^*V_2).$$

Assuming the validity of Eq. (1), either procedure gives

$$P_2 = \frac{\frac{1}{2}|Y_eV_1|^2}{G_2(1 + 4Q_2^2\delta_2^2)}.$$  (7)

The "circuit efficiency" $\eta_l$, or fraction of $P_2$ that is dissipated in the external load $G_L$, is given by

$$\eta_l = \frac{G_L}{G_2};$$  (8)

hence the power $P_L$ delivered to this external load is $P_L = \eta_l P_2$, or

$$P_L = \frac{\frac{1}{2}|Y_eV_1|^2 G_L}{G_2^2(1 + 4Q_2^2\delta_2^2)}.$$  (9)

It may be observed from the relation between $G_2$ and $G_L$ in Eq. (4) that $G_L$ affects $P_L$ through the factor $G_L/(G_{BR} + G_L)^2$, which has its maximum value of $1/4G_{BR}$ when $G_L = G_{BR}$. Thus at this optimum load

$$P_L = \frac{|Y_eV_1|^2}{8G_{BR}(1 + Q_{BR}^2\delta_2^2)}.$$  (10)

Hence, at optimum load for an amplifier to which Eq. (1) applies, that is, when $G_L = G_{BR}$, half the power is delivered to the load and half to the internal power losses represented by $G_{BR}$. If $G_L$ is decreased from the optimum value, the amount of power abstracted from the beam is increased, and $V_2$ builds up to a higher value; but since the circuit efficiency $\eta_l$ decreases more rapidly than $P_2$ increases, the net value of $P_L$ decreases.

This matching of load to generator is not limited to klystrons; specific klystron properties have not yet been considered. In all subsequent discussions of voltage amplifiers it is assumed that the load is optimized— that is, that $G_L = G_{BR}$. Two later instances where this is not assumed are carefully noted. In power amplifiers there may be, as already noted, a situation where $|V_2|$ has an upper limit and is not given by Eq. (1); here $G_L = G_{BR}$ is not the optimum load. In oscillators, contrary to the tacit assumptions made above, $i$ depends on $V_2$; again, therefore, $G_L = G_{BR}$ is not necessarily the optimum load.

The input-signal power $P_1$ required to generate an input-gap voltage $V_1$ is given by

$$P_1 = \frac{1}{2}|V_1|^2 G_1.$$

Since the first cavity is ordinarily unloaded, $G_1$ is simply the value of $G_{BR}$ for the first cavity, for example, $G_{BR1}$. If the $G_{BR}$ of the output cavity is denoted by $G_{BR2}$, the final expression for the power gain is

$$\frac{P_L}{P_1} = \frac{|Y_e|^2}{4G_{BR1}G_{BR2}}.$$  (11)

Note the similarity between this equation and Eqs. (5·22) and (6·7).

**10·3. Two-resonator Voltage Amplifiers; Gain.** *Electronic Transadmittance in the Voltage-amplifier Klystron.*—All the foregoing relations hold true for any amplifier to which Eq. (1) applies. They may now be particularized to the voltage-amplifier klystron by use of the corresponding explicit expression for $Y_e$.

The expression for the fundamental component of the bunched beam current, which is derived in Sec. 9·2, is

$$i_1 = 2I_0 J_1(X)e^{-i\theta_0}. \tag{12}$$

This equation needs to be modified in two ways for application to the voltage amplifier. In the first place, since the discussion is concerned with weak signals ($X \ll 1$), $2J_1(X) \approx X$. In the second place, "debunching" may well be a predominant factor and should therefore be taken into consideration as soon as possible. As to this last point, it may be recalled from Sec. 9·3 and from Eqs. (13) and (21) of Sec. 9·3 that the leading terms in the reduction of the bunched beam current are $1 - X(hl)^2/12$ for transverse debunching, and $1 - (hl)^2/6$ for longitudinal debunching. Thus for weak signals the longitudinal debunching is the larger effect, and it contributes a factor $(\sin hl)/hl$ to $i_1$ and $Y_e$. (In the present chapter, $l$ denotes drift-tube length, as distinct from the use of $x$ in Chap. 9 as a general coordinate measured along the length of the beam.)

When $2J_1(X)$ is replaced by $X$ in Eq. (12) and the effects of longitudinal debunching are included, and when from Sec. 9·2 it is recalled that $V_1 = -jV$, the electronic transadmittance of Eq. (5) becomes

$$Y_e = je^{-i\theta_0}G_e \frac{\sin hl}{hl}, \tag{13}$$

in which $G_e$, the "small-signal electronic transconductance," is given by

$$G_e \equiv \frac{M_1 M_2 \theta_0 G_0}{2}, \tag{14}$$

where $G_0$ is the beam conductance $I_0/V_0$. It may be noted that $G_e$ is defined "omitting debunching," and also that $G_e$ is the absolute value, not the real part, of the corresponding $Y_e$. Since $G_e \propto \theta_0 \propto l$, the dependence of $Y_e$ on $l$ is contained completely in the term $\sin hl$. The first (and best) maximum of $Y_e$ comes at $hl = \pi/2$.

In comparison with Eq. (13) the electronic transadmittance based upon the unmodified $i_1$ of Eq. (12) is written

$$Y_e = \frac{je^{-i\theta_0}G_e 2J_1(X)}{X}. \tag{15}$$

This equation describes the strong-signal situation when debunching is a minor factor; an eventual diminution of $Y_e$ occurs, but as a result of overbunching rather than of debunching. As with Eq. (13), $G_e/X$ is independent of $l$ and the dependence of $Y_e$ on drift distance is contained completely in $J_1(X)$, which has a maximum at $X = 1.84$.

In Fig. 10·2 are shown the functions $\sin hl/hl$ and $2J_1(X)/X$, which appear in Eqs. (13) and (15).

A numerical example may serve to emphasize the importance of debunching. Suppose $V_0 = 600$ volts, $I_0 = 40$ ma, $a = 0.5$ cm, $\lambda = 10$ cm; then by Eq. (9·11) it follows that $h = 0.6$ cm$^{-1}$. Thus $|Y_e|$ has its maximum value for $hl = \pi/2$ or $l = 2.6$ cm. On the other hand, for $V/V_0 = 10^{-2}$, overbunching takes place $(X \approx 2)$ for $l \geqq 30$ cm; and the equation $V/V_0 = 10^{-2}$ corresponds to the not-at-all-small signal power of about a milliwatt in a conventional cavity resonator at this frequency.

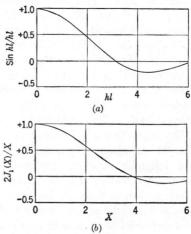

FIG. 10·2a.—Longitudinal debunching factor, $\sin hl/hl$, as a function of $hl$.

FIG. 10·2b.—Conductance compression, $2J_1(X)/X$, as a function of bunching parameter $X$.

Two points now arise in Eq. (13). In the first place, although $G_e$ is a convenient over-all parameter for describing a design goal or an actual tube, its use in Eq. (13) does not display well the dependence of $Y_e$ on the various tube parameters, such as the drift distance $l$. In the second place, the maximum of $Y_e$ as set by debunching occurs at $hl = \pi/2$; this is a condition that is independent of signal level and is therefore one of the first to be satisfied in a well-designed tube. Therefore, in the following equation, $hl$ has been set equal to $\pi/2$, the value of $\theta_0 G_0$ required by this condition has been inserted in Eq. (14) and thence in Eq. (13), and the detailed tube parameters appear explicitly:

$$Y_e = je^{-j\theta_0} M_1 M_2 \frac{\pi a}{\lambda} \sqrt{\frac{G_0}{60\beta}}, \qquad \left( hl = \frac{\pi}{2} \right). \tag{16}$$

Since $Y_e$ has been maximized with respect to debunching, it is proportional to $G_0^{1/2}$ instead of to $G_0$ as it would be (through $G_e$) if debunching were ignored in Eq. (13). This is true simply because Eq. (16) implies that if $G_0$ is increased, $l$ is decreased to keep $hl = \pi/2$; hence the product $\theta_0 G_0$, to which the optimum $Y_e$ is proportional, increases only as $G_0^{1/2}$. The beam radius $a$ in Eq. (16) arises in the same way; because $h \propto a^{-1}$, it follows that as $a$ increases the optimum drift distance and gain increase.

*Voltage-amplifier Klystron Power Gain.*—From Eqs. (11) and (16) the over-all power gain of the voltage-amplifier klystron at resonance may readily be obtained if optimum drift distance is assumed; thus, with $G_{BR} = G_{BR1} = G_{BR2}$,

$$\frac{P_L}{P_1} = \frac{M_1^2 M_2^2}{4\beta} \left(\frac{\pi a}{\lambda}\right)^2 \frac{60 G_0}{(60 G_{BR})^2}, \qquad \left(hl = \frac{\pi}{2}\right). \tag{17}$$

If there were no beam-loading, $G_0$ would not influence $G_{BR}$ at all, and the power gain with continually optimized $l$ would be directly proportional to $G_0/\beta$. Since $G_0/\beta$ is independent of $V_0$, the gain would then be independent of $V_0$, except for the dependence of the factor $M_1^2 M_2^2$ on $V_0$. At that value of $V_0$ for which the two gap-transit times are each one-half cycle, $M_1^2 M_2^2 = 0.16$. A four-fold increase in $V_0$ cuts the transit time down to one-quarter cycle and raises $M_1^2 M_2^2$ by about a factor of 4 to 0.66; however, no further increase in $V_0$ can raise $M_1^2 M_2^2$ above unity. Hence, at voltages such that the gap-transit times are less than a quarter cycle, and in the absence of beam loading, the power gain is practically independent of the beam voltage.

This incipient proportionality between gain and $G_0/\beta$ is a temptation, in designing a voltage amplifier, to go to very high values of $G_0/\beta$ and very short values of $l$. Eventually, however, in this process the beam-loading conductance $G_B$ becomes so large that it predominates in $G_{BR}$. As will shortly become evident, $G_B$ may reasonably be assumed to be proportional to $G_0$, and in that case the gain becomes inversely, instead of directly, proportional to $G_0$. The question now rises as to what is the optimum value of $G_0$. The answer involves some comment on beam-loading in general.

*Beam Loading.*—One type of beam-loading loss is that which occurs whenever a d-c beam passes through an r-f gap in a nonzero fraction of a cycle. In Chap. 3 it is shown that the contribution to $G_B$ from this source is $\theta_g^2 G_0/24$ ($\theta_g$ = gap-transit angle, assumed $\ll \pi$). This quantity simply corresponds to the energy consumed in velocity-modulating a d-c beam. Beam-loading losses measured experimentally in cavity resonators with some form of grid in the gap (see, for example, Fig. 12·19) are too large to be explained by this effect. The most likely source of these losses seems to be slow-speed secondary electrons that are knocked out of the grids with almost zero energy by the high-speed primaries of the beam. Such electrons oscillate back and forth in the gap under the influence of the r-f field, and they will eventually leave the gap, carrying with them some of the energy of the r-f field. Not much more is known of this effect at present than that it contributes to cavity losses a shunt conductance that is proportional to $I_0$ and is approximately independent of the beam voltage.

Let

$$G_B = bG_0. \tag{18}$$

Here $b$ may depend on gap spacing, is approximately proportional to $V_0$ over small ranges of $V_0$, and certainly depends on the secondary-emitting properties of the gap surfaces. The contribution of the term $\theta_g^2 G_0/24$ is not explicitly included. By a comparison of Eqs. (4), (17), and (18) it is seen that $G_0$ enters the expression for the gain in the form $G_0/(G_R + bG_0)^2$. When $V_0$ is held constant, this expression is maximized with respect to $G_0$ when $bG_0 = G_R$; and in this case

$$\frac{P_L}{P_1} = \frac{M_1^2 M_2^2}{16\beta} \left(\frac{\pi a}{\lambda}\right)^2 \frac{1}{60bG_R}. \tag{19}$$

*Further Maximization of Amplifier Gain.*—This expression for the maximum gain of a voltage-amplifier klystron is as far as one may proceed without more detailed knowledge of beam loading. As a particular example, at very low voltages and currents one might find the beam loading to be predominantly the type of loading by the primary beam that was discussed in Chap. 3; then $G_B = \theta_g^2 G_0/24$ and $b = \theta_g^2/24$. Given this particular explicit expression for $b$ and a knowledge of the way in which $G_R$ depends upon resonator dimensions, a further maximization of $P_L/P_1$ has been carried out[1] but is not reproduced in detail here. In the work referred to, it was found that $P_L/P_1$ has no absolute maximum; the maximum of $P_L/P_1$ at a given $\lambda$ and d-c input increases monotonically but increasingly slowly with increasing d-c power input.

*Comment on Design of Amplifiers for Maximum Gain.*—The optimum tube design that gives the gain of Eq. (19) is one in which $G_L = 2G_R$ and $G_B = G_R$. Thus, of the r-f power delivered to the output resonator by the fundamental component of the bunched beam, 50 per cent is delivered to the external load, 25 per cent is dissipated in ohmic losses in the output cavity resonator, and 25 per cent is consumed by losses introduced by the d-c component of the beam current. Furthermore, if input and output resonators are assumed to be identical except for the absence of external load on the input resonator, 50 per cent of the input-signal power goes into resonator ohmic losses, 50 per cent into beam loading.

The assumption of the equality of the values of $G_{BR}$ for both cavities, made in order to simplify Eq. (11), may be justified by repeating the discussion without making this assumption. It will be found that the gain is maximized when the ratio $b/G_R$ is the same for both cavities and when the products $M_1 M_2$ and $G_{R1} G_{R2}$ have their maximum value;

[1] W. W. Hansen and E. Feenberg, "Klystron Voltage Amplifiers," Sperry Gyroscope Co. Report 5221-108, Sept. 22, 1943.

barring unusual beam-loading conditions, these conditions are satisfied by identical cavities. This point is mentioned here because, if the input and output cavities are identical, then the optimum connections from cavity to external transmission line are also the same for both cavities. The optimum condition for the input connection to the first cavity is that the cavity should present a match to the line at resonance when the beam current is turned on. This condition is also the condition for loading the resonator so that $G_2 = 2G_{BR}$ when the line is terminated in its characteristic impedance looking away from the resonator. Thus a complete symmetry of the amplifier usually corresponds to optimum input and output conditions.

A comparison of some of these results with experiment is made in Sec. 10·7, which shows the agreement to be good.

*Relation Between Input- and Output-signal Voltages.*—All of the foregoing discussion of amplifier gain has been concerned solely with the power gain at resonance—that is, $\omega = \omega_1 = \omega_2$ and $\delta_1 = \delta_2 = 0$. Nothing has been said about bandwidth or about the way in which the relative phase of the input and output voltages depends upon frequency.

If it is assumed, merely to avoid arbitrary constants, that input and output transmission lines have the same characteristic impedance, then the absolute value of the ratio of output to input voltages $|V_L/V_S|$ is given at resonance by

$$\left|\frac{V_L}{V_S}\right| = \sqrt{\frac{P_L}{P_1}}. \tag{20}$$

The ratio $V_L/V_S$ is compounded of three factors: $V_1/V_S$, $V_2/V_1$, and $V_L/V_2$. The first and last of these ratios depend purely on circuits and do not involve any properties peculiar to the klystron; $V_L/V_2$ is essentially independent of frequency; $V_1/V_S$ is given, within a multiplicative constant, by

$$\frac{V_1}{V_S} \approx (1 + 2jQ_1\delta_1)^{-1}.$$

For any voltage amplifier, by Eq. (6),

$$\frac{V_2}{V_1} = -\frac{Y_e}{G_2(1 + 2jQ_2\delta_2)}.$$

Since, for a symmetrical amplifier with optimum load, it has been found, in general, that $G_1 = G_{BR}$ and $G_2 = 2G_{BR}$, $Q_1$ and $Q_2$ may be written $Q_{BR}$ and $\frac{1}{2}Q_{BR}$ respectively. When all these factors are combined and normalized by Eq. (20),

$$\frac{V_L}{V_S} = e^{-j\theta_0}\sqrt{\frac{P_L}{P_1}}\,(1 + 2jQ_{BR}\delta_1)^{-1}(1 + jQ_{BR}\delta_2)^{-1}$$

within an arbitrary complex multiplicative constant; here $P_L/P_1$ is the power gain at resonance.

The phase and bandwidth properties indicated in Eq. (21) are those of any amplifier with tuned input and output circuits. By staggered tuning ($\omega_1 \neq \omega_2$), the bandwidth may be increased at the expense of gain. The only characteristic klystron property is the factor $e^{-j\theta_0}$. This factor points up the ease of phase-modulating a klystron amplifier. A given percentage of modulation of the beam voltage produces half this percentage of modulation of $\theta_0$; the larger $\theta_0$ is (60 radians is an easily obtained value), the larger will be the resultant phase modulation of the output signal. In the absence of beam loading, and possibly in its presence, there will be no accompanying amplitude modulation. To the same degree that gain is independent of beam voltage, as discussed above, there will be no amplitude modulation accompanying the phase modulation.

**10·4. Voltage-amplifier Klystrons: Noise.**—One of the most obvious applications of a voltage amplifier is to enlarge weak r-f signals before they are detected or are mixed with local-oscillator signals in a receiver. Any amplifier has an inherent output noise power, however, which, if large enough, makes the amplifier useless as an r-f preamplifier. Questions of noise are thus vital to voltage amplifiers.

Noise may arise from any of several sources in a klystron amplifier. One such source is the thermal voltage fluctuations across the r-f gap, which are exactly analogous to the voltage fluctuations across the terminals of a resistor ("Johnson noise"); the well-known equation for the mean-square fluctuation voltage is

$$\overline{V_T^2} = \frac{4kT\,\Delta f}{G} \qquad (\text{volts})^2, \qquad (22)$$

where $\Delta f$ is the bandwidth of the measuring device, $T$ is the absolute temperature of the resistor, the conductance of which is $G$, and $k$ is Boltzmann's constant ($1.4 \times 10^{-23}$ joules/°K). In the klystron amplifier the conductance $G$ corresponds to the shunt conductance of the input cavity including the effects of any external load that is coupled into this cavity. In an ideal receiver, the available signal power needed to give unity signal-to-noise ratio in the receiver output would be $kT\,\Delta f$; $\Delta f$ is the limiting bandwidth of the receiver, whatever the factor may be which determines this bandwidth. If the input-cavity thermal noise were the only source of noise in klystron r-f amplifiers, then the necessary signal power would still be $kT\,\Delta f$, and there would be no advantage to placing this ideal klystron r-f amplifier ahead of the ideal receiver. However, as receivers (including the mixer) do not have ideal sensitivity, an r-f amplifier with input circuit noise that is predominantly thermal noise would be a very useful device. Thermal noise thus serves as a standard by which to measure other sources of noise in the amplifier.

Another of such sources of noise lies in the fluctuations in the beam current (shot effect). Any such random fluctuations in the beam current correspond to an intensity modulation of the beam current at all frequencies simultaneously—including, of course, the frequency to which the first resonator is tuned. If it is assumed, for the sake of simplicity, that the input signal is matched into the input cavity of the amplifier, the shunt conductance of the input cavity will be $2G_{BR}$, where $G_{BR}$ is the shunt conductance of the beam-loaded cavity by itself. If $\overline{i_N^2}$ is the mean-square current fluctuation that is due to shot noise, this fluctuating current delivers a noise power $P_N$ to the input cavity, where

$$P_N = \frac{1}{2} \frac{M_1^2 \overline{i_N^2}}{G_{BR}}.$$

The resulting random voltage will velocity-modulate the beam.

At low frequencies it is well known that, when the current $I_0$ is drawn from a temperature-limited cathode, $\overline{i_N^2} = 2eI_0 \, \Delta f$; here $e$ is the charge on the electron, $1.6 \times 10^{-19}$ coulombs. When the current $I_0$ is drawn from a space-charge-limited cathode, the low-frequency fluctuations in $I_0$ are smoothed out by the reaction of the potential minimum ("virtual cathode"). However, a fluctuation in electron emission so rapid that it takes place in a time less than a "time of reaction" of the potential minimum will not be smoothed out. Thus at microwave frequencies the quieting effect of space-charge limitation seems small (see page 160).

If it is still assumed that the shunt conductance of the input cavity has been increased to $2G_{BR}$ by the associated signal-input circuits, the noise power delivered to the input cavity by shot effect in the electron beam is thus $M_1^2 eI_0 \, \Delta f/G_{BR}$ watts, which corresponds to a mean-square fluctuation voltage, arising from the shot effect, of

$$\overline{V_N^2} = \frac{M_1^2 eI_0 \, \Delta f}{2G_{BR}^2}. \tag{23}$$

Even if the beam current were not at all intensity-modulated by the shot effect as it leaves the cathode, intensity modulation would result at the anode (first gap) simply as the result of the thermal spread in the velocity of the electrons as they leave the cathode. This thermal spread in velocity is the same as the result of a random velocity modulation, and during passage of the beam from cathode to anode there ensue the usual bunching effects and the resulting intensity modulation. The theory of bunching in a space-charge-limited potential, which is necessary in a discussion of this question, is complicated and is not reviewed here.

Equations (22) and (23) must suffice for estimating orders of magnitude of noise effects.

The relative influence of shot noise and Johnson input-circuit noise is measured by the ratio of the corresponding mean-square fluctuation voltages across the input gap. If the mean-square voltage fluctuation due to thermal (Johnson) noise is written as $\overline{V_T^2}$, and if $G = 2G_{BR}$ is placed in Eq. (22), Eqs. (22) and (23) give for this ratio

$$\frac{\overline{V_N^2}}{\overline{V_T^2}} = \frac{M_1^2 e I_0}{2G_{BR} \cdot 2kT}. \tag{24}$$

The effect of some of the factors in Eq. (24) may be seen in Fig. 10·3, which shows the noise charac-teristics of a 3000-mc/sec receiver preceded by a three-resonator klys-tron amplifier.[1] These character-istics are expressed in terms of the noise figure, which is the ratio to $kT \, \Delta f$ of the minimum input-signal power for which unity signal-to-noise ratio may be obtained at the output terminals of the r e c e i v e r. Also shown in the figure is the power gain of the klystron amplifier and the noise figure of the receiver without the klystron r-f amplifier; this latter noise figure, 19 db, is determined pri-marily by the crystal-mixer noise.

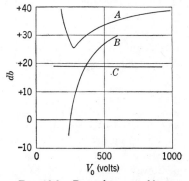

Fig. 10·3.—Dependence on klystron beam voltage of: (*A*) the over-all noise figure for 3000-Mc/sec receiver preceded by klystron amplifier; (*B*) amplifier gain; and (*C*) receiver crystal noise figure.

At the upper end of the beam-voltage range in Fig. 10·3, the amplifier gain is much higher than the noise figure of the receiver. Hence the noise from the input of the amplifier here masks the receiver (crystal) noise and is the determining factor in the over-all noise figure, which is now simply the ratio $\overline{V_N^2}/\overline{V_T^2}$ given by Eq. (24). Since both $M_1^2$ and $I_0$ decrease with decreasing beam voltage, the over-all noise figure also decreases with the beam voltage in this region of high gain. This effect appears in Fig. 10·3.

Eventually, however, a decrease of beam voltage brings a very sharp drop of gain caused by the approach of $M_1^2$ to zero as the input-gap transit angle approaches $2\pi$ radians. This effect is very marked in Fig. 10·3; the gain has a value of approximately zero for $V_0 \leq 225$ volts. This voltage corresponds to a gap-transit time of about $2\pi$ radians as calculated from the resonator dimensions. In the limit, as gain approaches zero,

[1] Data provided by E. Barlow, Sperry Gyroscope Co. Research Laboratories, Garden City, N.Y.

the noise contributed by the amplifier input circuit (but not necessarily by the amplifier output circuit) may be neglected; since the primary effect is the attenuation of the input signal, the over-all noise figure becomes inversely proportional to amplifier gain and increases with decreasing beam voltage.

The combined effect of these two trends is to produce a minimum in the noise figure, which for the tube used in Fig. 10·3 occurs at $V_0 = 270$ volts. It is clear from the figure that there is no advantage, at least as concerns ultimate sensitivity, in using this particular tube as an r-f amplifier ahead of the crystal mixer, even if the amplifier is operated at the position of minimum noise figure.

It is interesting to note how the noise figures of Fig. 10·3 compare with those that may be calculated from Eq. (24). Consider the situation at $V_0 = 600$ volts. Here $I_0 = 16$ ma, $G_{BR} \approx 1.0 \times 10^{-5}$ mhos, $M_1^2 \approx 0.37$; this value for $M_1^2$ is deduced from the value $M_1^2 \approx 0$ at $V_0 = 225$ volts. At $T = 300°$K, these figures give

$$\frac{\overline{V_N^2}}{\overline{V_T^2}} = 4900 = 37 \text{ db,}$$

as compared with the observed $35\frac{1}{2}$ db shown in Fig. 10·3.

So far no low-noise klystron amplifiers have been developed that are satisfactory as r-f preamplifiers. A promising approach to this problem is, however, suggested by Eq. (24) and data such as that of Fig. 10·3. A diminution of $I_0$ diminishes $\overline{V_N^2}/\overline{V_T^2}$, no matter how the $I_0$ diminution is brought about. On the other hand, except for beam-loading effects, the amplifier gain may, by Eq. (17), be made independent of a reduction in $I_0$—provided this is carried out by a reduction of beam voltage at constant electron-gun perveance and is accompanied by a change in resonator dimensions such that $M_1$ and $G_R$ are unaltered. This process thus requires a whole series of compensating design changes. Without analyzing these points in detail, two warnings may be made. First, the requisite small voltages imply minute physical structures, which are difficult to fabricate. Furthermore, there may be a relative "velocity modulation" that is due to a thermal spread in the electron-emission velocity; if this were present it would be considerably increased at low values of $V_0$ and might give rise to enhanced bunching and random fluctuations in $I_0$.

**10·5. Two-resonator Power-amplifier Klystrons; Bunching Conditions.**—In discussing voltage amplifiers in Secs. 10·2, 10·3, and 10·4 it is assumed that the main function of the amplifier is the amplification of small signals. This assumption implies that gain is of paramount importance. Also, the input signal is assumed to be so small that $X \ll 1$, in which case the efficiency is always negligibly small; therefore an increase in gain at the expense of efficiency might be considered profitable. On the other hand, there are also applications in which the maximum obtainable efficiency is desired but the amount of gain is comparatively unimportant, as in the buffer amplifier.

The present section is concerned with two-resonator amplifiers designed for, or operated at, conditions approximating maximum efficiency. Since this dichotomy of all amplifiers into "power amplifiers" and "voltage amplifiers" in the sense used here is somewhat artificial, a few points regarding operation at high signal levels, but not at maximum efficiency, are also discussed. It should be noted that cascade amplifiers (Secs. 10·8 through 10·10) combine some of the features of both voltage and power amplifiers.

*Optimum Bunching and Overbunching.*—The most striking feature of the power amplifier, or of any other klystron operating at optimum bunching, is the nonlinear dependence on the bunching parameter of the r-f components of the bunched beam current. The eventual diminution of any of these components as $X$ increases is known as "overbunching" and has been discussed in Sec. 9·2; overbunching has also been noted in Sec. 10·3 by way of comparison with the diminution of r-f current components by debunching. The values of $i_1$ and $Y_e$, if debunching is neglected, are repeated from that section for ease of reference:

$$i_1 = 2I_0 J_1(X)e^{-i\theta_0}, \tag{12}$$

$$Y_e = je^{-i\theta_0}G_e \frac{2J_1(X)}{X}, \tag{13}$$

and

$$G_e = \frac{M_1 M_2 \theta_0 G_0}{2}. \tag{14}$$

The function $J_1(X)$ is shown in Fig. 9·5, and $2J_1(X)/X$ is shown in Fig. 10·2. The function $2J_1(X)/X$ is known as the "conductance compression."

The maximum output power occurs at $X = 1.84$ ("optimum bunching"), at which point $|i_1|$ has its maximum value of $1.16\,I_0$. For $X = 1.84$, $|Y_e|$ is diminished from its small-signal value $G_e$ by the factor $2J_1(X)/X = 0.63$; hence the power gain given by Eq. (11) is diminished from its small-signal value by the factor $(0.63)^2 = 0.40$. This result may be altered somewhat by debunching and by limitations on the output-gap voltage, both of which phenomena are discussed shortly.

Customary operation of a power amplifier, then, is in the vicinity of $X = 1.84$; in the remainder of this section, it is therefore assumed that $X \approx 2$.

The diminution of output power with overdrive gives rise to an output characteristic like that of Fig. 10·4; if the r-f drive power is enough to produce overbunching with the input cavity tuned to resonance, optimum bunching is obtained with the input cavity somewhat detuned in order to cut down the input-gap r-f voltage.

*Debunching.*—The effects of debunching for $X \approx 2$ are not nearly so clear-cut as they are for $X \ll 1$. It may be recalled that derivation of longitudinal debunching effects takes the form of finding the change in the bunching parameter effected by debunching; the results are strictly valid only when the resulting $X$ is less than, or equal to, unity. If the condition $V/V_0 \leqq h\beta\lambda/\pi$ is satisfied, $X$ never exceeds unity, and there ensues a clear-cut situation in which none of the electron trajectories in an

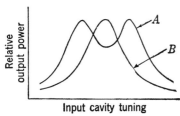

Applegate diagram (see Fig. 9·2) would ever intersect. It is thus immediately apparent that, in order to get something approximating optimum bunching in a power amplifier, the input r-f drive must be such that $V/V_0 > h\beta\lambda/\pi$, or, what is the same thing, $X_0 > hl$. Here $X_0$ is the value of $X$ in the absence of debunching. If $X_0 > hl$ so that $X$ may exceed unity, the theory of Sec. 9·2 breaks down because at least some of the electron

Fig. 10·4.—Klystron amplifier output characteristic: (*A*) excess drive producing overbunching at resonance and (*B*) optimum r-f drive.

trajectories are now intersecting. A perturbation calculation starting from the known conditions at $X = 1$ might well shed considerable light on the situation, but has not been carried out. Very qualitative considerations indicate that for good bunching in the vicinity of $X_0 = 2$, the condition $X_0 > hl$ should be met with a factor of safety of 2—that is,

$$hl \leqq 1. \tag{25}$$

In this case the bunched beam current may be diminished somewhat less than by the factor $(\sin hl/hl) \approx (1 - (hl)^2/6)$, which holds for $X < 1$. Wall effects also lessen the longitudinal debunching effect, as already noted.

The calculation of transverse debunching in Sec. 9·3 is approximate because it is based upon a center-of-the-bunch charge density proportional to $X$; this assumption is probably not very inaccurate for $X \leqq 2$. The calculation gives a spreading of the bunch proportional to $X^3$ or $l^3$, and a consequent fractional loss of current from the original beam area that amounts to $(hl)^2/6$ when $X = 2$. (These results can hardly be applied for $X > 2$, where charge densities are decreasing rather than increasing with $X$.) The loss of current is the same as the naively calculated longitudinal debunching loss; the latter is, however, suspected of being less, in fact, than the naive calculation indicates. The presence of one type of debunching diminishes the space-charge forces that give rise to the other type; hence it seems safe to assume, for the net effect of both types of debunching, a reduction by a factor of $1 - (hl)^2/6$ at $X = 2$.

If Eq. (25) is satisfied, the debunching loss in $i_1$ and $Y_e$ will not exceed about 16 per cent. The 16 per cent loss for $hl = 1$ could be halved by reducing $hl$ to $1/\sqrt{2}$. If this were done by a reduction in $l$, an increase in $V^2$ and in the r-f drive power by a factor of 2 would be required for the resultant 8 per cent increase in output-circuit driving current; or, if $hl$ were reduced to $1/\sqrt{2}$ by a 50 per cent reduction in $I_0$, the output would be halved for an increase in efficiency by one part in twelve. Ordinarily, neither procedure is very profitable. Hence, good design seems to indicate $hl = 1$, or somewhat less than the value of $\pi/2$ deduced for the voltage amplifier; therefore, in later discussions of efficiency it is assumed that $i_1$ has been reduced by debunching from $1.16I_0$ to $\frac{5}{6} \times 1.16I_0$ or $0.97I_0$.

**10·6. General Klystron Power-amplifier Relations.**—In Sec. 10·2 a number of general voltage amplifier relations are considered; these relations hold true for any voltage amplifier, regardless of the manner in which the output-circuit driving current is derived from the input signal. The present section deals with certain general relations that characterize any power amplifier, whether klystron or microwave triode; these relations have been touched upon, in less detail, in connection with the discussion of triode amplifiers in Chap. 6. Early in the present section, however, the explicit distribution of electron energies in a velocity-modulated beam enters into the equations; this fact makes improper a direct application of all the subsequent details to triodes.

*The Limitation on Output-gap Voltage.*—The basis of Sec. 10·2 is Eq. (1), which describes the driving of the output resonator by an r-f current. As long as this equation remains valid, most of the development of Secs. 10·2 and 10·3 for voltage amplifiers holds true for power amplifiers also; it is necessary, in dealing with klystron amplifiers, to take account in $Y_e$ only of the changes in bunching and debunching that have just been discussed in Sec. 10·5.

Equation (1) assumes that properly phased electrons are able to deliver an amount of energy $eM_2|V_2|$ to the output resonator in passing through the gap. In an output r-f gap with negligible transit angle, this assumption is obviously untrue if $|V_2| > V_0$, for then an electron entering the gap at the moment of retarding peak r-f voltage will actually be reflected from the gap. Far from delivering all its initial kinetic energy, the electron will actually regain some of its energy in retracing its path out of the gap and will return to the drift space with an energy equal to $|V_2| - V_0$. The bunch will not have delivered so much energy to the field as would be delivered if $|V_2| = V_0$, and yet more power is required to maintain a gap voltage $|V_2| > V_0$ than is required for $|V_2| = V_0$. Thus the gap voltage $V_2$ will never rise above $V_0$.

Strictly speaking, this deduction from the physical picture of the mechanism in the output gap holds true only when $V(\equiv |V_1|) = 0$ and when the output-gap transit angle is zero. If $V > 0$, half the electrons have less energy than $eV_0$ and therefore may be turned back for some value of $|V_2| < V_0$; a more exact calculation[1] for zero gap transit angle shows that the maximum value of $|V_2|$ is related to $V$ by the approximate relation

$$|V_2| \leqq V_0 - V. \tag{26}$$

The effect of the output-gap transit angle is not well known, but probably it affects the efficiency more through beam-loading than through influence on maximum $V_2$. Nevertheless, the foregoing comments and the succeeding deductions are rigorous only for $M_2 \approx 1$.

Thus, the simple Eq. (1) for the driving of the output resonator is invalid whenever it predicts the physically impossible situation

$$|V_2| > V_0 - V$$

—that is, whenever

$$M_2|i_1| \geqq (V_0 - V)|Y_2|. \tag{27a}$$

Whenever the condition of Eq. (27a) is met and Eq. (1) is made invalid, the latter equation is then to be replaced by

$$|V_2| = V_0 - V. \tag{27b}$$

The phase of $V_2$ is the same[2] as the phase of $i_1/Y_2$.

Equations (27) have an unexpected consequence in that they make the amplifier gain once more a relevant quantity in the power amplifier because a low gain means a high $V/V_0$ for optimum bunching, with the resulting low $|V_2|$ and low efficiency.

*Output Power in the Power Amplifier.*—The principal questions that have to be answered in the light of this new limitation imposed on $V_2$ by Eq. (26) have to do with the way in which the output power $P_L$ depends upon the various tube parameters such as $|i_1|$, $V_0$, and $G_L$. It is convenient initially to consider only what happens when $\omega = \omega_2$; what happens when the output resonator is tuned off resonance is easily appended later.

---

[1] E. Feenberg, "Theory of Bunching," Sperry Gyroscope Co. Report 5221-105, Nov. 24, 1942.

[2] It seems more convenient in this section to use $M_2i$, instead of its equivalent $Y_eV_1$ because $V_1$ has lost much of its previous importance, and $|i_1|$ always has a known value of approximately $I_0$.

The power dissipated in cavity-plus-load in the presence of a gap voltage $(V_0 - V)$ is $\frac{1}{2}(V_0 - V)^2 G_2$. This power must therefore also be that delivered by the beam at the gap whenever Eq. (27a) is satisfied. The circuit efficiency is still $G_L/G_2$; hence, when Eq. (27a) holds true, the power delivered to the load is

$$P_L = \tfrac{1}{2}(V_0 - V)^2 G_L. \tag{28a}$$

This equation expresses several fairly obvious facts. When excess driving current is available, an increase in this current does not increase $P_L$, as is shown by the absence of $i_1$ from Eq. (28). When excess driving current is available, an increase in $G_L$ does not cause a decrease in $V_2$; hence $P_L$ increases directly with $G_L$.

When the condition in Eq. (27a) does not hold, $P_L$ is given by Eq. (9), which for convenience is rewritten here with $G_2$ written as $G_{BR} + G_L$, $Y_e V_1$ written as $M_2 i_1$, and $\delta_2 = 0$:

$$P_L = \tfrac{1}{2} M_2^2 |i_1|^2 G_L / (G_{BR} + G_L)^2. \tag{28b}$$

For comparison with Eqs. (28a) and (28b) it is instructive to consider what the maximum value of $P_L$ may be for a given value of $(V_0 - V)$ and $M_2 i_1$. This maximum value of $P_L$ will be obtained when all of the current $M_2 i_1$ is effective in driving the output cavity—that is, when any larger value of $G_L$ would make $|V_2| < (V_0 - V)$—and when none of the power delivered by the electron stream is wasted in cavity or beam-loading losses—that is, $G_{BR} = 0$. In this case $P_L$ will have the value $P_{max}$ given by

$$P_{max} = \tfrac{1}{2} M_2 |i_1| (V_0 - V). \tag{29}$$

This illustration may be further idealized by setting $M_2 = 1$, $V \ll V_0$, and $|i_1| = 1.16 I_0$; then the over-all efficiency of the amplifier,

$$\frac{P_{max}}{I_0 V_0},$$

is 58 per cent. This percentage derives from the fact that the maximum value of $J_1(X)$ is 0.58 and is the basis of the common statement, "The maximum efficiency of the klystron is 58 per cent." (In Secs. 9·5 and 9·8 it is shown that bunching with a finite input-gap transit angle and cascade bunching may produce a waveform for which the "58 per cent" becomes "74 per cent.")

At the end of this section the factors that modify this "58 per cent" are collected and reviewed; for the moment, $P_{max}$ serves simply as a convenient normalizing factor for expressing the values of $P_L$. It is convenient to define one more normalizing quantity, a critical conductance $G_C$ given by

$$G_C \equiv \frac{M_2 |i_1|}{(V_0 - V)}. \tag{30}$$

This $G_C$ is not the transfer conductance; it is simply a measure of the output-circuit driving current in units that are convenient for expressing the condition stated in Eq. (27a). By comparing Eqs. (27a), (28a), (28b), (29), and (30) it is seen that the behavior of the output power of an amplifier with its output cavity tuned to resonance is completely described by the following equations:

$$P_{\max} = \tfrac{1}{2}(V_0 - V)^2 G_C; \tag{31a}$$

for

$$G_C \geqq G_2 \equiv G_{BR} + G_L, \qquad \frac{P_L}{P_{\max}} = \frac{G_L}{G_C}; \tag{31b}$$

and for

$$G_C \leqq G_2 \equiv G_{BR} + G_L, \qquad \frac{P_L}{P_{\max}} = \frac{\left(\dfrac{G_L}{G_C}\right)}{(G_{BR}/G_C + G_L/G_C)^2}. \tag{31c}$$

The relation between $P_L/P_{\max}$ and $G_L/G_C$ for various values of $G_{BR}/G_C$ is shown in Fig. 10·5. Here the value of $P_L/P_{\max}$ given by Eq. (31c)

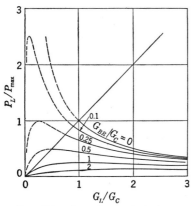

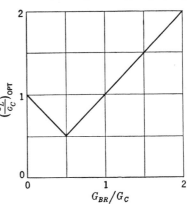

FIG. 10·5.—Dependence of relative output power $P_L/P_{\max}$ on normalized load conductance $G_L/G_C$, for various values of the normalized internal-loss conductance $G_{BR}/G_C$; dotted lines represent form that curves would have if $V_2$ were not limited.

FIG. 10·6.—Value of the normalized load conductance $(G_L/G_C)_{\mathrm{opt}}$ which maximizes output power, as a function of normalized internal-loss conductance $G_{BR}/G_C$.

is shown as a dotted line for that region in which this equation is inapplicable because of the limitation on $V_2$.

Let the value of $P_L/P_{\max}$ at optimum $G_L/G_C$ be $(P_L/P_{\max})_{\max}$; then it is apparent from Fig. 10·5 and Eqs. (31) that

for

$$\frac{G_{BR}}{G_C} \geqq 0.5, \qquad \left(\frac{P_L}{P_{\max}}\right)_{\max} = \frac{G_C}{4G_{BR}}; \tag{32a}$$

for

$$\frac{G_{BR}}{G_C} \leqq 0.5, \qquad \left(\frac{P_L}{P_{\max}}\right)_{\max} = 1 - \frac{G_{BR}}{G_C}. \tag{32b}$$

Equation (32a) is the result previously derived [cf. Eq. (10)] with no attention paid to the limitation on $V_2$; the optimum load is $G_L = G_{BR}$. For the region covered by Eq. (32b), for which $|V_2| = V_0 - V$, the optimum $G_L$ is given by $G_L/G_C = 1 - G_{BR}/G_C$. The dropping of $P_L/P_{\max}$ below unity for $0 < G_{BR}/G_C < 0.5$ is caused by the corresponding decrease of circuit efficiency below unity; when $G_{BR}/G_C > 0.5$, the circuit efficiency remains constant at $\frac{1}{2}$, but a continuing diminution of $P_L/P_{\max}$ is caused by the decrease in $V_2$, which now sets in.

Figure 10·6 shows this relation between $G_{BR}/G_C$ and the optimum value of $G_L/G_C$; Fig. 10·7 gives the dependence of the corresponding maximum value of $P_L/P_{\max}$ on $G_{BR}/G_C$. Figure 10·7 and Eq. (29) express the essence of all that has been said concerning loading conditions and limitation on output gap r-f voltage in the power amplifier. The resulting diminution in efficiency is seen to depend only on $G_{BR}/G_C$. In the absence of beam loading, $G_{BR}/G_C$ gets smaller and the efficiency gets higher as $i_1$ is increased; but beam loading, if it is

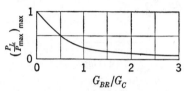

FIG. 10·7.—Dependence of normalized output power at optimum load $(P_L/P_{\max})_{\max}$, on normalized internal-loss conductance $G_{BR}/G_C$.

present at all, will eventually dominate in $G_{BR}$, and $G_{BR}/G_C$ will then asymptotically approach a nonzero lower limit as $I_0$ or $i_1$ is increased. Writing $G_B = bG_0$ as before, this lower limit is given by

$$\frac{G_{BR}}{G_C} \geqq \frac{bI_0(1 - V/V_0)}{M_2|i_1|}. \tag{33}$$

The dependence of output power on tuning of the output resonator is now fairly obvious. At values of $\delta_2$ for which

$$G_C \geqq |Y_2| = G_2|1 + 2jQ_2\delta_2|,$$

Eq. (28a) for $P_L$ will still hold true, and in particular $P_L$ will be independent of $\delta_2$; thus the center portion of the resonance curve will be flat-topped. When $\delta_2$ is so large that $G_C < |Y_2|$, the usual form of resonance curve will obtain. Thus the distortion of the form of the resonance curve is one way of identifying the onset of the limitation of $V_2$.

**10·7. Comparison of Theory and Experiment for Two-resonator Amplifier Klystrons.**—After this discussion of the various factors that enter into voltage-amplifier and power-amplifier operation, it is interesting to combine them for a specific case and see how the result compares with experiment. The type 410R klystron, perhaps the best-known two-resonator klystron amplifier, of which a schematic diagram is shown in Fig. 10·1, will be used for this purpose.   In Fig. 10·8 is shown a graph of output power as a function of input r-f power at $V_0 = 2070$ volts and with zero volts on the beam-focusing electrode.[1]   The functional form of this curve is discussed later; for the moment the quantities of interest are the maximum efficiency, the small-signal power gain, and the input and output r-f powers at maximum r-f output.   These quantities are optimized at a negative bias of 60 volts on the control electrode, and the optimum values that will be used are therefore not identical with those shown in Fig. 10·8.

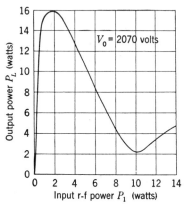

Fig. 10·8.—Dependence of output power $P_L$ on input r-f power $P_1$ in the type 410R amplifier klystron.

The operating characteristics (and other relevant data) to be observed at $V_0 = 2070$ volts are as follows:

$V_0$ .................................... 2070 volts
$\beta$ ....................................... 0.091
$I_0$ ....................................... 92 ma
Maximum $P_L$ ........................... 18 watts
Corresponding $P_1$ ........................ 1.8 watts
Maximum $\eta_L$ (over-all efficiency) ........... 9.5 per cent
Small-signal $P_L/P_1$ ...................... 25
$l$ ....................................... 3 cm
$a$ ....................................... 0.5 cm
$\lambda$ ....................................... 10 cm
Equivalent gap spacing .................... 0.23 cm (both cavities)
Grid transmission loss .................... 0.08 per grid
$G_R$ ....................................... $0.75 \times 10^{-5}$ mhos.

The number of grids through which the beam has passed at any given stage may be ascertained from Fig. 10·1; in calculations based on current at any point, the beam current will be $0.92^n \times 92$ ma, where $n$ is the number of grids traversed to reach the point in question.   The relevant factors affecting operation may now be summarized.

Debunching: Effective beam current $= 92 \times (0.92)^3$ ma $= 71$ ma; from this, $h = 0.29$, $hl = 0.87$.   Thus the design is very close to the optimum for debunching specified in Eq. (25).   Debunching diminishes $|i_1|$ by the factor $1 - (hl)^2/6 = 0.87$.

[1] Sperry Gyroscope Co. Technical Information Sheet on the type 410R klystron.

Beam-coupling coefficient: Since $\beta\lambda = 0.91$ cm, an equivalent gap spacing of 0.23 cm means a quarter-cycle gap-transit angle, for which $M = 0.90$.

Depth of modulation $V/V_0$: In the expression $X = \pi l M V/\beta V_0 \lambda$, the above values of $l$, $M$, $\beta$, and $\lambda$ give $V/V_0 = 0.20$ at optimum bunching ($X = 1.84$).

Bunched-current component $i_1$ and critical conductance $G_C$: With four grid absorptions before the current enters the output gap, if optimum bunching is assumed and the above debunching diminution included,

$$|i_1| = 2J_1(1.84) \times [1 - (hl)^2/6] \times (0.92)^4 \times 92 \text{ ma} = 66 \text{ ma}.$$

These values make $G_C = M_2|i_1|/(V_0 - V) = 3.6 \times 10^{-5}$ mhos.

Beam-loading: From measurements of $Q_{BR}$ as a function of beam current in this tube[1] it is known that $G_{BR}/G_R = 1 + I_0(\text{ma})/34$. The value of $G_R$ given in the above summary of operating conditions is an average of values obtained by velocity-spectrograph measurements[2] and by calculation.[3] The effective beam currents in the first and second r-f gaps are $92 \times (0.92)^2 = 78$ ma and

$$92 \times (0.92)^4 = 65 \text{ ma}$$

respectively; these values give $G_{BR1} = 2.5 \times 10^{-5}$ mhos,

$$G_{BR2} = 2.2 \times 10^{-5} \text{ mhos}.$$

Maximum efficiency: Since $G_{BR2}/G_C = 0.61$, $|V_2|$ has not quite reached the value $(V_0 - V)$, and, by Eq. (32a), $(P_L/P_{\max})_{\max} = 0.41$. Thus, all told, the presence of circuit and beam-loading losses (nonzero $G_{BR}$) has reduced the circuit efficiency and has so reduced the output gap voltage that the load receives 41 per cent of the power that it would receive if $G_{BR}$ were zero. If $G_{BR}$ were zero, the conversion efficiency would be

$$\frac{P_{\max}}{I_0 V_0} = \frac{1}{2}\left(1 - \frac{V}{V_0}\right)^2 \left(\frac{G_C V_0}{I_0}\right) = 0.26;$$

thus debunching, grid-absorption losses, beam-coupling coefficient, and the limitation of $|V_2|$ to $(V_0 - V)$ have reduced the ideal "58 per cent" to a semi-ideal 26 per cent that would obtain if there

---

[1] Data communicated to author by M. Chodorow, Sperry Gyroscope Co. Research Laboratories, Garden City, N.Y.

[2] J. J. Caldwell, "Velocity Spectrograph Measurements of Beam Loading," Sperry Gyroscope Co. Report 5221-1015, Oct. 23, 1944.

[3] *Microwave Transmission Design Data*, Sperry Gyroscope Co., Publication No. 23-80, Brooklyn, N.Y., 1944.

were no circuit or beam-loading losses. The over-all efficiency is the product of the two factors just discussed, or

$$\eta_L = 0.41 \times 0.26 = 10.6 \text{ per cent.}$$

Hence the predicted value of $P_L$ is 20.2 watts, which is in good agreement with the observed value of 18 watts.

Power gain at optimum bunching: The calculated required input r-f power is $P_1 = V^2/2G_{BR1} = 2.15$ watts; hence, at optimum bunching the power gain to be expected is given by $P_L/P_1 = 9.4$.

Small-signal power gain: The calculated small-signal electronic transconductance is $G_e = M_1 M_2 \theta_0 G_0/2 = 27 \times 10^{-5}$ mhos; if the factor 0.87 is allowed for debunching, $|Y_e| = 23.5 \times 10^{-5}$ mhos at resonance. And when Eq. (11) is generalized for $G_{BR1} \neq G_{BR2}$, the predicted small-signal power gain becomes

$$\frac{P_L}{P_1} = \frac{|Y_e|^2}{4G_{BR1}G_{BR2}} = 25.$$

The final comparison between theoretical and experimental values is then as follows:

|  | Theoretical | Experimental |
|---|---|---|
| Efficiency, per cent............................... | 10.6 | 9.5 |
| Output r-f power (optimum bunching), watts.......... | 20.2 | 18 |
| Input r-f power (optimum bunching), watts........... | 2.15 | 1.8 |
| Power gain (optimum bunching)..................... | 9.4 | 10 |
| Power gain (small signal). ........................ | 25 | 25 |

The most dubious ingredient in this generally close agreement is the assumed value of $G_R$, to which a " $\pm 30$ per cent" might reasonably have been appended. It would not be surprising if the errors in the debunching estimates were nearly of this order of magnitude also; therefore, the agreement may be in fact fortuitous. But the consistency of the calculation of output power and gain takes some of the sting away from this word of caution.

*Comparison of Theory and Experiment at High Input-gap Voltage.*— Figure 10·8 provides an interesting check of the bunching theory for large values of $V/V_0$ in Sec. 9·4. The coordinates in this figure are powers, not voltages or bunching parameter; hence, if the simplest bunching theory holds true, $P_L \propto |i_1|^2 \propto [J_1(X)]^2$ and this figure should be geometrically similar to a plot of $[J_1(X)]^2$ versus $X^2$. Since $J_1(3.84) = 0$, this relation implies that $P_L = 0$ for an input r-f power $(3.84/1.84)^2 = 4.4$ times the drive power for optimum bunching, or 7.9 watts. Actually, $P_L$ passes through a nonzero minimum at a drive power of 10 watts, and at the value of 7.9 watts, where simple theory indicates that there should be a zero in $P_L$, the output power is 30 per cent of the maximum output power.

This phenomenon suggests that the more exact equation for the bunched current components, Eq. (9·28), should be compared with the experimental data.   Under the assumed conditions, $\theta_0 \approx 20$; by Table 9·1 the drift-space coefficients that appear in Eq. (9·28) are thus given by $a_1 = 1$, $a_2 = 0.075$, $a_3 = -0.00625$.   When $|i_1|$ is evaluated by Eq. (9·28) at the point of the expected zero ($X = 3.84$), it is found that $|i_1| = 0.62I_0$ instead of zero.   The same calculation gives $|i_1| = 1.16I_0$ at $X = 1.84$—that is, at this latter point the higher-order corrections are negligible.   The ratio of the two values of $|i_1|^2$ is 0.29, in perfect agreement with the observed ratio, 0.30.   The use of Eq. (9·28) to predict the complete curve of Fig. 10·8 beyond this single check point is left as an exercise for the reader.

**10·8.  Voltage Cascade-amplifier Klystrons.**—It has been seen in Sec. 10·3 that there are definite upper limits to the gain of a two-resonator voltage-amplifier klystron with a given d-c input power.   It is obvious that a gain higher than that allowed by these limits may be obtained by using more than one stage of amplification.   One simple two-stage arrangement would be to lead the output power from one two-resonator amplifier into the input resonator of a second amplifier.   The so-called "cascade amplifier" is a much better way of accomplishing the same end by having both stages of amplification located within the same vacuum envelope and utilizing the same electron beam.   In the simplest form, three resonators are arranged along an electron beam.   The middle resonator abstracts power from the beam as the "output" cavity of the first stage; the second-gap r-f voltage that is thereby developed proceeds to velocity-modulate the beam further as the input-gap voltage of the second stage.

This arrangement has a number of advantages.   There is one electron beam instead of two and hence half the d-c input power; there are three resonators to tune instead of four, and none of the complications introduced by having two coupled resonators are present; moreover, the overall gain is at least four times as high as it would be for the same two stages of amplification operating on separate beams.   This factor of 4, although perhaps at first glance somewhat surprising, is based upon the simple considerations that follow.   With two intermediate resonators, one serving as output cavity for the first stage and one serving as input cavity for the second stage, the intermediate-circuit losses are doubled, thus doubling the shunt conductance that the output cavity of the first stage presents to the beam.   The power abstracted from the beam by this cavity is therefore only half the power that would be abstracted by the single intermediate cavity of the cascade amplifier, and this reduced amount of power must furthermore be divided between two cavities instead of exciting a single cavity.   Hence the power available for developing the input-gap voltage for the second stage is only one-quarter as much in the two-tube two-stage amplifier as it is in the two-stage cascade amplifier.

These general comments assume that the two stages of amplification act more or less independently—that is, that the voltage across the r-f

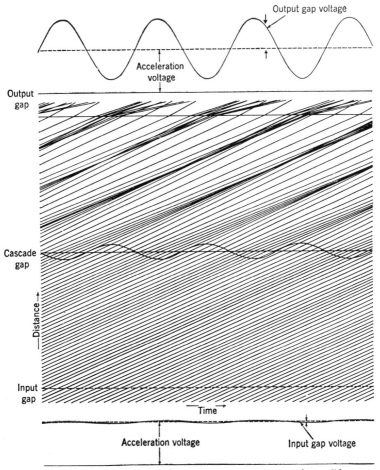

Fig. 10·9.—Applegate diagram of electron trajectories in cascade amplifier.

gap of the second resonator proceeds to velocity-modulate the beam and to be amplified just as if it existed across the first gap of a two-resonator voltage amplifier. It may be seen shortly that in a high-gain cascade amplifier this situation holds to an approximate degree.

Regarding the cascade voltage amplifier the question is sometimes asked: "If the maximum gain has been extracted from the beam in the first stage, how can one get still more gain out of the beam by hanging a third resonator on it?" A few comments prior to the detailed analysis may help to explain this point. In the first place, when the beam enters the second gap it is assumed to have a small degree of intensity modulation and velocity modulation; thus, for all intents and purposes, the second gap r-f voltage has a d-c beam to work on. In the second place, this beam delivers energy to the second resonator by virtue of its intensity modulation, not its velocity modulation; therefore, the further velocity modulation that the beam receives as it delivers this energy does not upset the process of energy transfer. Finally, after the beam has passed through the second gap, it has received a velocity modulation much larger than it received in the first gap, and its subsequent bunching is therefore determined almost entirely by the second-gap velocity modulation.

These facts are put into graphic form by Fig. 10·9,[1] which shows an Applegate diagram for a typical cascade amplifier. (See Sec. 9·2 for a single-stage Applegate diagram and a discussion of its significance.)

*Particularization of Cascade-bunching Theory to the Cascade Amplifier.* The theory of cascade bunching is developed in Sec. 9·8, and the notation of that section is adopted without further comment. The results of Sec. 9·8 that are applicable to small-signal cascade amplifiers may be summed up in the following statement. Cascade bunching in a small-signal cascade amplifier results in waveform components and relative current components just like those of simple bunching; the equivalent bunching parameter $X'$, which determines the waveform and current components for cascade bunching, is given by

$$X'e^{j\theta'} = X_{13} - jX_{23}e^{j\beta}. \tag{9·56}$$

(Here $\theta'$ gives the phase of the bunching relative to that which would result from first-gap velocity-modulation alone, and $\beta$ is used as a phase parameter, not as the ratio of electron velocity to velocity of light.) This simple description is valid when

$$X_{12}X_{23} \ll 2X'; \tag{34}$$

this condition is met in a high-gain cascade amplifier working at low levels. What happens when this condition is not met is discussed in the next section.

The behavior of the equivalent bunching parameter $X'$ is thus the key to the anatomy of the cascade voltage amplifier and the only point that distinguishes the latter from the single-stage voltage amplifier.

In deriving Eq. (9·56) for the equivalent bunching parameter $X'$,

[1] A. E. Harrison, "Graphical Methods for Analysis of Velocity-modulation Bunching," *Proc. I.R.E.*, **33**, 20 (1945).

the following gap voltages were assumed:

$$V_1 = -j\alpha_1 V_0 \qquad V_2 = -\alpha_2 V_0 e^{j(-\theta_{01}+\beta)}. \qquad (9\cdot49)$$

The parameters $\alpha_2$ and $\beta$, which specify the amplitude and phase of the second-gap voltage, have been left completely arbitrary because in Sec. 9·8 no hypothesis is made concerning the origin of the second-gap voltage. In the present case $V_2$ results from the driving of the second resonator by the current $M_2 i_{12}$; hence by Eq. (1),

$$V_2 = \frac{-M_2|i_{12}|e^{-j\theta_{01}}}{G_2(1 + 2jQ_2\delta_2)}.$$

This equation is made equivalent to the assumed form, Eq. (9·49b), by writing

$$\beta = -\tan^{-1} 2Q_2\delta_2 \qquad (35)$$

and

$$\alpha_2 V_0 = \frac{M_2|i_{12}| \cos \beta}{G_2}. \qquad (36)$$

Thus $\beta$ gives the phase angle between the driving current $M_2 i_{12}$ and the second-gap r-f voltage and is determined by the tuning of the second cavity; $\beta = 0$ at resonance.

Since $\alpha_2 \propto \cos \beta$, $X_{23} \propto \cos \beta$; hence

$$X_{23}(\beta) = X_{23}(0) \cos \beta. \qquad (37)$$

Thus Eq. (9·56) for the effective bunching parameter $X'$ becomes

$$X'(\beta)e^{j\theta'} = X_{13} - jX_{23}(0)e^{j\beta} \cos \beta. \qquad (38)$$

Many of the more important features of the cascade amplifier result simply from the explicit dependence of $X_{23}$ and $X'$ on the tuning parameter $\beta$ as shown in Eqs. (37) and (38); hence the consequences of Eq. (38) are explored in some detail before further specification of the values of $X_{13}$ and $X_{23}(0)$.

*Dependence of $X'$ on Middle-resonator Tuning.*—Without further detailed knowledge of $X_{13}$ and $X^{23}(0)$ the most important questions to be asked concerning Eq. (38) are these: How does $X'$ depend on $\beta$, and what is the maximum value of $X'$ obtained by varying $\beta$ (tuning the middle resonator)?

The answers are indicated in Fig. 10·10, in which Eq. (38) is represented graphically by showing the addition of the two complex vectors that make up $X'e^{j\theta'}$. The locus of the end point of the vector $X'e^{j\theta'}$ is seen to be a circle that is tangent to the real axis at $X_{13}$. One interesting point about Fig. 10·10 is that the maximum value of $X'$ does not occur with $\beta = 0$ and the middle resonator tuned to resonance. Rather, $X'$ is maximized when $\beta$ is somewhat positive; by Eqs. (35) ,and (3) this condition corresponds to tuning the second resonator to a frequency $\omega_2$ higher than the driving frequency $\omega$. Thus $X'$ is a maximum when the bunched current contributed by the second-gap velocity modulation is somewhat diminished in magnitude, but is more advantageously phased with respect to the contribution of the first-gap velocity modulation.

This fact suggests a second interesting point about Fig. 10·10. When the general subject of cascade amplification was introduced and roughly evaluated, the independence of first- and second-stage bunching was tacitly assumed; this was equivalent to the assumption that $X' = X_{23}(0)$. It is now apparent that when the continuation of the first-stage bunching into the second stage—that is, the influence of $X_{13}$ on $X'$—is considered, the net effect is to cause an additional increase in $X'$ and hence in the power gain. This effect is not

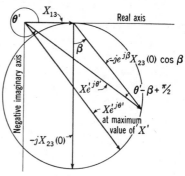

FIG. 10·10.—Graphical construction of Eq. (38).

$$X'e^{j\theta'} = X_{13} - je^{j\beta}X_{23}(0)\cos\beta.$$

numerically important in the cascade voltage amplifier, but it is the forerunner of an analogous and important effect in power amplifiers.

The various details of the behavior of $X'$, including the extent of this increase of $X'$ over $X_{23}(0)$, are easily listed. From Eq. (38) it may be deduced that $X'$ is a maximum or a minimum when

$$\tan 2\beta = \frac{2X_{13}}{X_{23}(0)}, \tag{39a}$$

or

$$\tan \beta = -\frac{X_{23}(0)}{2X_{13}} \pm \sqrt{\frac{X_{23}^2(0)}{4X_{13}^2} + 1}. \tag{39b}$$

The upper and lower signs correspond to the position of the maximum and minimum values of $X'$ respectively. By Eqs. (35) and (39b) the difference between the corresponding values of the second-cavity resonant frequencies, $\omega_{max}$ and $\omega_{min}$, is given by

$$Q_2(\delta_{max} - \delta_{min}) = Q_2 \frac{\omega_{max} - \omega_{min}}{\omega} = \sqrt{\frac{X_{23}^2(0)}{4X_{13}^2} + 1}. \tag{40a}$$

The maximum and minimum values of $X'$ are given by

$$X'^2_{\substack{max \\ min}} = \frac{X_{23}^2(0)}{2}\left[1 \pm \sqrt{1 + \left(\frac{2X_{13}}{X_{23}(0)}\right)^2}\right] + X_{13}^2. \tag{41a}$$

In a high-gain amplifier—in which it is obvious that $X_{13} \ll X_{23}(0)$—Eqs. (40) and (41) may be written

$$Q_2(\delta_{\max} - \delta_{\min}) \approx \frac{X_{23}(0)}{2X_{13}} \left[ 1 + \frac{2X_{13}^2}{X_{23}^2(0)} + \cdots \right], \qquad (40b)$$

$$X'_{\max} \approx X_{23}(0) \left[ 1 + \frac{X_{13}}{X_{23}(0)^2} + \cdots \right], \qquad (41b)$$

and

$$X'_{\min} \approx \frac{\sqrt{2}\, X_{13}^2}{X_{23}(0)} + \cdots . \qquad (41c)$$

Thus, the higher the gain (the higher $X_{23}(0)/X_{13}$), the less $X'_{\max}$ is increased above $X_{23}(0)$ by the continuation of first-stage bunching into

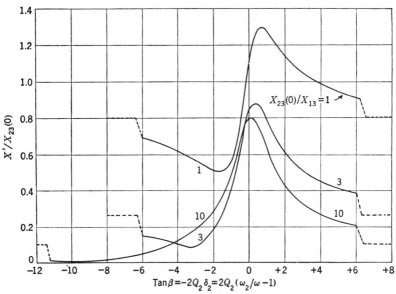

Fig. 10·11.—Middle resonator tuning curves of the cascade amplifier; effective bunching parameter at resonance, $X'$, as a function of middle resonator tuning for several values of $X_{23}(0)/X_{13}$.

the second stage; and the higher the gain the less detuning of the second resonator is required to maximize $X'$.

The effects that have just been described are illustrated in Fig. 10·11, in which is shown the theoretical dependence of $X'/X_{23}(0)$ on tuning of the second resonator; this tuning is specified by $2Q_2(\omega_2/\omega - 1)$, which is also written $-2Q_2\delta_2$. The curves are plotted for three values of $X_{13}/X_{23}(0)$. A comparison of the different curves shows the dependence on $X_{13}/X_{23}(0)$ of $X'_{\max}/X_{23}(0)$ and $X'_{\min}/X_{23}(0)$ as in Eqs. (41), and of

$\omega_{max}$ and $\omega_{min}$ as in Eqs. (40). The general dependence of "bandwidth" is also shown, although bandwidth is a somewhat nebulous property except when $X_{13}/X_{23}(0)$ is small. The case $[X_{13}/X_{23}(0)] = 1$ is a somewhat academic one because it corresponds to a very low second-stage voltage gain such as would not be used in a voltage amplifier.

Equations (40) and (41) and Fig. 10·11 suggest the use of experimentally observed middle-resonator tuning curves to determine the tube parameters. Thus by Eq. (41), the following relation holds true between the maximum and minimum $X'$ and the value of $X'$ for the middle resonator completely detuned ($\beta = \pi/2$):

$$X'_{max} : X'\left(\beta = \frac{\pi}{2}\right) : X'_{min} \approx \frac{X_{23}(0)}{X_{13}} : 1 : \frac{\sqrt{2}\,X_{13}}{X_{23}(0)}. \tag{42}$$

This relation provides two determinations of $X_{13}/X_{23}(0)$, which may be checked for self-consistency. The value of $Q_2(\delta_{max} - \delta_{min})$ that corresponds to the value of $X_{13}/X_{23}(0)$ may be found from Eq. (40b). This calculated value of $Q_2(\delta_{max} - \delta_{min})$, in conjunction with the observable quantity $(\delta_{max} - \delta_{min})$, provides a determination of $Q_2$.

*Condition for Validity of "Equivalent Bunching Parameter" in Power Amplifier Operating at Optimum Bunching.*—It should be noted that the foregoing discussion is valid for more general conditions than are involved solely in voltage amplifiers, in the sense in which this term is used in Sec. 10·2. It has been assumed that $X_{12} \leq 0.4$ and that therefore $|i_{12}| = I_0 X_{12}$, and it has been assumed that $X_{12}X_{23} \ll 2X'$, or, approximately, $X_{12} \ll 2$ for a high-gain amplifier. When the gain is high, for instance, so high that

$$\frac{X_{12}}{X_{23}} \leq 0.1, \tag{43}$$

neither of these conditions will be invalidated by operation at optimum bunching, $X' = 1.84$. In this case the calculation of $i_{13}$ may be extended into the range where $|i_{13}| = 2I_0 J_1(X')$. Although operation at this level might come under the heading of "power-amplifier operation" as the term has been used in this chapter, these comments on it fit more logically into the present section.

*Cascade Amplifiers with More Than Two Stages.*—The principles that have been discussed here for the two-stage amplifier apply, with additional complication of detail, to an $n$-stage cascade amplifier. However, as more stages are added and the gain is rapidly increased, it becomes more difficult to prevent feedback and regeneration. Self-sustaining oscillations or rapid fluctuations in gain therefore occur as the input signal is increased. These phenomena have been observed under certain conditions even in two-stage cascade amplifiers;[1] the feedback mechanism has been traced to the few secondary electrons that traverse the tube in a direction opposite to that of the initial beam. Such effects have made cascade amplifiers of more than two stages infeasible.

**10·9. Voltage Cascade Amplifier Gain; Comparison with Experiment.** *Electronic Transadmittance and Amplifier Gain.*—In finding the over-all gain of the amplifier it is assumed that $X'$ has been maximized with respect to middle-resonator tuning and is therefore given by Eq. (41b).

The absolute value of the electronic transadmittance is then given by

$$|Y_e| = \frac{M_3 |i_{13}|}{\alpha_1 V_0} = \frac{M_3 G_0 X'_{\max}}{\alpha_1}.$$

Equation (41b) gives $X'/X_{23}(0)$; the definition of $X_{23}$ gives $X_{23}(0)/\alpha_2$; and Eqs. (6) or (36) give $\alpha_2/\alpha_1$ for $\beta = 0$. From these it is found that

$$|Y_e| = \frac{G_{e1}G_{e2}}{G_2} \frac{\sin hl_1}{hl_1} \frac{\sin hl_2}{hl_2} \left[ 1 + \left( \frac{X_{13}}{X_{23}(0)} \right)^2 + \cdots \right], \qquad (44)$$

where $G_{e1}$ and $G_{e2}$ are the small-signal electronic transconductances defined for the first and second stages by exact analogy to Eq. (14). The small correction term in the square bracket may be evaluated by means of the relation

$$\frac{X_{13}}{X_{23}(0)} = \frac{G_2}{G_{e1}} \frac{M_1}{M_2} \frac{\theta_{01} + \theta_{02}}{\theta_{02}}. \qquad (45)$$

Debunching effects have been included in Eq. (44), but not in Eq. (45).

The power gain is given by writing Eq. (11) with the value of $|Y_e|$ as given by Eq. (44), with $G_2 = G_{BR2}$. Because the middle resonator is not normally loaded externally,

$$\frac{P_L}{P_1} = 4 \frac{G_{e1}^2}{4G_{BR1}G_{BR2}} \frac{G_{e2}^2}{4G_{BR3}G_{BR2}} \cdot \left( \frac{\sin hl_1}{hl_1} \frac{\sin hl_2}{hl_2} \right)^2$$
$$\left[ 1 + 2 \left( \frac{X_{13}}{X_{23}(0)} \right)^2 + \cdots \right]. \qquad (46)$$

More briefly, the power gain is four times the product of the single-stage gains of the individual stages, times the factor in square brackets, which is somewhat larger than unity. It is apparent that the optimization of the gain of each stage may be carried out independently in accordance

---

[1] E. Barlow and A. E. Harrison, "Klystron Resonator Coupling," Sperry Gyroscope Co. Report 5224-139, Feb. 14, 1944.

with the principles of Sec. 10·3. If the loss of beam current by grid absorption and possible beam spreading is not taken into account, the optimum design will be a symmetrical one with $l_1 = l_2$ and all three resonators identical.

*Illustrative Comparison of Cascade Amplifier Theory and Experiment.*—In Fig. 10·12 there is shown the relative output voltage (and hence relative $X'$) of an experimental high-gain cascade amplifier, observed as a function of $\delta_2$, the fractional frequency deviation of the middle resonator.[1] The power gain, which is not indicated in the figure, was measured as approximately 1000. The operating characteristics and other relevant data follow:[2]

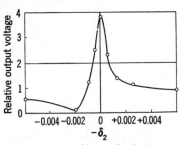

FIG. 10·12.—Observed relative output voltage of cascade amplifier klystron as a function of middle resonator detuning, $-\delta_2 = \omega_2/\omega - 1$.

| | |
|---|---|
| $V_0$ | 1600 volts |
| $\beta \equiv (v_0/c)$ | 0.080 |
| $I_0$ | 63 ma |
| $\lambda$ | 10 cm |
| $a$ | 0.5 cm |
| $l_1$ | 2.3 cm; $\theta_{01} = 18.3$ |
| $l_2$ | 1.3 cm; $\theta_{02} = 10.4$ |
| $G_R$ | $0.75 \times 10^{-5}$ mhos |
| $Q_R$ | 3500 |
| Gap spacing | 0.060 in. |

The electron gun and the resonators are the same as in the type 410R, the performance of which as a single-stage amplifier is analyzed in Sec. 10·7. The grid-transmission losses and the beam-loading effects are therefore the same as those given in that discussion.

In a comparison of the predictions of theory with the data of Fig. 10·12, the values of $X_{13}/X_{23}(0)$ and $Q_2$ are deduced from Fig. 10·12 by the procedure discussed in connection with Eq. (42); the same quantities are then calculated by dead reckoning through the use of Eq. (45) and the known beam loading. The power gain is then calculated.

If the effects of debunching, grid absorption, and beam loading are included, from the above operating characteristics the following values may be calculated:

[1] E. C. Levinthal, A. E. Harrison, E. Feenberg, "Cascade Amplification with Multiple-resonator Klystrons," Sperry Gyroscope Co. Report 5221-109, Oct. 15, 1943.

[2] Data on $Q_R$ provided by M. Chodorow, Sperry Gyroscope Co. Research Laboratories, Garden City, N. Y.

$$G_{BR2} = 1.75 \times 10^{-5} \text{ mhos}$$
$$G_{e1} = 21.6 \times 10^{-5} \text{ mhos}$$
$$G_{e2} = 10.2 \times 10^{-5} \text{ mhos}$$
$$\frac{\sin hl_1}{hl_1} = 0.91$$
$$\frac{\sin hl_2}{hl_2} = 0.98$$
$$M_1 = M_2 = M_3 = 0.87.$$

From the above values of $G_{BR2}$, $G_R$, and $Q_R$, $Q_{BR2}$ is found by use of the relation $Q_{BR2}/Q_R = G_R/G_{BR2}$ to have the value $Q_{BR2} = 1500$.

The application of these numerical values of Eq. (45), with $G_2$ set equal to $G_{BR2}$, gives $X_{23}(0)/X_{13} = 4.7$. Since the above values of $(\sin hl)/hl$ indicate that debunching is not serious, Eq. (45) is not greatly affected by its neglect of debunching.

In Fig. 10·12 the voltages at the points of maximum output voltage, complete middle-resonator detuning, and minimum output voltage are observed to be in the ratio $5.2{:}1{:}\sqrt{2}/8.2$. The two values of $X_{23}(0)/X_{13}$ that result, 5.2 and 8.2, are not very consistent. Since the value 8.2 is based upon $X_{\min}$, which involves a very small crystal-current reading, it may be inaccurate; the theoretical 4.7 agrees well with the other value, 5.2.

Figure 10·12 also indicates that $\delta_{\max} - \delta_{\min} = 0.0019$; a value for $X_{23}(0)/X_{13}$ of 5.2 in Eq. (40b) predicts $Q_{BR2}(\delta_{\max} - \delta_{\min}) = 2.85$, from which may be deduced a value of $Q_{BR2}$ equal to 1500. This result is in full agreement with the value of 1500 predicted from the known resonator $Q$ and beam loading.

From the above list of calculated shunt conductances and electron transconductances and from Eq. (44), the theoretical power gain is found to be 1150, which is within the limits of experimental error of the observed value of 1000.

With the exception of the already noted inconsistency, which would be removed if the value of the minimum relative voltage in Fig. 10·12 were in error by two, the quantitative agreement between theory and experiment is seen to be good.

**10·10. Power Cascade-amplifier Klystrons.**—There are two basic points involved in the discussion of two-resonator power amplifiers in Secs. 10·5 and 10·6. The first (Sec. 10·5) concerns the dependence of output-circuit driving current on input drive power and tube parameters when these quantities are such as to make the tube operate outside the "small-signal" range. The second concerned the effect that the physical limitation $|V_2| \leq (V_0 - V)$ had on optimum loading conditions and efficiency. This second point is common to all power amplifiers and need not be considered anew for power cascade amplifiers.  The first point, concerned with the factors that determine the maximum obtainable value of the output-circuit driving current $M_3 i_{13}$, does sometimes involve features peculiar to the cascade amplifier.

The essence of the discussion of cascade voltage amplifiers in Sec. 10·8 is the calculation of the equivalent bunching parameter $X'$.  It is noted that under certain conditions characteristic of high-gain amplifiers, namely,

$$\gamma \equiv \frac{X_{12} X_{23}}{2X'} \ll 1, \tag{47}$$

the bunched-beam-current component would be given by

$$|i_{13}| = 2I_0 J_1(X').$$

In such an instance there is very little to distinguish the single-stage amplifier from the cascade power amplifier.  The maximum obtainable value for $|i_{13}|$ is $1.16I_0$ for both amplifiers; and if too much r-f drive power is supplied, with the result that the beam is overbunched at the last resonator, then a detuning of any one of the two prior resonators will reduce the degree of bunching to the optimum point at which $X' = 1.84$ and $|i_{13}| = 1.16I_0$.  This process is noted in Fig. 10·4 of Sec. 10·5.

It is easily possible, however, in a low-gain cascade amplifier to have Eq. (47) invalidated.  Furthermore, it is apparent from Eq. (47) that, since $X_{12}$, $X_{23}$, and $X'$ are all proportional to the input-gap voltage $\alpha_1 V_0$, there is for every amplifier some level of r-f drive power above which Eq. (47) no longer holds and the bunching is no longer described by the effective bunching parameter $X'$.  It turns out that under such conditions of low gain or overdrive the maximum obtainable value of $|i_{13}|$, and hence of the output power, is increased by a factor of roughly 5/4.  It is with this phenomenon and its ramifications that the present section is concerned.

*Applicability of "Harmonic Bunching" to the Present Case.*—The discussion of cascade bunching in Sec. 9·6 is intended to be just sufficiently detailed to allow the drawing of some conclusions concerning the general manner in which this increase in the maximum value of $|i_{13}|$ is caused by the presence of harmonic terms in the kinematical equation.  Any exact treatment of this feature of cascade amplifiers would necessitate the use of a kinematical equation more exact than Eqs. (9.53) and (9.58).  In deriving these equations it is assumed that $X_{12} \leqq 0.4$, which by Eq. (59) implies $\gamma \leqq 0.2 X_{23}/X'$; it is apparent from Fig. 10·10 that in the cascade amplifier the quantities $X_{23} = X_{23}(0)$ cos $\beta$ and $X'$ are usually of the same order of magnitude.  Hence Eqs.

(53) and (58), when applied to cascade amplifiers, contain the implicit assumption $\gamma < 0.2$ (at least). But these same equations predict maximum $|i_{13}|$ at $\gamma = 0.4$. At $\gamma = 0.4$ an appreciable third-harmonic term is present in the kinematical equations; it does not, however, appreciably alter the maximum obtainable $|i_{13}|$. Therefore, in a sketchy discussion of the low-gain or overdriven amplifier there seems little point to going into the exact theory; the discussion is based upon a simple application of the results of Sec. 9·6.

To summarize the results referred to: An increase of the maximum value of $|i_{13}|$ by a factor 1.28 over the value predicted by simple bunching theory occurs when $X' \approx 2$, $\gamma \approx 0.4$, and $\theta' - \beta + \pi/2 = 0$. If $X'$ and $\gamma$ are in the vicinity of these optimum values and $\theta' - \beta + \pi/2 \neq 0$, $|i_{13}| \propto \cos \frac{1}{2}(\theta' - \beta + \pi/2)$. The dependence of $|i_{13}|/2I_0$ on $X'$ and on $\gamma$ for $\theta' = \beta - \pi/2$ is indicated in Fig. 9·11.

*Influence of Tube Parameters on the Increase in* $|i_{13}|$.—The general behavior of $X'$, $\gamma$, and $\theta' - \beta + \pi/2$ may be seen most readily with reference to Fig. 10·10. The deviations of $\cos \frac{1}{2}(\theta' - \beta + \pi/2)$ from unity are a measure of the lack of proper phase relation between the first- and second-harmonic components of the bunching. It is seen that in a high-gain tube $(X_{23}(0)/X_{13} \gg 1)$, the deviations of $\cos \frac{1}{2}(\theta' - \beta + \pi/2)$ from unity are very minor for any value of $\beta$. For $X_{23}(0)/X_{13} \geqq 1$ they are still minor for $\beta > 0$ but may be sizable for $\beta < 0$. This condition means that for $X_{23}(0)/X_{13} \gg 1$ the dependence of $|i_{13}|$ on $X'$ and $\gamma$ will be very close to that given in Fig. 9·11, regardless of the value of $\beta$; but when $X_{23}(0)/X_{13} > 1$ by no very large amount, and when $\beta < 0$, $|i_{13}|$ will be diminished from the value shown in that figure.

What is the condition for obtaining the optimum combination $X' = 2, \gamma = 0.4$? It will be observed that both $X'$ and $\gamma$ are proportional to the r-f input driving voltage; therefore if there is some value of $\beta$ at which the ratio $\gamma/X'$ has the value $0.4/2 = 0.2$, then there is some amount of r-f input drive power that will give $\gamma$ and $X'$ simultaneously the correct absolute values. This necessary condition, $\gamma/X' = 0.2$, may for ease of reference be written

$$\frac{X_{12}}{X_{13}} \frac{X_{13}}{X'} \frac{X_{23}}{X'} = 0.4, \tag{48}$$

in which $X_{12}/X_{13}$ is a quantity less than unity.

*Application to the High-gain Amplifier.*—Consider now the case of the high-gain amplifier for which $X_{23}(0)/X_{13} \gg 1$. Over most of the range of $\beta$, except for $\beta$ near $\pm\pi/2$, $X_{13}/X' \ll 1$ and $X_{23}/X' \approx 1$; hence Eq. (48) cannot be satisfied. If it is to be satisfied anywhere, it will be for $\beta \approx \pm\pi/2$. For such values of $\beta$ the situation is as shown in Fig. 10·13, which is an enlarged section of the relevant part of Fig. 10·10 when $X_{13}/X_{23}(0) \ll 1$. This figure shows that to a good approximation, the product of two of the factors in Eq. (48) has the value

$$\frac{X_{13}X_{23}}{X'^2} = \frac{X_{23}/X_{13}}{(1 \pm X_{23}/X_{13})^2}, \qquad \left(\beta \approx \pm \frac{\pi}{2}\right).$$

The expression with the upper sign ($\beta \approx +\pi/2$) has at $X_{23} = X_{13}$ a maximum value of $\frac{1}{4}$. Thus Eq. (48) cannot be completely satisfied for $\beta \approx +\pi/2$. The optimum condition $X' = 2$, $\gamma = 0.4$ cannot be reached for $\beta > 0$ as long as the gain is high enough for Fig. 10·13 to describe the facts when the equations $X_{13}/X' \ll 1$ and $X_{23}/X' \approx 1$ do not describe them. But on the other hand, for $\beta \approx -\pi/2$, Eq. (48)

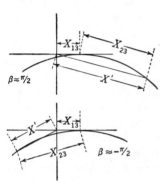

FIG. 10·13.—Determination of effective bunching parameter in high-gain cascade amplifier with $\beta \approx \pm \pi/2$ (middle resonator strongly detuned). Compare with Fig. 10·10.

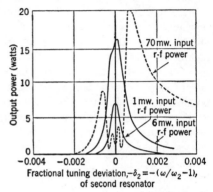

FIG. 10·14.—Output power of type 2K35 klystron cascade amplifier as function of middle resonator tuning, for three values of input r-f power.

will be satisfied some place in the vicinity of $X' = X_{13} = \frac{1}{2}X_{23}$. If, for the sake of a definite example, $X_{12}/X_{13}$ is taken as 0.4, and if the drive is then adjusted to optimize $X'$, the ideal combination is $X_{13} \approx 1.3$, $X_{23} \approx 3.3$, $X' \approx 2$, and $\gamma \approx 0.4$.

Thus, by drastic detuning and overdriving, the additional factor 1.28 in $|i_{13}|$ may be obtained from a high-gain amplifier; but this result is accomplished at the cost of detuning—a cost so great that $X_{13}$ has nearly the value required for optimum bunching in the absence of the second resonator. Thus, the gain of the device is of the same order of magnitude as the gain of a single-stage amplifier of the same construction.

When $\beta$ is not near $\pm\pi/2$, $\gamma$ is small, and therefore $|i_{13}|$ is once more given by $2I_0J_1(X')$; but since $X'$ increases rapidly as $\beta$ approaches zero, there is drastic overbunching and diminution of the output power.

*Illustrative High-gain Amplifier Tuning Curves.*—Some of these points are illustrated by Fig. 10·14, in which is shown the amplification characteristic[1] of the type 2K35—a 3000 Mc/sec high-gain cascade amplifier

[1] E. C. Levinthal, A. E. Harrison, E. Feenberg, "Cascade Amplification with Multiple-resonator Klystrons," Sperry Gyroscope Co. Report 5221-109, Oct. 15, 1943.

that is very similar to the type 410R in electron optics and resonator structure. The data in this figure correspond to operating conditions of $V_0 = 1800$ volts, $I_0 = 77$ ma. Although this figure is intended primarily as an illustration of the dependence of output power on middle-resonator tuning at high r-f input power, it should be noted in passing that the small-signal gain is shown to be about 7000.

In this figure the output power is shown as a function of middle-resonator tuning for three different values of drive power. The smallest of these drive powers, 1 mw, corresponds to small-signal high-gain operation. It is seen from the figure that the next highest value of drive power, 6 mw, is just slightly more than is necessary to maximize the output power at $\beta = 0$. The highest drive power shown, 70 mw, is insufficient to make $X' \approx 2$ at the amount of detuning required to make $\gamma = 0.4$; a higher drive power would produce a still higher amount of output power at a still greater degree of detuning. Nevertheless, a 35 per cent increase in output power is already apparent at the detuned peak. (Since this tube is probably operating with $|V_3| < V_0$, the ideal 28 per cent increase in $|i_{13}|$ that is to be expected from the cascade bunching process with overdrive would correspond to a 64 per cent increase in output power.) The rapid fluctuations in output power that are caused by overbunching are also apparent at the center of the tuning curve for the overdriven case.

*Application to the Low-gain Amplifier.*—Considerations similar to the above may be carried out for an inherently low-gain amplifier $(X_{23}(0)/X_{13} \approx 1)$. It will be found that the optimum value of $\beta$ will be positive and much nearer zero than in the high-gain amplifier. For example, with $X_{12}/X_{13} = 0.8$ and $X_{23}(0)/X_{13} = 1$, the optimum combination is $\beta = 0$, $X_{13} = 1.4$, $X_{23} = 1.4$, $X' = 2$, and $\gamma = 0.4$. This combination has about the same over-all gain as the detuned high-gain amplifier discussed above.

The results of the present section may be summed up in the following way. In a power amplifier that is supplied with enough input r-f power to maximize the output power, the use of an intermediate resonator in a power amplifier does not increase or decrease the gain, but it does increase the fundamental component of the bunched beam current by a factor up to 1.28. Also, if not enough input r-f power is supplied to reach the absolute maximum of output power, a very sizable increase in gain may be obtained over the two-resonator power amplifier.

The influence, on the harmonic components $i_{m3}$, of an intermediate resonator tuned to the fundamental or a harmonic frequency has been investigated;[1] this work is not discussed here.

[1] E. Feenberg, "Theory of Cascade Bunching," Sperry Gyroscope Co. Report 5221-1043, Aug. 22, 1945.

# CHAPTER 11

## FREQUENCY MULTIPLIER KLYSTRONS AND TWO-RESONATOR KLYSTRON OSCILLATORS

### By D. R. Hamilton

**11·1. Frequency Multiplier Klystrons.**—In Sec. 9·2 the unusual waveform of the bunched beam current in a klystron is noted, and typical waveforms for the simplest type of bunching are shown in Fig. 9·4. These waveforms are characterized by sharp peaks that are very rich in harmonic content. The Fourier analysis of these peaks, carried out in Sec. 9·2, shows that the current components at the $m$th harmonic, $i_m$, are given by

$$i_m = 2I_0 e^{-im\theta_0} J_m(mX). \tag{9·9}$$

The resulting dependence of $i_m$ on $X$ is indicated in Fig. 9·5. This figure indicates two interesting features: the slow diminution of the maximum value of $i_m$ as $m$ increases, and the more rapid narrowing of this first maximum as $m$ increases.

The maximum value of $J_m(mX)$ is approximately equal to $0.65m^{-1/3}$; hence the r-f power available (with operation at $|V_2| < (V_0 - V)$) should be proportional to $m^{-2/3}$. The exact values for the maxima of $J_1$ and $J_{10}$ indicate that the efficiency at the tenth harmonic should be 28 per cent of that at the fundamental (that is, that of an amplifier). A number of factors act to reduce the experimental results below this first hopeful estimate, but the general fact of the unusually high harmonic content remains and has been utilized in the development of frequency multiplier klystrons.

The second feature of Fig. 9·5, the small range of values of $X$ at which $i_{10}$ is appreciable, indicates that a 50 per cent diminution in $|i_{10}|^2$ would be caused by a change of the bunching parameter by $\pm 15$ per cent. This sensitivity of output power to input r-f drive could be inconvenient. However, it will be seen that the actual situation may be greatly improved over the predictions of simple theory in this respect.

A typical frequency multiplier klystron, the type 2K37, is shown schematically in Fig. 11·1. The resonant frequencies of the input and output cavities are, respectively, about 300 and 3000 Mc/sec. As a matter of mechanical convenience, the input cavity is not simply a scaled-up-by-ten version of the output cavity; by fairly heavy capacitance

285

loading the size of the input cavity is made not much larger than that of the output cavity.

*Applications of Frequency Multiplier Klystrons.*—The primary use to which frequency multipliers have been put is the generation of microwave power at some integral multiple of the reference frequency of a quartz crystal. Generators of such crystal-controlled microwave frequencies have been used as frequency standards; cascade amplifiers driven by the crystal-controlled output of a frequency multiplier have been used to provide 100 watts of frequency-stabilized power for various types of experimental microwave communication equipment. In a typical frequency-multiplication chain for such uses one might start with a 5-Mc/sec quartz crystal; successive stages of conventional frequency multiplication would produce power in the vicinity of 300 Mc/sec, which would then be used to drive a multiplier klystron with output at 3000 to 6000 Mc/sec.

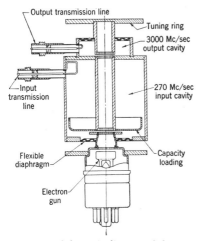

Fig. 11·1.—Schematic diagram of the type 2K36 klystron frequency multiplier.

The optimum frequency at which to make the transition from triodes to klystrons in such a chain depends upon the state of development and the inherent capabilities of the two tube types. Very good lighthouse tubes and other planar triodes have been developed in the 300- to 1000-Mc/sec range; on the other hand, for a klystron with a given electron beam and a given drift space the r-f drive voltage required to produce optimum bunching varies inversely to the drive frequency, and the r-f output increases as the order of multiplication is decreased. These factors indicate that the optimum frequency for the transition from triodes to klystron may be about 1000 Mc/sec.

*Influence of Debunching in Frequency Multipliers.*—Debunching, which is always very relevant in klystrons, attains increased importance in frequency multipliers through an interesting chain of circumstances. In the first place, with a given ratio $V/V_0$ of input-gap r-f voltage to beam voltage, the drift length required for a given value of $X$ is inversely proportional to the input frequency. The tendency, then, would be to economize on r-f drive powers by using a long drift space. The debunching wave number $h$ depends, however, only on the d-c properties of the beam and is independent of frequency; this makes it impossible to hold constant the product of drift distance times input frequency without sustaining serious debunching losses. But holding the drift distance constant to avoid debunching then makes the input r-f voltage inversely proportional to input frequency. The consequence at low drive frequencies is that $V > V_0$.

In one way this excess of gap voltage over beam voltage is, however, a blessing in disguise; for as is discussed in Sec. 9·6, having $V > V_0$ makes the output r-f power very insensitive to r-f drive. This same fact, however, also raises the r-f drive power, thereby making the latter more important than the d-c klystron input power as a factor of over-all efficiency.

The accuracy of the theory of longitudinal debunching as given in Sec. 9·3 is diminished as the drive frequency $\omega_1$ is decreased. Aside from the violation of the assumption $V \ll V_0$ as $\omega_1$ decreases, there is the additional fact that, whereas the distance $\beta\lambda_1$ between bunches is increasing, the longitudinal-debunching theory of Sec. 9·3 assumes $\beta\lambda_1 \ll a$. It has already been noted in that section that in the part of the beam adjacent to the conducting walls of the drift tube there can be no longitudinal electric field and hence no debunching. Physically speaking, the effect of increasing $\beta\lambda_1/a$ is to give this wall effect more prominence and thus to reduce longitudinal debunching.

On the other hand, the accuracy of the theory of transverse debunching is increased as $\beta\lambda_1/a$ is increased; and in the limit of large $\beta\lambda_1/a$, the presence of a conducting wall at the outer edge of a beam doubles the transverse debunching because of the image forces arising in the conductor. The effects just noted have been considered in some detail by Feenberg.[1]

*Experimentally Observed Debunching in Multiplier Klystrons.*—These considerations regarding the relative importance of the two types of debunching make it worth while to compare debunching theory and experiment under circumstances to which simple bunching theory may be applied, before going on to the implications of the designs with the large $V/V_0$ that debunching makes necessary. This procedure is given point, over and above the question of multipliers, by the probability that experimental debunching effects may be more clear-cut in multipliers, for which $X \approx 1.2$ at optimum bunching, than they are in amplifiers with $X \approx 1.8$ at optimum bunching. This probability arises from the thought that the theory, which is not strictly applicable above $X = 1$, should have more semblance of truth at $X = 1.2$ than at $X = 1.8$. Thus a comparison between theory and experiment at this point is of interest to the whole subject of debunching as well as to multipliers.

[1] E. Feenberg, "Theory of Bunching," Sperry Gyroscope Co. Report 5221-105, Nov. 24, 1942; and "Small-signal Theory of Longitudinal and Transverse Debunching," Sperry Gyroscope Co. Report 5221-114, Apr. 12, 1944.'

Debunching has a readily observable influence on the operation of any given tube. Transverse debunching causes a diminution in the current passing through the output gap. Longitudinal debunching causes a diminution in bunching parameter at the output gap which may be compensated for by a corresponding increase in r-f drive voltage. These points are readily checked experimentally; Figs. 11·2 and 11·3 give relevant experimental data.[1]

In each of these figures one of the coordinates is "exciter plate voltage," which is the voltage on the plate of the exciter tube just preceding the input to the multiplier. The r-f voltage appearing across

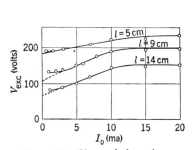

Fig. 11·2.—Observed dependence on beam current $I_0$ of the exciter plate voltage $V_{exc}$ for optimum output power from an experimental klystron frequency multiplier; beam voltage 500 volts, input and output frequencies 270 and 2970 Mc/sec.

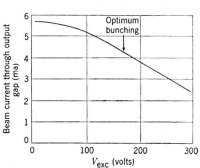

Fig. 11·3.—Diminution of beam through last resonator with increase of input r-f drive. Experimental klystron multiplier, $l = 5$ cm, $V_0 = 400$ volts.

the input gap of the multiplier should be approximately proportional to this exciter plate voltage. To determine the constant of proportionality, measurements were made of the maximum voltage required to stop electrons that had passed through the input r-f gap. These measurements indicated that the exciter plate voltage and the input-gap r-f voltage are the same to within $\pm 5$ per cent; this similarity is mostly fortuitous.

In Fig. 11·2 the exciter plate voltage required for optimum bunching is shown as a function of $I_0$ for different values of $l$.

At optimum bunching—that is, with $X$ fixed at 1.2—the product $(V/V_0)$ $(\sin hl)/hl$ is constant; hence the exciter plate voltage required for any beam current is proportional to

$$\frac{hl}{\sin hl} \approx 1 + \frac{1}{6}(hl)^2 \approx 1 + \left(\frac{l}{a}\right)^2 \frac{10G_0}{\beta}.$$

[1] A. E. Harrison, R. O. Haxby, "Klystron Frequency Multipliers," Sperry Gyroscope Co. Report 5221-115, Apr. 12, 1944.

This approximately linear dependence of drive voltage on beam current in Fig. 11·2 appears except at very low beam current and near the maximum beam current. At low current the high negative control-grid voltage used for diminishing $I_0$ has a focusing action such that the current is simultaneously reduced in magnitude and concentrated in a smaller beam. The debunching therefore does not decrease in proportion to the decrease in $I_0$. It is known that the electron gun used in this tube likewise gives a divergent beam when the control-grid voltage is run too positive; this accounts for the leveling off of the curves at high $I_0$.

When all space-charge effects at the low-current end are eliminated by extrapolating the linear portion of the curves to zero beam current and by setting the exciter plate voltage equal to $V$, values of $V/V_0 = 0.368$, 0.216, and 0.128 are obtained for $l = 5$, 9, and 14 cm respectively. The input cavity is tuned to $\lambda_1 = 110$ cm; and $\beta = 0.045$ at $V_0 = 500$ volts, hence the corresponding values of the bunching parameter, $\pi l V/V_0\beta\lambda$, are 1.18, 1.23, and 1.15. The agreement with the theoretical value of 1.2 is good and provides gratifying agreement with simple bunching theory.

An increase in exciter power with increasing klystron beam current could also be produced by beam loading in the input cavity. This increase would not affect the comparison between theory and experiment that has just been made, but it would affect any conclusion about debunching that might be drawn from Fig. 11·2. It is known that there is some beam loading in this input resonator, but it has not been accurately measured. It seems safe to ignore it for the following reason. First, the $G_R$ of the input cavity is calculated to be higher by a factor of 5 than that of typical 3000-Mc/sec cavities because of the heavy capacitance loading used in reducing the cavity size. A correspondingly higher beam-loading conductance $G_B$ would be required in order to produce a given effect. But the beam current in Fig. 11·2 is very low by the criteria used in the estimates of beam loading at earlier points in the previous chapter.

Having checked simple bunching at zero current in Fig. 11·2, the behavior at finite beam current in this figure will now be analyzed on the assumption that it is caused by debunching. The relative increase in the exciter plate voltage over its value at zero current should be $hl/\sin hl$. At $I_0 = 7$ ma the exciter plate voltage is increased over its zero-current value by factors of 1.15, 1.56, and 1.85, which correspond to $hl = 0.9$, 1.53, and 1.80 or $h = 0.18$, 0.17, and 0.13 for $l = 5$, 9, and 14 cm respectively. For this beam voltage and for the radius of the drift tube, $a$, equal to 0.5 cm, these values of $h$ would be produced by values of $I_0$ of 3.1, 2.7, and 1.6 ma.

Because most debunching takes place just before the beam enters the output gap, the actual cathode-emission current should be reduced by two factors before comparing with the above values: a factor of 0.85 for grid-absorption losses before entering the drift tube, and a factor $1 - (X/6)(hl)^2 = 1 - 0.2(hl)^2$ for transverse-debunching losses of the beam current. If the effects of these two factors are included, the actual beam currents at the output gap are calculated to be 5.0, 3.1, and 2.1 ma respectively. The beam currents that are necessary to explain the observed longitudinal debunching thus seem 25 per cent lower than the actual beam currents; this is probably the extent of the diminution of longitudinal debunching as caused by the conducting wall effect.

In Fig. 11·3 a measurement of beam loss due to transverse debunching is shown as a function of exciter-plate voltage, for $l = 5$ cm. Since $V_0 = 400$ volts, Fig. 11·3 is not directly comparable to Fig. 11·2; because $I_0$ is proportional to $V_0^{3/2}$ and in Fig. 11·3 is measured after being diminished by 0.71 by four grid absorptions, the zero-drive beam current of 5.7 ma would correspond to 11.2 ma in Fig. 11·3. Since $h = 0.89$ for $I_0 = 7$ ma, $hl = 0.89 \sqrt{11.2/7.0} = 1.13$ here. The resulting theoretical transverse-debunching current reduction of

$$1 - \left(\frac{X}{6}\right)(hl)^2 = 0.75$$

compares well with the observed value $4.5/5.7 = 0.79$.

The conclusions from these comparisons are as follows: The effect of longitudinal debunching on the drive voltage required for optimum bunching in this series of three tubes is less than elementary debunching theory predicts; the difference may very well be due to the wall effect. The beam loss that is due to transverse spreading is slightly greater than that predicted by elementary debunching theory. The over-all agreement is perhaps better than might have been expected.

**11·2. Frequency Multiplier Klystrons; Comparison of Theory and Experiment.** *The Theoretical Effects of Debunching on Multiplier Output Power.*—What effect does this debunching have on output power of the multiplier? Transverse debunching predicts simply a certain loss of current from the bunch, and hence a diminution of output power proportional to the square of the current. Longitudinal debunching, as applied to a beam of infinite width for $X \leqq 1$, implies no diminution of output power or change of waveform, but simply an increase in the value of $V/V_0$ required for optimum bunching.

As already noted in Sec. 9·3, however, in a beam of finite cross section with a conducting wall there is no longitudinal debunching at the outer edge of the beam. This fact has already been called upon to explain the way in which, in Fig. 11·2, the drive voltage for optimum bunching does not increase with beam current so rapidly as expected. "Optimum bunching," of course, must now be taken to mean an average over the beam width because the bunching parameter now varies with radial position in the beam.   If $X$ varies over a wider range than corresponds to the width of the first maximum of $J_m(mX)$, then a large part of the beam contributes nothing to the average value of $i_m$, or may even diminish it.   Thus longitudinal debunching probably diminishes output power more by virtue of its variation with radial distance from the axis of the beam than it does by virtue of its mere presence.   A glance at Fig. 9·5 shows that a slight variation of $X$ across the width of the beam becomes increasingly serious as $m$, the harmonic order, is increased; this is the reason for discussing the subject in connection with multipliers.

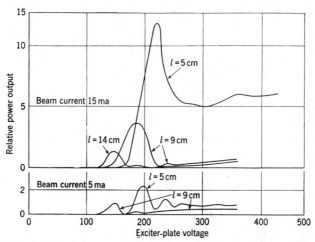

Fig. 11·4.—Observed relative multiplier output power as function of exciter-plate voltage for various values of beam current and drift length.   Same tubes as used in Figs. 11·2 and 11·3.

*The Observed Influence of Debunching on Multiplier Output Power.*— These comments serve as background for Fig. 11·4, in which is shown the variation of the relative output power with exciter plate voltage for the same tubes as were used for the data of Figs. 11·2 and 11·3.   Since the relative output powers were measured with a crystal rectifier that was probably saturating at the higher power levels, an accurate quantitative interpretation of the relative powers cannot be made.   However, the relative output powers will be compared with what would be expected on the basis of transverse debunching alone.

Before making this comparison, it should be noted that debunching will not only cause differences between various curves in Fig. 11·4, but will also affect the shape of an individual curve.   In spite of the effect of debunching on an individual curve, the similarity to the ideal bunching curves of Fig. 9·5 is striking provided it is noted that Fig. 9·5 shows $|i_m|$, and Fig. 11·4 shows relative $|i_m|^2$.

In analyzing Fig. 11·4 it is to be noted that although the higher beam current is normally 15 ma, it appears likely, from Fig. 11·2 and from the known divergence of the beam at higher currents, that the equivalent cathode-emission current is less—say 12 ma for $l = 5$ cm, and 10 ma each for $l = 9$ and 14 cm. Scaling up to these currents the values of debunching wavenumber estimated for $I_0 = 7$ ma from Fig. 11·2, one may obtain the values of $hl$, sin $hl/hl$, and $I_0^2[1 + 0.1(hl)^2]^{-4}$ shown in Table 10. Of these quantities, (sin $hl)/hl$ gives the ratio of bunching parameter at the edge of the beam to "mean" bunching parameter, by virtue of the way in which the values of $h$ were derived empirically from Fig. 11·2. The quantity $[1 + 0.1(hl)^2]^{-4}$ gives the diminution of output power by transverse debunching, and is used instead of the approximate $[1 - 0.2(hl)^2]^2$. The quantity $I_0^2[1 + 0.1(hl)^2]^{-4}$ should therefore be proportional to the total output power if the longitudinal effects do not greatly predominate. In calculating this quantity, $I_0$ is taken not as the nominal 15 ma of Fig. 11·2 but rather as the values 12, 10, and 10 ma discussed above.

TABLE 11·1.—COMPARISON OF OBSERVED RELATIVE OUTPUT POWERS OF FIG. 11·4 AND THE RELATIVE OUTPUT POWERS PREDICTED ON THE BASIS OF TRANSVERSE DEBUNCHING

| $l$, cm | Nominal $I_0$, ma | $hl$ | $\dfrac{\sin hl}{hl}$ | $I_0^2[1 + 0.1(hl)^2]^{-4}$ $\propto$ relative $P$ (predicted) | Normalized $P$ (predicted) | Relative $P$ (observed) | Normalized $P$ (observed) |
|---|---|---|---|---|---|---|---|
| 5 | 5 | 0.75 | 0.90 | $5^2 \times 0.81 = 20$ | 1 | 2.4 | 1 |
|  | 15 | 1.16 | 0.78 | $12^2 \times 0.60 = 86$ | 4.3 | 12.0 | 5.0 |
| 9 | 5 | 1.30 | 0.73 | $5^2 \times 0.53 = 13$ | 0.65 | 1.0 | 0.42 |
|  | 15 | 1.84 | 0.52 | $10^2 \times 0.31 = 31$ | 1.55 | 3.7 | 1.54 |
| 14 | 15 | 2.54 | 0.123 | $10^2 \times 0.14 = 14$ | 0.69 | 1.35 | 0.56 |

The experimentally observed output powers also are listed in Table 11·1. In order to simplify the comparison of prediction and experiment, the predicted and observed relative power outputs are normalized to unity for $l = 5$ cm and $I_0 = 5$ ma.

It is apparent that the general behavior of the observed relative powers is in agreement with the behavior that is predicted by taking into consideration only the transverse-debunching losses. From the width of the peaks in Fig. 11·4—approximately 20 per cent at half-power—one would conclude that output power should be reduced 50 per cent by a uniform spread of $\pm 20$ per cent in the values of the bunching parameter at different radial positions in the beam. The fact that there are no such unexplained diminutions in relative output power that may be ascribed to longitudinal effects, and the fact that the simple longitudinal theory predicts fairly well the relation between beam current and r-f drive voltage, seem to indicate that any wall effects do not extend very far into the beam.

*Absolute Multiplier Efficiency.*—All these deductions have been based on relative measurements. It is relevant to make a comparison of theory and absolute output power. The absolute output power measured for the tube with $l = 5$ cm, actual $I_0 = 12$ ma, $V_0 = 500$ volts is about 25 mw, corresponding to an efficiency of 0.4 per cent. If transverse debunching loss, absorption of beam current by grids, and the beam-coupling coefficient of the output gap are allowed for, and if $G_{BR} = 10^{-5}$ mhos for the output cavity, the calculated power output is 90 mw for a predicted efficiency of 1.5 per cent. This agreement is not as good as that obtained in previous sections for other types of klystrons.

This calculation assumes that $|i_m| \approx 2I_0 \times 0.65m^{-\frac{1}{3}}$, as given by simple bunching theory. A deviation from this expression would have a marked influence on the predicted output power; it should therefore be noted that evidence has been presented[1] tending to show that in at least one multiplier $|i_m|$ is proportional to $m^{-\frac{3}{4}}$ for $10 < m < 30$. Whatever the source of this more rapid diminution with $m$, it probably does not hold true for $1 < m < 10$ because it would then make the calculated absolute efficiency half the size of the observed efficiency in the above example. It may be that this $m^{-\frac{3}{4}}$ behavior for $10 < m < 30$ represents the influence of the longitudinal wall effect, which gets worse as $m$ increases.

*Multiplier Operation at High Input-gap Voltage.*—The zero-current values of $V/V_0$ that were deduced for optimum bunching in the tubes just under consideration ranged up to $V/V_0 = 0.37$ for $l = 5$ cm. This value of $V/V_0$ is sufficient to cause the smoothing out of the zero of output power for $l = 5$ cm by the second-order high-$V$ effects described in Sec. 9·4, as is discussed in Sec. 10·7 in connection with the similar amplifier data of Fig. 10·8. It is interesting to note the greatly increased smoothing-out for $l = 5$ cm, $I_0 = 15$ ma. It may be that the second-order high-$V$ effects are beginning to merge into the $V > V_0$ effects of Secs. 9·6 and 9·7 here because $V/V_0 \approx 0.8$ at an exciter plate voltage of 400 volts.

Be that as it may, all the data and analysis so far have been by way of exploring the phenomena that force one to still shorter drift distance and higher $V/V_0$. Figure 11·5 shows the analogous curves of output power vs. input-gap r-f voltage for a multiplier with the same input

---

[1] A. E. Harrison, R. O. Haxby, "Klystron Frequency Multipliers," Sperry Gyroscope Co. Report 5221-115, April 12, 1944.

frequency as those just considered, but with $V_0 = 400$ volts, $l = 2.5$ cm, and hence $\theta_0 \approx 3.5$ radians. The independent variable in Fig. 11·5 is the input-gap voltage as measured by the voltage required to stop all the electrons of the beam (see discussion following Fig. 11·3).

The fact that the output power is at the 19th harmonic in this tube does not affect the present discussion. Here $V/V_0 \approx 0.7$ at optimum bunching. Figure 9·17 predicts, for $\theta_0 \approx 3.5$, that beyond the simple optimum bunching the output power will level off at 15 to 20 per cent of the optimum-bunching peak. Actually, as may be seen in Fig. 11·5, the output power rises continually instead of leveling off, and it rises considerably above the level of the first peak.

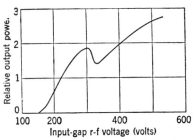

FIG. 11·5.—Dependence of relative output power at the 19th harmonic on input gap r-f voltage. Input frequency 270 Mc/sec, $l = 2.5$ cm; $V_0 = 400$ volts; $\theta_0 = 3.5$ radians.

This continual rise is probably due to the fact that the electrons of the bunch are now those that have been the most accelerated by the large input-gap r-f voltage. Thus the higher the input-gap r-f voltage, the less is the effect of debunching and the output-gap beam-coupling coefficient in reducing the driving current in the last resonator. The fact that this bunched current for $V > V_0$ is greater than that for $V < V_0$, instead of less as predicted by Fig. 9·17, is probably a combination of the high-electron-velocity factor already mentioned and the greater simplicity of the bunching process for $V > V_0$.

**11·3. Two-resonator Klystron Oscillators.**—The preceding chapter and the first two sections of the present chapter have been concerned solely with klystrons in which no energy is fed back from the output to the input circuit. A klystron amplifier, like any other amplifier, can be converted into a free-running oscillator by installing the proper feedback. The maximum ideal efficiency of such an oscillator is 58 per cent with simple bunching, and 74 per cent if a second harmonic is added to the bunching by the processes described in Secs. 9·5 and 9·8. This often-quoted ideal efficiency assumes $|V_2| = V_0$, a circuit efficiency of unity, no beam loading or resonator losses, no debunching, and no grid interception. The factors thus assumed are common to both oscillators and amplifiers, and have already been discussed in Secs. 10·7 and 10·9.

More basic to the operation of multiresonator oscillators than these factors are the constraints introduced by feedback. A concise presentation of the features that are peculiar to oscillators requires the passing over of those points which oscillators share with amplifiers; the modifying effect of such factors may be seen in the conclusions reached by this discussion.

It is particularly to be noted that the simplifying assumption, $|V_2| < (V_0 - V)$, is hereby made in order to avoid the complications of Sec. 10·6 that arise when output-gap voltage reaches the upper limit $(V_0 - V)$. It is also advantageous to simplify the discussion of oscillator-circuit features by assuming an extremely simple form of feedback—a frequency-insensitive mutual inductance $M_c$ between output and input circuits.[1]     This simple mutual inductance[2] is a good representation of the feedback coupling when the latter is provided by a slot or loop connecting two adjacent cavities.     When the feedback coupling is provided by a comparatively long transmission line, there are, of course, various resonances and frequency sensitivities associated with the latter, but when the oscillation frequency is distant from any such resonant frequencies, the general coupled-circuit features of the oscillator are well represented by the coupling assumed above.

Over and above these particular assumptions is the intention to discuss only two-resonator oscillators in detail.     Two other related types of oscillators should, however, be mentioned in passing.

One is the so-called "floating drift-tube" oscillator, in which practically all the wall dividing the first and second cavities has been removed, leaving only enough material to provide a means of mechanical support for the drift tube.     As a result, that which was originally a pair of separately-tuned cavities is now a single cavity, with a consequent increased ease of tuning.     On the other hand, it is still possible to retain the advantage of using an input-gap r-f voltage that is smaller than the output-gap voltage, because these two gaps are separated.     A tube of this type thus combines the ease of tuning of the reflex klystron (see succeeding chapters) with one of the r-f advantages of the two-resonator oscillator.     An example of such an oscillator with floating drift-tube is the 2K40, developed at the Bell Telephone Laboratories.

The other multiresonator oscillator that should be noted is the oscillator-buffer klystron.     Here a third resonator is placed along the axis of the beam, separated by a very short drift space from the second resonator.     The first two resonators constitute an ordinary two-resonator oscillator, which has, however, no external load.     If the drift space between the second and third resonators is short, the waveform of the bunched beam current will not be changed appreciably in passing from

---

[1] The "input" and "output" nomenclature, although derived from amplifier usage, remains convenient and unambiguous in discussing oscillators.

[2] Note the subscript that distinguishes the mutual inductance $M_c$ from the beam-coupling coefficient $M$ (which is assumed the same for both cavities).

second to third resonator; hence the third (or "buffer") resonator is able to abstract from the beam and deliver to an external load nearly as much power as could the second resonator if it were properly loaded. The primary utility of this oscillator-buffer arrangement lies in the fact

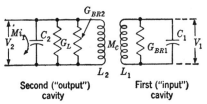

that any change of the load caused by the buffer resonator is unable to influence the frequency of oscillation because the latter is determined by the first two resonators. The oscillator-buffer klystron thus provides a very stable source of power. A typical klystron of this type is the 2K34, produced by the Sperry Gyroscope Company; this

Fig. 11·6.—Lumped-constant equivalent circuit for the two-resonator klystron oscillator.

klystron is similar in construction and performance to the type 410R, which is discussed in some detail in the preceding and present chapters.

*Representation of the Two-resonator Klystron Oscillator.*—As a result of these various simplifications, the two-resonator klystron oscillator under discussion is represented in a lumped-constant manner by Fig. 11·6. The influence of the bunched beam current on the output circuit is represented by the driving current $Mi_1$, applied across the shunt resonant output circuit, as discussed in Chap. 3. The effect of the

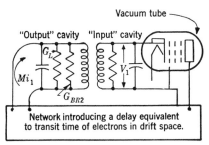

Fig. 11·7.—Hypothetical oscillator using circuit of, and having characteristics of, a two-resonator klystron oscillator (Fig. 11·6), but deriving $Mi_1$ from $V_1$ by conventional means rather than by velocity modulation and bunching.

external load applied to the output circuit is represented by the additional shunt conductance $G_L$; and the shunt conductances of the respective beam-loaded cavities are $G_{BR1}$ and $G_{BR2}$. Thus $G_2 = G_{BR2} + G_L$ and $G_1 = G_{BR1}$.

Figure 11·6 is not concerned with the manner in which $V_1$ produces $Mi_1$ by velocity modulation and bunching. As a matter of interest in structure, Fig. 11·7 illustrates a hypothetical oscillator using conventional low-frequency electronics and having the same characteristics as the klystron oscillator; here the generation of $Mi_1$ by $V_1$ is simulated by the action of a conventional multigrid vacuum tube that has no coupling between input and output circuits, and which is followed by a delay line that introduces a delay equal to the transit time of the electrons in the drift space.

It is clear from Fig. 11·4 that, if $Mi_1$ is given, the r-f voltage across the first gap $V_1$ is uniquely determined by the usual laws of circuit theory. This fact does not depend upon any knowledge of the origin of $Mi_1$. It is equally clear that the fact that this is a klystron oscillator—that is, that $Mi_1$ is produced by $V_1$ by the physical mechanism of velocity modulation and bunching—also uniquely determines the ratio $Mi_1/V_1$. In a steady state of oscillation these two relations between $Mi_1$ and $V_1$, arising from two different sets of physical circumstances, must be satisfied. This requirement may be expressed as follows: the circuit transfer admittance $Y_c$ (or "transadmittance"), must equal the electronic transadmittance $Y_e$; that is, with the sign convention noted in the next section,

$$Y_e = Y_c. \tag{1}$$

**11·4. Condition for Oscillation.**—The condition stated in Eq. (1) is sufficient to determine all the characteristics of oscillator behavior. The present section is devoted to a discussion of these two transadmittances and some of the consequences of the condition for oscillation.

*The Electronic Transadmittance.*—By Eq. (9·9) $i_1 = 2I_0e^{-i\theta_0}J_1(X)$, where $V_1 = -jV$. Although the assumption of this particular phase for $V_1$ is not retained, the phase of the electronic transadmittance is independent of the assumed phase of $V_1$; and from the above expressions the electronic transadmittance has already been found to be

$$Y_e = \frac{Mi_1}{V_1} = je^{-i\theta_0}G_e\frac{2J_1(X)}{X}. \tag{10·15}$$

It may be recalled from the discussion of amplifier theory in Sec. 10·3 that $G_e$ is the small-signal electronic transconductance, $G_e \equiv M^2\theta_0G_0/2$, which is independent of beam voltage for the customary constant-perveance electron gun; the conductance compression, $2J_1(X)/X$, which gives the diminution of $Y_e$ when $X$ is more than infinitesimal, is shown in Fig. 10·2.

*The Circuit Transadmittance.*—A few comments about sign conventions are in order before writing down the circuit transadmittance. The primary sign conventions that have so far been made are the following: (1) the instantaneous value of the bunched-beam-current component is positive during the "passage of the bunch," and (2) the instantaneous r-f gap voltage is positive when accelerating the electrons of the beam. As a consequence of these two conventions, the average power $P$ delivered to the output circuit is given by

$$P = -\tfrac{1}{2}\mathrm{Re}(Mi_1^* V_2) = -\tfrac{1}{2}\mathrm{Re}(Y_e^* V_1^* V_2).   \quad (2)$$

To these conventions must be added another: the mutual inductance $M_c$ and the circuit-coupling coefficient $k(k^2 \equiv M_c^2/L_1 L_2)$ is taken to be positive when $V_1 \propto -jV_2$ at resonance of both circuits to the frequency of the driving current. (It should be noted that in circuit considerations based on Fig. 11·6, $V_1$ and $V_2$ are the secondary and primary voltages respectively.) This convention is necessary because the sign of $k$ may be reversed by a simple change in coupling such as the one shown in Fig. 11·8.

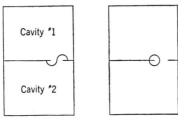

Fig. 11·8.—Illustration of means of changing sign of the coupling coefficient $k$ by a change in the symmetry of a feedback loop.

Given this sign convention, a conventional lumped-constant circuit analysis shows that the circuit transconductance is given by

$$Y_c \equiv \frac{Mi_1}{V_1} = jG_2 \sqrt{\frac{L_2}{L_1}} \frac{[(1 + 2jQ_1\delta_1)(1 + 2jQ_2\delta_2) + k^2 Q_1 Q_2]}{kQ_1}.   \quad (3)$$

Here, as usual, $\delta_1 \equiv (\omega - \omega_1)/\omega_1$, and a similar relation holds for $\delta_2$; $Q_2$ is the $Q$ of the output circuit including the effect of the load conductance $G_L$. However, Eq. (3) is not a convenient form because the frequency of the driving current (that is, the frequency of oscillation) appears both in $\delta_1$ and $\delta_2$. A better form may be obtained by use of the following notation:

$$\delta \equiv \frac{\omega - (\omega_1 + \omega_2)/2}{\sqrt{\omega_1 \omega_2}}   \quad (4a)$$

and

$$\delta_0 \equiv \frac{(\omega_2 - \omega_1)}{2\sqrt{\omega_1 \omega_2}}.   \quad (4b)$$

Thus $\delta$ is the fractional deviation of $\omega$ from the mean frequency of the two resonant cavities, and $\delta_0$ is one-half the fractional detuning of the two cavities from each other. It is also useful to define

$$K^2 = k^2 Q_1 Q_2.   \quad (5)$$

At the critical coupling, $K^2 = 1$. The term "critical" refers to the usual circuit terminology and does not refer to any critical condition for oscillator operation. Utilizing the relation $Q = 1/\omega LG$, Eq. (3) may now be rewritten

$$Y_c = \frac{\sqrt{G_1 G_2}}{K} \{ -2[(Q_1 + Q_2)\delta + (Q_1 - Q_2)\delta_0]$$
$$+ j[(1 + K^2 + 4Q_1 Q_2 \delta_0^2) - 4Q_1 Q_2 \delta^2] \}. \quad (6)$$

*The Condition for Oscillation.*—It has already been noted that steady-state oscillations exist only when the circuit and electronic transfer admittances are equal, that is, when

$$Y_e = Y_c. \quad (1)$$

If the values of the transfer admittances $Y_e$ and $Y_c$ given in Eqs. (10·15) and (6) are used, this condition may, for convenience, be written in full as follows:

$$\frac{je^{-j\theta_0} G_e 2J_1(X)}{X} = \frac{\sqrt{G_1 G_2}}{K} \{ -2[(Q_1 + Q_2)\delta + (Q_1 - Q_2)\delta_0]$$
$$+ j[(1 + K^2 + 4Q_1 Q_2 \delta_0^2) - 4Q_1 Q_2 \delta^2] \}. \quad (7)$$

The questions asked concerning the oscillator are usually such as to suggest the following classification of the various quantities in Eq. (7). The d-c transit angle of electrons from input to output gap, $\theta_0$, is the independent variable; it is proportional to $V_0^{-\frac{1}{2}}$ and a change in this independent variable simply describes a change in beam voltage. The dependent variables are $\delta$ and $X$, which specify the frequency and amplitude of oscillation. The basic circuit parameters are the relative detuning of the resonators $\delta_0$, the normalized circuit-coupling coefficient $K$, the unloaded $Q$ of first cavity $Q_1$, the loaded $Q$ of second cavity $Q_2$, and the product $GQ = \omega C$ for each cavity. The basic electronic parameter is $G_e$, the small-signal electronic transconductance. It should be recalled particularly that $\theta_0 \propto V^{-\frac{1}{2}}$ and that usually (i.e., electron gun of constant perveance) $I_0 \propto V_0^{\frac{3}{2}}$ and $G_0 \approx V_0^{\frac{1}{2}}$; hence $G_e$, which is proportional to $\theta_0 G_0$, is independent of $\theta_0$ and $V_0$ except for the usually minor dependence of $M$ on $V_0$.

The dependent variable $X$ does not give very much information about the output power because $X \propto |V_1|$, whereas the output power involves $V_2$. A subsidiary relation to Eqs. (1) and (7) giving the relation between $V_1$ and $V_2$ is needed, which follows from simple circuit analysis:

$$V_2 = \frac{jV_1 \sqrt{G_1/G_2} [1 + 2jQ_1(\delta + \delta_0)]}{K}. \quad (8)$$

The discussion is, for some time, concerned not with output, but simply with the values that $X$ assumes under various circumstances; nevertheless Eq. (8) is inserted at this point to call attention to the way in which

$|V_2/V_1|$ and the output power for a given $X$ increase as $\delta + \delta_0$ increases or as $K$ decreases.

Returning now to Eq. (7), it is worth while to inspect the way in which the variables $\theta_0$, $X$, and $\delta$ appear. Since the circuit elements are all linear, $X$ does not appear in $Y_c$; neither does the purely electronic variable $\theta_0$. Thus, both the phase and the absolute value of the circuit transadmittance are determined by the frequency deviation $\delta$. In the electronic transadmittance the phase is determined solely by $\theta_0$ and the absolute value by $X$ alone.

The way in which $X$ and $\delta$ are determined by $\theta_0$ may thus be visualized somewhat as follows. Suppose that all the circuit and electronic parameters have been fixed, and that someone now sets the beam voltage at a particular value and thus determines the value of $\theta_0$. This determines the phase of the electronic and hence of the circuit transadmittance; the frequency deviation $\delta$ is thus immediately determined as the value that gives $Y_c$ the correct phase. But, in thus meeting the phase condition, $\delta$ also completely determines the absolute value of $Y_c$. The amplitude of oscillation, as indicated by $X$, must therefore now be such as to give $Y_e$ this same absolute value. Thus one might say that $\theta_0$ determines $\delta$ and that $\delta$ determines $X$.

Sometimes these various conditions are incompatible. The maximum absolute value of $Y_e$ for any $X$ is $G_e$, and this value occurs for $X \approx 0$. If the value of $\delta$ as determined by $\theta_0$ is such as to make $|Y_c| > G_e$, then no oscillation can be supported. For example, as $\theta_0 \to 2\pi \times$ (integer $+ \frac{1}{2}$), $Y_c$ becomes negative imaginary; if $K$ is positive then $Y_c$ becomes negative imaginary only as $\delta \to \pm \infty$; but at the same time $|Y_c| \to \infty$. Hence oscillations can never occur for a positive $K$ at $\theta_0 = 2\pi \times$ (integer $+ \frac{1}{2}$). Similarly for a negative $K$, oscillations can never occur at

$$\theta_0 = 2\pi \times \text{ integer.}$$

Thus a plot of strength of oscillation versus $V_0$ or $\theta_0$ shows discrete modes of oscillation separated by regions of no oscillation. The larger $G_e$ is, the narrower these regions of no oscillation will be.

Equations (7) also verify the physically obvious fact that with small enough coupling ($K$) or large enough detuning ($\delta_0$), $|Y_c|$ will be so large at all frequencies that no oscillation is possible for any $\theta_0$.

Figures 11·9 and 11·10 show the way in which oscillation ceases at certain values of $\theta_0$ (or $V_0$), with the adjacent zeros of output separated by one cycle of electron-transit time.

These figures[1] show the frequency of oscillation and output power of the 410R klystron as a function of beam voltage. The 410R has already

[1] Type 410R Technical Information Sheet, Sperry Gyroscope Co., Greak Neck, N.Y.

been referred to as an "amplifier klystron"; it may be converted to an oscillator by attaching an external feedback line for which connections are provided. Various features of these figures are discussed at a later point; their relevancy to the present discussion lies in their illustration of the existence of discrete "modes of oscillation." It is to be noted that "mode" is here used in a sense different from that involved in "modes of free oscillation of coupled circuits"; the modes in Figs. 11·9 and 11·10 differ not in circuit features but only in electron-transit time.

In Fig. 11·10, for example, the centers of the regions of zero oscillation occur at $V_0$ = 560, 770, 1200, and 1950 volts; from the facts that $\lambda$ = 10 cm and the drift length $l$ = 3 cm, the corresponding transit

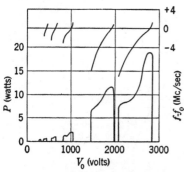

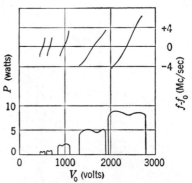

FIG. 11·9.—Typical output power and oscillation frequency characteristics in the type 410R two-resonator klystron oscillator. Feedback and detuning adjusted for maximum output power. Zero focus voltage. Center frequency $f_0$ = 3000 Mc/sec.

FIG. 11·10.—Typical output power and oscillation frequency characteristics in the type 410R two-resonator klystron oscillator. Feedback and detuning adjusted for uniform output power characteristic. Focus voltage zero. Center frequency $f_0$ = 3000 Mc/sec.

times are found to be 6.38, 5.36, 4.35, and 3.40 cycles. These numbers are not integers or integers plus one-half because, in comparison to the simple mutual-inductance model of Fig. 11·6, operation of the 410R involves an additional transit time—that of the feedback signal around the external feedback line. This fact also explains the slight shift in the modes in going from Fig. 11·10 to Fig. 11·9; the shift occurs because the length of the feedback line has been intentionally changed to produce the difference in the shapes of the modes in the two figures. The region of no oscillation that one would expect to find centered at 2.37 cycles or 4000 volts under the conditions of Fig. 11·10 is considerably broadened because the cathode begins to be temperature-limited, thus diminishing $G_e$ above 2500 volts; the zeros below 2000 volts also become increasingly wide (in percentage) as $V_0$ is decreased, because of the accompanying diminution of $M$ and hence of $G_e$.

**11·5. Transadmittance Diagrams.**—Analytically, the condition for oscillation as expressed in Eq. (7) is somewhat cumbersome. A more intuitive and simpler way of expressing this condition is made possible by considering the loci of $Y_e$ and $Y_c$ in the admittance plane. The condition for oscillation, $Y_e = Y_c$, then simply reduces to the condition that the loci of $Y_e$ and $Y_c$ intersect. Before considering the various stages involved in thus expressing the condition for oscillation, however, the general anatomy of these transadmittance loci themselves must be considered in some detail.

*Locus of the Circuit Transadmittance.*—The real part of $Y_c$ is a linear function of $\delta$; the imaginary part is a quadratic function of $\delta$ and hence

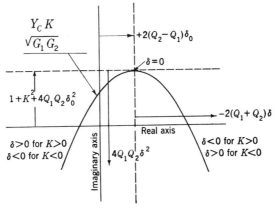

Fig. 11·11.—Locus of circuit transadmittance $Y_c$, normalized as $Y_cK/\sqrt{G_1G_2}$, as a parametric function of frequency deviation $\delta$.

of the real part; the locus of $Y_c$ is therefore a parabola with axis parallel to the imaginary axis of the admittance plane; each point on this parabola corresponds to a single value of $\delta$. The geometry of this parabola is summarized in Fig. 11·11, in which is shown the locus of $Y_cK/\sqrt{G_1G_2}$.

If $K > 0$, then Fig. 11·11 also shows $Y_c$ to within a scale factor, but if $K < 0$ (see Fig. 11·8), then the locus of $Y_c$ will be the negative of the one shown—that is, each point will be inverted through the origin. The vertex of the parabola always lies above the real axis by an amount $(\sqrt{G_1/G_2}/K)\,(1 + K^2 + 4Q_1Q_2\delta_0^2)$; this distance is thus always increased by increasing the relative resonator detuning, is decreased by heavy loading of the output cavity, and is a minimum with respect to coupling when $K^2 = 1 + 4Q_1Q_2\delta_0^2$. The distance of the vertex from the imaginary axis is proportional to the detuning, but would always be zero if both cavities were loaded to the same $Q$.

*Locus of the Electronic Transadmittance.*—The locus of $Y_e$ is more simple. As shown in Fig. 11·12, for any given value of $X$ the locus of

$Y_e$ is a circle about the origin of radius $G_e \cdot 2J_1(X)/X$; the radii for several values of $X$ are shown in Fig. 11·12, and the more exact dependence of $J_1(X)/X$ on $X$ may be obtained from Fig. 10·2.

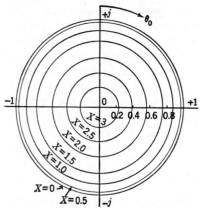

FIG. 11·12.—Dependence of $Y_e/G_e$, ratio of electronic transadmittance to small-signal electronic transconductance, on bunching parameter $X$ and electron-transit angle $\theta_0$; $Y_e = je^{-i\theta_0} G_e 2J_1(X)/X$.

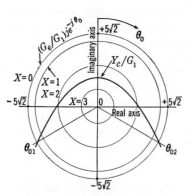

FIG. 11·13.—Transadmittance diagram (loci of $Y_c/G_1$ and $Y_e/G_1$) for critical coupling, no detuning ($K = 1$, $\delta_0 = 0$); $Q_2 = \frac{1}{2}Q_1$, $G_e/G_1 = 5\sqrt{2}$.

The condition for oscillation, Eq. (7), now finds simple expression in terms of these transadmittance loci. Figure 11·13 shows the loci of $Y_e$ and $Y_c$ for the simple case of critical coupling and no detuning ($K = 1$, $\delta_0 = 0$).[1] Oscillation will only occur for the range $\theta_{01} < \theta_0 < \theta_{02}$ for which $|Y_c| < G_e$, that is, for which the parabola lies within the $X = 0$ circle of radius $G_e$. For any value of $\theta_0$ within this range, $X$ will assume the value corresponding to the $Y_e$ circle intersected by the parabola at this value of $\theta_0$. Similarly, to within an additive constant, the value of $\delta$ at any $\theta_0$ is proportional to the horizontal (real)

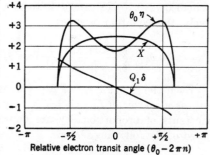

FIG. 11·14.—Dependence of electronic efficiency $\eta$, bunching parameter $X$, and oscillation frequency deviation $\delta$, on electron transit time $\theta_0$, for conditions as given in transadmittance diagram in Fig. 11·13.

projection of the parabola at the corresponding value of $\theta_0$. The dependence of $X$ and $\delta$ on $\theta_0$ as thus graphically derived from the transadmittance diagram of Fig. 11·13 is shown in Fig. 11·14. The limits of oscillation are the $\theta_{01}$ and $\theta_{02}$ of the previous figure.

[1] Certain values of $Q_1/Q_2$ and $G_e/G_1$ are assumed to make these curves identical with some that will appear later as part of a family of characteristics.

Some of the general conclusions to which this use of the transadmittance diagram leads are discussed later. It should be noted, however, that while this procedure gives the output-frequency deviation $\delta$, it does not give the output power, but only the bunching parameter $X$. The connection between output power and $X$ will now be discussed.

**11·6. General Oscillator Characteristics.**—*Relation between Electronic Efficiency $\eta$ and Bunching Parameter $X$.*—The determination of the output power—or better, the output efficiency—really comprises two steps: (1) the determination of the electronic efficiency, and (2) the determination of the circuit efficiency. The electronic efficiency $\eta$ is the efficiency of delivery of power by the electron stream to the output resonator. The circuit efficiency $\eta_c$ is the fraction of this power that gets delivered to the external load as represented by $G_L$ in Fig. 11·6. Thus the over-all efficiency $\eta_L$ is given by

$$\eta_L = \eta\eta_c. \tag{9}$$

As discussed in deriving Eq. (10·7) for the power $P_2$ delivered to the output cavity, the electronic efficiency $\eta$ is given by

$$\eta = \frac{\text{Re}\ (Y_e^* V_1^* V_2)}{2I_0V_0}$$
$$= -\frac{1}{2I_0V_0}\ \text{Re}\left(Y_e^*\ \frac{V_2}{V_1}\ |V_1|^2\right).$$

Using Eqs. (10·15), (8), and (9·2) to give values of $Y_e$, $V_2/V_1$, and $X$, respectively, this equation becomes

$$\theta_0\eta = \frac{2XJ_1(X)}{K}\ \sqrt{\frac{Q_2}{Q_1}}\ [\cos\theta_0 - 2Q_1(\delta + \delta_0)\sin\theta_0]. \tag{10}$$

Even the above form of Eq. (10) is hardly convenient analytically; but, as a matter of fact, it has a very simple physical content. If the constants of proportionality are omitted, this expression for $\eta$ is composed of the following factors:

1. $2J_1(X)$, the relative r-f component of bunched beam current.
2. $X\sqrt{1 + 4Q_1^2(\delta + \delta_0)^2}/K$, the magnitude of the output-gap r-f voltage.
3. $[\cos\theta_0 - 2Q_1(\delta + \delta_0)\sin\theta_0]/\sqrt{1 + 4Q_1^2(\delta + \delta_0)^2}$, the cosine of the phase between the bunched current $i_1$ and the output-gap r-f voltage.

The factor $[\cos\theta_0 - 2Q_1(\delta + \delta_0)\sin\theta_0]$ in Eq. (10) thus describes two separate effects: the changes in the magnitude of $V_2$, and in the relative phase of $i_1$ and $V_2$ as $\theta_0$ varies at constant $X$.

Consider, as an example, the case of no detuning ($\delta_0 = 0$). Here the transit angle $\theta_0 = 2\pi n$, where $n$ is an integer, gives $\delta = 0$ and

$$\theta_0 \eta = 2XJ_1(X) \sqrt{Q_2/Q_1}/K.$$

As $\theta_0$ increases two effects occur: $|V_2/V_1|$ increases, and the cosine of the angle between $V_2$ and $i_1$ decreases. These two effects have opposite influences on the efficiency; which will predominate? Equation (10) shows that, if $-\delta$ increases sufficiently rapidly with $\theta_0$, the increase in $|V_2|$ predominates over the increasingly unfavorable phase angle between $i_1$ and $V_2$, and the efficiency is a maximum at $\sin \theta_0 = \pm 1$. This is the usual case; it gives rise to behavior such as that shown in Figs. 11·9 and 11·10, where the efficiency shows local maxima just before the tube goes out of oscillation. The other alternative occurs only for small values of $G_e/G_2$.

In an oscillator with a sizable $G_e$, it is apparent from what has just been said that $i_1$ and $V_2$ are not in phase at the maximum efficiency available for $\delta_0 = 0$. This fact indicates the advantage of a relative detuning of the resonators, for the optimum efficiency will occur with the combination of maximum $|V_2|$ and zero phase angle between $i_1$ and $V_2$. The illustration of these points in detail by an exhaustive discussion of the contours of constant $\eta$ in the admittance plane is too lengthy a procedure to be carried out here. The present comments should suffice to indicate the physical factors at work; graphical illustrations of the effect of detuning on efficiency are given later.

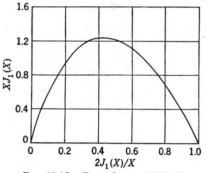

Fig. 11·15.—Dependence of $XJ_1(X)$ on $2J_1(X)/X$, that is, on radial position in the transadmittance diagram.

The relative contribution to $\eta$ by the factor $XJ_1(X)$ is easily seen. In Fig. 11·15 is shown the dependence of this function on $2J_1(X)/X$ (that is, on the relative distance from the center of the transadmittance diagram).

It should also be noted that, since $K$ occurs in the denominator of the right-hand member of Eq. (10), it might appear that an infinitesimally small coupling leads to an infinite $\eta$. But the normalization factor in Fig. 11·11 shows that as $K$ is decreased the absolute scale of the circuit transadmittance locus is increased; hence, too small a value of $K$ causes the locus of $Y_c$ to expand far beyond the locus of $Y_e$, and thus makes oscillation impossible long before any infinite $\eta$ is reached.

*The Circuit Efficiency.*—The circuit efficiency $\eta_c$ is the ratio of the power dissipated in the load $G_L$ to the power dissipated in $G_1$ and $G_2$; hence

$$\eta_c = \frac{|V_2|^2 G_L}{(|V_2|^2 G_2 + |V_1|^2 G_1)}.$$

By Eq. (8) this becomes

$$\eta_c = \frac{G_L}{G_2}\left[1 + \frac{K^2}{1 + 4Q_1^2(\delta + \delta_0)^2}\right]. \tag{11}$$

When $K \ll 1$, that is, when very little of the r-f power developed is returned to the first resonator to be there dissipated, this expression reduces to the simple equation $\eta_c = G_L/G_2$, which was used for amplifiers. The same is true when $Q_1\delta_0 \gg 1$, that is, when the detuning of the first resonator with respect to the second is very great.

The basic point about Eq. (11), however, is really the simple fact that the circuit efficiency depends on $\delta$ and hence, implicitly, on $\theta_0$ and $V_0$. This dependence is in sharp contrast to the situation, for example, in the reflex klystron.

*The Frequency of Oscillation.*—It has already been noted in discussing Eq. (7) that the frequency of oscillation is determined by the condition

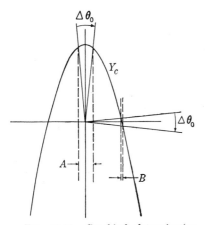

FIG. 11·16.—Graphical determination of the relative frequency changes, $A$ and $B$, produced at $\theta_0 = 2\pi n$ and $\theta_0 = 2\pi n + \pi/2$ by a given increment of $\theta_0$, $\Delta\theta_0$. Strong circuit coupling.

that the phase of the circuit transadmittance $Y_c$ shall be equal to the phase of the electronic transadmittance $Y_e$; and the latter, $\pi/2 - \theta_0$, is determined solely by the mean electron-transit time. The dependence of $\delta$ on $\theta_0$ is thus purely a circuit matter and is not at all influenced by amplitude of oscillation; the functional relation between $\delta$ and $\theta_0$ is determined by simple considerations involving the analysis of coupled circuits.

In the transadmittance diagram (see Fig. 11·11), the real part of $Y_c$ is linear in $\delta$. Thus, in terms of this diagram, $\delta$ may be determined from the $Y_c$ parabola for any value of $\theta_0$ by drawing a line from the origin at an angle $\theta_0$ to the imaginary axis; the real part of the admittance point where this line intersects the parabola is proportional to a constant minus $\delta$.

This graphical construction allows simple conclusions about the dependence of $\delta$ on $\theta_0$. In Fig. 11·16 is shown the $Y_c$ parabola for strong coupling, $K = 3$, with $\delta_0 = 0$. A change $\Delta\theta_0$ at $\theta_0 = 0$ makes a change $A$ in Re $(Y_c)$ that is much larger than the change $B$ produced by the same $\Delta\theta_0$ at $\theta_0 = \pi/2$. Hence $d\delta/d\theta_0$ is much larger at $\theta_0 = 0$ than at $\theta_0 = \pi/2$.

Similar reasoning may be applied to other values of $K$ and $\delta_0$, and will disclose the dependence of $\delta$ on $\theta_0$, which is shown in Fig. 11·17 for $\delta_0 = 0$ with $K \ll 1$, $K = 1$, $K = 3$, and for $\sqrt{Q_1 Q_2}\,\delta_0 = \pm 1$ with $K = 1$ (critical coupling). It may be noted that at critical coupling $\delta$ is practically linear in $\theta_0$ for $-\pi/2 < \theta_0 - 2\pi n < \pi/2$. Detuning produces a characteristic asymmetry; it may be deduced by a comparison of Figs. 11·9, 11·10, and 11·17 that $\delta_0 > 0$ in Fig. 11·9 whereas $\delta_0 < 0$ in Fig.

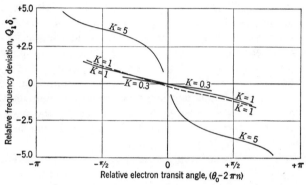

FIG. 11·17.—Oscillator frequency deviation $\delta$ as a function of electron-transit angle $\theta_0$, for $M = 1$, $Q_2 = \frac{1}{2}Q_1$, $G_e/G = 5\sqrt{2}$. Combinations of coupling and detuning as indicated. $Q_1\delta_0 = 0$ (solid curve); $Q_1\delta_0 = 0.5$ (broken curve).

**11·10.** Overcoupling produces linear regions (effectively, points of inflection) at $\theta_0 - 2\pi n = \pm\pi/2$ instead of at $\theta_0 - 2\pi n = 0$, as was the case with critical coupling.

It appears that the largest approximately linear variation of frequency with $\theta_0$ (that is, with a change in beam voltage) occurs for $\delta_0 = 0$ and $K = 1$; it has already been noted that this combination produces a somewhat lowered efficiency. It would also appear that the total range of frequency change, regardless of linearity, increases with increased overcoupling. This latter point is rather illusory, since the overcoupling will later be seen to split the main mode into two separate modes centered at $\theta_0 - 2\pi n = \pm\pi/2$; these two separate modes of oscillation correspond to the two "normal modes of free oscillation" of two coupled circuits, and the centers of gravity of the frequency of these two modes separate as $K$ increases. This fact emphasizes that the limits of oscillation must be taken into account in drawing conclusions from Fig. 11·17.

An analytical relation between $\delta$ and $\tan \theta_0$ may be derived from Eq. (7), but it serves more as a point of reference in calculation than as a source of understanding. For reference purposes, it is

$$- \frac{1}{2} \tan \theta_0 = \frac{(Q_1 + Q_2)\delta + (Q_1 - Q_2)\delta_0}{1 + K^2 + 4Q_1Q_2\delta_0^2 - 4Q_1Q_2\delta^2}. \quad (12)$$

Equation (12) shows that the decrease of $\delta$, that accompanies the increase of $\theta_0$, is unaffected by the sign of the coupling parameter $K$. It will be found by checking into the derivation of Eq. (10) that, when $\theta_0$ is increased from the value at which $i_1$ and $V_2$ are in phase, $\delta$ always decreases; this decrease tends to minimize the efficiency-reducing phase difference between $i_1$ and $V_2$. It might be said that the sign of $d\delta/d\theta_0$ is determined by the instinct of self-preservation!

*Typical Modes.*—The foregoing comments on the variation of $X$, $\delta$, and $\eta$ in the two-resonator oscillator may be most easily illustrated by presenting the transadmittance diagrams and mode shapes for typical combinations of $K$ and $\delta_0$. For this purpose, some assumptions must be made about $G_e$, $G_1$, $G_2$, $Q_1$, and $Q_2$. It will be assumed that $G_2 = 2G_1$ and $Q_1 = 2Q_2$ (i.e., $C_1 = C_2$). This value would be optimum load for a small-signal amplifier, but is only approximately optimum for the two-resonator oscillator. As already noted, however, in the present case the optimum load varies with $\theta_0$, and therefore there is no one load that is optimum over the whole mode.

A purely illustrative assumption must also be made about the relative size of $G_e$ and $G_1$, which determines the relative size of the $Y_e$-parabola and the $Y_e$-circle in the transadmittance diagram. The value of $G_e/G_1$ is taken as $5\sqrt{2}$.

In Fig. 11·18 is shown the transadmittance diagram for $\delta_0 = 0$, $K = 0.3$, 1, and 5—that is, undercoupling, critical coupling, and overcoupling of the circuits. (The "over" and "under" is circuit nomenclature, and does not necessarily mean "nonoptimum" so far as the oscillator is concerned.) In Fig. 11·19 is shown the transadmittance diagram for critical coupling ($K = 1$) and for $Q_1\delta_0 = 0$ and $+0.5$. In Fig. 11·20 is shown the dependence of $X$ on $\theta_0$, which may be deduced from these transadmittance diagrams. In Fig. 11·21 is shown the corresponding dependence of $\eta$, which may be deduced from Eqs. (9), (10), and (11). For completeness, there is also repeated in Fig. 11·21 the dependence of $\delta$ on $\theta_0$, which has already been given in Fig. 11·17.

The particular combinations of $K$, $\delta_0$, and $G_e/G_1$ to which these modes correspond have been chosen as typical of the various modes encountered in oscillator operation. The characteristic features of each type of mode may be summed up as follows.

The mode for $K = 5$ and $\delta_0 = 0$ shows the way in which strong coupling splits one mode into two separate modes. The center frequencies of these modes are separated by an amount that increases with $K$, just

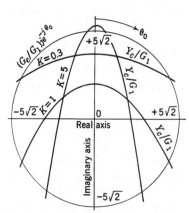

FIG. 11·18.—Transadmittance diagram for $\delta_0 = 0$, $G_e/G_1 = 5\sqrt{2}$, $Q_2 = \frac{1}{2}Q_1$.

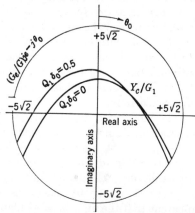

FIG. 11·19.—Transadmittance diagram for $K = 1$ (critical coupling), $G_e/G_1 = 5\sqrt{2}$, $Q_2 = \frac{1}{2}Q_1$.

as the two normal frequencies of free oscillation of two coupled circuits separate as $K$ increases. By the proper adjustment of $G_e/G_2$—that is, by the proper adjustment of the output load—these modes become

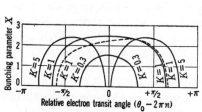

FIG. 11·20.—Dependence of bunching parameter $X$ on electron-transit angle $\theta_0$, for the combinations of coupling and detuning as indicated, and for $Q_2 = \frac{1}{2}Q_1$, $G_e/G_1 = 5\sqrt{2}$. $Q_1\delta_0 = 0$ (solid curve); $Q_1\delta_0 = 0.5$ (broken curve). See Figs. 11·18 and 11·19 for corresponding transadmittance diagrams.

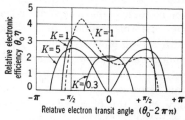

FIG. 11·21.—Electronic efficiency $\eta$ as function of electron transit angle $\theta_0$ for $Q_2 = \frac{1}{2}Q_1$, $G_e/G_1 = 5\sqrt{2}$. $Q_1\delta_0 = 0$ (solid curve); $Q_1\delta_0 = 0.5$ (broken curve). Compare with Figs. 11·17 through 11·20.

efficient. Operation in an overcoupled state is therefore a common practice. It is seen that with such operation the voltage modes of oscillation may be divided into two families, the mean frequencies of which are separated by an amount that increases with $K$. As the beam voltage is changed the modes of oscillation alternate between these two families.

The mode for optimum coupling with no detuning ($K = 1$, $\delta_0 = 0$) has an efficiency that is almost constant over a large range of $\theta_0$, and a frequency that (as already noted) is quite linear in $\theta_0$. The price of this advantageous behavior is a slight loss in efficiency.

The mode with $\delta_0 = 0$ and $K = 0.3$ (weak coupling) shows primarily the loss in efficiency caused by lack of sufficient feedback to maintain optimum bunching; it is apparent from the transadmittance diagram that a slight additional diminution in $K$ would cause the oscillations to cease entirely.

The mode with detuning ($Q_1\delta_0 = 0.5$) and $K = 1$ shows the results of detuning, namely, mode asymmetry and increased peak efficiency.

By presenting a number of such curves, enough information may be made available to allow a detailed analysis of the output efficiency of any oscillator. The discussion will not be carried, however, beyond what has been shown about general oscillator characteristics, for it is now apparent that the number of available degrees of freedom of adjustment of a given oscillator should make it possible to obtain an output power that is equal, essentially, to that of the corresponding power amplifier diminished by the power required to excite the first cavity.

Using as an example the 410R klystron to which so much reference has already been made, an amplifier output of 18 watts was quoted for $V_0 = 2070$ volts and $I_0 = 92$ ma. The oscillator data of Figs. 11·9 and 11·10 may be interpolated to $V_0 = 2070$ and allowance made for the increase of efficiency with a negative focusing voltage on the electron gun. If this is done, an oscillator output of 14.3 watts as compared with the amplifier output of 18 watts is obtained. The amplifier data indicate a necessary r-f input to the first cavity of 1.8 watts, or an ideal oscillator output of 16.2 watts. A large part of the difference between this figure and 14.3 watts may be loss in the external feedback line; in any case, the observed oscillator efficiency closely approximates that predicted by the amplifier performance.

# CHAPTER 12

## REFLEX KLYSTRON OSCILLATORS

### By J. K. KNIPP AND D. R. HAMILTON[1]

The reflex klystron oscillator is a high-frequency single-resonator tube employing the principles of velocity modulation and bunching for the purpose of production of r-f power. A stream of electrons from a cathode is accelerated to a potential of a few hundred volts in a region forming an electron gun (see Fig. 12·1). This stream passes through the gap of the resonator into a reflector region. Here the electrons are stopped by a strong retarding field and reflected back through the gap.

**12·1. General Behavior.**—If an r-f field exists across the gap, the stream is velocity-modulated on emerging from the gap after the first transit of the electrons. As a result of this initial velocity modulation, the stream is density-modulated on returning to the gap after being reflected. The degree to which the stream is density-modulated depends on the exact nature of the reflector region and on the magnitude of the initial velocity modulation. During the second transit, the modulated current interacts with the gap fields. If the relative phase of this current and the r-f gap voltage lies in the proper range, power can be delivered from the stream to the resonator. If this power is suffi-

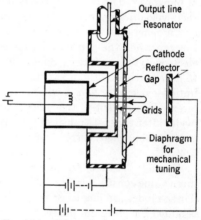

FIG. 12·1.—Schematic drawing of reflex oscillator with coaxial-line loop output.

cient for the losses and the load, steady oscillations can be sustained. The frequency of these oscillations will be near the principal resonant frequency of the resonator. The degree to which it differs from it will depend on the effective capacitance of the resonator and the reactive portion of the electron transadmittance, the latter being controlled by the phase of the reflected current.

[1] Sections 12·3 and 12·4 by D. R. Hamilton; the remainder of Chap. 12 by J. K. Knipp.

*Optimum Phase.*—The condition of optimum phase is determined by the fact that the center of the bunches in the returning stream should pass through the gap when the gap field has its greatest retarding effect, for then the greatest number of electrons lose the largest possible amount of energy during the passage and the maximum power is extracted from the beam.

Electrons forming the center of a bunch on the second transit are readily identified as those passing through the gap on the first transit at a time when the field is changing from one that is accelerating the electrons to one that is decelerating them.   Consider the group of electrons that passes through the gap in a short interval of time extending a small fraction of a cycle before and after this time.   Because the faster electrons penetrate deeper into the reflector region, their return takes a longer time than that of the slower ones.   In fact, in a constant reflector field, the time required for electrons to return is proportional to the velocity of injection.   Hence, if the earlier electrons in the group are also the faster, as they are if the earlier were accelerated and the later were decelerated during the first transit, conditions are right for the formation of bunches.   The center of the bunch is composed of electrons that have their velocities unaffected by the transit.

In general, if the phase is to be optimum, this center must arrive at the gap when the gap field exerts the maximum retarding effect on the electrons at the center.   Since the gap field changes from acceleration to deceleration on the first transit, it does not oppose returning electrons until $\frac{1}{2}$ cycle later and it will have its maximum retarding effect $\frac{3}{4}$ cycle later.   Subsequently the maximum retardation occurs $1\frac{3}{4}$, $2\frac{3}{4}$, $\cdots$ cycles after the first transit of the gap.   Hence the optimum phase angles between bunched current and gap field are $\theta_n = 2\pi(n + \frac{3}{4})$, $n = 0$, 1, 2, 3, $\cdots$ .

*Possible Modes of Operation.*—Oscillation with a phase near an optimum value constitutes a possible mode of operation of the reflex oscillator. These modes are identified by $n$, the number of whole cycles to which $\frac{3}{4}$ is added for optimum phase.

The relative phase of the bunched current and the gap voltage can be controlled by changing the reflector voltage.   A change in reflector voltage changes the average time spent by the electrons in the retarding field, and hence the number of cycles that have elapsed between first and second transits.   It is therefore very simple to change from one mode to another by making a change in the reflector voltage.   There exists a succession of discrete values of the reflector voltage corresponding to the sequence of numbers for optimum phase, with the less negative values having the larger values of $n$.   There are, of course, limitations in a tube of particular design on the phases that can actually be reached.   For example, the depth of the reflector region places an upper limit on the total time that an electron of a given initial velocity can spend in that region.

*Weak Modulation.*—The initial oscillations start from noise fluctuations, which are ever present in both the beam current and the gap voltage. The manner in which the oscillation builds up depends on how the various fields are applied. It is significant that under ideal conditions the phase of the bunches relative to the gap voltage does not depend to any marked degree on the amplitude of the gap voltage, and hence undergoes only negligible change during the buildup of oscillation provided the d-c conditions are not changed.

In order to simplify the discussion, suppose the transit angle of the gap is negligibly small.[1] The bunching parameter for negligible gap-transit angle is

$$X = \theta V/2V_0.$$

In the initial oscillations the bunching parameter is very nearly zero because of the smallness of the gap-voltage amplitude $V$ compared with the beam potential $V_0$. As the oscillation builds up, $X$ increases until the steady-state value is reached.

The velocity modulation that is due to the action of the gap

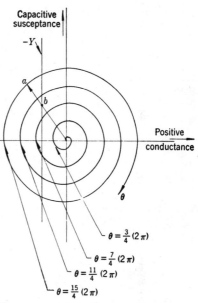

Fig. 12·2.—Small-signal electronic transadmittance. $Y_e \approx \dfrac{G_0}{2} j\theta e^{-i\theta}$.

voltage during the first transit has an amplitude that is the product of the average velocity of the electrons $v_0$ and the ratio $V/2V_0$. If the modulation is extremely weak, the amplitude of the bunched current caused by this velocity modulation is simply the product of the amplitude of the velocity modulation, the average charge density, and $-j\theta e^{-i\theta}$ (compare Sec. 3·3 and Sec. 9·3). This current can be used to define a small-signal electronic transadmittance. It is

$$Y_e \approx \frac{G_0}{2} j\theta e^{-i\theta}, \tag{1}$$

where $G_0$ is the beam conductance at the gap. If $\theta$ is regarded as a parameter that starts from zero, $Y_e$ as given by this formula traces a

[1] See J. R. Pierce, "Reflex Oscillators," *Proc. I.R.E.* **33**, 112 (1945).

spiral in the complex admittance plane, as shown in Fig. 12·2. This spiral starts at the origin with infinite slope and moves in a clockwise direction in ever increasing loops. It cuts the negative real axis at the angles $\theta_n = 2\pi(n + \frac{3}{4})$, $n = 0$, 1, 2, $\cdots$ . These are values of $n$ for which the electronic admittance is a pure negative conductance.

*Bunching Parameter.*—If conditions are such that the gap voltage increases, $X$ grows in value and the bunching process becomes less simple. As already noted, the phase angle does not ordinarily change. From bunching theory it is found that the effect on the electronic admittance is given by the factor $2J_1(X)/X$. This factor, which is plotted in Fig. 12·3, has the value unity for $X = 0$, and drops to zero at $X = 3.83$. It follows that a point on the spiral representing the initial electronic admittance for very weak modulation will move inward along the radius vector from the origin as the oscillation builds up. The shrinkage along the radius vector is given by Fig. 12·3 as a function of the bunching parameter. The process of initial build-up is discussed in Chap. 16, Sec. 16·8.

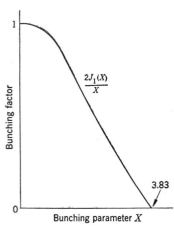

FIG. 12·3.—Factor giving effect of bunching parameter on electronic transadmittance.

*Steady Oscillation.*—The resonator and load can be represented at the gap by a conductance $G$ and variable susceptance $2jC(\omega - \omega_0)$, which is zero at the effective resonant angular frequency $\omega_0$. Hence the circuit admittance at the gap is

$$Y = G + 2jC(\omega - \omega_0).$$

Regarded as a function of $\omega$, the circuit admittance traces out a vertical line in the admittance plane with an intercept with the real axis at $G$.

The condition for steady-state oscillation is the familiar one that the total admittance is zero,

$$Y + Y_e = 0.$$

This relation gives at once the point at which the shrinking process must stop. In Fig. 12·2, $-Y$ has been indicated as a vertical line on the electronic admittance diagram. The steady-state condition has been satisfied when the electronic admittance that has the initial value indicated by the point $a$ changes by moving along the radius vector toward the origin until it reaches the point $b$, which is the intercept of this vector with the line $-Y$. Steady oscillations are established at this point.

It is seen that the process described can take place only if the initial point on the spiral lies to the left of the constant circuit-conductance line, for otherwise the radius vector does not intercept that line.   Only points to the left of the line can lead to steady oscillation.   Hence it becomes apparent that of the possible modes of oscillation, only those having electronic conductance for weak modulation at optimum phase greater in magnitude than the circuit conductance can operate with these conductances unchanged.   For a given beam conductance and a given circuit conductance, there is in the sequence of possible modes a lowest value of $n$ corresponding to the smallest intercept on the spiral from which steady oscillations can be initiated.

The point $b$ not only establishes the magnitude of the gap potential, through the dependence on $X$ as given in Fig. 12·3, but also determines the frequency of the oscillations by giving the amount of circuit susceptance that is needed. The frequency of oscillation will be the resonant frequency $\omega_0$ only if the point $a$, and hence $b$, is on the real axis.   Otherwise the frequency will deviate above or below $\omega_0$ by an amount depending on $C$, $G_0$, and $\theta$. If in the $n$th mode $\theta$ is greater than $2\pi(n + \frac{3}{4})$, the frequency of oscillation will be less than $\omega_0$; and if it is less than this value, the frequency will be greater than $\omega_0$.

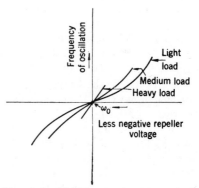

FIG. 12·4.—Electronic tuning in a given mode.

*Electronic Tuning.*—The qualitative behavior under electronic tuning can be seen from the spiral diagram.   If the point $a$ is on the negative real axis and to the left of the constant circuit-conductance line, the point $b$ is also on the axis and the tube oscillates in the center of the mode. If the reflector voltage is made less negative, $\theta$ increases, the point $a$ moves upward along the spiral in the clockwise manner, and the point $b$ moves upward along the vertical line.   At the same time, the frequency of oscillation decreases, though not fast enough to cause a decrease in the product of frequency and time spent in the reflector region.   When the two points meet, the gap voltage is reduced to zero and oscillation stops.   Hence the two points of intersection of the vertical line with that portion of the spiral belonging to the $n$th mode define the limits of oscillation and the frequency range under electronic tuning.   The higher the mode, the greater the separation of these extreme points and the greater the tuning range.   For a given mode the frequency changes more rapidly with voltage at the center of the mode for a heavy load than for a light load because the point $b$ is nearer $a$ for the heavy load and hence moves more nearly at the same rate (see Fig. 12·4).

Since the spiral is not symmetrical above and below the center of the mode, electronic tuning is not completely symmetrical, the asymmetry being greater for lower modes. Other causes for asymmetry will become apparent in this and later chapters.

*Power Production.*—The r-f current in the gap depends on the gap voltage through the factor $J_1(X)$. It has a maximum that is the same in magnitude for all modes and occurs at the first maximum of $J_1(X)$, which comes at $X = 1.84$. Since $X = \theta V/2V_0$ and $\theta$ is larger for higher modes, the maximum of $J_1(X)$ comes at smaller gap voltages for higher modes. Thus, it is to be expected that the maximum total r-f power produced is less for higher modes because the largest currents are at lower voltages. More exactly, the power is proportional to $XJ_1(X)/\theta$; hence the power falls from mode to mode as $1/(n + \frac{3}{4})$. The maximum of $XJ_1(X)$ occurs at $X = 2.40$. For a particular mode there is a value of the circuit conductance $G$ that leads to this value of the bunching parameter at the center of the tuning range under steady oscillation. Larger and smaller circuit conductances (heavier and lighter loads) have smaller total power.

Because of the losses to the beam and to the resonator, not all the power produced is delivered to the load. The fraction of useful power that is produced is given by the circuit efficiency, which is the ratio of the load conductance to the total circuit conductance. The remaining power goes into losses in the cavity walls and in the beam.

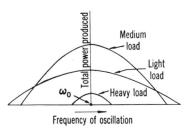

FIG. 12·5.—Total r-f power produced during electronic tuning.

The frequency of oscillation is usually as readily measured as the reflector voltage; since a unique relation exists between them in a given mode, the power is often regarded as a function of the frequency. Illustrative curves are shown in Fig. 12·5. At the resonant frequency $\omega_0$ the total power is less than maximum for heavy loads ($b$ near $a$ in Fig. 12·2 and $X < 2.40$) and for light loads ($b$ near origin and $X > 2.40$). The frequency range between zero-power points increases the lighter the load.

*Gap Transit Angle.*—A finite gap transit angle $\theta_1$ causes the gap voltage to be not fully effective in producing bunching and the bunched current not fully effective in driving the resonator. The first effect arises because the field changes during the time of passage through the gap, and hence an average value less than the maximum value becomes operative. The second effect is due to the partial cancellation in phase of the current in the gap, again because of the finite time of transit of the gap. Each introduces a factor $M = \sin (\theta_1/2)/(\theta_1/2)$ into the small-signal driving current.

The first effect introduces a factor $M$ into the bunching parameter. In addition the gap transit angle exerts an additional influence because the phase angle that is effective in bunching must be measured from the center of the gap; hence, if $\theta_3 = \omega T_3$, where $T_3$ is the average time spent by the electrons in the reflector region, the phase angle is $\theta = \theta_1 + \theta_3$ because the time required to go from the center of the gap back to the center of the gap is longer by two contributions, each of which is equal to $T_1/2$, the time of passage across half the gap. The angle that enters in the bunching parameter is also affected by the finite time of passage of the gap but not in the same way. For a linear reflecting field this angle, which is called the effective bunching angle, $\theta_e$, is equal to $\theta_3$ minus the gap-transit angle; thus $\theta_e = -\theta_1 + \theta_3$. The negative sign is due to the fact that, in the process of bunching due to velocity modulation, the extra time $T_1$ spent in the gap is similar in its effect to time spent in a field-free drift space. As is pointed out in Chap. 9, bunching caused by free drift and bunching caused by the action of a reflecting field give density modulations that are opposite in sign. The angle that enters as a factor in the small-signal transadmittance is the effective bunching angle $\theta_e$. In Eq. (1) it is written as $\theta$ since (for a linear reflecting field) the two angles are the same for $\theta_1 = 0$.

With these changes arising from the finite gap-transit angle, $X = \theta_e M V/2V_0$ and the electronic transadmittance is the expression,

$$Y_e = \frac{G_0}{2} M^2 \frac{2J_1(X)}{X} j\theta_e e^{-i\theta}. \tag{2}$$

The combination $G_{ne} = \theta_{ne} M^2 G_0/2$, where $\theta_{ne} = \theta_n - 2\omega_0 T_1$ is the value of $\theta_e$ at the center of the $n$th mode, is the negative of small-signal electronic conductance at the center of that mode.

The maximum possible total power produced in a given mode is affected by gap transit angle only by a factor $\theta/\theta_e$ to first approximation, for the optimum value of the bunching parameter is unchanged. This optimum value occurs for a value of $G$ that is smaller by $M^2\theta_e/\theta$ and for a value of $V$ that is larger by $\theta/M\theta_e$ than the corresponding values for zero gap transit angle; since the total power is $\frac{1}{2}GV^2$, its maximum is increased by the factor $\theta/\theta_e$. However, it is to be remembered that design considerations do not always allow the optimum value of $G$.

**12·2. Oscillator Theory for High Modes.**—There are three principal reasons why velocity-modulated tubes, of which the reflex oscillator is an example, are subject to fairly reliable theoretical treatment: the geometry is simple, the current densities are low, and the velocities in the gaps are high. The electrons travel very nearly along straight and parallel lines. The circuit is composed of one or more resonators and, except for coupling devices, it has a high degree of axial symmetry. The resonator gaps, through which the electrons pass, have depths that are usually small compared with the diameters of the openings. The principal mode of excitation of each resonator is generally such that the electrical field in the gap is directed along the axis of the tube and has a space-constant amplitude. Because of the low current densities and high velocities of injection, space charge usually has only a slight effect on the beam. It can cause spreading and debunching and, where the velocities drop to zero as in the reflector region of the reflex oscillator, it can have an effect on the time of passage. Such effects are present in varying degrees under different operating conditions and affect the action of the tubes in a quantitative manner. However, they rarely change in any marked degree the qualitative aspects of the tube behavior. Because of the high velocities, the thermal velocity spread of the beam has but slight effect on the operation of the tube.

In this section the simple theory of the reflex oscillator is developed. This theory is based on space-constant gap and reflector fields and has its greatest degree of validity for high modes. In low modes (small $n$) various correction terms in the electronic admittance are important [they contain extra factors $1/\theta_e$ (see Sec. 9·4 and Sec. 12·5)]. Also, for the lowest modes the amplitude of the gap voltage required for bunching sometimes becomes so large that some electrons are stopped in their return passage through the gap. This complication does not arise for high modes because the large values of the bunching angle in the bunching parameter $X$ make optimum bunching possible with small gap voltages.

*Electronic Transadmittance.*—In formulating simple bunching theory in Sec. 9·2, a field-free drift space was assumed. However, it was then found in Sec. 9·4 that with the exception of a possible change in the sign of the bunched beam current the results of Sec. 9·2 could be adopted *in toto* for the present case of a linear reflecting field. Here there will be used a sign convention for the bunched current that makes Eq. (9·9) applicable without change. Since the gap voltage is given by the real part of $-jVe^{j\omega t}$ as in Eq. (9·1), it follows that the electronic transadmittance for the present case can be written as

$$Y_e = \frac{G_0}{2} M^2 \frac{2J_1(X)}{X} j\theta_e e^{-j\theta},\qquad(2)$$

where $G_0 = kI_0/V_0$ is the beam conductance of the stream that returns to the gap; $k$ is the fraction of the beam returning.

*Condition for Oscillation.*—For steady oscillation to take place the total admittance measured at the gap must be zero. The circuit admittance $Y$ is the sum of three contributions: the load admittance $Y_L$, the resonator admittance $Y_R$, and the beam-loading admittance $Y_B$, all measured at the gap. Hence the condition for oscillation is

$$Y_L + Y_R + Y_B + Y_e = 0.$$

The circuit admittance is written in the form

$$Y = Y_L + Y_R + Y_B = G_L + G_{BR} + 2jC(\omega - \omega_0),$$

where $G_L$ is the load conductance, $G_{BR} = G_B + G_R$ is the conductance arising from the beam loading and the resonator, $C$ is the effective capacitance, and $\omega_0$ is the frequency of oscillation at the center of the mode —that is, it is the frequency of oscillation for $\theta = \theta_n = 2\pi(n + \frac{3}{4})$.

In a particular mode, it is convenient to measure the phase angle from its value at the center by writing $\theta = \theta_n + \phi$. On introducing the new symbols and separating real and imaginary part, the condition for oscillation yields the two equations

$$\left.\begin{array}{l} G = \dfrac{G_0}{2} M^2\theta_e \dfrac{2J_1(X)}{X} \cos \phi, \\[2mm] 2C(\omega - \omega_0) = -\dfrac{G_0}{2} M^2\theta_e \dfrac{2J_1(X)}{X} \sin \phi, \end{array}\right\} \tag{3}$$

where $G = G_L + G_{BR}$ is the total circuit conductance.

The two equations above serve to determine the gap voltage and frequency of oscillation. It is convenient to regard $\phi$ as a parameter, which is assigned values in an interval corresponding to the tuning range, from which $X$ and $\omega$ are calculated. If the second equation is divided by the first, there is obtained

$$\frac{\omega_0 - \omega}{\omega_0} = \frac{1}{2Q} \tan \phi. \tag{4}$$

where $Q = \omega_0 C/G$ is the loaded $Q$ of the circuit. From the definitions of $\theta$ and $\theta_e$, $\theta_e = \theta_n - 2\theta_1 + \phi$. The bunching angle at the center of the mode has the value $\theta_{ne} = \theta_n - 2\omega_0 T_1$. At the center of the mode the negative of the small-signal transconductance is $G_{ne} = \theta_{ne}M^2G_0/2$. A conductance parameter is introduced, which is defined as $\gamma = G/G_{ne}$. The first equation then becomes

$$\gamma = \frac{2J_1(X)}{X} \cos \phi, \tag{5}$$

where the ratio $\theta_e/\theta_{ne}$ has been set equal to unity because its dependence on $\phi$ is negligible in high modes.

For steady oscillation to take place in a particular mode, the conductance parameter for that mode must be less than unity. This condition has been noted in the first section of this chapter, where it was observed that the magnitude of the small-signal transconductance for a particular mode must exceed the circuit conductance if steady oscillation is to be maintained. The bunching parameter for $\phi = 0$ is shown plotted as a function of the conductance parameter in Fig. 12·6.

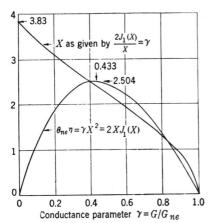

$X$ as given by $\frac{2J_1(X)}{X} = \gamma$

$\theta_{ne}\eta = \gamma X^2 = 2XJ_1(X)$

Conductance parameter $\gamma = G/G_{ne}$

Fig. 12·6.—Dependence at center of mode of the bunching parameter and total electronic efficiency on conductance parameter. $G_{ne} = \theta_{ne}M^2G_0/2$;

$\theta_{ne} = 2\pi(n + \tfrac{3}{4}) - 2\omega_0 T_1$;

$n = 0, 1, 2, 3 \cdots$.

*Starting Current.*—If the tube is to be operated with the injected current $-I_0$ but is started cold with the reflector voltage adjusted to the center of the tuning range for an operating mode, oscillations will not start until $G_{ne}$, which is proportional to the injected current, is greater than $G$. As the cathode temperature is increased, the injected current, and hence $G_{ne}$, increases. When $G_{ne}$ becomes greater than $G$, oscillations become possible. The larger $G$ is, the greater is the starting current; or again the lower $Q$ as the result of a large $G$, the greater the starting current. The ratio of the magnitude of the starting current to the operating current is $\dfrac{2J_1(X)}{X}$, which for a given conductance itself depends on $I_0$.

*Efficiency and Output Power.*—The total r-f power generated and the r-f output power are $\tfrac{1}{2}GV^2$ and $\tfrac{1}{2}G_LV^2$, respectively. The electronic efficiency $k\eta$ and the over-all electronic efficiency to the load $k\eta_L$ are given by the equations,

$$\eta = \frac{GV^2}{2kI_0V_0} \qquad \text{and} \qquad \eta_L = \frac{G_LV^2}{2kI_0V_0}. \tag{6}$$

In this section and in Sec. 12.5 the $\eta$'s are defined for convenience as efficiencies with respect to the beam current returning through the gap. The $\eta$'s can readily be rewritten:

$$\eta = \frac{\gamma X}{\theta_{ne}} = \frac{2XJ_1(X)}{\theta_e}\cos\phi; \qquad \eta_L = \frac{\gamma_L X^2}{\theta_{ne}} = \frac{G_L}{G_L + G_{BR}}\cdot\frac{2XJ_1(X)}{\theta_{ne}}\cos\phi,$$
$$\tag{7}$$

where $\theta_{ne}/\theta_e^2$ has been replaced by $1/\theta_{ne}$ and $\gamma_L = G_L/G_{ne}$ is the load conductance parameter. At the center of the mode the product $\theta_{ne}\eta = 2XJ_1(X)$ and is shown plotted in Fig. 12·6. It has a maximum at $X = 2.40$, which is the value of the bunching parameter for optimum total power conversion. At this point $\gamma = 0.433$ and $2XJ_1(X) = 2.504$. Since this value is the same for all modes, the maximum total electronic efficiency changes as $1/\theta_{ne}$ from mode to mode, or roughly as $1/2\pi(n + \frac{3}{4})$. It is small, since even for $n = 2$, the maximum value of $(\theta_{ne}/\theta_n)\eta$ is only 0.144.

It is well to check the assumption $V/V_0 < \frac{1}{2}$, which guarantees that no electrons are stopped in the gap. Since $\theta_e M^2$ is less than $\theta_n$ at the center of the mode, $V/V_0 > 2X/\theta_n$. For $X = 2.4$, $2X/\theta_n$ is 1.02, 0.44, and 0.278 for $n = 0$, 1, and 2, respectively. Hence for maximum total power conversion the condition is certainly violated for the $(n = 0)$ mode. For $X = 3.83$, for which the power conversion is zero, $2X/\theta_n$ is 1.62, 0.696, and 0.442 for $n = 0$, 1, and 2, respectively and the condition is certainly violated for the two lowest modes. It is seen, therefore, that for this reason alone the theory of this section has very little meaning in the lowest two modes, except for $X < 2.4$, a fact that must be kept in mind in using the equations and curves. However, for completeness, curves will

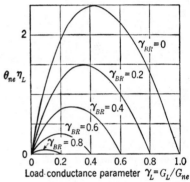

FIG. 12·7.—Dependence of output efficiency at center of mode on the load-conductance parameter for five values of internal-conductance parameter.

$$\gamma_{BR} = \gamma_B + \gamma_R = (G_B + G_R)/G_{ne}.$$

be given for low as well as high values of $n$, although these curves have certain validity only for the high modes.

Usually the internal conductance (resonator and beam) is a quantity that cannot be easily changed. The power conversion to the load is of primary consideration and it can be varied by changing the load conductance. Since in this simple theory the phase does not change with changes in gap voltage—that is, it does not change with $X$, a tube in the center of the mode remains in the center of the mode as the load conductance is varied. In Fig. 12·7 the product $\theta_{ne}\eta_L$ for $\phi = 0$ is shown plotted for a number of fixed values of the internal conductance parameter $\gamma_{BR} = (G_B + G_R)/G_{ne}$.

It is readily shown that for maximum output power

$$\gamma_L = J_2(X), \qquad \gamma_{BR} = J_0(X). \qquad (8)$$

In Fig. 12·8 $\gamma_L$, $\gamma$, and also the ratio $\gamma_L/\gamma$, which is circuit efficiency, are plotted as functions of $\gamma_{BR}$ for the condition that $\gamma_L$ has been adjusted to give the maximum output power for the indicated value of $\gamma_{BR}$. The

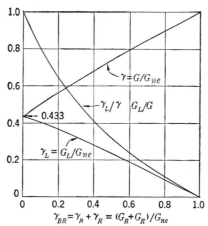

Fig. 12·8.—Conductance parameter, load-conductance parameter, and circuit efficiency for maximum power output as functions of internal-conductance parameter.

best condition for output power is, of course, achieved by having the internal conductance parameter as small as possible, for then the internal losses are minimized. As the internal losses increase, the circuit efficiency

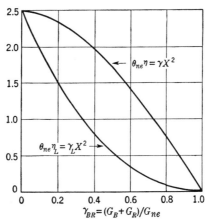

Fig. 12·9.—Dependence of total electronic efficiency and output efficiency for maximum power output on internal-conductance parameter.

drops rapidly, approaching zero as $G_{BR}$ approaches $G$. The actual efficiencies with $\gamma_L$ adjusted to maximum power output are obtainable from Fig. 12·9, if the internal conductance parameter is known.

Returning to a discussion of the starting current, it is noted that, if the total power conversion is to be a maximum, $X = 2.40$ and the ratio of the starting current to the operating current should not be less than 0.433. If the load conductance has been adjusted to give maximum output power, the ratio of the starting current to the operating current for particular values of the internal-conductance parameter is not less than the corresponding value of $\gamma$ in Fig. 12·8.

*Electronic Tuning.*—Within a mode, changing the reflector voltage from the value for operation at the center of the mode changes the frequency of oscillation and the bunching parameter. The range of the frequency of oscillation is bounded by the zero gap-voltage points, for

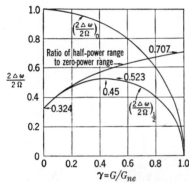

FIG. 12·10.—Dependence of total half-power range, total zero-power range, and their ratio on the conductance parameter.

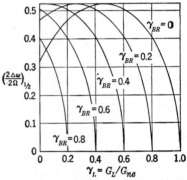

FIG. 12·11.—Dependence of total half-power range on load-conductance parameter for five values of internal-conductance parameter.

which $X = 0$. At these points $\cos \phi = \gamma$; hence [from Eq. (4)] the frequency range is $\dfrac{\omega_0}{Q} \dfrac{\sqrt{1 - \gamma^2}}{\gamma} = \dfrac{G}{C} \dfrac{\sqrt{1 - \gamma^2}}{\gamma} = \dfrac{G_{ne}}{C} \sqrt{1 - \gamma^2}$. The frequency width, $2\Omega \equiv G_{ne}/C$, is the total half-power width of the loaded resonator with the resonator so loaded that the frequency range for electrical tuning has been just reduced to zero ($G = G_{ne}$). The total frequency range between zero-power points is $2\Omega \sqrt{1 - \gamma^2}$, and the total frequency range between half-power points is given by the formula,

$$\left(\frac{2\Delta\omega}{2\Omega}\right)_{\frac{1}{2}} = \left\{ \left[\frac{2J_1(X_0/\sqrt{2})}{X_0/\sqrt{2}}\right]^2 - \left[\frac{2J_1(X_0)}{X_0}\right]^2 \right\}^{\frac{1}{2}}, \qquad (9)$$

where $X_0$ is the value of the bunching parameter at the center of the mode. These quantities and their ratio are plotted in Fig. 12·10 as functions of the conductance parameter $\gamma$. The total zero-power frequency range is equal to $2\Omega$ for $\gamma = 0$ and drops steadily to zero as $\gamma$ approaches unity.

The half-power frequency range starts at $0.65\Omega$ at $\gamma = 0$, has a maximum, which is $1.04\Omega$ at $\gamma = 0.45$, and goes to zero for $\gamma = 1$. The half-power frequency range divided by $2\Omega$ is shown in Fig. 12·11 plotted as a function of $\gamma_L$ for the particular values of $\gamma_{BR}$ used in Fig. 12·7.

*Operating Conditions.*—In order to compare different modes a new parameter, $\Gamma = \theta_n \gamma$, is introduced; it is proportional to $2G/G_0$ and is

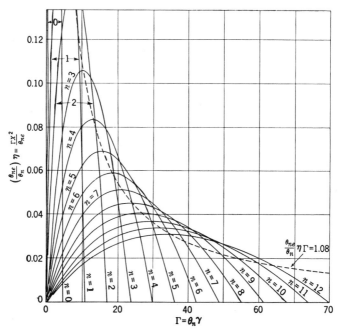

Fig. 12·12.—Dependence of total electronic efficiency on total conductance.

$$\Gamma = \frac{2G}{M^2 G_0}\left(\frac{\theta_n}{\theta_{ne}}\right);$$

$$\theta_n = 2\pi(n + \tfrac{3}{4}); \ \theta_{ne} = 2\pi(n + \tfrac{3}{4}) - 2\omega_0 T_1. \quad n = 1, \left(\frac{\theta_{ne}}{\theta_n}\right)\eta_{\max} = 0.226; \ n = 2,$$

$$\left(\frac{\theta_{ne}}{\theta_n}\right)\eta_{\max} = 0.144.$$

approximately constant from mode to mode. In Fig. 12·12, $(\theta_{ne}/\theta_n)\eta$ at the center of the modes is plotted against $\Gamma$ for successive values of $n$. It is of particular interest to note that, if the total power conversion for a given value of $\Gamma$ is a maximum for a given mode, it decreases for higher modes for fixed $\Gamma$ but, on going to lower modes, it increases before dropping suddenly. Hence, for a fixed total conductance the total power conversion is the greatest for a mode below that for which the total power conversion is nearest its own maximum.

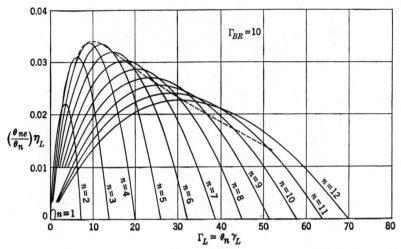

FIG. 12·13.—Dependence of output efficiency on load conductance with fixed internal conductance ($\Gamma_{BR} = 10$).

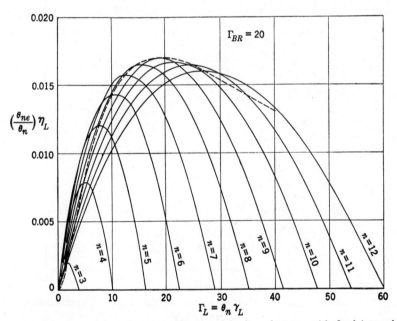

FIG. 12·14.—Dependence of output efficiency on load conductance with fixed internal conductance ($\Gamma_{BR} = 20$).

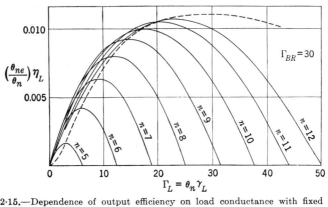

FIG 12·15.—Dependence of output efficiency on load conductance with fixed internal conductance ($\Gamma_{BR} = 30$).

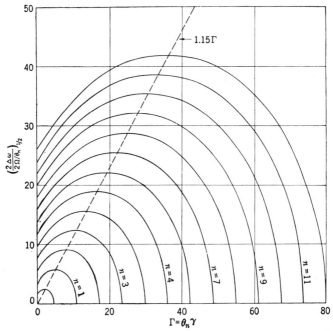

FIG. 12·16.—Dependence of total half-power electronic tuning range on total conductance.

$$2\Omega/\theta_n = G_{ne}/\theta_n C = \frac{M^2 G_0}{2C}\left(\frac{\theta_{ne}}{\theta_n}\right); \; \Gamma = \frac{2G}{M^2 G_0}\left(\frac{\theta_n}{\theta_{ne}}\right).$$

Of greater interest are Figs. 12·13, 12·14, and 12·15, which show $(\theta_{ne}/\theta_n)\eta_L$ at the centers of the tuning range as functions of $\Gamma_L = \theta_n\gamma_L$ for the lowest operating modes for three values of $\Gamma_{BR} = \theta_n \gamma_{BR}$.

In Fig. 12·16 functions proportional to the half-power tuning ranges in successive modes are plotted against $\Gamma$. Since the tuning range depends only on $\Gamma$ and not on $\Gamma_L$, curves for particular values of $\Gamma_{BR}$ as functions of $\Gamma_L$ are given by Fig. 12·16 by starting with $\Gamma = \Gamma_{BR}$ as the new abscissa origin. For example, if $\Gamma_{BR} = 20$, that part of Fig. 12·16 to the right of $\Gamma = 20$ gives the tuning ranges as functions of $\Gamma_L$; the output power is zero for $\Gamma_L = 0$ but the tuning range is not zero in this example for modes above $n = 2$. For a fixed value of $\Gamma_{BR}$, the maximum half-power tuning range of each mode cannot be reached in the lowest of the operating modes. Thus, if $\Gamma_{BR} = 20$, the maxima can be reached by varying $\Gamma_L$ only in modes above $n = 6$.

It is instructive to investigate the locus of the maxima of the output power curves for fixed $\Gamma_{BR}$ (dashed lines in Figs. 12·12, 12·13, 12·14, and 12·15) and to make comparisons of the half-power tuning ranges. Since for maximum output power [by Eqs. (8)],

$$\left.\begin{array}{l} \Gamma_L = \theta_n J_2(X) \\ \\ \Gamma_{BR} = \theta_n J_0(X), \end{array}\right\} \tag{10}$$

and

the output conversion efficiency to the load is given by the expression

$$\left(\frac{\theta_{ne}}{\theta_n}\right)\eta_L = \frac{X^2 J_0(X) J_2(X)}{\Gamma_{BR}}, \tag{11}$$

as is found by using $\Gamma_L$ and $\Gamma_{BR}$ to eliminate $\gamma_L$ and $\theta_n$ in the equation $(\theta_{ne}/\theta_n)\eta_L = \gamma_L X^2/\theta_n$. Moreover, at the maximum

$$\Gamma_L = \frac{\Gamma_{BR} J_2(X)}{J_0(X)}.$$

This equation combined with Eq. (11) gives a parametric relation between the maximum of the output efficiency and $\Gamma_L$. The locus of the maxima of $(\theta_{ne}/\theta_n)\eta_L$ against $\Gamma_L$ starts at zero at $\Gamma_L = 0$, rises to a maximum at $\Gamma_L = \Gamma_{BR}$, where $X^2 J_0(X) J_2(X) = 0.34$, and thereafter decreases towards zero for larger $\Gamma_L$. At the highest point the locus gives

$$\left(\frac{\theta_{ne}}{\theta_n}\right)\eta_L = \frac{0.34}{\Gamma_{BR}}$$

From Fig. 12·8, it is seen that the point $\Gamma_L = \Gamma_{BR}$ corresponds to $\Gamma_L = \Gamma_{BR} = 0.32\,\theta_n$, $\Gamma = 0.64\,\theta_n$. The maximum half-power tuning range in a particular mode is seen from Fig. 12·10 to have the value $0.52\,\theta_n(G_{ne}/\theta_n C)$ and comes at $\Gamma = 0.45\,\theta_n$. At $\Gamma = 0.64\,\theta_n$, the half-

power tuning range in the same mode has dropped only six per cent to
the value $0.49\theta_n(G_{ne}/\theta_nC)$. However, the output power at $\Gamma = 0.45\ \theta_n$
in the mode having its maximum output power nearest $\Gamma = 0.64\ \theta_n$
is about 40 per cent less than the value at the maximum, for the change
from $\Gamma_L = 0.32\ \theta_n$ to $\Gamma_L = 0.13\ \theta_n$ is a change in $\theta_{ne}\eta_L$ from 1.05 to 0.64,
as is found by using Fig. 12·6.

The conclusion is that, if the load conductance is varied and the
mode chosen to give the maximum output power, the half-power tuning
range is only a few per cent below the maximum for that mode. Under
these conditions the internal conductance is roughly equal to the load
conductance. Approximate formulas for the output conversion efficiency
and half-power tuning range are $0.34M^2G_0/G_L$ and $1.6G_L/C$, respectively.
(It is to be remembered that tuning ranges in this section are for angular
frequencies.)

The frequency of oscillation is sensitive to small changes in the
reflector and beam voltages. It is easily shown that

$$\left(\frac{\partial\omega}{\partial V_r}\right)_{\omega_0} \approx -\frac{\omega_0}{V_0 - V_r^0}\left(\frac{\theta_n}{2Q + \theta_n}\right), \tag{12}$$

where $V_r$ is the reflector voltage with respect to the cathode (not the
absolute value of this voltage) and $V_r^0$ is its value at the center of the
mode. A simple calculation gives

$$\left(\frac{\partial\omega}{\partial V_0}\right)_{\omega_0} \approx \frac{\omega_0}{V_0 - V_r^0}\left(\frac{\theta_n}{2Q + \theta_n}\right)\frac{V_0 + V_r^0}{2V_0}. \tag{13}$$

Since $V_0$ is positive and $V_r$ is negative, this quantity vanishes for
$V_r^0 = -V_0$. Therefore, frequency stability with regard to beam voltage
can be obtained and still keep high frequency sensitivity to reflector
voltage for the purposes of tuning.

The addition of a susceptance, whether mechanically, through the
load, or through beam loading can change both the resonant frequency
and the effective capacitance. If the addition at the gap is

$$B_B + (\omega - \omega_0)C_B,$$

then

$$2(\omega - \omega_0)C + B_B + (\omega - \omega_0)C_B = 2(\omega - \omega_0')C',$$

where $C' = C + C_B/2$, $\omega_0' = \omega_0 - B_B/2C'$. If the tube was originally
at the center of the tuning range and the reflector voltage is not
changed, the change in frequency is given by the equation,

$$\omega' - \omega_0 + \frac{G}{2C'}\tan\left[\frac{\theta_n(\omega' - \omega_0)}{\omega_0}\right] = \omega_0' - \omega_0;$$

for small changes

$$\omega' - \omega_0 \approx \frac{(\omega_0' - \omega_0)2Q}{(2Q + \theta_n)};$$

also

$$\omega_0' - \omega' \approx \frac{(\omega_0' - \omega_0)\theta_n}{(2Q + \theta_n)}.$$

Hence, if the resonant frequency is increased by the introduction of a negative susceptance, the frequency of operation increases almost as much as the change in the resonant frequency, assuming $\theta_n/2Q \ll 1$, but the tube will operate at slightly less than the new resonant frequency. It is easily seen that the rate at which the reflector voltage must be changed in order to keep the tube in the center of the tuning range is given by

$$- \frac{\omega_0}{V_0 - V_r^0} \frac{dV_r^0}{d\omega_0} \approx 1. \tag{14}$$

**12·3. Observed Characteristics of the Reflex Klystron.**—The idealized theory of the reflex klystron that has just been discussed involves only the simpler details of reflex-klystron operation. It becomes a matter of immediate interest to know how adequately actual reflex-klystron behavior is described by the theory.

Many features of observed behavior differ in various details from those predicted in this chapter. These divergences may, however, be adequately explained by refining the theory. It is with such details of behavior that the next five chapters are concerned; and these chapters in themselves present experimental data that indirectly provide striking confirmation of reflex-klystron theory when simple theory is used as the basis for more complicated considerations.

The present section reviews some of the simpler aspects of theory that may be compared with experiment; points for which comparison is implicit in the consideration of later chapters are noted only briefly, but additional data that do not logically occur in any of these later chapters are presented here.

*Phase Relations for Oscillation.*—One of the simplest points of reflex-klystron theory is the prediction that maximum r-f output power is generated when the reflection transit angle is given by the relation $\theta = 2\pi(n + \frac{3}{4})$, where $n$ is an integer. This and associated phase relations are responsible for the existence of discrete modes of oscillation. In the following chapter, as an introduction to consideration of the generalized reflector, there is discussed the relation between the various electrode voltages at which local maxima of output power occur; it is shown there that the observed location of the modes of oscillation is in good agreement with the above condition $\theta = 2\pi(n + \frac{3}{4})$.

*General Functional Relations Within an Individual Mode.*—To the user of the reflex klystron, one of the klystron characteristics most generally referred to is the way in which the output power and the frequency of oscillation depend upon the reflector voltage for a given mode of oscillation. By the methods described in Chap. 13, values of reflector voltage may be transformed into values of reflection transit time, which is conveniently measured in terms of the relative reflection transit angle $\phi$ given by $\phi = \theta - 2\pi(n + \frac{3}{4})$. In Figs. 12·4 and 12·5 are shown the predictions of simple theory about the way in which the frequency of oscillation and the relative output power are expected to depend on the reflector voltage and the oscillation frequency. In the actual reflex klystron the individual modes always show characteristics that bear a basic resemblance to those set forth in these figures.

One such reason for a divergence from behavior as predicted in these figures is the fact that they have been explicitly deduced for a "high mode"—that is, one for which $\theta_e$ is so large that the percentage variation

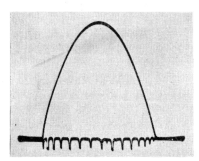

Fig. 12·17.—Oscilloscope photograph of mode of type 2K33 reflex klystron; output power and frequency as functions of reflector voltage. Adjacent frequency markers indicate frequencies separated by 5 Mc/sec.

of $\theta_e$ across a mode is negligible. For a "low mode" an asymmetry is introduced into the mode shape. Another typical distortion of mode shape occurs when, for any reason, the phase of the return bunched beam current depends upon the amplitude of bunching. A rather more drastic change in the mode may be produced by electrons that make three or more transits of the r-f gap. In addition to changes in mode shape, the latter two effects may also give rise to an electronic tuning hysteresis in which the amplitude and frequency of oscilla-

tion depend upon the direction from which the operating value of the reflector voltage is approached. All these phenomena are discussed in Chap. 14.

Hysteresis and mode distortion may also arise when the klystron operates into a resonant or frequency-dependent load, as discussed in Chap. 15.

In spite of these various perturbing influences, mode shapes similar to those of Figs. 12·4 and 12·5 are observed in well-designed oscillators operating on a high mode and into a good load. Typical of such operation is the mode shown in Fig. 12·17 for a type 2K33 klystron. This figure is an oscilloscope photograph in which output power and oscillation frequency are shown as functions of reflector voltage, the horizontal coordinate. Frequencies occurring at various reflector voltages are indicated by the frequency markers lying along the horizontal base line; adjacent markers are separated by 5 Mc/sec.

*Nature of the Small-signal Electronic Transconductance.*—The relation between $\theta_e$ and the small-signal electronic transconductance may perhaps best be observed by means other than those involving actual oscillation of the klystron in question. In Fig. 12·18 are shown data obtained on a type 417A klystron in which the beam current is reduced to a value too low to sustain oscillation.[1] The $Q$ and the resonant frequency of the resonant cavity of the 417A are measured by means of usual techniques involving an external signal generator. The figure shows the dependence of the measured $Q$ and the resonant frequency upon the reflector voltage, that is, upon the reflection transit phase.

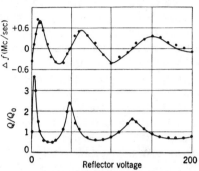

Fig. 12·18.—Resonant frequency shift $\Delta f = f - f_0$ and ratio $Q/Q_0$ of effective $Q$ to zero beam-current $Q$, for type 417A reflex klystron operating with beam current less than starting current.

The over-all klystron-cavity admittance is the sum of the intrinsic admittance of the cavity and the contribution of the electronic trans-admittance. Under the condition of this experiment, with the r-f gap voltage provided by an external signal generator, small-signal conditions prevail and the electronic transadmittance is given by Eq. (1). The real part of this transadmittance, which affects the over-all $Q$ in this experiment, oscillates about zero with increasing amplitude as $\theta$ is increased (reflector voltage less negative); this situation corresponds, in the figure, to the oscillation of $Q$ about the intrinsic $Q$ of the resonator with an amplitude that increases as reflector voltage is lowered. Similarly, the electronic susceptance and the over-all resonant frequency of the cavity oscillate with increasing amplitude about zero and about the intrinsic resonant frequency of the cavity. Zero electronic susceptance is seen to correspond to maximum absolute value of electronic conductance and vice versa. These phenomena are in agreement with the predictions of Eq. (1) concerning the electronic transadmittance.

*Relative Dependence of Output Power and Electronic Tuning Range Upon Load.*—According to simple theory the output power and electronic-

[1] E. L. Ginzton and A. E. Harrison, "Reflex Klystron Oscillators," *Proc. I.R.E.*, **34**, 97(1946).

tuning range should depend upon the load that the oscillator sees, in a manner described in the last paragraphs of Sec. 12·2. This subject is discussed at length in Chap. 15; there it is shown that under properly simplified operating conditions there is good agreement between simple theory and experiment.

**12·4. Quantitative Comparison of Theory and Experiment.**—The preceding section has been concerned with some general qualitative comparisons between theory and experiment. It is instructive to make the comparison more quantitative, particularly with respect to the two characteristics of greatest practical importance—the output power and the electronic tuning range. The present section is concerned with the details of such a comparison as carried out with one particular type, the 3K23 reflex klystron.

*Operating Condition.*—The data in question are all taken at $V_0 = 900$ volts, $n = 2$, $\lambda = 30.5$ cm. The cathode emission current (intentionally reduced in taking some of the data) is normally 60 ma. The beam passes through a total of four grids before it finally makes its second transit of the r-f gap; at each passage through a grid 6 per cent of the current is absorbed with the result that the beam current $kI_0$ effective in oscillator operation is 78 per cent of the cathode emission current $I_0$. (The ratio is somewhat lower at the highest values of current used, apparently because of a slight beam spreading.)

*Beam Coupling Coefficient.*—The actual gap spacing is 0.25 cm; that is a spacing between rather coarse grids; and with this type of grid, measurement of the beam voltage for which $M = 0$ indicates that the gap spacing that is effective in determining the beam-coupling coefficient is about 0.35 cm. At the specific $V_0$ and $\lambda$ this gives $M = 0.94$, $M^2 = 0.88$.

*Beam Loading.*—A basic factor in the over-all operation of an oscillator is the effective value of the cavity $Q$ and the cavity shunt conductance $G$ or the shunt "impedance" $R = 1/G$. Although the shunt conductance is not easily measured by direct means,[1] there are two general types of methods available for measuring $Q$. The results of these two measurements of $Q$ are of interest not only in themselves, but also because a comparison of the results provides one of the best tests of reflex-klystron theory. One of the types of method referred to includes any method that is based on the use of an external signal generator, such as the measurement of the bandwidth of the cavity operated as a filter. The second method is based on Eq. (4), the derivative of which states that at the center of a mode (i.e., $\phi = 0$) the rate of electronic tuning is given by

$$\frac{1}{f_0}\frac{df}{d\phi} = -\frac{1}{2Q}. \tag{15}$$

[1] See, however, R. L. Sproull and E. G. Linder, *Proc. I.R.E.*, **34**, 305 (1946).

By the first method the $Q$ of the resonant cavity of the type 3K23 with no beam current is found to be 2000 ± 10 per cent. (This limit of error is not indicative of the much smaller limits applicable to a more careful experiment.)

Measurement of the values of $Q$ indicated by the second means, observation of the center-of-mode tuning rate, is made at a number of values of the effective beam current $kI_0$, as indicated in Fig. 12·19. During these measurements the tube is oscillating and, as only an infinitesimal amount of power is coupled out of the resonator for purposes of measurement of tuning rate, the resulting $Q$ should be $Q_{BR}$, the $Q$ of the resonator as loaded by the beam only.

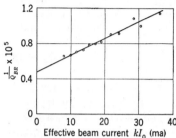

FIG. 12·19.—Observed dependence of $Q_{BR}$ ($Q$ of beam-loaded cavity) on effective beam current $kI_0$, in a type 3K23 reflex klystron.

The data in Fig. 12·19 are well represented by the empirical relation

$$\frac{1}{Q_{BR}} = 0.48 \times 10^{-3}(1 + 0.039kI_0), \tag{16}$$

where $kI_0$ is the effective beam current in milliamperes. Thus it appears that a beam loading is present that may be represented by a beam-loading conductance linear in $I_0$, and which will reduce the inherent resonator $Q$ by a factor of 2 when $kI = 26$ ma or $I_0 = 33$ ma. Since the normal operating current is 60 ma, it is seen that beam-loading losses ordinarily predominate over resonator losses in this tube. This result is basic to the subsequent analysis.

The data of Fig. 12·19 extrapolate to $Q = 2100$ at zero current. This value compares very well with the value of 2000 indicated by the first method, and constitutes good experimental verification of the theory of electronic tuning.

*Starting Current.*—The starting current, or the minimum current that will sustain oscillation, depends directly upon the effective shunt conductance of the resonant cavity; conversely, measurement of starting current gives information about this shunt conductance provided that the theory is correct in its statements about starting current.

With the stated operating conditions of the type 3K23, and with observation of oscillation carried out by coupling an infinitesimal amount of power out to an external load, it is found that with zero external load, oscillations occur for an effective beam current given by $kI_0 \geqq 2.35$ ma. It will become apparent from the subsequent discussion of Fig. 12·20 that this current is the same as the starting current shown in that figure.

From the above beam-loading data, $G_{BR} = 1.09G_R$ at $kI_0 = 2.35$ ma. If a linear reflector field is assumed (as will very nearly be the case at these low currents), the simple theory states that $G_{BR} = \pi(n + \frac{3}{4})M^2G_0$ if $G_0$ is the beam conductance corresponding to the effective starting current. From the already stated values of $M$, $n$, $V_0$ and the above values of starting current and $G_{BR}/G_R$, it is deduced that

$$G_R = 18 \times 10^{-6} \quad \text{mhos.}$$

*Comparison of Observed and Predicted $Q_R$ and $G_R$.*—From the dimensions of the 3K23 cavity and from cavity-resonator charts of Chap. 4, the theoretically predicted values of $Q_R$ and $G_R$ are found to be 2030 and $8.3 \times 10^{-6}$ mhos respectively. The predicted value of $Q_R$ agrees very well with the observed values of 2000 and 2100; but the predicted value of $G_R$ is half of the value calculated from oscillator theory and the observed starting current. This discrepancy may arise from any of several sources. The calculated shunt impedances or conductances of Chap. 4 are admittedly approximate, although an error of two is not to be expected. Also, the discrepancy is in the same direction as that produced by phase aberration in the reflector—that is, by a difference in the d-c transit times or the values of $\phi$ associated with different electron trajectories in the reflector region. Such phase aberrations are discussed in Chap. 13, where it is shown that they may be expressed by a factor $\overline{(\cos \phi)}_{max}$ by which efficiency and effective beam current are reduced. Thus, to explain completely the present discrepancy, a phase-aberration factor of $8.3/18$ or approximately 0.5 would have to be postulated.

Finally, there are undoubtedly some electrons that make more than two transits of the r-f gap; and it may be seen in Chap. 14 that the influence of these multiple-transit electrons is particularly marked in the vicinity of the starting point.

*The Parameter $\gamma_{BR}$ and its Dependence on $kI_0$.* The parameter $\gamma_{BR}$ is defined as the ratio $2G_{BR}/M^2\theta_eG_0$. More generally, with the beam-loading contribution of $kI_0$ included in $G_{BR}$, $\gamma_{BR}$ is the ratio of zero-external-load effective starting current to effective beam current $kI_0$. Since $G_{BR}$ increases with $kI_0$, $\gamma_{BR}$ is not exactly inversely proportional to $kI_0$.

The usefulness of the parameter $\gamma_{BR}$ lies in the fact that the electronic-tuning range $\Delta f$ (Note that $\Delta f \equiv 2\Delta\omega/2\pi$) and the efficiency $\eta_L$ at optimum loading are known functions of $\gamma_{BR}$ (see Figs. 12·9, 12·10, and 12·11). If it is assumed that the experimentally observed value of the starting current is not influenced by some effect that is more important at low amplitudes than at high amplitudes (for example, multiple transits), then the observed beam loading and the observed zero-external-load effective starting current yield the following relation:

$$\gamma_{BR} = \left(\frac{21.5}{kI_0}\right)(1 + 0.039 \, kI_0). \tag{17}$$

Utilizing Eq. (16) for $Q_{BR}$ and Eq. (17) for $\gamma_{BR}$, the curves in Figs. 12·8, 12·9, and 12·10 may be used to deduce the predicted dependence of $\eta_L$ and $\Delta f$ shown in Figs. 12·20 and 12·21. The efficiency predicted in Fig. 12·20 is the over-all efficiency, and allowance has been made in this figure for the loss of 22 per cent of the beam current in grid interception. The ideal efficiency for a reflex klystron working in the $(n = 2)$-mode is 14.5 per cent; the current loss in grid interception reduces this to 11.3 per cent; the difference between this latter figure and the effi-

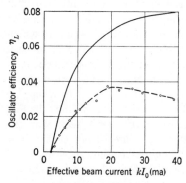

FIG. 12·20.—Dependence of oscillator efficiency $\eta_L$, on effective beam current $kI_0$ for a type 3K23 reflex klystron. Experimental data (broken curve). Dependence predicted on basis of simple oscillator theory, observed beam-loading, observed starting current (solid curve).

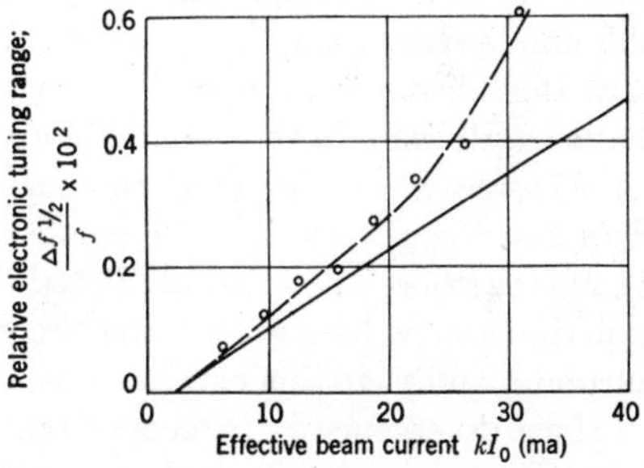

FIG. 12·21.—Dependence of electronic-tuning range on effective beam current for a type 3K23 reflex klystron. Experimental data (broken curve); calculated from observed starting current (solid curve).

ciencies predicted for various currents in Fig. 12·20 represents the efficiency loss that is anticipated as a result of resonator and beam-loading losses.

*Experimentally Observed Dependence of Efficiency on Effective Beam Current.*—Figure 12·20 summarizes the experimental data on this point. It is seen that there is considerable discrepancy between the predicted and observed behavior. The discrepancy takes two forms. In the first place, at low currents the experimental curve lies below the predicted curve by a constant factor of 2.3. In the second place, at high currents the shapes of the two curves differ markedly, with the experimental efficiency eventually decreasing with increasing current.

The first of these points is reminiscent of the factor 2.2 by which the starting current is found to differ from the value predicted on the basis of theoretical cavity shunt conductance. One of the tentative hypotheses advanced to explain this previous discrepancy was a phase-aberration factor $(\overline{\cos \phi})_{\text{max}} = 0.5$. The same hypothesis explains the low-current data of Fig. 12·20 because the efficiency should be reduced by this same factor. On the other hand, the hypothesis that the calculation of $G_R$ in Chap. 4 is inaccurate by a factor of two will explain the starting-current anomaly but will do nothing to bring observed and predicted efficiencies into line. The same is true of any simple hypothesis concerning multiple-transit electrons. The indication of phase aberration is thus reinforced.

The second point about Fig. 12·20, the drooping of the experimental efficiency at high currents, seems to be related to space-charge distortion of the reflector field of the sort discussed in more detail in Chap. 13. This space-charge distortion occurs in the 3K23 at current densities at which no trouble would arise with shorter-wavelength klystrons in which the anode-reflector spacing is correspondingly smaller. It will be seen that this phenomenon is probably an important factor in setting a long-wavelength limit to the profitable operation of the reflex klystron.

*Experimentally Observed Dependence of Electronic Tuning Range on Effective Beam Current.*—The empirically observed data is shown in Fig. 12·21 together with the predicted values of $\Delta f$. It is seen that the experimental values exceed the theoretical by some 20 per cent at low currents, and that this excess increases at higher currents.

This divergence is in general agreement with and corroborates the conclusions already reached in connection with the efficiency data. A phase-aberration factor will not affect the relation between $\Delta f$ and $\gamma_{BR}$ when (as here) the latter is determined empirically from the starting current. The slight excess of observed over predicted values at low currents is probably caused by a slight curvature of the reflector field; it is seen in Chap. 13 that a corresponding 20 per cent diminution in efficiency would then accompany this increase in $\Delta f$. This 20 per cent diminution of efficiency is masked by the larger phase-aberration effect. Similarly, the abnormal increase of $\Delta f$ at high current is exactly what would be expected if the unexpected decrease of $\eta$ at high currents were due to space-charge distortion of the reflector field.

*Conclusions.*—It is apparent from this example that the behavior of a single reflex-klystron type may contain sizable quantitative deviations from simple theory. It has been noted that the reasons for these discrepancies are susceptible to analysis and that the elaborations of theory that are necessary for obtaining quantitative agreement are discussed in subsequent chapters. Given these subsequent elaborations of theory there do not seem to be any large gaps in the understanding of the reflex klystron. It should be noted, however, that in some cases (notably the matter of space charge in the reflector region) these elaborations of theory are sketched in these later chapters, but not developed in full detail.

**12·5. Detailed Theory of Idealized Oscillator.**—The theory of the reflex oscillator as presented in Sec. 12·2 is based on the simplest possible assumptions and approximations. Most of the remainder of this book is concerned with the phenomena occurring when the operating conditions or theoretical assumptions of Sec. 12·2 are made more general. The present section is concerned with the generalizations that are introduced by applying to the idealized oscillator of Sec. 12·2 a less approximate mathematical treatment than was given there. It will be found that this procedure alters the oscillator behavior in several interesting details, but not in basic characteristics. In order to make the present section more self-contained some of the material of Chap. 9 is repeated here.

In the remaining six chapters of this book many phenomena encountered in reflex oscillators that are not accounted for under the idealizations of this section are discussed. Of particular interest and importance is the effect of a nonideal reflector, the field of which is not constant along the axis of the tube and therefore changes the transit-time and bunching relationships. This is the subject of the next chapter. Nonideal behavior as manifested in hysteresis is the subject of Chap. 14. In Chap. 15 the effect of load is discussed in detail. The next two chapters deal with the modulation of the oscillations, intentionally and because of noise. The final chapter is a summary of the characteristics of practical reflex tubes.

In the present section some of the results of the following chapter are anticipated by generalizing the assumed oscillator in one respect over that of Sec. 12·2. Four instead of three regions in the tube, separated by ideal grids, are considered: the acceleration region, the gap, a field-free drift space, and the reflector region. The field-free drift space may be built into the tube, or it may be an idealization of a thick grid, or it may not be present at all; it is of interest principally because of differences in the bunching caused by this region and in the bunching caused by the reflector region.

In relation to the cathode the resonator is at the positive d-c potential $V_0$ and the reflector is at the negative d-c potential $V_r$. The total potential drop in the reflector region is therefore $V_0 - V_r$. The current injected into the gap from the acceleration region is $-I_0$ ($I_0$ is positive). The beam conductance is most conveniently defined in terms of the current that returns to the gap, $G_0 = kI_0/V_0$.

The velocity $v_0$ of injection of the electrons is given by the beam potential, $V_0 = mv_0^2/2e$. In the absence of the r-f field, the one-way transit time of the gap is $T_1 = d/v_0$, where $d$ is the spacing of the gap grids. The one-way transit time in the field-free drift space is $T_2$, and the complete transit time in the reflector region is $T_3$. The time that the electrons take in going from the center of the gap back to the center of the gap, in the absence of r-f fields, is $T = T_1 + 2T_2 + T_3$.

*Nature of the Driving Current.*—The driving current is the sum of parts coming from the injected and reflected electrons,

$$i(t) = i^+(t) + i^-(t).$$

These parts are the space averages of the injected and reflected currents, respectively,

$$i^+(t) = \frac{1}{d} \int_0^d dx \, i^+(x,t), \qquad i^-(t) = \frac{1}{d} \int_0^d dx \, i^-(x,t).$$

Following the treatment of Chap. 3, Sec. 3·5, two-way transmission of a high-velocity gap can be considered as the simultaneous injection of electrons into the gap through both grids; each injected stream can have both density and velocity modulation. The method of analysis indicated there can be used in developing the theory of the reflex oscillator. It is necessary to calculate the density and velocity modulation of the reflected stream as it enters the gap from the properties of the stream as it emerges from the gap after the first transit. This procedure gives readily the first approximation to the electronic admittance as in Eq. (12·2). However, if an attempt is made to improve the calculation, two difficulties arise: the calculation of the properties of the reflected stream from its properties before reflection is very difficult, and it is apparent that a consistent description requires a more careful analysis of the action of the gap than is contained in the considerations of Sec. 3·5.

In the treatment here presented all phenomena in the gap are traced back, with the aid of kinematical relations derived from Newton's law, to the time of first injection of the electrons into the gap. In the mathematical formulation phase factors occur that can be calculated from the model with any degree of accuracy desired. Since both the current and the velocity of the injected stream are assumed to be unmodulated, this method of attack is particularly suited to the problem of this section. In Chap. 17 the theory of noise in the reflex oscillator is developed using also this method of treatment; in the noise problem neither the injection velocity nor the injection current is constant.

It is convenient in this chapter and also in Chap. 17 to use the Fourier-integral theorem. In order to give mathematical validity to its use, a time interval is introduced that is much longer than the period corresponding to any of the frequencies which are considered; and, outside that time interval, all time-varying quantities are considered equal to their average values.   The integrations over the time are carried out with the aid of the Dirac delta function and its integral representation. This function $\delta(\omega')$ has the property that if $F(\omega')$ is an arbitrary function of $\omega'$,

$$\int_{-\infty}^{\infty} d\omega' \, \delta(\omega')F(\omega') = F(0).$$

Its integral representation is

$$\delta(\omega') = \frac{1}{2\pi} \int_{-\infty}^{\infty} d\tau' e^{i\omega'\tau'}.$$

By the Fourier-integral theorem

$$i^+(x,t) = \int_{-\infty}^{\infty} \frac{d\omega'}{2\pi} e^{j\omega't} \int_{-\infty}^{\infty} d\tau i^+(x,\tau)e^{-i\omega'\tau},$$

$$i^-(x,t) = \int_{-\infty}^{\infty} \frac{d\omega'}{2\pi} e^{j\omega't} \int_{-\infty}^{\infty} d\tau i^-(x,\tau)e^{-i\omega'\tau}.$$

In order to express these quantities in terms of the injected current at the first grid suppose in each case that an electron arriving at $x$ at time $\tau$ first entered the gap at $x = 0$ at time $\tau'$.   Then

$$\left. \begin{array}{l} \int_{-\infty}^{\infty} d\tau i^+(x,\tau)e^{-i\omega'\tau} = \int_{-\infty}^{\infty} d\tau' i^+(0,\tau')e^{-i\omega'\tau}, \\[2mm] \int_{-\infty}^{\infty} d\tau i^-(x,\tau)e^{-i\omega'\tau} = -k \int_{-\infty}^{\infty} d\tau' i^+(0,\tau')e^{-i\omega'\tau}, \end{array} \right\} \tag{18}$$

where $i^+(0,\tau')$ is the injected current at the time $\tau'$ and $ki^+(0,\tau')$ is that portion of the injected current that is reflected back into the gap.   These identities are the result of the continuity and single-valued nature of $\tau$ when regarded as a function of $\tau'$.

In order to establish the validity of the second of the identities, the observation is made that the reflected electrons that pass through the plane $x$ at time $\tau$ in the time interval $\Delta\tau$ have a total charge $-i^-(x,\tau)\,\Delta\tau$. Since $\tau'$ is not necessarily a single-valued function of $\tau$, these electrons can have been first injected into the gap at several earlier times $\tau'$. If the positive time interval at $\tau'$ during which those injected at $\tau'$ first pass through the first grid is $\Delta\tau'$, the ratio $\Delta\tau/\Delta\tau'$ is given by $|d\tau/d\tau'|$ for that value of $\tau'$.   Since these electrons have the total charge $ki^+(0,\tau')\,\Delta\tau'$,

$$i^-(x,\tau)\,\Delta\tau = -k \sum_{\tau'(\tau)} i^+(0,\tau')\,\Delta\tau',$$

where the sum is over all $\tau'$ having the same $\tau$.   If the left member of this equation is multiplied by $e^{-i\omega'\tau}$ and summed over all $\tau$, the left

member of the second identity results in the limit.   If the right member
is multiplied by $e^{-i\omega'\tau}$ and summed over all $\tau$, the double sum can be
replaced by a single sum over $\tau'$ and the right member of the second
identity results; there is no overlapping of the intervals $\Delta\tau'$ since $\tau$ is a
single-valued function of $\tau'$ and the total range of $\tau'$ is covered since that
function is continuous.   The first identity follows by a similar argument.
Therefore

$$i^+(x,t) = \int_{-\infty}^{\infty} \frac{d\omega'}{2\pi} e^{i\omega't} \int_{-\infty}^{\infty} d\tau' i^+(0,\tau') e^{-i\omega\tau^+(x;\tau')},$$
$$i^-(x,t) = -k \int_{-\infty}^{\infty} \frac{d\omega'}{2\pi} e^{i\omega t} \int_{-\infty}^{\infty} d\tau' i^+(0,\tau') e^{-i\omega\tau^-(x;\tau')}$$

(19)

where $\tau^+(x;\tau')$ and $\tau^-(x;\tau')$ are the arrival times at the plane $x$ of electrons
that were injected into the gap at $x = 0$ at time $\tau'$ and which have come
directly or been reflected, respectively.   The driving current is

$$i(t) = \int_{-\infty}^{\infty} \frac{d\omega'}{2\pi} e^{i\omega't} \int_{-\infty}^{\infty} d\tau' i^+(0,\tau') \frac{1}{d} \int_0^d dx[e^{-i\omega'\tau^+(x;\tau')} - ke^{-i\omega'\tau^-(x;\tau')}] \quad (20)$$

In this chapter both the injected current and the velocity of injection are
considered to be constant.

This description of the current has a generality beyond the use made
of it in this chapter.   For instance, $i^+(0,\tau')$ need not be set equal to a
constant; it can be a periodic function of the time as determined by some
earlier condition (as by an additional resonator), or it can be a random
variable (such as a current with noise components).   Similarly, the injection velocity need not be constant, a consideration that can affect the
calculation of the arrival times.   It is to be noted that the two identities
above (Eqs. 18) are valid if $e^{-i\omega'\tau}$ is replaced by an arbitrary function of $\tau$.

In this method of determining the driving current the essential step
is the calculation of the space averages of the phase factors containing
the arrival times.   These arrival times are obtained with the aid of
Newton's law from the fields through which the electrons move.

*Motion of the Electrons.*—The arrival times $\tau^+(x;\tau')$ and $\tau^-(x;\tau')$
depend on the velocity of injection $v_0$, as determined by the beam potential, $V_0 = mv_0^2/2e$, and on the transit times $T_1$, $T_2$, $T_3$, all of which are
independent of the r-f field; in addition, they depend on the frequency,
amplitude, and phase of the gap potential $V \sin \omega t$.   Of particular
importance are the three transit angles $\theta_1 = \omega t_1$, $\theta_2 = \omega T_2$, $\theta_3 = \omega T_3$, and
the phase angle $\theta = \theta_1 + 2\theta_2 + \theta_3$, which is measured from the center
of the gap to the center of the gap.   The condition $V/2V_0 < \frac{1}{4}$ is assumed,
for otherwise if $\theta_1$ were small enough, some of the electrons could be

stopped in the gap. Such a stoppage, although not impossible, is not considered in this chapter since a special treatment of the problem is required. Of interest are the relative magnitudes of the four quantities $T_3/T_1$, $T_2/T_1$, $1$, $V/2V_0$. The assumption is made that $T_3/T_1$ and $T_2/T_1$ are (or can be) much larger than unity. The distinction is made between $T_3$, $T_2$, $T_1$, $(V/2V_0)T_3$, and $(V/2V_0)T_2$, which are zero-order quantities, and $(V/2V_0)T_1$, $(V/2V_0)^2T_3$, and $(V/2V_0)^2T_2$, which are first-order quantities. This distinction is made in order that the implicit functional relations that are obtained for the desired arrival times can be solved explicitly to first-order quantities. The calculation of the driving current is carried out to first order.

With the gap potential $V \sin \omega\tau$, Newton's law is

$$m \frac{d^2x}{d\tau^2} = \frac{eV}{d} \sin \omega\tau.$$

If the first passage through the gap is considered, Newton's law can be integrated to give

$$\left.\begin{array}{l} m(v - v_0) = -\dfrac{eV}{d\omega} (\cos \omega\tau - \cos \omega\tau'), \\[2ex] mx = mv_0(\tau - \tau') - \dfrac{eV}{d\omega^2} [\sin \omega\tau - \sin \omega\tau' - \omega(\tau - \tau') \cos \omega\tau'] \end{array}\right\} \quad (21)$$

If the second equation is rearranged and $eV/d\omega mv_0 = V/2V_0\theta_1$ is substituted, there is obtained

$$\tau = \tau' + \frac{x}{v_0} + \left(\frac{V}{2V_0}\right)\frac{T_1}{\theta_1^2} [\sin \omega\tau - \sin \omega\tau' - \omega(\tau - \tau') \cos \omega\tau'], \quad (22)$$

which is an exact expression. Hence, to the first order,

$$\tau^+(x;\tau') = \tau' + \frac{x}{d} T_1 + \left(\frac{V}{2V_0}\right)\frac{T_1}{\theta_1^2}\left[ \sin\left(\omega\tau' + \frac{x}{d}\theta_1\right) - \sin \omega\tau' - \frac{x}{d}\theta_1 \cos \omega\tau'\right]. \quad (23)$$

It is interesting to express the time of arrival at the second grid, as obtained from the expression just derived, in terms of the functions of the gap-transit angle, $M$ and $N$, introduced in Chap. 3. These functions are unity for $\theta_1 = 0$ and become small for large values of $\theta_1$. The following equation results

$$\tau^+(d;\tau') = \tau' + T_1 - \left(\frac{V}{2V_0}\right)\frac{T_1}{2}\left[ M \sin\left(\omega\tau' + \frac{\theta_1}{2}\right) - \frac{\theta_1 N}{6} \cos\left(\omega\tau' + \frac{\theta_1}{2}\right)\right].$$

It is to be noted that to this approximation the effective phase is that which the electron would have had at the center of the gap, if the r-f field had not been present, modified by the additional angle $- \tan^{-1} (\theta_1 N/6M)$. This angle arises from the cosine term in the above; this term also modifies the magnitude of the effective gap voltage (see Fig. 3·8).

Considering next the passage through the field-free drift space and the reflection in the reflector region, if $v_d$ is the velocity of the electron as it first emerges from the gap, the time spent in the field-free drift space (both ways) is $2T_2 v_0/v_d$. Under the assumption of a constant reflector field, the time spent in the reflector region is $T_3 v_d/v_0$.

In order to get all the first-order terms in the total time between emerging from the gap and entering it again, $v_0/v_d$ and $v_d/v_0$ are needed, to the second order, in $V/2V_0$. The expression for $v_d$ is

$$v_d = v_0 - \left(\frac{V}{2V_0}\right)\frac{v_0}{\theta_1} (\cos \omega\tau - \cos \omega\tau'). \tag{24}$$

From this equation is found, to the second order, with the aid of the first-order expression for $\tau$,

$$v_d = v_0 \left\{ 1 + \frac{MV}{2V_0} \sin\left(\omega\tau' + \frac{\theta_1}{2}\right) - \frac{1}{2}\left(\frac{MV}{2V_0}\right)^2 \sin^2\left(\omega\tau' + \frac{\theta_1}{2}\right) \right.$$
$$\left. + \frac{\theta_1}{12}\left(\frac{V}{2V_0}\right)^2 \left[ -2P\sin\left(\omega\tau' + \frac{\theta_1}{2}\right)\cos\left(\omega\tau' + \frac{\theta_1}{2}\right) + \theta_1 \frac{MN}{2} \right]\right\}. \tag{25}$$

Terms that remain in the limit of zero gap-transit angle have been separated out and are recognizable as terms in the expansion of

$$v_0 \left[ 1 + \frac{MV}{V_0} \sin\left(\omega\tau' + \frac{\theta_1}{2}\right) \right]^{\frac{1}{2}}.$$

The remaining terms vanish for $\theta_1 = 0$. The quantity $P$ is given by

$$P = \frac{6}{\theta_1^3} (\theta_1 - \sin\theta_1);$$

and, like $M$ and $N$, is unity for $\theta_1 = 0$ and becomes small for large values of $\theta_1$ (see Fig. 3·3). It is significant that the second-order terms introduce the frequency $2\omega$. Since the bunching process is not a linear one, terms of this frequency in the arrival times contribute to the principal harmonic of the driving current.

The time of reentry can now be calculated to first order.  It is

$$
\tau^-(d;\tau') = \tau' + T + (-2T_2 + T_3)\left(\frac{MV}{2V_0}\right)\sin\left(\omega\tau' + \frac{\theta_1}{2}\right)
$$
$$
- (-6T_2 + T_3)\frac{1}{2}\left(\frac{MV}{2V_0}\right)^2 \sin^2\left(\omega\tau' + \frac{\theta_1}{2}\right)
$$
$$
- \frac{T_1}{2}\left(\frac{V}{2V_0}\right)\left[M\sin\left(\omega\tau' + \frac{\theta_1}{2}\right) - \frac{\theta_1 N}{6}\cos\left(\omega\tau' + \frac{\theta_1}{2}\right)\right] \quad (26)
$$
$$
+ \frac{T_1}{12}(-2\theta_2 + \theta_3)\left(\frac{V}{2V_0}\right)^2\left[-2P\sin\left(\omega\tau' + \frac{\theta_1}{2}\right)\right.
$$
$$
\left.\cos\left(\omega\tau' + \frac{\theta_1}{2}\right) + \frac{\theta_1 MN}{2}\right],
$$

where $T = T_1 + 2T_2 + T_3$.  In the equation for the arrival time $T_2$ and $T_3$ enter in the first-order terms with opposite signs because the effect of the velocity change is not the same in the field-free drift space and the repeller region.  The difference is the greatest in its effect on the coefficient of $\sin^2(\omega\tau' + \theta_1/2)$, where the extra factor of 3 comes from the addition in the expansion of $v_0/v_d$ that is due to the contribution of $\sin(\omega\tau' + \theta_1/2)$.

Considering, finally, the return passage in the gap, since the electron is now moving in the opposite direction, the effect of the field is the negative of the effect on injected electrons.  The exact expression is

$$
\tau = \tau^-(d;\tau') + \frac{v_0}{v_d}\left\{\left(\frac{d-x}{d}\right)T_1 - \left(\frac{V}{2V_0}\right)\frac{T_1}{\theta_1^2}\left[\sin\omega\tau - \sin\omega\tau^-(d;\tau')\right.\right.
$$
$$
\left.\left. - \omega(\tau - \tau^-(d;\tau'))\cos\omega\tau^-(d;\tau')\right]\right\} \quad (27)
$$

Two facts are significant: the speed of the reentry is $v_d$, not $v_0$, and the time of reentry is $\tau^-(d;\tau')$.  However, in the time interval $\tau - \tau^-(d;\tau')$ the latter appears in the high-order term.  With the aid of first-order expression for $v_d$, there is obtained to first-order,

$$
\tau - \tau^-(d;\tau') = \left(\frac{d-x}{d}\right)T_1 - \left(\frac{d-x}{d}\right)T_1\left(\frac{MV}{2V_0}\right)\sin\left(\omega\tau' + \frac{\theta_1}{2}\right)
$$
$$
- T_1\left(\frac{V}{2V_0}\right)\frac{1}{\theta_1^2}\left\{\sin\left[\omega\tau' + \theta + Z\sin\left(\omega\tau' + \frac{\theta_1}{2}\right)\right.\right.
$$
$$
\left.+ \left(\frac{d-x}{d}\right)\theta_1\right] - \sin\left[\omega\tau' + \theta + Z\sin\left(\omega\tau' + \frac{\theta_1}{2}\right)\right]
$$
$$
\left. - \left(\frac{d-x}{d}\right)\theta_1\cos\left[\omega\tau' + \theta + Z\sin\left(\omega\tau' + \frac{\theta_1}{2}\right)\right]\right\}, \quad (28)
$$

where $\theta = \omega T$, and $Z = \omega(-2T_2 + T_3)\frac{MV}{2V_0}$.  It is to be noted that the first-order terms contain all harmonics of the oscillation frequency because the arguments of the sine and cosine functions contain sines themselves.

*Phases and Phase Factors.*—The first-order contributions to the phases $\omega'\tau^+(x;\tau')$ and $\omega'\tau^-(x;\tau')$ are conveniently expressed in terms of the following three functions:

$$
\left.\begin{aligned}
F^{+\prime}(x;\tau') &= \frac{\theta_1'}{\theta_1^2}\left[\sin\left(\omega\tau' + \frac{x}{d}\theta_1\right) - \sin\omega\tau' - \frac{x}{d}\theta_1\cos\omega\tau'\right], \\
F'(x;\tau') &= -(-6\theta_2' + \theta_3')\left(\frac{MV}{2V_0}\right)\frac{M}{2}\sin^2\left(\omega\tau' + \frac{\theta_1}{2}\right) \\
&\quad - \frac{\theta_1'}{2}\left[M\sin\left(\omega\tau' + \frac{\theta_1}{2}\right) - \frac{\theta_1 N}{6}\cos\left(\omega\tau' + \frac{\theta_1}{2}\right)\right] \\
&\quad + Z'\frac{\theta_1}{12M}\left[-2P\sin\left(\omega\tau' + \frac{\theta_1}{2}\right)\cos\left(\omega\tau' + \frac{\theta_1}{2}\right) + \frac{\theta_1 MN}{2}\right] \\
&\quad - \left(\frac{d-x}{d}\right)\theta_1' M\sin\left(\omega\tau' + \frac{\theta_1}{2}\right), \\
F^{-\prime}(x;\tau') &= \frac{-\theta_1'}{\theta_1^2}\left\{\sin\left[\omega\tau' + \theta + Z\sin\left(\omega\tau' + \frac{\theta_1}{2}\right) + \left(\frac{d-x}{d}\right)\theta_1\right]\right. \\
&\quad - \sin\left[\omega\tau' + \theta_1 + Z\sin\left(\omega\tau' + \frac{\theta_1}{2}\right)\right] \\
&\quad \left. - \left(\frac{d-x}{d}\right)\theta_1\cos\left[\omega\tau' + \theta + Z\sin\left(\omega\tau' + \frac{\theta_1}{2}\right)\right]\right\}.
\end{aligned}\right\} \quad (29)
$$

Therefore, the phases $\omega'\tau^+(x;\tau')$ and $\omega'\tau^-(x;\tau')$ may be written as follows:

$$
\left.\begin{aligned}
\omega'\tau^+(x;\tau') &= \omega'\tau' + \frac{x}{2}\theta_1' + \left(\frac{V}{2V_0}\right)F^{+\prime}(x;\tau'), \\
\omega'\tau^-(x;\tau') &= \omega'\tau' + \theta' + Z'\sin\left(\omega\tau' + \frac{\theta_1}{2}\right) + \left(\frac{d-x}{d}\right)\theta_1' \\
&\quad + \left(\frac{V}{2V_0}\right)F'(x;\tau') + \left(\frac{V}{2V_0}\right)F^{-\prime}(x;\tau').
\end{aligned}\right\} \quad (30)
$$

In the phase factors, $e^{-i\omega'\tau^+(x;\tau')}$ and $e^{-i\omega'\tau^-(x;\tau')}$, the exponentials containing first-order terms can be expanded and quadratic and higher terms dropped. Hence, the space-averages of the phase factors, which are the quantities that occur in the driving current, are

$$
\left.\begin{aligned}
\frac{1}{d}\int_0^d dx\, e^{-i\omega'\tau^+(x;\tau')} &= e^{-i\omega'\tau'}\frac{1}{d}\int_0^d dx\, e^{-j\frac{x}{d}\theta_1'}\left[1 - j\left(\frac{V}{2V_0}\right)F^{+\prime}(x;\tau')\right], \\
\frac{1}{d}\int_0^d dx\, e^{-i\omega'\tau^-(x;\tau')} &= e^{-j\left[\omega'\tau' + \theta' + Z'\sin\left(\omega\tau' + \frac{\theta_1}{2}\right)\right]}\frac{1}{d}\int_0^d dx\, e^{-j\left(\frac{d-x}{d}\right)\theta_1'} \\
&\quad \left[1 - j\left(\frac{V}{2V_0}\right)F'(x;\tau') - j\left(\frac{V}{2V_0}\right)F^{-\prime}(x;\tau')\right].
\end{aligned}\right\} \quad (31)
$$

These averages need be carried out only for $\omega' = \omega$ because only the coefficient of $e^{j\omega t}$ in the driving current is desired. The result is

$$\frac{1}{d}\int_0^d dx e^{-j\omega\tau^+(x;\tau')} = M e^{-j\left(\omega\tau'+\frac{\theta_1}{2}\right)} - \left(\frac{V}{2V_0}\right)\frac{\theta_1}{12}\left[Ne^{-j\frac{\theta_1}{2}} - Pe^{-j(2\omega\tau'+\theta_1)}\right],$$

$$\frac{1}{d}\int_0^d dx e^{-j\omega\tau^-(x;\tau')} = e^{-j\left[\omega\tau'+\theta+Z\sin\left(\omega\tau'+\frac{\theta_1}{2}\right)\right]}M e^{-j\frac{\theta_1}{2}}$$

$$- j\left(\frac{V}{2V_0}\right)e^{-j\left[\omega\tau'+\theta+Z\sin\left(\omega\tau'+\frac{\theta_1}{2}\right)\right]}M e^{-j\frac{\theta_1}{2}}\left\{-(-6\theta_2+\theta_3)\right.$$

$$\left(\frac{MV}{2V_0}\right)\frac{M}{2}\sin^2\left(\omega\tau'+\frac{\theta_1}{2}\right) - \frac{\theta_1}{2}\left[M\sin\left(\omega\tau'+\frac{\theta_1}{2}\right) - \frac{\theta_1 N}{6}\right. \qquad (32)$$

$$\left.\cos\left(\omega\tau'+\frac{\theta_1}{2}\right)\right] + \frac{Z\theta_1}{12M}\left[-2P\sin\left(\omega\tau'+\frac{\theta_1}{2}\right)\right.$$

$$\left.\cos\left(\omega\tau'+\frac{\theta_1}{2}\right) + \frac{\theta_1 MN}{2}\right] - \frac{\theta_1}{2}\left(M - j\frac{\theta_1 N}{6}\right)\sin\left(\omega\tau'+\frac{\theta_1}{2}\right)\right\}$$

$$+ \left(\frac{V}{2V_0}\right)\frac{\theta_1}{12}\left\{Ne^{-j\frac{\theta_1}{2}} - Pe^{-j\left[2\omega\tau'+\theta_1+2\theta+2Z\sin\left(\omega\tau'+\frac{\theta_1}{2}\right)\right]}\right\}.$$

*Zero-order Terms in the Driving Current.*—Since a description of the general behavior of the reflex oscillator is to be found in the zero-order terms, they are considered separately. The arrival times to zero-order are simply

$$\left.\begin{aligned}
\tau^+(x;\tau') &= \tau' + \frac{x}{d}T_1, \\
\tau^-(x;\tau') &= \tau' + (-2T_2+T_3)\left(\frac{MV}{2V_0}\right)\sin\left(\omega\tau'+\frac{\theta_1}{2}\right) + \left(\frac{d-x}{d}\right)T_1.
\end{aligned}\right\} \qquad (33)$$

From these expressions the space-averages of the phase factors for the injected and reflected currents are readily calculated. They are, respectively,

$$\left.\begin{aligned}
&e^{-j\left(\omega'\tau'+\frac{\theta_1'}{2}\right)}M(\theta_1'), \\
&e^{-j\left[\omega'\tau'+\frac{\theta_1'}{2}+\theta'+Z'\sin\left(\omega\tau'+\frac{\theta_1}{2}\right)\right]}M(\theta_1'),
\end{aligned}\right\} \qquad (34)$$

where

$$\theta_1' = \omega'T_1, \qquad \theta' = \omega'T, \qquad Z' = (-2\theta_2'+\theta_3')\frac{MV}{2V_0},$$

$$M(\theta_1') = \sin\frac{\theta_1'}{2}\bigg/\frac{\theta_1'}{2}.$$

The driving current is

$$i(t) = -I_0\int_{-\infty}^{\infty}\frac{d\omega'}{2\pi}e^{j\omega't}\int_{-\infty}^{\infty}d\tau' e^{-j\left(\omega'\tau'+\frac{\theta_1'}{2}\right)}$$

$$M(\theta_1')\left\{1 - ke^{-j\left[\theta'+Z'\sin\left(\omega\tau'+\frac{\theta_1'}{2}\right)\right]}\right\}. \qquad (35)$$

Since

$$\int_{-\infty}^{\infty} d\tau' e^{-i\omega'\tau'} = 2\pi\,\delta(\omega'),$$

the first term is merely $-I_0$. As expected, the average current on its first transit is unmodulated in this approximation. The phase factor in the reflected current can be resolved into an infinite sum of harmonic contributions by means of the Bessel-function expansion

$$e^{-jZ'\sin\left(\omega\tau' + \frac{\theta_1}{2}\right)} = \sum_{-\infty}^{\infty} J_m(Z')e^{jm\left(\omega\tau' + \frac{\theta_1}{2} - \pi\right)}. \tag{36}$$

Since

$$\int_{-\infty}^{\infty} d\tau' e^{-i(\omega'-m\omega)\tau'} = 2\pi\,\delta(\omega' - m\omega),$$

the reflected current is the familiar sum of harmonic contributions with Bessel functions in the amplitudes; the driving current is

$$i(t) = -I_0\left[1 - k\sum_{-\infty}^{\infty} M(m\theta_1)J_m(mZ)e^{-jm(\theta+\pi)}e^{jm\omega t}\right]. \tag{37}$$

The electronic transadmittance is $-2j/V$ times the coefficient of $e^{j\omega t}$ in the driving current. Hence

$$Y_e \approx \frac{-2j}{V}\,kI_0MJ_1(Z)e^{-i(\theta+\pi)}.$$

In this expression $Z = (-2\theta_2 + \theta_3)MV/2V_0$. The quantity $(-2\theta_2 + \theta_3)$ is the angle that is effective in the combined bunching action of the field-free drift space and the repeller space. Since these two spaces tend to form bunches in opposition, the bunching angle is effectively reduced. It is not unreasonable to think of half of the gap as part of the drift space, in which case the bunching takes place from the center of the gap to the center of the gap. Such a picture is already implied in the phase of the driving current $\theta = \theta_1 + 2\theta_2 + \theta_3$. The effective bunching angle then is $\theta_e = -\theta_1 - 2\theta_2 + \theta_3$ and the bunching parameter $X = \theta_e MV/2V_0$. Since

$$\frac{2jkI_0M}{V} J_1(X)e^{-i\theta} \approx \frac{2jkI_0M}{V}\left[J_1(Z) + J_1'(Z)\left(-\frac{\theta_1 MV}{2V_0}\right)\right]e^{-i\theta},$$

where $J_1'(Z) = dJ_1(Z)/dZ$, the change that is introduced is not a zero-order contribution.

*Additions to the Admittance.*—When the first-order terms are included in the phase factors, $-2j/V$ times the coefficient of $e^{j\omega t}$ in the driving current is found to be the rather cumbersome expression

$$G_0 \frac{M^2}{2} \left[ \frac{2J_1(Z)}{Z} j(-2\theta_2 + \theta_3) - J_1'(Z)2j\theta_1 \right.$$

$$\left. + (-6\theta_2 + \theta_3)\left(\frac{MV}{2V_0}\right)J_1''(Z) \right] e^{-j\theta}$$

$$- G_0 \frac{\theta_1}{12} \left[ \theta_1 M N J_0(Z) - \frac{\theta_1 M N}{2} Z J_1(Z) + j2P J_2(Z) \right] e^{-j\theta}$$

$$+ G_0 \frac{\theta_1}{12} jNe^{-j\frac{\theta_1}{2}}\left(\frac{1}{k} + 1\right) + \frac{G_0\theta_1}{12} P J_2(2Z)e^{-j\left(2\theta + \frac{\pi}{2}\right)}. \quad (38)$$

The first term, $\dfrac{G_0 M^2}{2} \dfrac{2J_1(Z)}{Z} j \, (-2\theta_2 + \theta_3)e^{-j\theta}$, is the zero-order contri-

bution. The second term, $-\dfrac{G_0 M^2}{2} J_1'(Z)2j\theta_1 e^{-j\theta}$, is the addition to this

contribution that is discussed in the last paragraph. It is caused by the
extension of the effective drift space by half the width of the gap. The

third term, $\dfrac{G_0 M^2}{2} (-6\theta_2 + \theta_3)\left(\dfrac{MV}{2V_0}\right)J_1''(Z)e^{-j\theta}$, is a first-order contribu-

tion to the electronic admittance that does not vanish with zero gap-
transit angle; it arises from one of the second-order terms in $v_d$. The
group of terms that follows arises from the combined effect of additional
second-order terms in $v_d$ and first-order terms, not included in the addition
to the zero-order contribution, that have their origin in the effective drift

action of the gap. The term $\dfrac{G_0}{2} \dfrac{j\theta_1 N}{6} e^{-\frac{j\theta}{2}}\left(\dfrac{1}{k} + 1\right)$ is the beam-loading

admittance arising from the double transit of the unmodulated current.
The last term is an addition to the beam loading which is due to the
modulation of the reflected current.

The terms containing $J_1''(Z)$, $J_0(Z)$, and $J_1(Z)$ are 90° out of phase
with the zero-order admittance. At the center of a mode, the term
containing $J_2(2Z)$ is 90° out of phase with the ordinary beam-loading
terms. Hence, at the center of a mode these out-of-phase terms do not
affect the magnitude of the oscillations directly, but do affect the frequency with which the oscillations take place.

All but the first two of these additions to the admittance are probably best regarded as variable additions to the circuit conductance and
susceptance arising from the presence of the beam. It is therefore convenient to define the electronic admittance as follows,

$$Y_e = G_0 \frac{M^2}{2} \left[ \frac{2J_1(X)}{X} j\theta_e + X_f J_1''(X) \right] e^{-j\theta}, \quad (39)$$

where $X = \theta_e MV/2V_0$, $\theta_e = -\theta_1 - 2\theta_2 + \theta_3$, and $X_f = \theta_f MV/2V_0$, $\theta_f = -3\theta_1 - 6\theta_2 + \theta_3$. The extra factor 3 in the drift contributions to $\theta_f$ is caused by the combined effect of pure second-order terms and squares of first-order terms in $v_0/v_d$; these terms and the second-order terms in $v_d/v_0$ become first-order terms because $\theta_2$ and $\theta_3$ can be large. Correspondingly, the beam-loading admittance is defined as

$$Y_B = -\frac{G_0}{2}\left(\frac{\theta_1}{6}\right)\left[\theta_1 MNJ_0(X) - \frac{\theta_1 MN}{2}XJ_1(X) + j2PJ_2(X)\right]e^{-i\theta}$$
$$+ \frac{G_0}{2}\frac{j\theta_1 N}{6}e^{-j\frac{\theta_1}{2}}\left(\frac{1}{k}+1\right) + \frac{G_0}{2}\left(\frac{\theta_1}{6}\right)PJ_2(2X)e^{-j\left(2\theta+\frac{\pi}{2}\right)}. \quad (40)$$

The sum $Y_e + Y_B$ contains all the terms of Eq. (38) but does not exclude some higher-order terms. The beam-loading admittance as defined is zero for zero gap-transit angle ($M$, $N$, and $P$ are shown plotted in Fig. 3·3).

*Condition for Oscillation.*—For ease of reference some of the important relations from Sec. 12·2 are reproduced here. For oscillation to take place the total admittance measured at the gap must be zero. Thus

$$Y_R + Y_L + Y_B + Y_e = 0,$$

where $Y_R$ and $Y_L$ are the resonator and load admittances measured at the gap.

The total circuit admittance is defined to include the beam-loading admittance: $Y = Y_R + Y_L + Y_B$. Using this modified formulation,

$$Y = G + j2C(\omega - \omega_R),$$

where $G$ is the effective conductance, $C$ is the effective capacitance of the gap, and $\omega_R$ is the effective resonant frequency. It should be remembered that these quantities depend on $\omega$ and $V$ to a certain extent, as did in fact the unmodified quantities.

On separating real and imaginary parts,

$$\left.\begin{array}{l}G = \dfrac{G_0 M^2}{2}\left[\dfrac{2J_1(X)}{X}\theta_e\cos\left(\theta+\dfrac{\pi}{2}\right) - X_f J_1''(X)\sin\left(\theta+\dfrac{\pi}{2}\right)\right], \\[3mm] 2C(\omega-\omega_R) = -\dfrac{G_0 M^2}{2}\left[\dfrac{2J_1(X)}{X}\theta_e\sin\left(\theta+\dfrac{\pi}{2}\right) \right. \\[3mm] \left. \qquad\qquad\qquad\qquad + X_f J_1''(X)\cos\left(\theta+\dfrac{\pi}{2}\right)\right].\end{array}\right\} \quad (41)$$

These two equations serve to determine the gap voltage and oscillation frequency.

As already noted, oscillation cannot take place for all values of the phase angle $\theta$. The values $\theta = \theta_n \equiv 2\pi(n + \frac{3}{4})$, $n = 0, 1, 2, \cdots$, are called the centers of possible modes of oscillation. At these points

$$G = \frac{G_0 M^2}{2} \frac{2J_1(X)}{X} \qquad \theta_e = G_0 \frac{M^2}{2} \frac{2J_1(X)}{X} (-2\theta_1 - 4\theta_2 + \theta_n), \quad (42)$$

because $\theta_e = -\theta_1 - 2\theta_2 + \theta_3$ and $\theta_3 = \theta - \theta_1 - 2\theta_2$. Since $2J_1(X)/X$ cannot be greater than unity, the tube cannot oscillate in the mode in question, or at least not for $\theta = \theta_n$, if $G/(\theta_e M^2 G_0/2)$ is greater than unity. This ratio at the center of the mode is defined in Sec. 12·2 as "the conductance parameter" and $-\theta_e M^2 G_0/2$ at the center of the mode is called the small-signal electronic transconductance. Let $\omega_0$ be the frequency of oscillation at the center. Then

$$\omega_0 = \omega_R - \frac{G_0}{2C} \frac{M^2}{2} X_f J_1''(X).$$

The fractional deviation from $\omega_R$ is

$$\frac{\omega_0 - \omega_R}{\omega_R} = - \frac{G}{2\omega_R C} \frac{X_f J_1''(X)}{2J_1(X)/X} \frac{1}{\theta_e}. \qquad (43)$$

Suppose, for example, $X = 2.4$; then $2J_1(X)/X = 0.433$ and

$$-XJ_1''(X) = 0.822.$$

Then $(\omega_0 - \omega_R)/\omega_R \approx 0.95/Q\theta_e$, where $Q = \omega_R C/G$; except for low modes the deviation is very small compared with the bandwidth of the circuit.

The mode is usually limited by its zero-voltage points. They are

$$G = G_0 \frac{M^2}{2} (-2\theta_1 - 4\theta_2 + \theta) \cos\left(\theta + \frac{\pi}{2}\right)$$

$$\omega - \omega_R = - \frac{G}{2C} \tan\left(\theta + \frac{\pi}{2}\right),$$

which give $\theta$ and $\omega$ at the two points.

*Efficiency.*—As noted in Sec. 12·2 the r-f power generated and the r-f power output are $\frac{1}{2}GV^2$ and $\frac{1}{2}G_L V^2$, respectively. In that section $\eta$ is taken as the total electronic efficiency and $\eta_L$ the electronic efficiency to the load, both defined using the current that returns to the gap. Then

$$\eta = \frac{GV^2}{2kI_0 V_0}, \qquad \eta_L = \frac{G_L V^2}{2kI_0 V_0}.$$

It is convenient to measure the phase in a particular mode from its value $\theta_n$ at the center of the mode and to write $\theta = \theta_n + \phi$. The effective bunching angle at the center of the $n$th mode is $\theta_{ne} = \theta_n - 2\omega_0(T_1 + 2T_2)$.

Let $-G_{ne}$ be the small-signal electronic transconductance at the center of the $n$th mode, $G_{ne} = \theta_{ne}M^2G_0/2$. The electronic transadmittance then is

$$Y_e = -G_{ne}\left[\frac{2J_1(X)}{X}\left(\frac{\theta_e}{\theta_{ne}}\right) - jX_fJ_1''(X)\frac{1}{\theta_{ne}}\right]e^{-j\phi}, \qquad (44)$$

and the total electronic efficiency becomes

$$\eta = \frac{\gamma_n X^2}{\theta_{ne}}\left(\frac{\theta_{ne}}{\theta_e}\right)^2,$$

where $\gamma_n = G/G_{ne}$ is the conductance parameter at the center of the $n$th mode.

In terms of these symbols and the loaded $Q$ of the circuit, $Q = \omega_R C/G$, the conditions for oscillation are

$$\gamma = \frac{2J_1(X)}{X}\left(\frac{\theta_e}{\theta_{ne}}\right)\cos\,\phi - X_fJ_1''(X)\frac{1}{\theta_{ne}}\sin\,\phi,$$

$$\frac{\omega - \omega_R}{\omega_R} = -\frac{1}{2Q\gamma}\left[\frac{2J_1'(X)}{X}\left(\frac{\theta_e}{\theta_{ne}}\right)\sin\,\phi + X_fJ_1''(X)\frac{1}{\theta_{ne}}\cos\,\phi\right]\cdot \quad (45)$$

On substituting for $\gamma$ in the efficiency

$$\eta = \frac{2XJ_1(X)}{\theta_{ne}}\left(\frac{\theta_{ne}}{\theta_e}\right)\cos\,\phi - \frac{X_fX^2J_1''(X)}{\theta_{ne}^2}\left(\frac{\theta_{ne}}{\theta_e}\right)^2\sin\,\phi, \qquad (46)$$

The maximum of $XJ_1(X)$ is at $X = 2.4$, for which $-X^3J_1''(X) = 4.74$. The above formula indicates, as has already been noted, that the efficiency decreases on going to higher modes. The factor $\theta_{ne}/\theta_e$ makes the power output unsymmetrical about the center of the mode. So also does $\sin\,\phi$, but in the opposite direction. The term containing $\sin\,\phi$ makes an appreciable contribution only in very low modes because of the extra factor $\theta_{ne}$ in the denominator; however, for such modes, the efficiency is considerably reduced by the beam loading, which has been concealed in the modified circuit conductance.

*Electronic Tuning.*—In a uniform reflector field the product

$$(V_0 - V_r)T_3$$

is a constant for a given velocity of injection. However,

$$\theta_3 = \frac{1}{2}\left(\theta + \theta_e\right) = \frac{1}{2}\left(\theta_n + \theta_{ne}\right) + \phi + \frac{1}{2}\left(\frac{\omega_0 - \omega}{\omega_0}\right)(\theta_n - \theta_{ne}).$$

If $T_3$ is eliminated and the reflector voltage $V_r^0$ at the center of the mode ($\omega = \omega_0, \phi = 0$) is introduced to remove the constant, it can be shown that

$$\frac{V_r - V_r^0}{V_0 - V_r^0} = \frac{\dfrac{2\theta_n}{\theta_n + \theta_{ne}}\left[\dfrac{\omega_0 - \omega}{\omega_0} + \dfrac{\phi}{\theta_n}\right]}{\left[1 + \dfrac{2\phi}{\theta_n + \theta_{ne}} + \left(\dfrac{\omega_0 - \omega}{\omega_0}\right)\left(\dfrac{\theta_n - \theta_{ne}}{\theta_n + \theta_{ne}}\right)\right]}.$$

A useful measure of the rate of electronic tuning is

$$-\frac{\omega_0}{V_0 - V_r^0}\left(\frac{\partial V_r}{\partial \omega}\right)_{\omega_0} = \frac{2\theta_n}{\theta_n + \theta_{ne}}\left[1 - \frac{\omega_0}{\theta_n}\left(\frac{\partial \phi}{\partial \omega}\right)_{\omega_0}\right];$$

but

$$\left(\frac{\partial \theta}{\partial \omega}\right)_{\omega_0} = -\frac{2C}{G} = -\frac{2Q_0}{\omega_0},$$

where $Q_0 = \omega_0/CG$.   Hence

$$-\left(\frac{V_0 - V_r^0}{\omega_0}\right)\left(\frac{\partial \omega}{\partial V_r}\right)_{\omega_0} = \left(\frac{\theta_n + \theta_{ne}}{2\theta_n}\right)\frac{1}{\left(1 + \dfrac{2Q_0}{\theta_n}\right)} \approx \frac{\theta_n}{\theta_n + 2Q_0}. \quad (47)$$

This equation gives the rate of change of frequency with change in reflector voltage at the center of the mode.

# CHAPTER 13

## NONIDEAL REFLECTORS

### By D. R. Hamilton

In the preceding chapter various idealizations were made in order to emphasize the most basic features of the reflex klystron. Among these idealizations the following may be noted:

1. The assumption of an "ideal" reflector, in which the potential varies linearly with distance, as would be produced by plane-parallel electrodes with no space-charge effects.
2. The assumption of small r-f gap voltages—that is, the assumption of a "high mode" $(n \gg 1)$.
3. The assumption that no electron makes more than one return transit through the gap—or the assumption of no "multiple transits," as this term will hereafter be used.

The next chapter is concerned with the phenomenon of "electronic-tuning hysteresis," which results when the third of the above assumptions is violated. Violation of the second assumption, with the resultant bunched-beam-current phase shifts, also gives rise to "hysteresis" and mode asymmetries that are closely related to those produced by multiple transits. The magnitude of these phase shifts is considerably dependent upon the first assumption. Violation of the second assumption also causes deviations from the simple bunching theory as discussed in Sec. 9·4; but in the reflex klystron these effects are minor compared with the effects that are introduced when the assumption of an ideal reflector is invalid.

The present chapter, then, is concerned primarily with some of the general relations that are applicable in practical cases when the assumption of an ideal reflector does not hold true. These general relations are of two types. One type is concerned with the purely d-c transit-time questions that are involved in the phase relations of bunched beam current and r-f gap voltage; the other type is concerned with the bunching process, and involves the derivatives of transit time with respect to initial electron velocity.

**13·1. D–c Electron Optics.**—The d-c motions of electrons in the reflection region involve, of course, standard problems of electron optics such as the question of how to reflect all the electrons back for a second transit through the r-f gap.    As a matter of fact, it may be seen in the next chapter that a supplementary and more difficult question is how to reflect all of them for a second transit, while ensuring that none are again reflected from the cathode region for additional transits through the gap. For all such purely geometrical questions regarding electron trajectories, commonly used electron-optical techniques are available.    One such technique is graphical ray-tracing in the electrostatic field of given electrodes, this field being calculated by electrostatic theory or plotted with an electrolytic tank; another technique makes use of the analogy between electrons moving in an electrostatic field and small balls rolling under the influence of gravity on a stretched elastic membrane.

The electron optics of reflection involves not only the requirement that electrons go to the right places, but also the requirement that all electrons of a given velocity spend the same amount of time in being reflected; the phase aberrations that result if this requirement is not met have adverse effects on performance and are discussed in Sec. 13·10. Both of the above-mentioned methods of finding out the path of the electrons—ray-tracing and ball-rolling—are easily adapted to give this additional information about transit time.    Neither of them includes directly the effect of space-charge forces on electron motion.    A convenient method that has been developed for including the effects of space charge in electron-gun design[1] does not seem to be directly applicable to general reflector design.

For further information on the background of electron optics that is relevant to these specific design questions just discussed, the reader is referred to the extensive literature on electron optics in general.    The present chapter and the next one are primarily concerned with those questions of electron motion that remain relevant to oscillator operation when the above two requirements (geometrically satisfactory electron trajectories, and uniformity of transit time) may be assumed to have been met.

The first question to be discussed concerns the way in which applied electrode voltages and reflector geometry affect the absolute value of the d-c transit time.    Such a discussion fulfills two functions.    One is that of introduction and ground work for the subsequent discussion of r-f effects.    Another equally important function arises from the fact that the d-c or equilibrium electron motions determine those combinations of oscillator parameters at which oscillation may or may not occur. The resulting interrelations of applied parameters that are required for oscillation are in themselves important operating characteristics of the practical oscillator; and in addition they may give, in any particular

---

[1] J. R. Pierce, *Jour. App. Phys.*, **11**, 548 (1940).

case, information about the nature of the reflector field that will be relevant to subsequent questions of r-f performance.

The procedure that is followed in discussing d-c transit-time relations is to consider these relations in various simplified reflector fields. The principal features of these fields are representative of the reflectors met in actual practice, and the simplifications that are involved are those which ensure the satisfaction of the primary condition of uniformity of transit time among the electrons. However, before dealing with specific reflector fields it is worth while to consider certain general relations that concern the effects of changing dimensions and electrode voltages in an electron-optical system; these relations serve as essential tools in the later discussion.

**13·2. General Scaling of Voltages and Dimensions.**—The general relations that are involved in the scaling of voltages and dimensions in a d-c electron-optical system follow in a straightforward manner from the dimensional relations in the three basic laws that describe the flow of electrons in a vacuum. These laws are:

1. The Coulomb law of force between charged particles, as expressed in Poisson's equation relating the space-charge density $\rho$ and the variation of the potential $\Phi$ with position:

$$\nabla^2\Phi \equiv \frac{\partial^2\Phi}{\partial x^2} + \frac{\partial^2\Phi}{\partial y^2} + \frac{\partial^2\Phi}{\partial z^2} = \rho. \tag{1}$$

2. The conservation of matter, as expressed in the requirement that as much charge flows into any given volume element as flows out of it. For a d-c system, i.e. for $\partial\rho/\partial t = 0$, this requirement is expressed by the relation

$$\boldsymbol{\nabla} \cdot (\rho\mathbf{v}) \equiv \frac{\partial}{\partial x}(\rho v_x) + \frac{\partial}{\partial y}(\rho v_y) + \frac{\partial}{\partial z}(\rho v_z) = 0 \tag{2}$$

where $\mathbf{v}$ is the electron-velocity vector and $\rho\mathbf{v} \equiv \mathbf{J}$, the current-density vector.

3. Newton's laws of motion, or conservation of energy applied to the relation between the electrostatic potential (measured with respect to the cathode) and the electron velocity:

$$\tfrac{1}{2}mv^2 = e\Phi. \tag{3}$$

Any electron-optical situation is described by the three variables, $\rho$, $\mathbf{v}$, and $\Phi$, that enter into these three equations. Given the conditions existing at the surface enclosing a given region—for example, the potential and electron-emission characteristics at every point—then these three equations determine uniquely the resulting values of $\rho$, $\mathbf{v}$, and $\Phi$ at every point in the region.

The above comments and relations should be generalized in one respect. Suppose that **v** is not a single-valued function of position—i.e., suppose that more than one stream of electrons passes through some points of space; the reflection region of the reflex klystron is a case in point. Then $\rho$ in Eq. (1) and $\rho\mathbf{v}$ in Eq. (2) are understood to represent the summation, over all these streams, of the values of $\rho$ and $\rho\mathbf{v}$ respectively associated with each of these streams. This is, however, a purely formal matter that does not affect any of the conclusions to be drawn from Eqs. 1-3 and therefore does not warrant a formal complication of these equations.

An explicit mathematical solution for $\rho$, **v**, and $\Phi$ in any particular case is usually not feasible unless the boundary conditions are especially simple. However, comparisons of the solutions to these equations in cases with complex but similar boundary conditions may be made easily and with profit.

Thus, suppose it is desired to compare the physical situations in two regions that are related to each other as follows:

1. They are geometrically similar—that is, all the dimensions of Region 2 are larger than those of Region 1 by the scale factor $a$.
2. In Region 2 the applied voltages at every boundary point, measured with respect to the cathode, are larger by the factor $b$ than the voltages at the geometrically analogous points in Region 1.
3. The electron-emitting surfaces in the two regions are geometrically similar and the electron emission from these surfaces is space-charge limited with the applied voltages that are involved—that is, the potential gradient at the emitting surfaces is always zero.

Two such regions are shown in Fig. 13·1. The position vectors of two geometrically similar points are denoted by $\mathbf{r}_1$ and $\mathbf{r}_2$ respectively; the geometrical similarity is thus expressed by the equation

$$\mathbf{r}_2 = a\mathbf{r}_1. \tag{4}$$

Suppose that in Region 1 the space-charge density, electron velocity, and electrostatic potential are the functions of position $\rho_1(\mathbf{r}_1)$, $\mathbf{v}_1(\mathbf{r}_1)$, and $\Phi_1(\mathbf{r}_1)$. Then, because of the specified similarity between the two regions and because of the way in which the various dimensions enter into Eqs. (1), (2), and (3), it is seen that for Region 2 a possible solution $\rho_2(\mathbf{r}_2)$, $\mathbf{v}_2(\mathbf{r}_2)$, $\Phi_2(\mathbf{r}_2)$ is the following:

$$\mathbf{v}_2(\mathbf{r}_2) \equiv \mathbf{v}_2(a\mathbf{r}_1) = b^{\frac{1}{2}}\mathbf{v}_1(\mathbf{r}_1) \tag{5a}$$

$$\rho_2(\mathbf{r}_2) \equiv \rho_2(a\mathbf{r}_1) = \left(\frac{b}{a^2}\right)\rho_1(\mathbf{r}_1) \tag{5b}$$

$$\Phi_2(\mathbf{r}_2) \equiv \Phi_2(a\mathbf{r}_1) = b\Phi_1(\mathbf{r}_1). \tag{5c}$$

It is well known, however, that there is only one possible solution to Eqs. (1), (2), and (3) for each region; hence the solution for Region 2 deduced in this manner from the solution for Region 1, and given in Eq. (5), must be the only solution for Region 2.   There are, therefore, the following simple and interesting results of the specified scaling of the boundary conditions in voltage and geometrical size: (1) the potential, at every point within the region, scales by the same factor as is applied to the boundary potential, (2) the electron trajectories remain geometrically similar, (3) the space-charge density, at every point, scales by the same constant factor $b/a^2$.

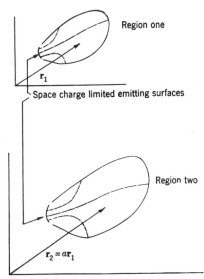

The third requirement initially applied to the derivation of these results, that of space-charge limitation of the emitting surfaces, is not necessary and could be replaced by a more general requirement on the scaling up of the potential gradient at the cathode by the factor $b/a$; this is, however, a very nonrealistic requirement on the physical electron-emitting characteristics of the cathode ex-

Fig. 13·1.—Graphical representation of the situation involved in the scaling of voltages and dimensions in an electron-optical system. Boundary conditions: in region one, on $\Phi = \Phi_1(\mathbf{r}_1)$ on boundary; in region two, $\Phi = \Phi_2(\mathbf{r}_2) = b\Phi_1(\mathbf{r}_1)$ on boundary.

cept for the space-charge-limited case of zero potential gradient.

From the behavior of the primary variables as shown in Eq. (5), the behavior of the "secondary" variables $\mathbf{J} = \rho\mathbf{v}$ (the current density), $I$ (the total emission current), and $T$ (the electron transit time between any geometrically similar pair of points) may be deduced.   These scale as follows (omitting the arguments of the functions):

$$\mathbf{J}_2 = \left(\frac{b^{3/2}}{a^2}\right)\mathbf{J}_1 \tag{6a}$$

$$I_2 = b^{3/2}I_1 \tag{6b}$$

$$T_2 = \left(\frac{a}{b^{1/2}}\right)T_1. \tag{6c}$$

Equations (6a) and (6b) express the functional dependence of current on dimension and voltage as given by the Langmuir-Childs law; these equations show that this functional dependence holds for any arbitrary geometry as long as the cathode is space-charge limited.

The regions of Fig. 13·1 may be subdivided into smaller regions, some of which would not contain the cathode surface. It may be seen from considering this case that the scaling behavior described in Eqs. (5), (6b), and (6c) applies equally well to any region into which current is injected instead of being drawn from a cathode within the region; it is necessary only that the injected current density be given by Eq. (6a)—or what is the same thing, it is necessary that the external cathode that supplies the injected current should be subjected to the same scaling process as is the region under consideration.

**13·3. Reflector Mode Patterns.**—The "reflector mode pattern" is one of the best ways of summarizing, for a given oscillator, either the d-c transit-time relations or the combinations of oscillator parameters for which oscillation occurs. A reflector mode pattern is a graphical presentation of the dependence, on some other parameter, of the reflector voltages corresponding to the centers of various modes of oscillation, that is, corresponding to the transit-time relation[1] $\theta_0 = 2\pi(n + \frac{3}{4})$ or $\phi = 0$. A reflector mode pattern is made up of a number of individual "mode loci" each one corresponding to a single mode (single value of $n$). It is to be particularly noted that "mode pattern" as here used has a meaning distinctly different from that of "mode shape"; the latter expression has been used to denote the dependence of frequency or output power on reflector voltage.

In some cases there may be a use for a mode pattern showing not only the loci of the points for which $\theta_0 = 2\pi(n + \frac{3}{4})$, but also showing contours of constant frequency, constant output power, etc; such a mode pattern, particularly the one involving output power, involves other properties of the reflector field beside the d-c electron-transit times and would therefore involve the bunching factors discussed in Sec. 13·7 and subsequently. The simple mode patterns here considered depend only upon d-c transit-time phenomena; this statement is based on the assumption that at the center of the bunch is an electron traveling with the d-c (the mean or unmodulated) velocity. This assumption is not always exactly true under non-small-signal conditions (see Sec. 9·4) and to this degree the conclusions of the present chapter are not exactly correct when applied to experimental data obtained at large amplitude of oscillation; but the errors are usually of the second order.

[1] Throughout this chapter the notation with regard to transit angle follows that of Chap. 9, i.e., $\theta_0$ = transit angle for $V_e = V_0$; $\theta$ is the transit angle for arbitrary $V_e$. This distinction was unnecessary in Chap. 12, where $\theta$ alone was used; the necessity in the present chapter appears later when the drift-space coefficients of Chap. 9 are used. The present $\theta_0$ need not be confused with $\theta_n(n = 0)$, since in practice the latter very seldom occurs.

The most generally useful mode pattern is that in which the values of $V_r$ for the center of the various modes are plotted against $V_0$. Such a $V_r$-vs.-$V_0$ reflector mode pattern, measured for the type 417A, is shown in Fig. 13·2.

As an introduction to the general relations that apply in such a mode pattern, the dotted construction line that passes through the point $(V_r = 0, V_0 = 0)$ in Fig. 13·2 should be considered. This line is the locus of those operating points for which the ratio $|V_r|/V_0$ has some constant value—what the particular value is does not matter in the present discussion. From the discussion of voltage scaling in an electron-optical

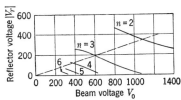

FIG. 13·2.—$V_r$-vs.-$V_0$ mode pattern for the type 417A reflex klystron operating at 10.0 cm.

system given in Sec. 13·2, it follows that if the cathode emission is space-charge limited throughout this range of beam voltage, that is, if $I_0 \propto V_0^{3/2}$, then all these points with some given value of $|V_r|/V_0$ must correspond to a given set of d-c electron trajectories. This holds true for any arbitrarily shaped reflector region and for any degree of space charge. Since the trajectories are geometrically identical and since the velocities at all points in the reflector region change as $V_0^{1/2}$, the total transit time must vary as $V_0^{-1/2}$ for points lying on the dotted line in Fig. 13·2.

The points of intersection of the dotted construction line with the various mode loci will now be considered. Each of these loci corresponds to the condition $\phi = 0$, or $\theta_0 = 2\pi(n + \frac{3}{4})$ when $n$ is an integer. But it has already been shown that along the line $|V_r|/V_0 = $ constant, $\theta_0 \propto V_0^{-1/2}$; hence the values of $V_0^{-1/2}$ at the intersections of the dotted line with the mode loci should be in the ratio of adjacent integers plus $\frac{3}{4}$, and the fulfilling of this condition will determine the integer $n$ associated with each mode.

In Table 13·1 below there are listed the values of $V_0$ and the relative values of $V_0^{-1/2}$ for the intersection of the mode loci and the line $|V_r|/V_0 = $ constant. Listed in adjacent columns are the values for the number of cycles transit time, as deduced for the two extreme modes

TABLE 13·1.—ASSIGNMENT OF MODE NUMBERS IN FIG. 13·2

| $V_0$ | Relative $V_0^{-1/2}$ | Relative $V_0^{-1/2}$ normalized to various choices of $(n + \frac{3}{4})$ for value of $\theta_0/2\pi$ in middle mode | | |
|---|---|---|---|---|
| 1090 | 1.0 | 2.04 | 2.78 | 3.53 |
| 600 | 1.346 | 2.75 | 3.75 | 4.75 |
| 370 | 1.718 | 3.51 | 4.78 | 6.06 |

from the relation $\theta_0 \propto V_0^{-\frac{1}{2}}$ when the values $2\frac{3}{4}$, $3\frac{3}{4}$, and $4\frac{3}{4}$ cycles are assigned to the middle mode. It is seen that the relations $\theta_0 \propto V_0^{-\frac{1}{2}}$ and $\theta_0 \propto (n + \frac{3}{4})$ are simultaneously satisfied for only one of the possible assignments of values of $n$, namely the assignment indicated in Fig. 13·2.

The above procedure is a very useful one for identifying modes; this identification, when compared with that predicted by dead reckoning from dimensions and voltages, in itself tells something about the electron optics of the reflector region. It illustrates, however, simply a special case of a more general property of the reflector mode pattern. This property may be stated as follows: All the mode loci in a $V_r$-vs.-$V_0$ reflector mode pattern are geometrically similar, differing only by a scale factor; if a single mode locus and the corresponding value of $n$ are known, then the remainder of the mode pattern may be deduced therefrom. The truth of this statement is easily seen by considering the effect of changing the direction of the dotted construction line in Fig. 13·2, for the distances from the origin at which the various mode loci intersect this construction line are in the ratio of $1/\sqrt{n + \frac{3}{4}}$ and this ratio is independent of the particular direction of the construction line in question.

Thus all the d-c transit-time relations for a given reflector field are completely described and specified by a single mode locus. It follows from the general discussion of Sec. 13·2 that the shape of this generalized mode locus is unaffected by an overall geometrical scaling that includes the space-charge-limited electron gun as well as the reflector region.

*The Reflector Mode Pattern for Plane-parallel Space-charge-free Reflector Field.*—In addition to giving information about the dependence of d-c transit time on electrode voltages, as has just been discussed, the reflector mode pattern also reveals something of the characteristics of the reflector

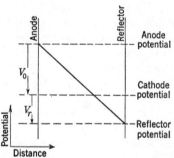

Fig. 13·3.—Variation of potential with position in plane-parallel space-charge-free reflector.

field. Since most reflector fields have their generic origin in the plane-parallel space-charge-free field, the mode pattern existing with this field provides a good point of departure for a discussion of the influence of reflector field on mode pattern.

For an electron entering (with energy $eV_0$) the reflector field shown in Fig. 13·3, the depth of penetration into the field is proportional to $V_0/(V_0 + |V_r|)$; the average velocity (in a uniform field such as this) is proportional to $\sqrt{V_0}$; the transit time of an electron into the reflection region and back out again is therefore proportional to $\sqrt{V_0}/(V_0 + |V_r|)$.

If this expression is set equal to a constant, and the voltages are measured in arbitrary units such that $|V_r| = 0$ when $V_0 = 1$, then

$$|V_r| = \sqrt{V_0} - V_0; \qquad (7)$$

or, what is the same thing, if the constant to which $\sqrt{V_0}/(V_0 + |V_r|)$ is set equal to unity, then $|V_r| = \sqrt{V_0} - V_0$. Since it has already been

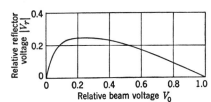

FIG. 13·4.—Normalized mode locus for plane-parallel space-charge-free reflector.

seen that all mode loci for a given reflector have the same shape, and since it is only the shape that is a matter of present concern, this nonchalance regarding absolute values is justified. Such a mode locus, passing though the point ($|V_r| = 0$, $V_0 = 1$) will be called a "normalized mode locus."

In Fig. 13·4 is shown the normalized mode locus described by Eq. (7). Physically, its shape arises as follows. For $V_0 \ll |V_r|$ the strength of the reflecting field is practically independent of $V_0$; in order to maintain a constant reflection time as $V_0$ (and the electron velocity) is increased, the strength of the reflection field and hence the size of $|V_r|$ must be rapidly increased with $V_0$ in order to prevent a too rapid increase in depth of penetration. On the other hand, when $V_0 \gg |V_r|$, the depth of penetration is hardly affected by an increase in $V_0$; and in order to compensate for the increased electron velocity, $|V_r|$ must be decreased to allow for deeper penetration.

*The Relation between Normalized Mode Locus and Over-all Reflector Mode Pattern.*—For purposes of comparison with the mode loci of other reflector fields, Fig. 13·4 illustrates all that need be said; but before going on to these other reflector fields it is worth while to note the

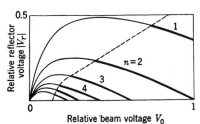

FIG. 13·5.—Idealized reflector mode pattern as derived from the normalized mode locus of Fig. 13·4 and the condition $G_e/G \gtrsim 1$.

relation between the normalized mode locus of Fig. 13·4 and the observed mode pattern of Fig. 13·2.

In Fig. 13·5 are shown a series of mode loci derived from the normalized mode locus of Fig. 13·4 and graduated in size to correspond to the values of $n$ indicated on each locus; that is, the normalized mode locus is scaled up by a factor proportional to $1/\sqrt{n + \frac{3}{4}}$.

The experimentally observed mode loci of Fig. 13·2 do not, however, extend down to $V_0 = 0$; the reason becomes apparent when consideration is given to the necessary condition for the starting of oscillation, $G_e/G \geqq 1$. For the present case $G_e = M^2\theta_0 G_0/2$; assuming a space-charge-limited electron gun, $G_0 = I_0/V_0 \propto \sqrt{V_0}$. Hence the boundary between the regions of oscillation and no oscillation in the reflector-mode pattern, specified by the relation $G_e/G =$ constant, is given for constant $G$ by the condition $M^2\theta_0\sqrt{V_0} =$ constant.

It has already been seen, however, that along a line from the origin in the mode pattern (that is, $|V_r|/V_0$ constant, identical electron trajectories), $\theta_0\sqrt{V_0}$ is constant. Hence for the range of beam voltages for which $M^2 \approx 1$, oscillation will occur in the region of the mode pattern for which $|V_r|/V_0 \leqq$ some constant. When the beam voltage gets low enough, $M^2$ starts to decrease and this boundary line sags, as is shown for a typical boundary in Fig. 13·5. The individual mode loci are continued to the left of this boundary as faint lines, indicating the form that the mode pattern would take if the boundary were shifted.

*The General Relation for "Radians per Volt."*—The general theoretical relations for the reflex klystron give output characteristics in terms of the electronic parameters $G_e$ and $\phi$. In most practical problems involving changes within a given mode (for example, electronic tuning and modulation), $G_e$ is sensibly constant and $\phi$ is altered by changing some electrode voltage. In these practical problems it is just as important to know the relation between electrode voltage and the absolute or relative transit time in radians ($\theta_0$ or $\phi$) as it is to know the relation between $\theta_0$ or $\phi$ and the output characteristics. This relation between transit time and applied voltage— or, more briefly, the "radians per volt," "radians per reflector volt,"

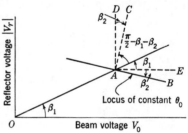

FIG. 13·6.—Mode pattern geometry.
$\beta_1 = \tan^{-1}(|V_r|/V_0)$;
$\quad\quad \beta_2 = -\tan^{-1}(\partial|V_r|/\partial V_0)_{\theta_0}$.

"radians per beam volt," etc.—may be deduced in a simple manner from that part of the mode locus in the vicinity of the operating point.

In Fig. 13·6, the encircled point $A$ in the $(V_r, V_0)$-plane represents the combination of values of $V_r$ and $V_0$ at which a knowledge of radians per volt is desired. Through this point are drawn two lines, $AO$ and $AB$. The line $AO$ is a geometrical construction line through the origin; the other line $AB$, the tangent to the locus of constant $\theta_0$ passing through the point $A$, is the only necessary bit of experimental data.

Since $\theta_0 \propto V_0^{-\frac{1}{2}}$ for motion along the line $OA$,

$$\left(\frac{\partial\theta_0}{\partial V_0}\right)_{V_r/V_0} = -\frac{\theta_0}{2V_0}. \tag{8}$$

Since $AB$ is the contour of constant $\theta_0$, however, the maximum gradient of $\theta_0$ is along the line $AC$ perpendicular to $AB$. By the construction shown in Fig. 13·6, this maximum gradient of $\theta_0$ is

$$\left(\frac{\partial \theta_0}{\partial \bar{V}}\right)_{\max} = \frac{\cos \beta_1}{\sin (\beta_1 + \beta_2)} \left(\frac{\partial \theta_0}{\partial V_0}\right)_{V_r/V_0} \tag{9}$$

where

$$\beta_1 = \tan^{-1} \frac{|V_r|}{V_0}$$

$$\beta_2 = -\tan^{-1} \left(\frac{\partial |V_r|}{\partial V_0}\right)_{\theta_0}. \tag{10}$$

Similarly, the gradient of $\theta_0$ along the line $AD$, that is, $(\partial \theta_0/\partial |V_r|)_{V_0}$, is given by

$$\frac{1}{\cos \beta_1 \cos \beta_2} \left(\frac{\partial \theta_0}{\partial |V_r|}\right)_{V_0} = \frac{1}{\sin (\beta_1 + \beta_2)} \left(\frac{\partial \theta_0}{\partial V_0}\right)_{V_r/V_0} \tag{11}$$

The derivative of $\theta_0$ with respect to any other change of voltage is easily found from Fig. 13·6, but only $(\partial \theta_0/\partial |V_r|)_{V_0}$, the most commonly useful of these derivatives, will be worked out explicitly with the aid of Eq. (10). Here Eqs. (8), (10), and (11) give

$$\left(\frac{\partial \theta_0}{\partial |V_r|}\right)_{V_0} = - \frac{\theta_0}{2V_0} \frac{1}{\dfrac{|V_r|}{V_0} - \left(\dfrac{\partial |V_r|}{\partial V_0}\right)_{\theta_0}} \tag{12}$$

This is a general relation that makes it possible to find $(\partial \phi/\partial |V_r|)_{V_0}$ when $|V_r|$, $V_0$, and $\theta_0$ are given, provided that the influence of reflector geometry as represented by $(\partial |V_r|/\partial V_0)_{\theta_0}$ is known. Not much more can be said on this point until the mode loci for various specific geometries are investigated at a later point. It may, however, be noted that the geometrical similarity of all mode loci for a given reflector makes $(\partial |V_r|/\partial V_0)_{\theta_0}$ a constant for constant $V_r/V_0$; hence from Eq. (12),

$$\left(\frac{\partial \phi}{\partial |V_r|}\right)_{V_0} = \left(\frac{\partial \theta_0}{\partial |V_r|}\right)_{V_0} \propto V_0^{-\frac{3}{2}} \propto \theta_0^3.$$

Thus the radians per reflector volt for a given electron trajectory increase rapidly as $V_0$ is lowered.

**13·4. Reflector Mode Patterns of $V_r$-vs.-$\lambda$.**—Most of Sec. 13·3 has been concerned with the specific properties of the $V_r$-vs.-$V_0$ reflector mode pattern. Another type of mode pattern that presents useful practical information about oscillator characteristics is the reflector voltage versus wavelength, or $V_r$-vs.-λ, mode pattern; and like the $V_r$-vs.-$V_0$ pattern, this one contains within itself the complete description of the d-c transit-time properties of a given reflector. A $V_r$-vs.-λ pattern as observed for the type 417A (the same tube as used for Fig. 13·2) is shown in Fig. 13·7.

The $V_r$-vs.-λ mode pattern is of practical importance in applications where λ must be changed over a considerable range without exceeding certain limits in reflector voltage range. Since the $V_r$-vs.-λ and the $V_r$-vs.-$V_0$ diagrams are directly derivable from each other, as is discussed shortly, either type of measurement may be used to obtain information. Thus the $V_r$-vs.-λ mode pattern is particularly important in tubes that operate over only a narrow range of beam voltages but over a relatively larger range of wavelengths.

Since $\theta_0 \propto T/\lambda$, $T$ is proportional to λ at constant $V_0$ and $\theta_0$ (that is, for a given mode in Fig. 13·7). Hence the $V_r$-vs.-λ mode pattern is essentially a plot of reflector voltage vs. transit time, or vice versa.

In the $V_r$-vs.-λ diagram, since it is taken at constant $V_0$, points corresponding to a given set of electron trajectories lie on a horizontal line of constant $V_r$. Along such a line of constant electron trajectory, the value of $\theta_0$ for any given λ is inversely proportional to λ. Hence from the mode locus for a single value of $\theta_0$ all the other mode loci may be derived; conversely, given a set of mode loci in the $(V_r, \lambda)$-plane the values of $\theta_0$ for each mode may be assigned by use of the requirement that $\theta_0 = 2\pi(\frac{3}{4}, 1\frac{3}{4}, 2\frac{3}{4}, \cdots)$ just as was done with the $V_r$-vs.-$V_0$ diagram.

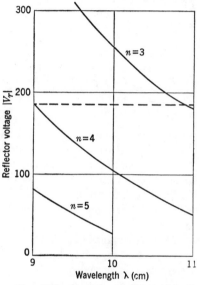

FIG. 13·7.—$V_r$-vs.-λ reflector mode pattern for the type 417A reflex klystron operating at $V_0 = 400$ volts.

Thus in Fig. 13·7, for $|V_r| = 185$ volts two modes occur with λ = 9.00, 10.91 cm. The ratio of these two wavelengths, 1.21, is closely the same as the ratio 4.75/3.75 = 1.21; hence the assignment of mode numbers shown in Fig. 13·7. It will be noted that this assignment agrees with that of Fig. 13.2.

Since a single mode locus in the $V_r$-vs.-λ plane determines all other mode loci in the manner described above, all mode loci are similar in the sense that they differ only by a horizontal (λ) scale factor. Thus a mode pattern may be represented by a single mode locus that may be conveniently normalized to pass through the point ($\lambda = 1$, $V_r = 0$). The normalized $V_r$-vs.-$V_0$ and $V_r$-vs.-$\lambda$ mode loci may be easily derived from each other with the help of the auxiliary normalized $V_r$-vs.-$\lambda^2$

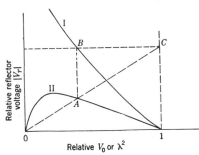

FIG. 13·8.—Geometrical construction for generation of the $V_r$-vs.-$\lambda^2$ normalized mode locus from the $V_r$-vs.-$V_0$ locus or vice versa. Curve (*I*), $V_r$-vs.-$\lambda^2$ mode locus; curve (*II*), $V_r$-vs.-$V_0$ mode locus.

mode locus; the $V_r$-vs.-$\lambda^2$ and the $V_r$-vs.-$V_0$ loci are related to each other by the simple geometrical construction of Fig. 13·8. The verification of this fact is left as an exercise for the reader, with the hint that in Fig. 13·8, the relation of point $C$ to points $A$ and $B$ should be considered.

The normalized $V_r$-vs.-$\lambda$ mode locus for a parallel plane reflector, no space charge, is shown in Fig. 13·9. In discussing the mode patterns of specific reflectors in the next two sections, only the normalized $V_r$-vs.-$V_0$ locus will be shown (Figs. 13·13 and 13·19). But it is apparent from Fig. 13·8 that the slope of the right-hand half of the $V_r$-vs.-$\lambda$ mode locus is roughly proportional to the corresponding slope in the $V_r$-vs.-$V_0$ mode locus; anything that affects one of these will affect the other in the same manner.

### 13·5. Normalized Mode Locus of a Space-charge-free Recessed Reflector.

—In actual practice the anode-reflector region is not bounded by two parallel planes. The reflector electrode is commonly somewhat recessed over a diameter somewhat greater than that of the electron beam, as is shown in various figures of Chap. 18. This has the effect of providing a radially inward force on electrons, which tends to counter-

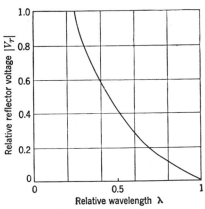

FIG. 13·9.—Normalized $V_r$-vs.-$\lambda$ mode locus for plane-parallel space-charge-free reflector.

act any inherent or space-charge-produced divergences in the beam. In the next chapter it is seen that it is sometimes advantageous to add other complications to the electrode shape in order to avoid more than two transits of the electrons through the r-f gap.

The particular recessed reflector with which the present section is concerned is shown in Fig. 13·10.    The relative dimensions, with reflector depth equal to half the reflector diameter, are more extreme than most of the practical reflectors shown in Chap. 18.    However, when space charge is neglected any equipotential lying between the two electrodes of Fig. 13·10 may be replaced by a conducting surface operated at a potential negative with respect to cathode; thus the solution of this reflector inherently contains the solution to a number of other convergent reflectors that are similar to the reflectors of Chap. 18.    For purposes of discussing this reflector field[1] it will be assumed that the electrons move along the axis without too great a divergence therefrom, in other words, that the diameter of the reflector is rather larger than the beam and that the beam is not initially very divergent.    In this case the reflector field is essentially

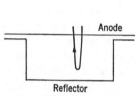

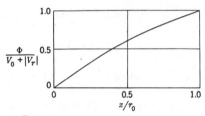

Fig. 13·10.—Geometry of the cup reflector to which Figs. 13·11 and 13·12 and 13·13 refer.

Fig. 13·11.—Variation of relative negative potential $\Phi/(V_0 + |V_r|)$ along the axis of cup reflector as function of $x/r_0$, distance from anode measured in units of the reflector radius $r_0$.

one-dimensional; in Fig. 13·11 is shown the dependence of electrostatic potential on $x/r_0$, distance along the axis as measured in units of the reflector radius.

Some of the properties of the mode locus of this reflector are immediately apparent from Fig. 13·11.    Thus, for $|V_r| \gg V_0$ (electron turn-around at $\Phi/(V_0 + |V_r|) \ll 1$), the behavior is essentially that of a plane-parallel reflector.    But for $|V_r| = V_0/2$ (electron turn-around at $\Phi/(V_0 + |V_r|) = \frac{2}{3}$ in Fig. 13·11), a further increase in $V_0$ increases the depth of penetration much more rapidly than in the plane-parallel case; thus not as large a compensating decrease in $|V_r|$ is necessary to hold the reflection time constant.

The dependence of transit time $T$ on incident energy $V_0$, with constant total potential difference $(V_0 + |V_r|)$ in the field of Fig. 13·11, is shown in Fig. 13·12.    The normalizing factor $T_0$ is the reflection time for a plane-parallel reflector with the same reflector spacing and

[1] This discussion of the tubular reflector is based upon the unreported work of J. B. Garrison of the Radiation Laboratory.

with reflector voltage zero. The square-root dependence of $T$ on $V_0$ for a plane-parallel reflector is also indicated in the figure. Similar curves giving the reflection time $T$ for reflectors derivable from the present recessed reflector by placing conductors at various

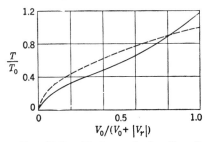

equipotentials may be obtained from Fig. 13·12 by a horizontal expansion of the curve in Fig. 13·12 sufficient to give the correct intercept at $V_0/(V_0 + |V_r|) = 1$.

Fig. 13·12.—Electron reflection time $T$ in the reflector field of Fig. 13·11 (solid line). Transit time in reflector of same spacing but with linear variation of potential (broken line); $T_0$ is the transit time in this linear field with $|V_r| = 0$.

The mode locus is in turn derivable from Fig. 13·12 by plotting $V_r$ vs. $V_0$ at constant $T$. The resulting normalized mode locus is shown in Fig. 13·13 with the mode locus for the plane-parallel reflector indicated for comparison. The flattening out of the locus as the reflector gets deeper is a monotonically progressing process. Considerations of power-supply convenience and the avoidance of reflector bombardment by fast electrons usually require operation with $0.2V_0 \leqq |V_r| \leqq 0.5V_0$;

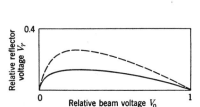

Fig. 13·13.—Normalized mode locus for the reflector potential of Fig. 13·11 (solid curve). Normalized mode locus for plane-parallel space-charge-free reflector (broken curve).

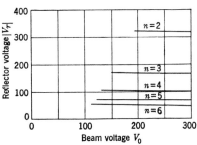

Fig. 13·14.—Reflector-mode pattern in experimental reflex klystron with hemispherical reflector.

and it is apparent from Fig. 13·13 that for a deep reflector the mode loci in this range of reflector voltages are practically horizontal lines—that is, the reflection-transit time and hence the oscillation frequency are nearly independent of beam voltage. Similarly, it is apparent from the previous discussion of the factors that determine radians phase change per reflector volt that this quantity is maximized for such a horizontal mode locus.

In Fig. 13·14 the mode pattern for an experimental reflex oscillator with a hemispherical reflector is shown; the correspondence with the behavior just discussed is obvious.

Some of the other implications of the deeper reflector are discussed when the effect of various reflectors on the bunching process is considered.

**13·6. Space-charge Transit-time Effects in the Plane-parallel Reflector.**—Space-charge effects are always present to some degree in any reflecting region. The only reflector for which they can be analyzed with any degree of facility is the plane-parallel reflector; the analysis of this reflector will serve to indicate orders of magnitude and the nature of end results.

The general question of one-dimensional flow of electrons between parallel planes has been thoroughly discussed elsewhere[1] without, however, giving in much detail the results that are applicable to the case of complete reflection of the electrons. (See also Sec. 3·6.) The mathematical analysis of the additional details[2] will not be reproduced here, the discussion being limited to stating the results and discussing their physical content.

According to Poisson's equation, the curvature of the potential function is proportional to the space-charge density. In a region into which a constant current is injected, the space-charge density at any point is inversely proportional to the electron velocity, or the square root of the potential, at that point; space-charge effects are then greatest at the turn-around point in the reflector region.

The order of magnitude of the effects involved may be seen from a simple case. In a plane-parallel diode with negligible cathode-emission current the potential varies linearly with distance from the cathode. If the cathode-emission current is increased until it is space-charge limited, the potential gradient at the cathode is zero and the potential varies with the $\frac{4}{3}$ power of distance from the cathode. Nearly the same $\frac{4}{3}$ power space-charge distortion of the electrostatic field would result, for the same geometry, if the current were injected at the anode and collected at the "cathode," now run slightly positive with respect to the zero equipotential. Furthermore, suppose that the current were injected at the anode, with the "cathode" now operated as a reflector at a voltage infinitesimally negative with respect to the source of the electrons, with the result that all the electrons are now returned to the anode; then if the "cathode" (reflector!)-anode spacing were decreased by the factor $1/\sqrt{2}$, nearly the same $\frac{4}{3}$ power variation of potential with distance would again result. This last factor of $1/\sqrt{2}$ comes in because the

---

[1] C. E. Fay, A. L. Samuel, and W. Shockley, *Bell Syst. Tech. J.*, **17**, 49 (1938). B. Salzberg, A. V. Haeff, *R.C.A. Review*, **2**, 236 (1938).

[2] Private communication from W. Sollfrey, Sperry Gyroscope Co. Research Laboratories, Garden City, N.Y.

injected current, since it is now reflected, is equivalent in its space-charge contribution to twice as much current in a one-way diode; and a decrease in diode spacing by the factor $1/\sqrt{2}$ doubles the emission current. These considerations suggest that a very useful parameter for use in dealing with space-charge effects in reflectors is the ratio $\sqrt{2}\,d/s$, where $d$ is the anode-reflector spacing and $s$ is the cathode-anode spacing in the "equivalent diode." By this last term is meant a space-charge-limited diode that would supply, at the given beam voltage, the current density which is injected into the reflector region. The ratio $\sqrt{2}\,d/s$ is proportional to the square root of the perveance of the electron gun. (Perveance $\equiv I_0/V_0^{3/2}$, a quantity that is independent of $V_0$ in a space-charge-limited electron gun.)

When $\sqrt{2}\,d/s = 1$ and the reflector is operated infinitesimally negative (it is assumed that the electrons have no velocity distribution), then the potential varies with the $\frac{4}{3}$ power of distance from reflector to anode. For $\sqrt{2}\,d/s \ll 1$ there is little space-charge influence and the potential

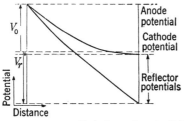

FIG. 13·15.—Variation of potential with distance in the presence of space charge; same $I_0$, $V_0$, reflector spacing, corresponding to $\sqrt{2}\,d/s = 1.4$; two different reflector voltages.

varies nearly linearly with distance. This latter case corresponds to the situation in a temperature-limited diode. This analogy between a diode and the reflecting region cannot be carried far, however, unless attention is given to the fact that a reflector is often run negative with respect to cathode. Thus, Fig. 13·15 shows the variation of potential in a reflection region with two different reflector voltages but with everything else constant. It is seen in this figure that a high reflector voltage, by pushing the electron turn-around point nearer to the anode, diminishes the total amount of space charge and the space-charge distortion of the field just as would a smaller anode-reflector spacing. The specific curves in Fig. 13·15 have been calculated for $\sqrt{2}\,d/s = 1.4$. In the type 3K23 reflex klystron, the operation of which is analyzed in Chap. 12, an even higher degree of space-charge is present, corresponding to $\sqrt{2}\,d/s = 2.5$. The curvature of the potential that sets in at low reflector voltages, to which was ascribed in Chap. 12 an observed decrease in efficiency in the type 3K23, is apparent in Fig. 13·15; the way in which this curvature influences bunching and efficiency is discussed in Secs. 13·7 to 13·9.

Some attention must also be given to what happens when $V_r = 0$ ("$V_r = 0$" hereafter means "reflector infinitesimally negative") and $\sqrt{2}\,d/s > 1$. In this case, as shown in Fig. 13·16, the turn-around point moves out from the reflector toward the anode; the potential maintains its same relative form, shrinking horizontally in the figure.

In finding the variation of potential in cases such as those of Fig. 13·15, it is necessary to join two solutions: the linear potential in the region between the reflector and the turn-around point, and the temperature-limited-diode potential between the turn-around point and the anode. These two solutions must join with continuous first derivatives at the turn-around point; hence, if $|V_r| > 0$, the solution for the potential in the space-charge-field region must have non-zero gradient at the turn-around point, just as does the potential in a temperature-limited diode.

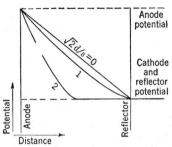

Fig. 13·16.—Variation of potential with position in the reflector region when $V_r = 0$, for various values of the beam current or of $\sqrt{2}\, d/s$.

Without reproducing the details of the derivation, the results of the considerations just outlined may be summarized. The notation used is as follows:

$x$ = distance measured into reflection region from the anode.

$\Psi$ = the electrostatic potential measured with respect to the cathode or the electron turn-around point in the reflector region, and normalized by dividing by $V_0$.

Then the relation between potential and distance in that part of the reflection region where current is present is given by

$$\frac{\sqrt{2}\, x}{s} = (1 - 2C)(1 + C)^{\frac12} - (\Psi^{\frac12} - 2C)(\Psi^{\frac12} + C)^{\frac12}. \qquad (13)$$

Here $C$ is a parameter the physical significance of which is shown by the relation

$$\frac{s}{\sqrt{2}}\left(\frac{d\Psi}{dx}\right)_{\Psi=0} = -\frac{4}{3}\, C^{\frac12}.$$

Thus $C$ is proportional to the square of the (suitably normalized) potential gradient at the electron turn-around point. This relation, however, is hardly convenient for finding the value of $C$ with which to enter Eq. (13) in any given situation. The value of the parameter $C$ may be determined from the relation

$$\frac{|V_r|}{V_0} = \frac{4}{3}\, C^{\frac12}\left[\frac{\sqrt{2}\, d}{s} - (1 - 2C)(1 + C)^{\frac12} - 2C^{\frac32}\right]. \qquad (14)$$

This equation is summarized graphically in Fig. 13·17, which gives the relation between $|V_r|/V_0$ and $C$ for various values of $\sqrt{2}\,d/s$. For $\sqrt{2}\,d/s \geqq 1$, there is no value of $C$ for which $|V_r|/V_0 = 0$. This condition corresponds to the physical fact that, if $\sqrt{2}\,d/s > 1$ and $V_r = 0$, the potential has the value zero for a finite distance in front of the reflector. The potential remains at zero up to the point $x = s/\sqrt{2}$; for smaller

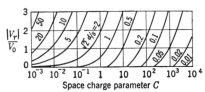

FIG. 13·17.—Dependence of the space-charge parameter $C$ on the parameters $|V_r|/V_0$ and $\sqrt{2}\,d/s$.

values of $x$, the potential depends upon distance just as it would if $d$ were given by $s/\sqrt{2}$.

The d-c transit times in the reflection region are conveniently normalized in terms of the value that the round-trip transit time assumes when the potential in the reflection region is just like that in a space-charge-limited diode—that is, when $\sqrt{2}\,d/s = 1$. In this latter case the transit time is $6s/v_0$. For any other case the transit time $T$ and the normalized transit time $\tau$ are given by

$$\tau \equiv \frac{Tv_0}{6s} = (1 + C)^{1/2} - C^{1/2}. \tag{15}$$

From this equation and the dependence of $C$ on $|V_r|/V_0$ and $\sqrt{2}\,d/s$ as shown in Fig. 13·17, one may deduce the dependence of the normalized transit time $\tau$ on $|V_r|/V_0$ and $\sqrt{2}\,d/s$ as shown in Fig. 13·18.

The behavior shown in Fig. 13·18 results from the interplay of two factors: the depth of penetration of the electrons into the reflector field, and the mean electron velocity in the reflector space. In the absence of space charge, a diminution of $|V_r|$ at constant $V_0$ increases the depth of penetration while leaving the mean electron velocity unchanged; as $|V_r|/V_0$ goes from unity to zero the transit time is doubled. This

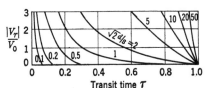

FIG. 13·18.—Dependence of the normalized reflection transit-time $\tau$ on the parameters $|V_r|/V_0$ and $\sqrt{2}\,d/s$.

behavior corresponds to the behavior shown in Fig. 13·18 for $\sqrt{2}\,d/s \ll 1$. (The curve for $\sqrt{2}\,d/s = 0.2$ is expanded horizontally over that for $\sqrt{2}\,d/s = 0.1$ because the transit time through the equivalent diode, to which $\tau$ is normalized, has been correspondingly decreased.) As space charge comes effective ($\sqrt{2}\,d/s \geqq 1$), it is apparent from Fig. 13·15 that the depth of penetration increases less rapidly as $|V_r|/V_0$ diminishes, but, because of the increasing potential curvature, an increasingly large fraction of the electron's path lies in the low-velocity region near the turn-around point. These two factors have opposite effects on the transit time. For $\sqrt{2}\,d/s \leqq 1$ the turn-around point for $V_r \approx 0$ is at the reflector and the turn-around point for $|V_r|/V_0 = 1$ is practically midway between anode and reflector just as in the absence of space charge; thus the increasing curvature of the potential as $V_r$ approaches zero (see Fig. 13·15) gives rise to an increase of transit time with diminishing $|V_r|$ that is more rapid than in the absence of space charge. However, as $\sqrt{2}\,d/s$ increases above unity (see Fig. 13·16), the depth of penetration at $V_r = 0$ becomes less and less. This effect tends to counterbalance the space-charge diminution of mean velocity that takes place as $|V_r|$ diminishes; the net result is that for $\sqrt{2}\,d/s \gg 1$ (very severe space-charge conditions) the transit time becomes more and more independent of $V_r$. This result is likewise apparent in Fig. 13·18.

The interplay of these various transit-time factors results in the normalized mode loci shown in Fig. 13·19 for various degrees of space charge. The most interesting feature here is the extreme distortion from the space-charge-free case under conditions of high space charge. This distortion is due to the effect just noted for, as $V_0$ is increased and

an attempt is made to hold $T$ constant by a decrease in $|V_r|$ to allow deeper penetration, this attempt is partially frustrated by the increasing curvature of the potential function. This increasing curvature must be compensated by a further decrease in $|V_r|$; this accelerating process brings $|V_r|$ rapidly to zero. The curves in Fig. 13·15 may also be used to illustrate this point because, since space-charge phenomena are inde-

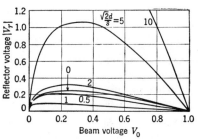

FIG. 13·19.—Normalized mode locus for plane-parallel reflector with varying degrees of space charge as indicated by varying values of $\sqrt{2}\,d/s$.

pendent of voltage in the presence of a space-charge limited cathode, the curves of Fig. 13·15 may correspond as well to constant $T$, variable $V_0$, as to the constant $V_0$, variable $T$ indicated in the caption. The value of $V_r$ would then be measured relative to the varying $V_0$; and with $T$ constant, the curve with low $|V_r|$ corresponds to high $V_0$.

Although Fig. 13·19 shows the mode loci normalized to $V_r = 0$ at $V_0 = 1$ for comparison with Figs. 13·4 and 13·13, the physical factors just discussed may be more easily seen in the unnormalized pattern of Fig. 13·20, which shows the locus for a single mode (single value of $T$) as $\sqrt{2}\,d/s$ is increased. This figure shows that as the electron-gun perveance per unit area is increased for a given reflector geometry, the maximum transit time obtainable with a given beam voltage eventually diminishes monotonically.

This maximum transit time is always obtained with $V_r = 0$. With a given geometry and $V_0$ and with $V_r = 0$, Fig. 13·16 illustrates why transit time eventually decreases monotonically with increasing current. At zero reflector voltage, an increase in current does not at first change depth of penetration but does increase potential curvature and transit time; however, as already noted, for $\sqrt{2}\,d/s \geqq 1$ a further increase in current simply moves the turn-around point nearer the anode without changing the relative shape of the potential, and hence diminishes the transit time.

These comments about the influence of space charge in the reflector region have been intended largely as background; the only clear-cut easily observable effect that has been discussed is the influence of space

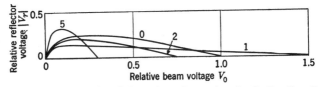

Fig. 13·20.—Unnormalized mode locus for a given value of reflection time $T$, showing relation between $V_r$ and $V_0$ as $d/s$ (that is, beam current at constant beam voltage) is increased. Curves labelled with values of $\sqrt{2}\,d/s$.

charge on the mode pattern. Aside from the usefulness of knowledge of mode patterns per se, and the implied possibility of exploring d-c space-charge effects and verifying these comments by observation of actual mode patterns, there are two important consequences of this discussion.

One has to do with the influence that the curvature of the potential in the region of the turn-around point has upon the bunching phenomenon, which is discussed later. The other point, related in part to the first, has to do with the influence of space-charge phenomena on the useful range of wavelengths for the reflex klystron.

As the operating wavelength of the reflex klystron is increased, the reflection time must be increased in the same proportion because, in order for oscillation to exist, the reflection time must have a minimum value of $\frac{3}{4}$ or preferably $1\frac{3}{4}$ cycles measured at the oscillation frequency. It is seen in the later discussion of the effects of space charge upon bunching that the effects of increasing space charge are eventually adverse. Hence, let it be supposed that in increasing the wavelength of the klystron the space-charge effects are maintained at some constant level; the dependence of relative potential upon relative position is therefore unchanged in the scaling process. The invariance of space-charge effects and the proportionality of reflection time to wavelength may be accomplished by holding $V_0$ constant and scaling the dimensions of the cathode and the reflector in proportion to the wavelength (see the previous discussion of the scaling of electron-optical systems). But this scaling process holds $I_0$ constant. Thus as the wavelength is increased, the d-c input power, the efficiency, and the r-f output power approach constant limiting values. At the same time, however, competition from other oscillators that are not limited in this manner comes into play and hence makes the reflex klystron increasingly less advantageous above some maximum wavelength.

This conclusion is not appreciably changed by considering other methods of scaling; hence it may be said that reflector space-charge effects, operating in the dimension parallel to the motion of the beam, set one long-wavelength limit to the competitive ability of the reflex-klystron oscillator. The same may be said concerning the effects of debunching in multiresonator klystrons. There, for a given beam voltage, the necessary drift length is proportional to the wavelength, but the debunching wave number, which determines the length of drift space for which debunching becomes harmful, does not involve the frequency of the r-f input-gap voltage.

It is not too irrelevant to note an interesting related fact, which is that the short-wavelength limit for klystron operation is set by another electron-optical effect, the existence of a maximum obtainable current density.[1] This maximum current density is a limitation involving dimensions transverse to the beam. The maximum current density is important because circuit losses increase as the wavelength decreases, and a larger total current is therefore required to sustain oscillation; at the same time the cavity size and the gap area available for this current decrease. Since the current density is limited, the two requirements collide head-on and set a lower limit to available operating wavelengths. Unfortunately, at present this lower limit is not influenced by competition from any markedly better oscillator, in contrast to the situation at the long-wavelength limit.

All told, the two limitations just described seem to limit the usefulness of the reflex klystron oscillator to the (not-so-small!) wavelength range extending from somewhat more than a millimeter to somewhat less than a meter.

**13·7. Influence of Reflector Field on Bunching.**—The effects of velocity modulation by a noninfinitesimal r-f gap voltage and of subsequent bunching in an arbitrary drift space are considered in detail in Sec. 9·4. There it is found that, even with the simplest drift spaces, the

---

[1] J. R. Pierce, *Jour. App. Phys.*, **10**, 715 (1939).

noninfinitesimal r-f gap voltage necessitated corrections to the results of the simple bunching theory of Sec. 9·2 and Eq. (9·9). Changes in both the phase and the amplitude of the bunched-beam-current components are indicated, and since these are primarily effects that increase with increasing amplitude of the gap voltage, they usually diminish with increasing $n$ in the reflex klystron. In generalizing these results to arbitrary drift spaces it is found that these effects of noninfinitesimal gap-voltage amplitude are dependent on the transit-time characteristics of the drift space.

It is also found, however, that the relation between bunching parameter and r-f gap voltage is dependent on the drift-space characteristics; and this is considerably more important to the present discussion. In the two simplest drift spaces, a field-free drift space and a linear reflecting field, $|X| = M\theta_0 V/2V_0$, where $\theta_0$ is the d-c transit angle in the drift space; however, for all other drift spaces, $X = a_1 M\theta_0 V/2V_0$, where the coefficient $a_1$ is a characteristic of the drift space given by Eq. (9·26b): $a_1 = -(2V_0/\theta_0)(d\theta/dV_e)_0$. This last effect is not, as were the previous ones, a matter of distortion of the bunch consequent upon modulation by a large r-f gap voltage; to the contrary, the waveform and phase of the bunched beam current are unaltered, and the simple zero-order Eq. (9·9) for the current components still holds. All that has happened is that the degree of bunching produced by a given $V/V_0$ is the same as that which would be produced in a linear reflecting field with a d-c transit angle $|a_1\theta_0|$ instead of $\theta_0$.

This fact is sometimes expressed by saying that in a nonlinear reflecting field the "equivalent bunching time" is different from the transit time. The equivalent bunching angle $|a_1\theta_0|$ thus governs all considerations of bunching and small-signal electronic conductance $G_e$, and the transit angle $\theta_0$ governs all considerations of bunching phase and the phase angle $\phi$. The main importance of the field coefficient $a_1$ lies in the fact that it does not depend on gap-voltage amplitude and hence is less likely to decrease with increasing $n$.

The consequences of an increase in equivalent bunching time over transit time ($|a_1| > 1$) are simple. They are the same as the consequences, already noted in detail in Chap. 12, of increasing $\theta_0$ in the linear reflecting field. Thus in the simplest terms (assuming high current efficiency), $\eta \propto 1/|a_1|\theta_0$ and $\Delta f_{\frac{1}{2}} \propto |a_1|\theta_0$. If by some means $\theta_0$ and $n$ could be held constant and $|a_1|$ increased, a decrease of $\eta$ and an increase of $\Delta f_{\frac{1}{2}}$ would result. Conversely, a decrease in $|a_1|$ increases efficiency and decreases electronic-tuning range.

Thus the principal subject of interest in the investigation of general reflector fields is the field coefficient $a_1$, which apparently can have such far-reaching effects on the simplest aspects of reflex-klystron behavior.

**13·8. D-c Transit Time Versus Effective Bunching Time.**—Since bunching depends upon differences in transit times, the resulting dependence of bunching parameter on the derivative $(d\theta/dV_e)_0$ in $a_1$ is to be expected. But the way in which $(d\theta/dV_e)_0$ depends on the general shape of the reflector field is perhaps not so obvious, and the physical origin of any such dependence is therefore worth some investigation.

What happens in the vicinity of the electron turn-around point has a pronounced effect on transit-time relations as the electron velocities in this vicinity are low and the time spent in this region is out of proportion to its geometrical extent. The various relations involved may perhaps most easily be seen with reference to Fig. 13·21. Here are shown schematically three reflector fields such as might be produced by placing an auxiliary grid between the anode and reflector at the position indicated.

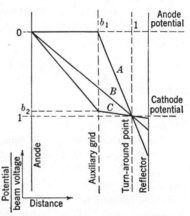

Fig. 13·21.—Illustrative reflector fields for discussion of transit time and bunching relations: (A) $b_1 = \frac{2}{3}, b_2 = 0$; (B) $b_1 = b_2$; (C) $b_1 = \frac{2}{3}, b_2 = 0.95$.

The transit-time relations in such a case are simple and are easily derived because the average velocity in traversing any segment of a linear potential is simply the average of the velocities at the beginning and at the end of the segment. These relations will be stated without derivation and with no discussion of their significance as analytical expressions; they are given explicitly simply for the convenience of anyone who may wish to experiment with combinations of parameters other than those shown in Fig. 13·21.

Let the relative position and potential of the imaginary "auxiliary grid" be given by $b_1$ and $b_2$, as shown in the figure; and let $\theta_{00}$ be the d-c transit angle when $b_1 = b_2$—that is, $\theta_{00}$ is the d-c transit angle for an ideal linear reflector with the same turn-around point as the reflector in question. Then the d-c transit angle $\theta_0$ is given by

$$\frac{\theta_0}{\theta_{00}} = \frac{b_1}{b_2} + \frac{b_2 - b_1}{b_2\sqrt{1 - b_2}}. \tag{16}$$

The rate of change of transit time with changing electron energy may be measured by a quantity similar to that used in defining $a_1$, $-(2V_0/\theta_{00})(d\theta/dV_e)_0$. This quantity is given, for the indicated reflector field, by

$$\frac{2V_0}{\theta_{00}}\left(\frac{d\theta}{dV_e}\right)_0 = \frac{b_1}{b_2} + \frac{b_2 - b_1}{b_2(1 - b_2)^{3/2}}. \qquad (17)$$

What do these relations say about the potential curves, $A$ $B$, and $C$ of Fig. (13·21), for which $b_1 = \frac{2}{3}$ and $b_2 = 0$, $\frac{2}{3}$ and 0.95 respectively? Equation (16) indicates transit times given by

$$\frac{\theta_0}{\theta_{00}} = 0.67, \ 1, \ \text{and} \ 2.02$$

respectively. This result is as it should be; the velocity at any given point in space has been progressively decreased in going from $A$ to $C$.

By Eq. (17), the rate of change of transit time with incident electron velocity is given by

$$\frac{2V_0}{\theta_{00}}\left(\frac{d\theta}{dV_e}\right)_0 = 0, \ 1, \ \text{and} \ 27;$$

hence

$$a_1 = 0, \ -1, \ \text{and} \ -13.4$$

for $A$, $B$, and $C$ respectively.

This result is rather surprising. It says that in the reflection field $A$ no bunching action at all occurs, and also that in field $C$, bunching occurs as easily as it would in a linear reflecting field with 13.4 times as large a d-c transit angle; in field $C$, $\eta$ is reduced by a factor 13.4 and $\Delta f_{1/2}$ increased by a factor 13.4 from the values in a linear field with the same d-c transit angle. What is happening here?

Consider first field $A$ of Fig. 13·21. This field is really a combination (in a proportion chosen with the intention of emphasizing a particular point) of two cases that have already been noted in detail: the ideal reflector and the field-free drift space. It will be recalled that the transit time of an electron with initial energy $V_e$ is proportional to $V_e^{1/2}$ in the ideal reflector and to $V_e^{-1/2}$ in a field-free drift space; hence in Case $A$, where $b_1$ is so chosen as to make the transit times in the two spaces equal, the total transit time is independent of $V_e$ for $V_e \approx V_0$. There thus can be no bunching by small r-f gap voltages with the field of Case $A$, as transit time is independent of electron energy.

This result does not hold true, of course, for any value of $b_1$ other than $\frac{2}{3}$. At $b_1 = \frac{2}{3}$ and $b_2 = 0$, $a_1$ goes through zero and changes sign; for $b_2 = 0$ and $b_1 > \frac{2}{3}$ the bunching is predominantly field-free in character and 180° out of phase with that for $b_2 = 0$, $b_1 < \frac{2}{3}$; with a reflector for which $b_2 = 0$ and $b_1 > \frac{2}{3}$, modes of oscillation can occur not at $\theta_0 = 2\pi(n + \frac{3}{4})$ but at $\theta_0 = 2\pi(n + \frac{1}{4})$.

Consider now Case $C$ of Fig. 13·21. What makes $(d\theta/dV_e)_0$ so large? This quantity has increased out of all proportion to the increase in $\theta_0$. The increase in $\theta_0$ results largely from the increase in the geometrical extent of the region where velocities are small; but the increase in $(d\theta/dV_e)_0$ arises because the gradient of the potential at the turn-around point is small. This small gradient means that a slight increase in incident electron energy makes a disproportionate increase in the depth of penetration and in the distance which the electron must travel at very low energy. This example illustrates the fact that the potential gradient at the turn-around point becomes of prime importance when it is small.

Case $C$ corresponds to the general shape of reflector field most commonly encountered in fact. A distortion in the same direction as this one is caused by space-charge effects between plane-parallel electrodes, as has already been seen in Figs. 13·15 and 13·16. Even in the absence of space charge, the provision of a radially inward focusing field at the reflector produces the same downward displacement of the potential function, as seen in Fig. 13·11. So an increase in the bunching time over the transit time, with the consequent decrease in efficiency and increase in electronic tuning range over that expected with a linear reflecting field, must be expected to be the rule rather than the exception.

*Dependence of the Field Coefficient $a_1$ on Position in the Reflector Mode Pattern.*—The factor $a_1$, which is usually increased by the common nonlinearities of reflector fields, is a dimensionless number that will always be the same for given d-c electron trajectories in a given reflector (with possible later reservations in the case of space-charge distortions of the field). It is shown in Sec. 13·3 that for any particular tube (with space-charge-limited cathode) a given value of $V_r/V_0$ always corresponds to the same set of electron trajectories, regardless of frequency of oscillation or absolute value of the electrode voltage. Thus the loci of constant values of $a_1$ are straight lines through the origin in the $V_r$-vs.-$V_0$ mode pattern, and horizontal straight lines in the $V_r$-vs.-$\lambda$ mode pattern.

The general trend of the further dependence of $a_1$ is also apparent from general considerations. In a reflector field in which curvature of the potential arises from a shaping of the electrodes to produce a focusing action on the beam—as in the recessed reflector of Sec. 13·5—a diminishing of $|V_r|/V_0$ allows a deeper penetration of electrons into the reflector, and the potential gradient at the turn-around point is thus diminished. In a plane-parallel reflector field with space charge a decrease in $|V_r|/V_0$ causes a rapid decrease in the potential gradient at the turn-around point. In normal operating conditions a decrease in $|V_r|/V_0$ accompanies an increase in $V_0$ or $\lambda$, as the reflector mode patterns of Figs. 13·2 and 13·7 illustrate; hence, for a given mode of oscillation, an increase in $V_0$ or $\lambda$ causes an increase in $|a_1|$ that is usually fairly slow at first and then becomes more rapid as $V_r$ approaches zero. If this effect is not accompanied by others, such as the phenomenon of phase aberration which will be discussed shortly, then the approach of $V_r$ to zero is accompanied by a rapid decrease of $\eta$ and a rapid increase in $\Delta f_{\frac{1}{2}}/f_0$.

*Illustrative Examples.*—An illustration of this action is shown in Fig. 13·22. In this figure are shown the dependence of output power and electronic-tuning range on $V_0$ for the $(n = 3)$-mode of the type 417A. The corresponding mode locus is shown in Fig. 13·2. Without trying to disentangle all the factors involved (the change in $M$ and the fact that

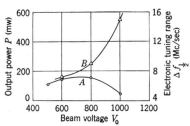

FIG. 13·22.—Variation of output power $P$ (curve $A$) and electronic tuning range $\Delta f_{\frac{1}{2}}$ (curve $B$) in the $(n = 3)$-mode of the type 417A reflex klystron. Compare with Figs. 12·20 and 12·21.

the cathode was not operated at exactly constant perveance), it appears that for $V_0 > 600$ volts or for $|V_r|/V_0 < \frac{1}{3}$ a rapid increase in $|a_1|$ occurs for this mode, with the attendant increase in $\Delta f_{\frac{1}{2}}$ and decrease in $\eta$. The type 417A has a rather flat reflector; therefore this effect can arise only in a minor degree from an increased depth of penetration into the curved potential which a recessed reflector provides. On the other hand, a comparison of Figs. 13·2 and 13·19 also suggests that space charge has considerably affected the reflector mode pattern. From the dimensions of the 417A, the beam diameter ($\frac{1}{4}$ in.) and the operating conditions ($I_0 = 25$ and 75 ma at $V_0 = 400$ and 1000 volts respectively—not constant perveance), one may calculate for $\sqrt{2}\,d/s$ the values 1.5 and 1.1 respectively for $V_0 = 400$ and 1000 volts. The mode pattern of Fig. 13·2 is consistent with values of $\sqrt{2}\,d/s$ of about 2.0 and 1.5 in these two cases. It is not known how space-charge effects and reflector-depth effects (the latter slight in this case) combine; hence this approximate agreement seems satisfactory and lends support to the suggestion that the increase in $|a_1|$, that may be deduced from Fig. 13·22, is due to space-charge effects.

Exactly similar conclusions may be drawn from the example of the type 3K23, discussed in Section 12·4.

*Elimination of Reflector Effects from Comparisons of Theory and Experiment.*—These general remarks also make clear another point: if one wants to compare the behavior of various modes in a reflex klystron with zero-order theory the only really satisfactory way to do it is under circumstances such that the same value of $a_1$ is operative for each mode during the comparison. One way to do this is to work with small currents and to use an accurately plane-parallel reflector. A better way, when this is possible, is to make the comparison under the condition of identical electron trajectories for each mode.

In Fig. 13·23 is shown the dependence of $V_r$ on $\lambda$ for the type SD835D, an external resonator tube developed[1] by Sylvania Electric Products, Inc.   In Fig. 13·24 is shown the dependence of output power on $\lambda$. Both these figures are taken at the same constant beam voltage, 325 volts.   The experimental points in Fig. 13·24 scatter considerably, probably in large part because of the necessity of changing cavities to cover the wavelength range and because of the difficulties of measuring power over wide wavelength ranges; it seems reasonable to idealize this

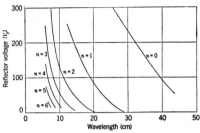

FIG.   13·23.—$V_r$-vs.-$\lambda$   mode   pattern   for SD835D reflex klystron; $V_0 = 325$ volts.

data by drawing the dashed line.   At any given wavelength the dependence of output power $P$ on mode number $n$ is very far from the relation $P \propto 1/(n + \frac{3}{4})$ predicted by the zero-order theory.

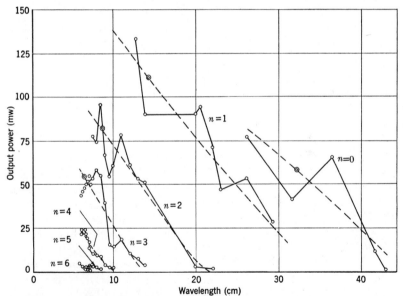

FIG. 13·24.—Dependence of output power on wavelength for various modes of SD835D reflex klystron; $V_0 = 325$ volts.   At double circles, $|V_r| = 200$ volts.

From Fig. 13·23 one may pick out the wavelengths at which the various modes have a given $V_r$ and hence have given d-c trajectories

[1] V. B. Corey and P. R. Malmberg, "SD835D Reflex Oscillator Tube," Sylvania Report D-62, Feb. 2, 1945,

Suppose that this is done for $|V_r| = 200$ volts. The points on the power curves of Fig. 13·24 that occur at the corresponding values of $\lambda$ and hence are obtained with a single set of electron trajectories are indicated in Fig. 13·24 by large circles. In Table 13·2 below are indicated the resulting values of power output for the various modes. If $\eta \propto 1/(n + \frac{3}{4})$ as simple theory predicts, then $(n + \frac{3}{4})P$ should be a constant for the values of $P$ and $n$ indicated. In the next column this product is found. It is seen that the constancy of the product $(n + \frac{3}{4})P$ is good except for $n = 0$.

It seems reasonable to conclude from this data that the predictions of the zero-order theory as to the variation of efficiency with $n$ are rather accurate for $n \geqq 1$ in this tube. It is interesting to note that this does not hold true for $n = 0$, and that the efficiency here is down by a factor of nearly five from a simple prediction based on the other two modes. This discrepancy may result from two factors: a value of $G_e$ and a beam current that are too small to sustain this mode well, and the high r-f gap voltage that is present in this low mode. (For $n = 0$, $V/V_0 \approx 1$ at $X = 2$.)

TABLE 13·2.—RELATION BETWEEN OUTPUT POWER $P$ AND MODE NUMBER $n$ FOR OPERATION AT $|V_r| = 200$ VOLTS, $V_0 = 325$ VOLTS IN THE SD835D REFLEX KLYSTRON

| $n$ | $P$, mw | $(n + \frac{3}{4})P$ |
|---|---|---|
| 0 | 58 | 44 |
| 1 | 112 | 196 |
| 2 | 83 | 228 |
| 3 | 54 | 203 |

The comparison of experiment with theory is discussed at this point not so much to check the theory as to indicate the transcendent importance of reflector optics. In a completely ideal (linear, space-charge-free) reflector, the power curves of Fig. 13·24 would become horizontal straight lines. Whether they are different from horizontal straight lines because of reflector nonlinearities or phase aberrations or beam-loading cannot be deduced from Fig. 13·24 without experimental evidence on the similar dependence of $\Delta f_{\frac{1}{2}}$ on $\lambda$ and $n$, which is unfortunately lacking. The manner in which such experimental data would be utilized is described after the discussion of phase-aberration effects.

**13·9. Bunching and Space Charge.**—It has already been seen, in discussing the d-c transit-time properties of the plane-parallel reflector with space charge, that the presence of space charge produces a diminution in the potential gradient at the turn-around point in the reflection region. It has been seen—as, for example, in Fig. 13·15—that a comparatively small change in $V_r$ near $V_r = 0$ may cause a large change in this turn-around gradient. It is apparent that important increases in $|a_1|$ are bound to occur under such circumstances, and it would be convenient to have a neat presentation of the effect of the various space-charge parameters on $a_1$ and $a_2$.

This presentation is no simple matter, however. The basic difficulty is the fact that the effects now considered arise from the interaction of electrons with each other rather than their interaction, as separate individuals, with external electrodes. The situation in this case is somewhat analogous to that of debunching in the field-free drift space—with an interesting difference. In the field-free case the space-charge effect of debunching is to slow down the bunching and decrease $X/V$; in the present reflector case, the indications are that the space-charge distortion of the reflecting field makes $X/V$ larger than would be calculated for a given $\theta_0$ in the absence of space charge. However, this point is only an interesting sidelight to the main points, for debunching in a field-free drift space is simple compared with that which takes place in a reflecting field. The most troublesome complication in the latter case is the fact that electrons with different energies penetrate to different distances, making the forces in the vicinity of the all-important turn-around point very complex.

One way of throwing some light on the situation is the following. In considering small-signal behavior, it might seem reasonable to investigate the motion of one test electron in the field of all the other electrons, which are assumed to be moving with the single d-c energy $eV_0$. In doing this a peculiar difficulty arises. There are inherent discontinuities in certain derivatives of the space-charge-influenced potential at the turn-around point; because of these, the derivatives of transit time with respect to incident energy, evaluated at $V_e = V_0$, are logarithmically infinite, and the field coefficients $a_1, a_2 \ldots$ therefore have no meaning in this calculation.

To be sure, this logarithmic infinity in derivative corresponds to a minor kink in a curve of $\theta$ vs. $V_e$. One possible solution might be to disregard the kink and use the calculated dependence of $\theta$ on $V_e$ to construct a $t_2$-vs.-$t_1$ diagram after the manner of Chap. 9. A numerical integration may be used to make a Fourier analysis of the waveforms corresponding to this $t_2$-vs.-$t_1$ diagram, and if this is done for several values of $V_e/V_0$ the numerical dependence of current components on $V_e/V_0$ is known. This information may be compared with Eq. (9·9) and may be used to predict the efficiency. The procedure, while not elegant, certainly has some significance.

A more accurate and probably more elegant procedure would be to carry out a self-consistent field calculation in the same manner as has been carried out by Hartree with such success in the theory of atomic structure.

These questions are left as a problem for the reader; the authors do not know the answers. It is apparent, however, that the answers are of great importance, particularly to longer-wavelength tubes operating at high d-c inputs.

**13·10. Reflector Fields with Phase Aberrations.**—The foregoing discussion has implicitly assumed that in the d-c case all electrons have the same total reflection transit time (same values of $\theta_0$), and therefore all parts of the bunch return to the r-f gap at the same time. If this condition is not fulfilled—that is, if "phase aberrations" are present—then the bunch loses some of its effectiveness because the condition for maximum power transfer, $\phi = 0$, cannot be fulfilled for all electrons by any given reflector voltage. The effective power factor is now $\overline{\cos \phi}$, the value of $\cos \phi$ averaged over all electrons; and the net results of the phase aberrations are two. The effective beam current is reduced by a factor $(\overline{\cos \phi})_{max}$, and, since a fraction of the beam current, $1 - (\overline{\cos \phi})_{max}$ is bound to be wasted, the maximum electronic efficiency is reduced by the factor $(\overline{\cos \phi})_{max}$. There is, in addition, a diminution in the operating circuit efficiency because of the diminution in beam current.

Any phase aberration can be very harmful, particularly in high modes, for it is the absolute phase aberration, not the relative phase aberration, that diminishes $(\overline{\cos \phi})_{max}$. For example, a $\pm 5$ per cent variation in a transit time of six cycles ($\theta_0 = 38$ radians) corresponds to

$$(\overline{\cos \phi})_{max} = 0.50$$

or a more than 50 per cent reduction in operating efficiency. This effect is thus a sizable factor in the requirements for high precision in the manufacture of short-wavelength reflex klystrons.

The degree of phase aberration depends on the depth of penetration into the reflector field and hence on $V_r/V_0$; for example, a wide beam would have little phase aberration in the recessed reflector of Fig. 13·10, with a very high reflector voltage, but for a smaller reflector voltage the aberration would be severe. The percentage phase aberration is a single valued function of $V_r/V_0$ just as are the field coefficients $a_1$, $a_2$, . . . . For a given $V_r/V_0$ and a given percentage phase aberration, the absolute aberration is proportional to $\theta_0$ or inversely proportional to $\sqrt{V_0}$; and since the absolute phase aberration is what is effective, phase aberration effects will be less for the low modes.

**13·11. Comparison of Phase Aberrations and Reflector Nonlinearities.** Either one of these effects (aberration or nonlinearity) may thus cause a decrease in oscillator efficiency; certain uncommon nonlinearities, such as Case $A$ of Fig. 13·21, can of course cause increased efficiency. The relative effects of aberration and nonlinearity are, however, distinguishable in several respects.

A phase aberration decreases $\Delta f_{\frac{1}{2}}$ as well as $\eta$, whereas a nonlinearity that diminishes $\eta$ increases $\Delta f_{\frac{1}{2}}$. Thus the effects of Fig. 13·22 are due to reflector-field nonlinearities, not to phase aberrations.

The effects of a nonlinearity are the same for all modes at a given $V_r/V_0$; the effects of phase aberration diminish at low modes. The constancy of the product $(n + \frac{3}{4})P$, which apparently verifies the zero-order theory in Fig. 13·24, holds true equally well over a wide range of values of $V_r/V_0$ in that figure. Since it is rather unlikely that the degree of phase aberration will be constant over a wide range of values of $V_r/V_0$, it seems probable that the diminution of output power with decreasing $|V_r|$ in the SD-835 is a straightforward matter of nonlinearity of the reflector field. Observation of the variation of $\Delta f_{\frac{1}{2}}$ with $V_r$ would check this point.

A simple linear reflector field differs from both the cases just discussed, of course, because in this case $\eta$ and $\Delta f_{\frac{1}{2}}$ should have the variations indicated by the zero-order theory independently of $V_r/V_0$.

# CHAPTER 14

## HYSTERESIS IN REFLEX KLYSTRONS

### By D. R. Hamilton

**14·1. Phenomenon of Hysteresis.**—In common usage "hysteresis" refers to a phenomenon in which a dependent physical variable assumes any one of several values for a single value of an independently variable parameter; which of these several values the dependent variable assumes is governed by the history of the independent variable. The term "hysteresis" is most commonly used in connection with reflex klystrons to denote the often encountered multiple dependence of output power and frequency on reflector voltage. The same factors that give rise to this particular type of hysteresis cause hysteresis with respect to changes in other parameters such as beam voltage, beam current, or resonator tuning; these other types of hysteresis will not be discussed further, but the methods used in treating reflector-voltage hysteresis are directly applicable to them.

In its milder form hysteresis is important less for its own sake than for the mode asymmetry that is associated with it. (See Fig. 12·4 for an ideal symmetrical mode.) Hysteresis, when not too pronounced, occurs at one edge of the mode (see Fig. 14·6 for example) and is accompanied by a mode asymmetry that looks as if it were produced by a compression of the reflector voltage scale on one side of the mode. The consequences are not bad if the frequency and output-power characteristics are compressed by the same amount, as in Fig. 14·6, but in many instances the two characteristics differ in the degree of asymmetry, making the frequency deviations between maximum-power point and the two half-power points on either side different. For many purposes— such as automatic frequency control of the reflex-klystron local oscillator in a receiver—this variance reduces the effective electronic tuning range to twice the smaller of these two frequency deviations.

In more extreme cases, as in Fig. 14·16, the hysteresis extends well into the mode, occurs in a series of small steps, and is accompanied by frequency discontinuities. The problem of asymmetry is minor in comparison.

Since, however, all forms of hysteresis are usually closely related to mode asymmetry, this chapter is concerned both with mode asymmetry and hysteresis even when the asymmetry arises from a cause that does not, in itself, cause hysteresis.

384

Mode asymmetry and hysteresis may arise either from load effects or from electronic causes; load effects are discussed in Chap. 15 and the electronic causes of these phenomena are discussed in the present chapter. There are at least three electronic causes: the appreciable variation across the width of a low mode of the small-signal electronic transconductance $G_e$, the dependence of the phase of the bunched beam current upon r-f gap voltage, and the effects of electrons making more than one return transit of the r-f gap.[1]

**14·2. Mode Asymmetry Produced by Dependence of $G_e$ on $\phi$ in Low Modes.**—In obtaining the idealized mode shape of Fig. 12·4, $n$ was assumed much greater than unity. The primary value of this assump-

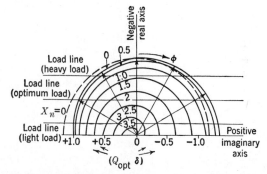

FIG. 14·1.—Admittance diagram for $n = 1$, assuming simple bunching. Loci of $Y_e$ for constant r-f gap voltage, as indicated by corresponding values of $X_n$ (continuous curves). Locus of small-signal admittance for this mode when variation of $\theta_0$ is neglected in calculating $G_e$ (broken curve). Values of $Q_{opt}\delta$ indicate relative frequency deviation associated with corresponding points on load lines; $\phi = \theta_0 - 2\pi(n + \frac{3}{4})$.

tion lies in the fact that the variation of $G_e$, the small-signal electronic transconductance, across the width of the mode can be neglected. In the admittance diagram of Fig. 12·2 this assumption corresponds to the assumption that $n$ or $\theta_0$ are so large that the spiral half-loop of small-signal electronic transadmittance is essentially a semicircle.

It is apparent from Fig. 12·2 that for modes with low $n$ this assumption is badly in error. A segment of the admittance diagram for a single value of $n$, $n = 1$, but for several levels of r-f voltage is shown in Fig. 14·1; here the higher-order corrections to the r-f component of the bunched beam current are neglected. The small-signal admittance, $-G_e e^{-i\phi}$ or $+jG_e e^{-i\theta_0}$, depends both in magnitude and phase on $\theta_0$; this polar plot of the admit-

---

[1] The origin, in multiple transits, of much hysteresis was first noted by W. G. Shepherd, Bell Telephone Laboratories Report MM-42-140-56. Most of the discussion and all the experimental data in the present chapter is taken from J. B. Garrison, "A Qualitative Analysis of Hysteresis in Reflex Klystrons," RL Report No. 650, Feb. 4, 1946.

tance includes the effect of the dependence of $G_e$ on $\theta_0$ as given[1] by

$$G_e = \theta_0 M^2 G_0/2.$$

The figure also shows the loci of the large-signal electronic transadmittance, $Y_e = je^{-i\theta_0}G_e 2J_1(X)/X$, for various values of the r-f gap voltage. Constant r-f gap voltage is indicated by constant $X_n$, which is the value of the bunching parameter for $\theta_0 = \theta_n \doteq 2\pi(n + \frac{3}{4})$; contours of constant $X$ would not serve here the desired purpose of indicating constant gap voltage since the ratio of bunching parameter to gap voltage is in itself dependent upon $\theta_0$. Also, for purposes of visual comparison, the dotted line in Fig. 14·1 is a semicircle, which shows where the locus of small-signal transadmittance would lie if the value of $\theta_0$ at the center of the mode were used in calculating $G_e$.

The three straight-line loci of constant circuit conductance in Fig. 14·1 correspond to heavy, optimum, and light loading. As discussed in Chap. 12, the various load lines are simply the loci of the circuit admittance for various conditions of loading. The fractional frequency deviation $\delta$ associated with a given point in a load line is proportional to the distance of this point from the real axis. The value of $\delta$ corresponding to a given horizontal location in Fig. 14·1 is indicated by the value of the product $Q_{opt}\delta$; $Q_{opt}$ is the value of the cavity $Q$ that corresponds to optimum load (maximum output power for ideal oscillator). From the asymmetrical occurrence of the intersections of the load lines with the admittance loci of constant $X_n$ in Fig. 14·1 it is apparent that there is

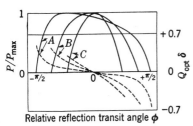

FIG. 14·2.—Dependence of normalized output power, $P/P_{max}$ (continuous curves) and normalized frequency deviation, $Q_{opt}\delta$ (broken curves) on relative reflection transit angle $\phi$ for $n = 1$ as deduced from Fig. 14·1. $\phi = \theta_0 - 2\pi(n + \frac{3}{4})$. ($A$ = light load; $B$ = optimum load; $C$ = heavy load.)

marked mode asymmetry, particularly at light load. This asymmetry, as deduced from Fig. 14·1, is shown in detail in Fig. 14·2. Since the curves of output power (proportional to the values of $X_n^2$) are normalized to unity for each mode the mode curves show only relative power within each mode. (In comparing this and subsequent mode shapes with experiment, it is to be borne in mind that increasing $\phi$ corresponds to decreasing absolute value of reflector voltage and decreasing frequency.)

---

[1] Note that $G_e$ depends upon $\theta_0$, as distinct from the $G_{ne}$ used in Chap. 12 for the value of $G_e$ at the center of the $n$th mode. Note also that the d-c transit angle, $\theta$ in Chap. 12, here is denoted by $\theta_0$ and is not distinguished from the bunching angle $\theta_e$.

These figures indicate that a definite asymmetry, in both output power and frequency of oscillation, is produced by the effect in question. This asymmetry is slight at optimum load and is greatest for very light load. Since the mode for which $n = 1$ is the lowest mode commonly used ($n = 0$ being unsatisfactory), and since the asymmetry diminishes rapidly as $n$ is increased, it is clear that the variation of $\theta_0$ across the mode is usually a minor factor in causing mode asymmetry.

**14·3. Hysteresis Caused by Phase Shifts Dependent Upon R-f Gap Voltage and Independent of $\theta_0$.**—All the forms of hysteresis that have an electronic origin have as their most essential characteristic a dependence of the phase of the bunched beam current on the amplitude of the r-f gap voltage. The simplest type of hysteresis results when this phase shift depends only upon r-f gap voltage amplitude and is unaffected by the value of $\phi$ or $\theta_0$.

Such a phase shift is encountered in Sec. 9·4, where it is shown that a finite gap voltage gives rise to a phase shift that is proportional to $a_2$, where $a_2$ is one of the field coefficients defined in Eq. (9·26). In general, $|a_2|$ increases as the mode number decreases; in a linear reflecting field, $|a_2| = \frac{1}{2}\theta_0$ by Table 9·1. This increase of phase shift with decreasing $n$ or $\theta_0$ is explained simply by the fact that the smaller the value of $\theta_0$, the larger the r-f gap voltage required for a given $X$. For $n = 1$ and $\theta_0 = 1\frac{3}{4} \times 2\pi$ (the lowest practical mode), and for $X = 2$, a phase shift of $-0.14$ radians results with a linear reflector field.

The phase shift may be markedly changed in magnitude and sign by the changes in the reflection-field coefficient $a_2$ in other than linear reflectors. A phase shift may also be brought about by other than purely transit-time effects, such as a velocity-dependent absorption or preferential focusing of electrons in the reflection space. The consequences of an amplitude-dependent phase shift are therefore discussed in general terms without immediate reference to any one model.

Any question of mode asymmetry or hysteresis is most easily discussed, as are the questions of the preceding section, in terms of the admittance diagram. The best way of representing the behavior of the electronic transadmittance in the admittance diagram is different for different behaviors. In all the previous applications of the admittance diagram the phase of the electronic transadmittance has been equal to $\phi$ plus a constant. It was, therefore, superfluous to show a series of radii representing the loci of $Y_e$ for constant $\phi$. Even the circles of the $Y_e$-loci for constant $X$ are somewhat superfluous, except that the spacing of these circles indicates the functional dependence of $Y_e$ on $X$. In Fig. 14·1, however, the loci of $Y_e$ at constant $V/V_0$ or $X_n$ have real significance because these loci are no longer simple.

For the present section it is assumed that a high mode ($n \gg 1$) is involved, and the effect considered in Sec. 14·2 may therefore be neglected. Since, by assumption, the dependence of $Y_e$ on $X$ is still the same as in the zero-order theory, the loci of $Y_e$ for constant $X$ are circles. However, the phase of $Y_e$ is not linearly dependent on $\phi$; hence the locus of $Y_e$ at constant $\phi$, which shows how the phase of $Y_e$ depends on $X$, becomes the most basic part of the diagram.

An admittance diagram for an assumed simple dependence of $Y_e$ on $X$ is shown in Fig. 14·3; it is assumed that the phase shift goes to zero for $X = 0$. Two $Y_e$-loci for constant $\phi$ are shown. It may be noted that they have the same shape and may be derived from each other by a simple rotation about the origin; this results from the assumption that the amplitude-dependent phase shift is independent of $\phi$. As is always true of any admittance diagram for a simple resonant circuit, the circuit admittance locus, or "load line," is a straight line parallel to the imagi-

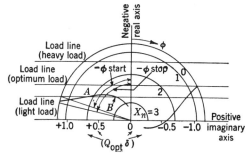

Fig. 14·3.—Admittance diagram for high mode, showing two typical loci of $Y_e$ when phase of $Y_e$ depends on r-f gap voltage as well as on reflection time. Because of this latter assumption the negative real axis is the origin of $\phi$ only for $X_n = 0$.

nary axis, with the circuit susceptance linear in frequency deviation. Such lines corresponding to light, optimum, and heavy load are indicated in Fig. 14·3.

As is also true of any admittance diagram, oscillation can occur for a given $\phi$ only if the electron admittance locus for that value of $\phi$ and the circuit admittance locus intersect at a point so that the condition $Y_e = -Y$ may be met. The resultant amplitude and frequency of oscillation are determined by the amplitude label of this point on the $Y_e$-locus and the frequency label of this point on the $Y$-locus. When this procedure is applied to Fig. 14·3 and the $Y_e$-locus is rotated about the origin (which corresponds to sweeping $\phi$ or reflector voltage), the three modes of Fig. 14·4 emerge.

The reasons for the shapes of these modes are simple. For the light and the optimum load lines it is clear that, as the $Y_e$-locus is rotated clockwise, a rotation corresponding to increasing $\phi$ through the starting-point, the intersection of the $Y_e$-locus moves through the frequency and amplitude scale at a rapid rate because of the changed shape of the $Y_e$-locus. At the other end of the mode a correspondingly diminished rate of change of $X$ and $\delta$ occurs; the result is a mode asymmetry.

For the lightest of the three loads indicated in Fig. 14·3 a new feature occurs. At the lower of the two values of $\phi$ for which a constant-$\phi$ locus of $Y_e$ is shown in Fig. 14·3, there are two points of intersection of the $Y_e$-locus and the

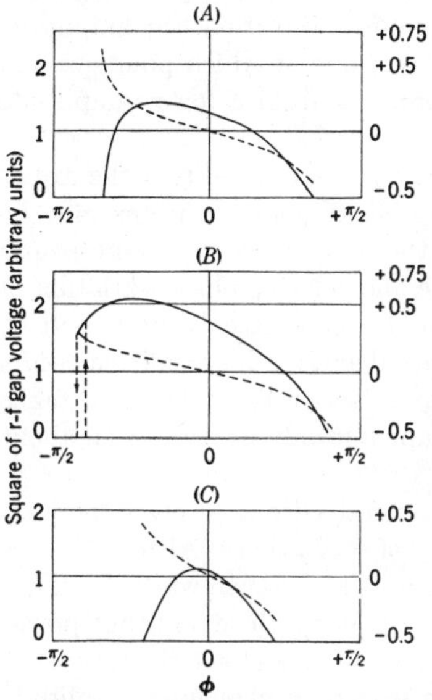

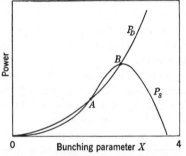

FIG. 14·4.—Dependence of normalized frequency deviation, $Q_{opt}\delta$ (broken curve) and square of r-f gap voltage (continuous curve) on relative reflection transit angle $\phi$, for the three loads of Fig. 14·3. Loads are as follows: $(A)$ optimum load; $(B)$ light load; $(C)$ heavy load.

FIG. 14·5.—Possible dependence on bunching parameter $X$ of $P_D$ (power dissipated in circuit) and $P_S$ (power supplied by electron stream); illustration of system in which stable oscillation may exist (at point $B$) but is not self-starting.

load line. In this situation oscillations are not self-starting. If oscillations exist at point $B$ they are self-sustaining.

These statements are most readily understood with reference to Fig. 14·5. The power dissipated by the circuit, $P_D$, and the power supplied to the circuit by the electron stream, $P_S$, are shown here as functions of the bunching parameter $X$ for the situation just discussed. At point $B$ any tentative overtures made by the oscillator in the direction of an increase in $X$ result in an excess of $P_D$ over $P_S$, an effect that discourages such overtures; any decrease of $X$ below point $B$ results in an invigorating excess of $P_S$ over $P_D$; therefore, point $B$ is, as usual, a point of stable equilibrium. The same line of reasoning shows that any oscillation existing between points $A$ and $B$ will build up to point $B$. Since below point $A$, however, $P_S < P_D$, any oscillation existing here will die down; no oscillation can build up through this region.

This figure makes clear the reason for the hysteresis phenomenon that appears in Fig. 14·4b. During the interval when $\theta_0$ and $\phi$ increase from below the starting point, oscillations are unable to start until the $X = 0$ point in the $Y_e$-locus reaches the load line; but once the oscillation starts it immediately builds up to its equilibrium amplitude. As $\phi$ passes through this same region in the opposite direction, the amplitude of oscillation decreases until $\phi$ reaches the value at which points $A$ and $B$ coalesce, then oscillation drops to zero, but from a lower amplitude than that to which it builds up on the return trip.

*General Properties of Simple Phase-shift Hysteresis.*—From the examples shown in Figs. 14·3 and 14·4 a number of generalizations may be drawn. These generalizations concern the occurrence of hysteresis and associated behavior when the magnitude and relative phase variation of $Y_e$ are arbitrary functions of $X$ but the reflection phase $\theta_0$ enters only in the factor $e^{-i\theta_0}$; in terms of the admittance diagram, this condition occurs when the various constant-$\theta_0$ or constant-$\phi$ loci of $Y_e$ in the admittance diagram differ from each other not in shape but only by a rotation about the origin.

One of the more important of these generalizations involves the relation between output power and frequency of oscillation. Although these quantities will be asymmetrical functions of $\theta_0$ and $\phi$ even when the phase shift is not great enough to cause hysteresis, nevertheless output power *will* be a symmetrical function of frequency. This effect shows up, for example, in Fig. 14·4a in the correlation in rate of change of amplitude and frequency. This effect has its origin in the assumption that the locus of $Y_e$ maintains its shape as it rotates about the origin with $\theta_0$, thus making the contours of constant bunching parameter in the admittance plane circles as in Fig. 14·3. Since the dependence of $X$ on $\delta$ is governed by the values of $X$ and $\delta$ at the intersection of the circles of constant $X$ with the load line, the values of $\phi$ required to bring about this intersection are completely irrelevant to the relation between $X$ and $\delta$.

It is also clear that the lighter the load the greater the tendency to hysteresis. Since circuit conductance $G$ has significance only in relation to the small-signal electronic transconductance $G_e$, at constant load the larger $G_e$ the more hysteresis. Thus the beam voltage $V_0$ will influence hysteresis only by its influence on $G_e$.

Hysteresis will occur at one end of the mode or the other but not at both. If the large-signal bunched beam current is retarded with respect to the small-signal current (as in Fig. 14·3), hysteresis will occur at the high-frequency end of the mode, and vice versa.

*Comparison of Theory and Experiment.*—In many cases simple phase-shift hysteresis is masked or complicated by the multiple-transit hysteresis described in the next section. If careful precautions are taken to avoid multiple transits, as discussed later, hysteresis with the characteristics just discussed may occur.   In Fig. 14·6 is shown a photograph of an oscilloscope trace (retouched with arrows), showing output power (vertical) as the reflector voltage (horizontal) is swept with a sine-wave sweep; also shown are equally spaced frequency markers which indicate

the frequency of oscillation at that point on the output-power trace directly above the frequency marker.   The reflector voltage is increasing and $\phi$ is decreasing to the left.   A sizable hysteresis at the high-frequency end of the mode is shown, with the klystron dropping out of oscillation at about the 20 per cent power point and coming back into oscillation at about the 80 per cent power point on the return sweep.   Although there is a marked asymmetry of mode shape, the curve of power vs. frequency

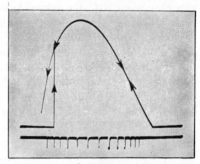

Fig. 14·6.—Oscilloscope photograph, retouched with arrows, showing output power and frequency of oscillation as functions of reflector voltage; absolute value of reflector voltage increasing to left.

plotted from this data and shown in Fig. 14·7 is seen to be symmetrical.

The degree of power-vs-voltage asymmetry occurring in a given mode may be expressed in terms of the differences in reflector voltage between the maximum power point and the two half-power points; more exactly,

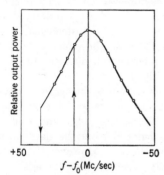

Fig. 14·7.—Relation between output power and frequency deviation $f - f_0$ for the mode of Fig. 14·6.

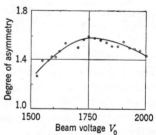

Fig. 14·8.—Observed degree of asymmetry as a function of beam voltage $V_0$, for the same type 2K33 klystron as used in Figs. 14·6, 14·7, and 14·9; $I_0 = 8$ ma, $\lambda = 1.25$ cm.

by "degree of asymmetry" is meant the ratio of the voltage difference between maximum-power and low-frequency half-power points to the voltage difference between maximum-power and high-frequency half-power points.

Observations of this asymmetry similar to those of Fig. 14·6 were made over a range of beam voltages with this same tube, a type 2K33. A summary of the observed asymmetry for constant oscillator loading is presented in Fig. 14·8. These data were taken not at constant electron-gun perveance but at constant beam current; as far as dependence on beam voltage is concerned, the small-signal electronic transconductance is therefore proportional to $M^2/V_0$, which is in turn proportional to $\sin^2(\theta_1/2)$, where $\theta_1$ is the transit angle through the r-f gap. The data in Fig. 14·8 therefore show not only the expected slow dependence of asymmetry on beam voltage, but also suggest that $\theta_1 = \pi$ for $V_0 = 1750$ volts. This value of $\theta_1$ implies an equivalent gap spacing of 0.042 in.

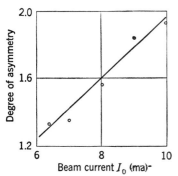

FIG. 14·9.—Observed degree of asymmetry as a function of beam current $I_0$, for the same type 2K33 klystron as used in Figs. 14·6, 14·7, and 14·8; $V_0 = 1800$ volts, $\lambda = 1.25$ cm.

for the operating wavelength of 1.25 cm of the 2K33. Since the r-f gap in the 2K33 is not a grid but simply two opposing 0.028-in. holes in two 0.005-in. copper sheets separated by a spacing of 0.007 in., an equivalent gap spacing of 0.042 in. is not out of line with the construction; the data of Fig. 14·8 probably provide as good an experimental measure of this quantity as can be obtained.

With the same tube, measurements were also made of the dependence of mode asymmetry on beam current at constant load. The asymmetry should decrease rapidly with decreasing beam current because the constant load becomes relatively heavier. This behavior is verified by the data shown in Fig. 14·9.

The type of behavior discussed in this section is thus seen to have a close counterpart in experimental data. In the case of the particular 2K33, for which data is plotted in Figs. 14·6, 14·7, 14·8, and 14·9, the sign and magnitude of the phase shift deduced from the data do not agree with those predicted by bunching theory. However, when this tube is in oscillation, it is experimentally observed that there is an r-f defocusing action causing the interception, by the resonator walls, of many electrons that in the nonoscillating state would be returned through the gap. Since this is a rather sizable amplitude-dependent effect, it is capable of producing the phase shift that is required to produce the observed hysteresis and mode asymmetry.

These data were taken with a 2K33 tube constructed to eliminate the multiple return transits of the electron through the r-f gap. This tube is not typical, for many of the 2K33 tubes show very little hysteresis.

In the next section the behavior produced in the same tubes by multiple transits is described.

**14·4. Bunching Theory for Multiple-transit Electrons.**—To sustain oscillation it is required only that the electrons in a reflex klystron make one return transit through the r-f gap after their initial transit. Unless very careful precautions are taken, however, there will always be some electrons that make more than one return transit in the normal form of reflex klystron. Such electrons are called "multiple-transit" electrons, as distinguished from the "single-transit" electrons that make only one return passage. It should be noted that "multiple" and "single" refer to the number of return transits, not to the total number of transits. Since the number of electrons making multiple return transits is small, it is sufficient for the present purpose to consider only those electrons that, after their first return transit, are reflected from the cathode region for a second return transit. These electrons give rise to a characteristic type of hysteresis that is discussed in the present section.

This stream of multiple-transit electrons leads a complicated life. But whatever the total effect produced on this stream by double velocity modulation, interception of electrons by the cathode, and the complicated d-c potentials through which the electrons pass, this third-transit stream is intensity-modulated and constitutes a driving current for the oscillator circuit. Its presence means that the electronic transadmittance is composed of two components, a single-transit admittance and a multiple-transit admittance.

It might be thought that no appreciable effect could arise from this multiple-transit electron stream, considering the diminutions in intensity produced by grid absorption losses and considering also the fact that the multiple-transit electrons have not received the careful attention provided for the single-transit electrons. This decrease in intensity, however, is counteracted by the fact that the reflection time in the cathode region is usually much longer than that in the reflector region; thus the naively calculated small-signal electronic transconductance $G_e$, which is (at least approximately) proportional to the product of drift time and beam current, may have for the multiple-transit stream a value comparable to that for the single-transit stream. If this is true, then multiple transits may be expected to have an important influence in the small-signal region near the edges of the modes of oscillation.

*Application of Cascade Bunching Theory to Multiple-transit Phenomena.*—The multiple-transit electrons in the reflex klystron are not found in the usual environment for bunching, for many of the electrons that enter the cathode region with a net increase in energy as the result of their two passages through the r-f gap collide with the cathode and are absorbed or cause secondary emission. This effect is best taken into consideration, however, only after discussing the relation that exists between the multiple-transit and single-transit bunched beam currents if the cathode-anode region has the attributes of an ordinary reflector region. When these conditions exist, the cascade-bunching theory of Sec. 9·8 is directly applicable to the calculation of the multiple-transit bunched beam current because it is concerned with the bunching that follows velocity modulation of a beam at two separated r-f gaps. The results of Sec. 9·8 are easily particularized to the present case.

In the application of the results of Sec. 9·8 serious consideration must be given to the questions of sign that are brought up by the fact that, in the present case, there is a single r-f gap with the single-transit and multiple-transit electrons going through it in opposite directions. The fundamental components of the single-transit and multiple-transit bunched beam currents must be considered first; these may be denoted by $i_{11}$ and $i_{12}$ respectively. The former is given, as usual, by Eq. (9.9) with the notation slightly modified as noted above and as in Sec. 9·8:

$$i_{11} = 2I_0 e^{-j\theta_{01}} J_1(X_{12}). \tag{1}$$

For $i_{12}$ any self-consistent sign convention may be adopted; the best convention seems to be the one that allows direct use of the results of Sec. 9·8 without change. If it is assumed that only the fraction $a$ of the single-transit electrons is reflected from the cathode for another transit of the gap, Eq. (9·58) then becomes (with slight modification of notation but with signs unchanged)

$$i_{12} = 2aI_0 e^{-j(\theta_{01}+\theta_{02}-\theta')} J_1(X'). \tag{2}$$

In the interests of self-consistency, the fact that $i_{11}$ and $i_{12}$ are flowing through the same gap in opposite directions must be taken into account by writing the total amount as

$$i_1 = i_{11} - i_{12}. \tag{3}$$

In Sec. 9·8 the complex first and second r-f gap voltages are written

$$V_1 = -j\alpha_1 V_0 \tag{9·49a}$$
$$V_2 = -\alpha_2 V_0 e^{j(-\theta_{01}+\beta)}. \tag{9·49b}$$

Here $\alpha_1 V_0$ and $\alpha_2 V_0$ are the absolute values of $V_1$ and $V_2$; because, in the present case, both refer to the same gap, the notation may be simplified by writing $\alpha_1 = \alpha_2 = \alpha$. In Sec. 9·8 the phase angle $\beta$ was an arbitrary parameter used to specify the relative phases of $V_1$ and $V_2$, and was to be determined in a particular instance by the constraints between $V_1$ and $V_2$.

If it is assumed, in the present case, that $|V_1| = |V_2|$, what is the relative phase of $V_1$ and $V_2$? The sign convention used in Eqs. (1), (2), and (3) must be followed; this is the convention of defining the sign of quantities by reference to the direction of the electron stream concerned. Consequently, $V_1 = -V_2$. Equation (9·49) then indicates that

$$\beta = \theta_{01} - 2\pi(n + \tfrac{3}{4}) + \pi = \phi + \pi. \tag{4}$$

Equation (9·56) for the effective bunching parameter $X'$ and the cascade-bunching phase shaft $\theta'$ then becomes

$$X'e^{i\theta'} = X_{13} + jX_{23}e^{j\phi}. \tag{5}$$

This equation, in conjunction with Eq. (2), completely specifies the multiple-transit current $i_{12}$.

A very convenient approximation may be introduced here. As already noted, this approximation corresponds closely to fact in most reflex klystrons and in particular in the type 2K33, with the performance of which the theory developed is compared. This approximation is given by the expression

$$X_{13} \approx X_{23} \quad \text{and} \quad X_{13} \gg X_{12}; \tag{6}$$

in approximately linear cathode-anode and anode-reflector fields this corresponds to assuming that $\theta_{02} \gg \theta_{01}$. Any inaccuracy in this assumption does not affect the general character of the conclusions that are drawn from these considerations.

The assumption of Eq. (6) simplifies Eq. (5) considerably: with the aid of trigonometric identities,

$$X'e^{i\theta'} \approx X_{13}(1 + je^{j\phi}) = X_{13}\sqrt{2(1 - \sin\phi)}\; e^{j\left(\frac{\phi}{2} + \frac{\pi}{4}\right)},$$

or

$$X' \approx X_{13}\sqrt{2(1 - \sin\phi)}, \tag{7a}$$

$$\theta' \approx \frac{\phi}{2} + \frac{\pi}{4}. \tag{7b}$$

Perhaps the most interesting fact about Eqs. (7) is the dependence of $X'$ on $\phi$. It is apparent that $X'$ increases steadily from almost zero at the high-$\phi$ (low-frequency) end of the mode to a value of approximately $2X_{13}$ at the low-$\phi$ (high-frequency) end of the mode. Thus any effects arising from multiple transits, whatever they may later be found to be in detail, will be much more marked at the high-frequency end of the mode. This result in Eq. (7a) corresponds to a simple physical fact that is illustrated in the partial Applegate diagram of Fig. 14·10. Here are shown the electron trajectories and the r-f fields that the corresponding electrons encounter when they make their initial transit and first return transit of the gap. For the particular case shown, $\theta_0 = 2\pi n$; hence $\phi = +\pi/2$. It is seen that the electrons that were speeded up and slowed down on the initial transit are respectively slowed down and speeded up by almost the same amount on the return transit—that is, the net velocity modulation after the return transit is almost zero, and corresponds to $X' \approx 0$ for $\phi = \pi/2$ in Eq. (7a). A similar line of reasoning for $\phi = 0$ and $\phi = -\pi/2$ shows the initial velocity modulation respectively unaffected and doubled by the return transit; this likewise corresponds to Eq. (7a).

By Eq. (7b), $\theta'$ ranges from 0, for $\phi = -\pi/2$, to $\pi/2$ for $\phi = +\pi/2$; and by Eq. (2), this positive phase shift of $\theta'$ corresponds to a diminution in the transit time of the bunch.

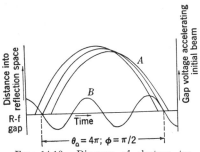

FIG. 14·10.—Diagram of electron trajectories (A) and r-f gap voltage (B) illustrating the almost complete cancellation of initial velocity modulation that occurs, on return transit, for $\phi = \pi/2$.

The immediately preceding comments have been concerned primarily with the values of $X'$ and $\theta'$ for use in Eq. (2) to obtain the current $i_{12}$. Before the application of the resulting value of $i_{12}$ to a determination of oscillator behavior is considered, the subject of cathode interception of electrons during their reflection from the cathode region should be discussed.

*Interception of Speeded-up Electrons by the Cathode Surface.*—It may be thought at first glance that all the electrons entering the cathode region with a velocity exceeding the d-c beam velocity would be absorbed by the cathode. This assumption would be true if all the electron trajectories were normal to the cathode surface. Actually, however, most electrons have some small radial component of velocity perpendicular to the axis of the beam. Therefore at no point in the process of reflection from the cathode do they have zero velocity and zero kinetic energy. As a result any given electron must have a finite amount of energy in excess of the d-c beam energy before it is absorbed. Since this excess energy required for absorption is different for different electron trajectories, therefore cathode-interception effects increase smoothly with the r-f gap voltage until all the speeded-up electrons are intercepted. Interception effects vary also with $\phi$. For example, at the center of the mode most of the electrons of the bunch are slowed down by the maximum r-f voltage and hence are not intercepted at the cathode. It has already been seen that at that mode edge for which $\phi \approx \pi/2$ the original velocity modulation is largely neutralized on the first return transit, whereas for $\phi \approx -\pi/2$ the original velocity modulation is increased. Thus the effects of cathode interception are most marked for the high-frequency edge of the mode, $\phi \approx -\pi/2$.

These effects are two: a diminution in $i_{12}$ because of the smaller number of electrons involved, and a shift in the phase of $i_{12}$ because of the asymmetry of the bunch produced by removing the fast electrons. The fast electrons of the bunch have a longer reflection time than the slow ones, but they start sooner from the gap and under small-signal conditions return sooner than the slow electrons; hence a removal of the fast electrons corresponds to a slowing down of the bunch—an increase in $\theta_{02}$, or a decrease in $\theta'$. Since this effect is most marked for $\phi < 0$, it is an effect of the same sign as the cascade-bunching phase shift described by Eq. (7b). The maximum magnitude of the phase shift produced by absorbing the fast electrons of a bunch is approximately $\pi/4$.

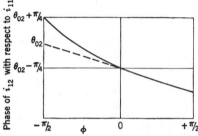

Thus the variation with $\phi$ of the sum-total phase difference between $i_{12}$ and $i_{11}$ is similar to that shown in Fig. 14·11. No analytical expression for the effect of this cathode interception is presented, but its qualitative effects are noted as occasion arises. They do not appear to be important except in a few isolated cases. (The discussion of Fig. 14·15c should be noted as an important example.)

Fig. 14·11.—Approximate dependence on $\phi$ of the phase of $i_{12}$ with respect to $i_{11}$: without cathode interception (broken curve); with cathode interception (continuous curve).

**14·5. Production of Hysteresis by Multiple-transit Electrons.**—The effects of cathode interception may be left for qualitative insertion at a later point, and the total electronic transadmittance may be written with the aid of Eqs. (1), (2), (9·49), and (7). If $G_e$ refers to the usual single-transit small-signal electronic transconductance, then

$$Y_e = -e^{-i\phi}G_e\left[\frac{2J_1(X_{12})}{X_{12}} - \frac{aX_{13}}{X_{12}}\frac{X'}{X_{13}}\frac{2J_1(X')}{X'}\,e^{-j\left(\theta_{02}-\frac{\phi}{2}-\frac{\pi}{4}\right)}\right]. \quad (8)$$

The contribution of the multiple-transit electrons is intentionally expressed in an expanded form in order to emphasize certain points. Thus the amplitude-independent quantity $aX_{13}/X_{12}$, in which $a \ll 1$ and $X_{13}/X_{12} \gg 1$, may of itself be comparable to unity; this argument was previously used in noting the possibility of sizable multiple-transit effects. In turn, the factor $X'/X_{13} \approx \sqrt{2(1 - \sin \phi)}$ is the dominant factor making multiple-transit effects so important at the high-frequency end of the mode.

The factor $2J_1(X')/X'$, while equal to unity for small signals just as is $2J_1(X_{12})/X_{12}$, nevertheless decreases much more rapidly than the latter as $\alpha$ increases because $X_{13} \gg X_{12}$, and hence, usually, $X' \gg X_{12}$.

Consequently at high amplitude

$$\frac{2J_1(X')}{X'} \ll \frac{2J_1(X_{12})}{X_{12}}$$

—that is, the multiple-transit current is easily overbunched and loses its relative influence. Its influence will thus be strongest at small amplitudes when $2J_1(X')/X' = 2J_1(X_{12})/X_{12} = 1$.

Further discussion of Eq. (8) proceeds most easily with the aid of a

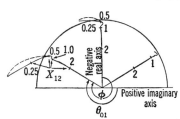

specific example based on the following assumptions: (1) that the electron optics of the cathode region are such that $aX_{13}/X_{12} = 0.25$, (2) that the beam voltage (which determines $\theta_{02}$) has a value such that to the nearest whole cycle $\theta_{02} = 3\pi/4$, and (3) that $X_{13} \approx 7X_{12}$. (This last assumption determines the relative rate of increase of $X'$ and $X_{12}$ with $\alpha$.) In Fig. 14·12 are shown the resulting loci of $Y_e/G_e$ for three different values of $\phi$. The points on the loci that correspond to various values of $X_{12}$ are so indicated.

FIG. 14·12.—Locus of normalized total electronic admittance, $Y_e/G_e$, as a parametric function of $X_{12}$ for $\phi = -60°$, $0$, $+60°$ and for other specialized conditions as described in text. Dotted line indicates the change in $(Y_e/G_e)$-locus introduced by including the effects of cathode interception.

The following points should be observed in Fig. 14·12:

1. The increasing distortion of the loci as the high-frequency (negative-$\phi$) end of the mode is approached.
2. The fact that the distortion produced by multiple transits dies down rapidly with increasing gap voltage or single-transit bunching parameter $X_{12}$.
3. The damped oscillatory variation of the phase of $Y_e$ as $X_{12}$ increases.
4. The change with $\phi$ of the relative angle of the multiple-transit "hook" on the end of the locus.

What effects do cathode interception have on Fig. 14·12? Since the interception is zero for zero gap voltage ($X_{12} = 0$) and then increases to a constant value at a larger value of $X_{12}$, and since the sign of the phase shift is as shown in Fig. 14·11, the net effect is as shown by the dotted lines in Fig. 14·12. Thus, there is no change in the basic character of the $Y_e$-locus produced by the cathode-interception effects.

Some of the finer details of experimentally observed hysteresis are later seen to require, for explanation, reference to some of the finer details of Fig. 14·12. But having shown these several accurate $Y_e$-loci, it is now apparent that, for discussing the basic structure of hysteresis, several simplifications may be made. One important question of basic characteristics that needs to be investigated deals with the variation of multiple-transit hysteresis with $\theta_{02}$, that is, with beam voltage.   For this purpose the $Y_e$-locus may, for ease of handling, be represented by two straight-

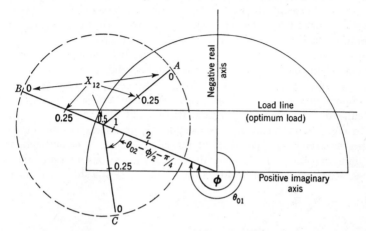

FIG. 14·13.—Admittance diagram showing three idealized total electronic-admittance loci ($A$, $B$, $C$) corresponding to a single value of $\phi$ and three values of $\theta_{02}$.   Compare with Fig. 14·12.

line segments as in Fig. 14·13.   The $X_{12}$-labels at the various points in these segments approximate those of the ($\phi = -60°$)-locus in Fig. 14·12.   The orientation of the segment representing the single-transit admittance depends only on $\theta_{01}$ or $\phi$; the orientation, relative to this segment, of the segment representing the contribution of the multiple-transit admittance depends only on $\theta_{02}$ because the dependence on $\phi$ is minor for small ranges of $\phi$.

Several such $Y_e$-loci for several values of $\theta_{02}$ are shown in Fig. 14·13. By rotating these loci about the origin (corresponding to changing $\phi$) and observing the intersection of the $Y_e$-locus with the load line, the shapes of the modes, the high-frequency ends of which are shown in Fig. 14·14, may be deduced.   These are purely schematic diagrams and no attempt has been made to show the asymmetry introduced into the mode shape; only the starting and stopping conditions are indicated.

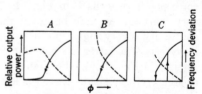

FIG. 14·14.—Schematic representation of the variation with $\phi$ of output power (continuous curves) and frequency deviation (broken curves) on the high-frequency side of a mode.   These three mode shapes correspond to those obtained by rotating the three admittance loci $A$, $B$, and $C$ of Fig. 14·13.

In Figs. 14·13 and 14·14 the two values of $\theta_{02}$ corresponding to the loci $A$ and $C$ correspond roughly to the two extreme mode shapes that will be obtained. With locus $A$, the direction of the frequency change is reversed and a very small amplitude oscillation diminishes gradually over a large range of $\phi$. With locus $C$, both the starting and stopping processes are discontinuous, and the discontinuous stopping occurs at a fairly low amplitude. As $\phi$ is made less negative (locus swinging clockwise) the starting process may at times be uncertain for, during the instant when the end of the locus is on the load line, the amplitude must build up most of the way to its large equilibrium value—at least past the point $A$ in Fig. 14·5. If the rate of sweeping of $\phi$ is too fast, the opportunity may be lost and oscillation may not start at all. This difficulty does not arise with mode $A$ in Fig. 14·13.

In Fig. 14·15 are shown three oscilloscope photographs showing mode shapes occurring in type 2K33 klystrons of an early version that have multiple transits. (For the significance of the various axes and the two traces, see the discussion of Fig. 14·6.) Figure 14·15$a$ shows a mode that

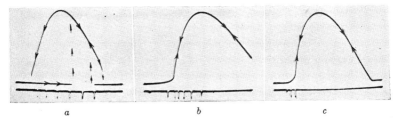

$a$            $b$            $c$

Fig. 14·15.—Oscilloscope photograph of typical mode shapes illustrating multiple-transit hysteresis and associated effects; taken with early model of type 2K33 klystron.

corresponds to locus $C$ in Fig. 14·13. The high-frequency hysteresis is very marked. It may be noted that the high-frequency stopping discontinuity is very slight and that there is also present some low-frequency hysteresis. The latter has not been discussed but may be readily deduced. Figure 14·15$b$ shows the high-frequency tailing-off phenomenon; the existence of oscillation far to the left of the apparent edge of the mode is shown by a faint frequency marker that could not be there unless the klystron were oscillating at that point. Figure 14·15$c$ shows the same phenomenon, but here the frequency-marker arrangement is adjusted to give an indication only at a single frequency rather than at evenly spaced frequency intervals as in the other pictures. It is seen that the same oscillation frequency occurs for three adjacent values of reflector voltage or of $\phi$.

Figures 14·13 and 14·14 predict a frequency-doubling but not such a frequency-tripling at the tailing-off point. However, if the curvature of the multiple-transit segment of the admittance locus, produced by cathode-interception phase shift (see Fig. 14·12), is taken into account, then this frequency-tripling seems explained.

The small low-frequency hysteresis phenomenon has already been noted in Fig. 14·15a. There may also be a low-frequency tailing-off phenomenon similar to that found at high frequencies but not so extended in range of $\phi$ or reflector voltage.

The damped oscillatory behavior of the $Y_e$-locus that occurs in the more exact loci of Fig. 14·12 can give rise, in a fairly obvious manner that will not be discussed in detail, to the mode discontinuities shown in the oscilloscope photograph of Fig. 14·16. These discontinuities, in which the amplitude jumps between two non-zero values, are accompanied by frequency hysteresis. This phenomenon does not

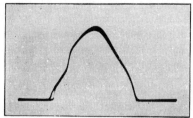

FIG. 14·16.—Oscilloscope photograph showing dependence of output power (vertical) on reflector voltage increasing in absolute value to the left; illustrative of mode irregularities produced by multiple transits.

occur in the variations of hysteresis previously discussed, and in many applications it is obviously more objectionable than amplitude hysteresis.

*Comparison between Multiple-transit Hysteresis and Simple Single-transit Phase-shift Hysteresis.*—Several points of comparison between multiple-transit hysteresis and the pure single-transit phase-shift hysteresis discussed in the previous section now present themselves. For one thing, Figs. 14·12 and 14·13 indicate that with multiple transits there is no single-valued relation between $X_{12}$ (that is, output power) and $Y_e$. From the discussion in Sec. 14·3, it follows that there is no symmetrical relation between power and frequency when the mode asymmetry is introduced by multiple-transit phenomena.

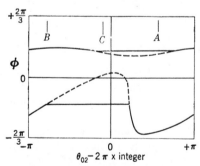

FIG. 14·17.—Dependence on $\theta_{02}$ of the values of $\phi$ at which oscillation begins (broken curves) and stops (continuous curves), calculated for the specific case to which Figs. 14·13 and 14·14 apply.

In the second place, it is apparent from Figs. 14·13 and 14·14 that with multiple transits there is a periodic variation of hysteresis with beam voltage, the frequency of this variation being rapid when the reflection time in the cathode region is a large number of cycles.

One further point: because of the peculiar folded-back form which the $Y_e$-locus assumes for some values of $\theta_{02}$ in the presence of multiple transits, multiple-transit hysteresis is not limited to light loads as is single-transit phase-shift hysteresis. (At least it is not so limited as it is when this phase shift is sizable only for sizable values of $X$.)

The second point above, the periodic variation of multiple-transit hysteresis with beam voltage, is perhaps the most characteristic. Since $\theta_{02}$ also varies with $\lambda$ and since focusing conditions may make it vary with $I_0$, a periodic dependence of multiple-transit hysteresis on these quantities may be expected also. In Fig. 14·17 is shown a calculated dependence on $\theta_{02}$ of the values of $\phi$ at which oscillations start and stop. This curve has been calculated for optimum loading with the numerical values of klystron characteristics that were assumed in constructing Figs. 14·12 and 14·13. These numerical characteristics correspond closely to those of the type 2K33 klystron, with which all the experimental data reproduced in this chapter have been taken. The details of

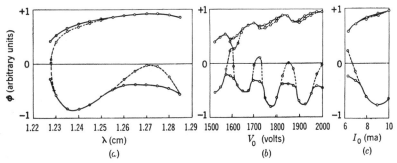

Fig. 14·18.—Variation of mode limits in a type 2K33 reflex klystron with multiple transits; starting point (broken curves) and stopping point (continuous curves). (a) Variation with wavelength, $\lambda$; $V_0 = 1800$ volts, $I_0 = 8$ ma; (b) Variation with voltage, $V_0$; $\lambda = 1.25$ cm, $I_0 = 8$ ma; (c) Variation with beam current, $I_0$; $V_0 = 1800$ volts, $\lambda = 1.25$ cm.

the derivation of Fig. 14·17 are not reproduced here because they follow closely the principles just outlined. The points in Fig. 14·17 that correspond to the three $Y_e$-loci of Fig. 14·13 and the corresponding mode shapes of Fig. 14·14 are indicated.

In Fig. 14·18 is shown the experimentally observed dependence on $V_0$, $\lambda$, and $I_0$ of the mode limits that are predicted in Fig. 14·17. In Fig. 14·18b may be seen the influence of the dependence of $G_e$ on $V_0$. This influence is discussed in the previous section in connection with the dependence of hysteresis on $V_0$ in a 2K33 tube from which multiple transits had been eliminated (see Fig. 14·8).

But such questions of the absolute values of the limits of oscillation shown in Fig. 14·18 are not nearly so interesting as the periodicity, which is apparent. Thus in Fig. 14·18b an increase of $V_0$ by 1.077 or an increase in $\sqrt{V_0}$ (that is, a decrease in $\theta_{02}$) by $1.038 = \frac{27}{26}$ takes the hysteresis through one full cycle. In Fig. 14·18a, a decrease in $\lambda$ from 1.285 cm to 1.230 cm—that is, an increase in $\theta_{02}$ by $1.285/1.230 = \frac{24}{23}$—takes the hysteresis through one complete cycle. These figures are consistent with each other, and with the geometry of the 2K33, in indicating a reflection time from the cathode region of the order of magnitude of twenty-five cycles. Since the reflector mode used in these studies of the 2K33 corresponds to $4\frac{3}{4}$ cycles reflection-time in the reflector region, the origin of some of the numbers used as bases for Figs. 14·12 and 14·13 is perhaps now more clear.

*The Elimination of Multiple Transits.*—It is thus seen that, although it may not produce a completely ideal mode, the elimination of multiple transits goes a long way toward clearing up the mode. The mode shown in Fig. 14·6 is a somewhat extreme sample of (presumably) single-transit phase-shift hysteresis in the 2K33, whereas the modes of Figs. 14·15 and 14·16 are mild compared with some of those produced by multiple transits. Furthermore, in most reflex tubes with grids in the r-f gap, there is not the possibility of the r-f focusing effect, which probably causes phase-shifting in the (gridless) 2K33. Thus the question of elimination of multiple transits is an important one.

The elimination in multiple transits is primarily an electron-optical problem. A satisfactory procedure, which was used by the Bell Telephone Laboratories in the type 726 klystron, and which was applied by the Raytheon Manufacturing Company to the 2K33, consists of placing a spike in the middle of the reflector to distort the reflection field in such a manner that a force is exerted on the electrons radially outward from the axis of the beam. The resulting divergence of the beam, although not enough to prevent the return of the electrons through the r-f gap, is enough to prevent another reflection from the cathode. There are, of course, refinements to the procedure, but this is the essence of the method, and the fact that it has been very successful in eliminating hysteresis further verifies the multiple-transit hypothesis concerning the origin of most hysteresis.

CHAPTER 15

## LOAD EFFECTS IN REFLEX KLYSTRONS

By J. B. H. KUPER

**15·1. Introduction.**—Up to this point the reflex klystron oscillator has been considered in terms of the rather simple equivalent circuit shown in Fig. 15·1a, which contains a gap (or pair of grids) represented by the capacitance $C$, the electronic admittance $Y_e$, the conductance $G_R$ and susceptance $B_R$ of the rest of the resonator, and the load admittance $Y_L$. This circuit is adequate for discussion of the electronics of the device and the major features of its practical behavior under load, but for predictions of engineering accuracy it will be necessary to use the more detailed circuit of Fig. 15·1b.

Here there is an output coupling device that may be a stepdown transformer. Physically, this might be a coupling loop inserted in a cavity or a coupling aperture between the cavity and a waveguide. This coupling will generally have appreciable losses. In a typical tube, the 2K25 or 723A/B, the output consists of a coupling loop to a coaxial line (which has a glass bead for the vacuum seal) and an antenna to excite a waveguide. A detailed analysis of such a device would be very

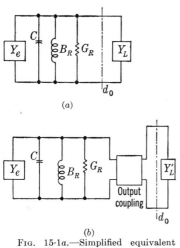

(a)

(b)

Fig. 15·1a.—Simplified equivalent circuit for reflex oscillator.
Fig. 15·1b.—Simplified equivalent circuit including an output coupling that may have losses.

tedious and fortunately it is unnecessary except for the actual designing of a tube. Even then it is necessary only to insure that the behavior of the coupling is fairly smooth over the contemplated frequency range. The load is now designated as $Y_L'$ to call attention to the fact that it is measured in waveguide or a coaxial line rather than referred to the gap.

Fortunately, a fairly simple measurement procedure, commonly known as "cold test" since the tube under test is not oscillating, will permit determination of the properties of the output coupler and of the

404

resonator with the exception of the "capacitance" $C$.  Depending on the construction of the tube, this parameter may be measured at low frequency, computed from the geometry, or estimated from the dimensions of the cavity and the resonant frequency (see Chap. 4).

Another type of test, in which the tube is in active operation, is required to obtain information on power output, frequency, and electronic tuning range as functions of load.  This information is commonly plotted in the form of contours on a circle diagram or Smith[1] chart, and is often referred to as a Rieke diagram.

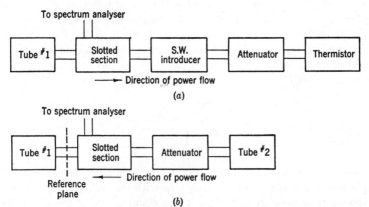

FIG. 15·2.—Block diagrams of apparatus for making (*a*) active tests (Rieke diagrams) or (*b*) cold tests.

Block diagrams of the apparatus required for active and cold tests are shown in Fig. 15·2.  The use of a spectrum analyzer for standing-wave measurements is a considerable convenience but not essential; any calibrated detector and frequency meter can be substituted.

In the succeeding sections methods of making these tests and their interpretation are discussed in detail, and the problem of avoiding discontinuous frequency jumps in the presence of a high-$Q$ load such as a reference cavity is treated briefly.

**15·2. Basis of the Cold Test.**—The theory of the cold test has been discussed by Slater.[2]  In Fig. 15·2*b*, the tube under test, Tube 1, is inoperative and power is supplied from another source indicated as Tube 2, which may or may not be of the same type.  Power is fed to the

[1] P. H. Smith, "Transmission Line Calculator," *Electronics*, **12**, 29 (1939); "An Improved Transmission Line Calculator," *Electronics*, **17**, 130 (1944).

[2] J. C. Slater, "Operation and Testing of Reflex Oscillators," RL Report No. 742, June 18, 1945.  The treatment of the cold test in this chapter, in general, follows that of Slater, with some minor changes.  See also J. C. Slater, "Microwave Electronics," *Rev. Mod. Phys.*, **18**, 441 (1946).

left, as indicated by the arrows, from the auxiliary source through an attenuator whose chief function is to decouple the source from the measuring equipment. The slotted section is used to measure impedances, referred to some plane indicated by the vertical dotted line, at various frequencies in the region in which Tube 1 would oscillate if active.

The method of analysis is independent of the particular type of output transformer used and depends only on the existence of a resonant cavity coupled to an output transmission line. The first problem is to consider the input impedance looking into the cavity across an arbitrary plane in the vicinity of the slotted section as a function of frequency.

*Impedance of a Lossless Cavity.*—If the special case of a cavity with no surface resistance losses and no electron loading, so that the impedance is purely reactive, is considered first, it can be shown perfectly generally[1] that the impedance looking into the cavity to the left across an arbitrary plane can be written in the form

$$\overleftarrow{Z} = \sum_n \frac{Z_n}{j\left(\dfrac{\omega}{\omega_n} - \dfrac{\omega_n}{\omega}\right)}. \tag{1}$$

The sum is taken over the infinite number of normal modes of the cavity. These modes are the natural oscillations with the output open-circuited at the plane of measurements; for if $\omega$ is equal to one of the $\omega_n$'s so one of the denominators vanishes, $\overleftarrow{Z}$ will be infinite. The $Z_n$'s are constants whose significance is discussed later. It is most convenient to express impedances in terms of the characteristic impedance of the measuring line so that $\overleftarrow{Z}$ and the $Z_n$'s are dimensionless and not affected by any conventions that may be involved in defining impedance (as in waveguide).

It is assumed that one of the resonant frequencies $\omega_n$ refers to the mode of particular interest, and that all other modes are widely separated from it. This assumption is safe for ordinary reflex oscillator cavities, provided that the transmission line out to the point of measurement is not too long. For a long line, coupling between cavity and line may result in modes that are close together. Let the particular resonant frequency of interest be $\omega_0$. Then for frequencies in this neighborhood, Eq. (1) can be written

$$\overleftarrow{Z} = \frac{Z_0}{j\left(\dfrac{\omega}{\omega_0} - \dfrac{\omega_0}{\omega}\right)} + Z_1, \tag{2}$$

[1] J. C. Slater, "Forced Oscillations in Cavity Resonators," RL Report No. 118, December 31, 1942.

where

$$Z_1 = \sum_{n \neq 0} \frac{Z_n}{j \left( \dfrac{\omega}{\omega_n} - \dfrac{\omega_n}{\omega} \right)}.$$

For small variations of $\omega$ around $\omega_0$, $Z_1$ will vary only slowly with frequency. Each individual term of $Z_1$ will be much smaller than the resonance term of Eq. (2), since the denominators do not approach zero, but the sum is finite. The quantity $Z_1$ represents the input reactance of the transmission line alone when the cavity is off resonance.[1]

*Choice of Reference Plane.*—By proper choice of the plane of measurements, $Z_1$ can be eliminated. Suppose first that the resonance term in Eq. (2) is eliminated by detuning the cavity without disturbing the transmission-line term $Z_1$, as can be done experimentally to a high degree of accuracy. Then $Z_1$ will vary as the plane of reference is moved along the line in the familiar manner—that is, the standing-wave ratio will be infinite, and

$$Z_1 = j \tan \frac{2\pi(d - d_0)}{\lambda_g}. \tag{3}$$

In this expression $d$ is the distance along the line from the cavity to the plane at which the impedance is measured, $d_0$ is the position of one of the standing-wave minima or zero impedance planes, and $\lambda_g$ is the wavelength in the guide or transmission line. If $Z_1$ is known as a function of wavelength across a particular plane $d$, Eq. (3) can be used to determine $d_0$ as a function of $\lambda_g$. Of course, there will be a number of values of $d_0$, a half guide wavelength apart, that will satisfy Eq. (3) equally well. Further, if one of the planes $d_0$ is chosen as the reference plane for all measurements, the $Z_1$ term in Eq. (2) will vanish, and the analysis is considerably simplified at the price of introducing a moving coordinate system in the standing-wave measurements.

*Inclusion of Losses.*—If the planes of reference $d_0$ are used, the impedance looking into the cavity (lossless) will be

$$\overleftarrow{Z}_{(d_0)} = \frac{Z_0}{j \left( \dfrac{\omega}{\omega_0} - \dfrac{\omega_0}{\omega} \right)}. \tag{4}$$

[1] Some authors immediately identify the reactance $Z_1$ with $j\omega L_1$ (suitably transformed) where $L_1$ is the inductance of the output loop; here the attempt is to use only quantities readily obtainable from external measurements. Both procedures are equally valid.

The behavior of a real (i.e., lossy) cavity can be represented in terms of a complex frequency[1] $\omega$ given by the equation

$$j\left(\frac{\omega}{\omega_0} - \frac{\omega_0}{\omega}\right) + \frac{1}{Q} = 0.$$
(5)

Provided that $Q$ is not too small it can be shown that this expression is equivalent to the definition of $Q$ as $2\pi \times \dfrac{\text{energy stored}}{\text{energy dissipated per cycle}}$.

It is also true (from considerations of continuity) that if a transmission line is broken at any plane *without disturbing the current or voltage* the impedances looking in the two directions from the plane will be given by $\overleftarrow{Z} + \overrightarrow{Z} = 0$.

Suppose that the cavity has no internal losses but is loaded by a matched output line. Then $\overrightarrow{Z}_{(d_0)} = 1$ and hence $\overleftarrow{Z}_{(d_0)} = -1$, and Eq. (4) reduces to

$$j\left(\frac{\omega}{\omega_0} - \frac{\omega_0}{\omega}\right) + Z_0 = 0.$$
(6)

It is customary to define the $Q$ of a circuit loaded only by a matched output as the "external $Q$," $Q_{\text{ext}}$. By comparison of Eqs. (5) and (6), it is evident that

$$\frac{1}{Q_{\text{ext}}} = Z_0.$$
(7)

Similarly, the internal losses in the cavity may be represented by the "unloaded $Q$," $Q_0$. This is the $Q$ obtained when the load is open-circuited. Equation (4) may now be rewritten

$$\overleftarrow{Z}_{(d_0)} = \frac{1/Q_{\text{ext}}}{j\left(\dfrac{\omega}{\omega_0} - \dfrac{\omega_0}{\omega}\right) + \dfrac{1}{Q_0}},$$
(8)

which obviously satisfies the special cases of matched load, $\overrightarrow{Z}_{(d_0)} = 1$, and open circuit, $\overrightarrow{Z}_{(d_0)} = \infty$.

By choosing the reference plane $d_0$ the reactive part of $Z_1$ can be made to vanish, but in any real device there will be a finite resistive term remaining to make the observed standing-wave ratio $\sigma_1$ less than infinity. Ordinarily this loss will be small, but in special cases it may be of considerable importance. It can conveniently be included by adding a term $\sigma_1$ to Eq. (8).

---

[1] The concept of a complex frequency to represent a damped wave is convenient although perhaps unfamiliar. For if $\omega = \beta + j\alpha$ then a disturbance

$$Ae^{j\omega t} = Ae^{j(\beta + j\alpha)t} = Ae^{-\alpha t}e^{j\beta t}.$$

*Effect of Electron Beam.*—Finally, although strictly speaking there will be no electron beam in a cold test, it may be desirable to include the effects of a beam to allow for conditions when the reflector voltage is set outside the oscillation range of a mode. The beam admittance

$$Y_e = -2G_e \frac{J_1(X)}{X} e^{-j\left(\theta + \frac{\pi}{2}\right)}$$

may be included by adding a term in the denominator of Eq. (8) of the form $Y_e/C\omega_0$. The justification for this is as follows. Let $Y_e = g + jb$ and consider for a moment only the conductance. Then $C\omega_0/g$ would be the $Q$ of the resonator loaded only by the beam conductance, here assumed positive—that is, reflector voltage set roughly midway between two oscillating modes. This expression would be analogous to that for $Q_0$, which could be written (referring to Fig. 15·1a) as $C\omega_0/G_R$. It can also be shown that the imaginary part of $Y_e$ predicts the electronic tuning effects correctly.

The final expression for the oscillator cavity is thus

$$\overleftarrow{Z}_{(d_0)} = \frac{1/Q_{\text{ext}}}{j\left(\dfrac{\omega}{\omega_0} - \dfrac{\omega_0}{\omega}\right) + \dfrac{1}{Q_0} + \dfrac{Y_e}{C\omega_0}} + \sigma_1. \tag{9}$$

This expression can be used not only as the basis of a cold test *but also* to predict active behavior. In a true cold test the $Y_e$ term will vanish.

**15·3. Cold-test Procedure.**—In making a test it is customary to record the locations of the standing-wave minima, designated here as the planes $d$, and the standing-wave voltage ratio $\sigma$.

The impedance looking into the resonant cavity across the plane $d$ of the standing-wave minimum is

$$\overleftarrow{Z}_{(d)} = \frac{1}{\sigma}. \tag{10}$$

Then the impedance across the plane $d_0$ is

$$\overleftarrow{Z}_{(d_0)} = \frac{\dfrac{1}{\sigma} - j \tan \dfrac{2\pi(d - d_0)}{\lambda_g}}{1 - \dfrac{1}{\sigma} j \tan \dfrac{2\pi(d - d_0)}{\lambda_g}}. \tag{11}$$

It is often more convenient to introduce the complex reflection coefficient **r** defined by the equations

$$\overleftarrow{r}_{(d)} = \frac{1/\sigma - 1}{1/\sigma + 1} = \frac{1 - \sigma}{1 + \sigma}$$

$$\overleftarrow{r}_{(d_0)} = \frac{\overleftarrow{Z}_{(d_0)} - 1}{\overleftarrow{Z}_{(d_0)} + 1}. \tag{12}$$

Now the reflection coefficients $\overset{\leftarrow}{\mathbf{r}}_{(d)}$ and $\overset{\leftarrow}{\mathbf{r}}_{(d_0)}$ are related by the equation

$$\overset{\leftarrow}{\mathbf{r}}_{(d_0)} = \overset{\leftarrow}{\mathbf{r}}_{(d)} e^{j4\pi\frac{d-d_0}{\lambda_g}}. \qquad (13)$$

The familiar circle diagram or Smith chart is actually a plot of $\overset{\leftarrow}{\mathbf{r}}_{(d_0)}$ in the complex plane. In practice, the transformation from the plane $d$ to plane $d_0$ is made with the aid of a circular transmission-line calculator[1] rather than by computation with Eq. (11).

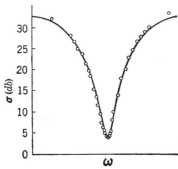

FIG. 15·3.—Typical cold test data, $\sigma$ (db) vs. frequency.

*Determination of Output Line Losses.*—As indicated above, the first step is to determine both $\sigma$ and $d_0$, with the cavity detuned, as functions of frequency in the region of interest. Since it is to be expected that $d_0$ will change rather rapidly with frequency, careful measurements are essential here. With the cavity sufficiently detuned, Eq. (9) reduces to $\mathbf{Z}_{(d_0)} = \sigma_1$. Standing-wave ratios are usually measured in decibels using the attenuator on a spectrum analyzer; conversion of standing-wave measurements in db to voltage ratios is to be made by the relation

$$\sigma_1(\mathrm{db}) = 20 \log_{10}\frac{1}{\sigma_1}. \qquad (14)$$

In an actual tube with a well-designed output line, $\sigma_1(\mathrm{db})$ may be about 35 db, corresponding to a $\sigma_1$ of 0.018.

*Determination of Cavity Parameters.*—The next step is to retune the cavity to the frequency at which measurements are to be made. Remembering that in a cold test $Y_e$ is zero, and hence $C$ cannot be determined, the remaining quantities in Eq. (9), $\omega_0$, $Q_0$, and $Q_{\mathrm{ext}}$, can be found. The most accurate way to determine these is by a plot of the standing-wave ratio in db, $\sigma(\mathrm{db})$, as a function of frequency throughout the resonance curve of the cavity. A typical plot of this sort appears in Fig. 15·3.

If the value of $\overset{\leftarrow}{\mathbf{Z}}_{(d_0)}$ at resonance is defined as $\sigma_0$, from Eq. (9) it is evident that

$$\sigma_0 \equiv \overset{\leftarrow}{\mathbf{Z}}_{(d_0)_0} = \frac{Q_0}{Q_{\mathrm{ext}}} + \sigma_1. \qquad (15)$$

[1] For example, the calculator manufactured by the Emeloid Co., Inc., 287 Laurel Ave., Arlington, N.J.

Since the quantity $\sigma_0$ may be greater or less than unity, two cases must be distinguished. In Case 1, the standing-wave maximum at resonance is found at $d_0$ and $\sigma_0$ is greater than unity; in Case 2, the coupling is weak, $\sigma_0$ is less than unity, and the standing-wave minimum will occur at $d_0$ as in the detuned case. The standing-wave ratio at resonance in db, called $\sigma_0(\text{db})$, is given by

$$\left.\begin{aligned} \sigma_0(\text{db}) &= 20 \log_{10} \sigma_0, &\quad \text{Case 1,} \\ \sigma_0(\text{db}) &= 20 \log_{10} \frac{1}{\sigma_0}, &\quad \text{Case 2.} \end{aligned}\right\} \tag{16}$$

Thus the ratio $Q_0/Q_{\text{ext}}$, and $\omega_0$ may be determined by measurements at resonance. To separate $Q_0$ and $Q_{\text{ext}}$, however, it is necessary to observe more of the resonance curve.

First let the abbreviation

$$\delta = Q_{\text{ext}}\left(\frac{\omega}{\omega_0} - \frac{\omega_0}{\omega}\right) \approx 2Q_{\text{ext}}\left(\frac{\omega - \omega_0}{\omega_0}\right) \tag{17}$$

be introduced, and Eq. (15) be rearranged to read

$$\frac{Q_0}{Q_{\text{ext}}} = \sigma_0 - \sigma_1.$$

If this equation is substituted in Eq. (9), there is obtained

$$\overleftarrow{\mathbf{Z}}_{(d_0)} = \frac{1}{j\delta + \dfrac{1}{\sigma_0 - \sigma_1}} + \sigma_1 \tag{18}$$

for the cold test. With Eqs. (12) and (18), a reflection coefficient can be written with a magnitude given by

$$|\overleftarrow{\mathbf{r}}| = \sqrt{\frac{(\sigma_1 - 1)^2(\sigma_0 - \sigma_1)^2\delta^2 + (\sigma_0 - 1)^2}{(\sigma_1 + 1)^2(\sigma_0 - \sigma_1)^2\delta^2 + (\sigma_0 + 1)^2}}. \tag{19}$$

Since $\sigma = (1 + |\mathbf{r}|)/(1 - |\mathbf{r}|)$ it is evident that, given $\sigma_1$ and $\sigma_0$, a curve of $\sigma$ as a function of $\delta$ can be constructed. Given an experimental curve such as that in Fig. 15·3, from which $\omega_0$, $\sigma_0$, and $\sigma_1$ can be read off, a possible procedure is to compute a theoretical curve of $\sigma(\text{db})$ as a function of $\delta$ and then to choose $Q_{\text{ext}}$ to give the horizontal scale in best agreement with experiment.

This procedure, although best from the standpoint of accuracy, is not often justified. Instead it is customary to determine the width of the resonance curve at some properly chosen value of $\sigma$, and thus to find $Q_0$ or $Q_{\text{ext}}$. In Case 1 it is convenient to take the width of the resonance curve between points $\delta = \pm 1$.  Then from Eq. (17)

$$\frac{\Delta f}{f} = \frac{1}{Q_{\text{ext}}}, \qquad (\text{Case 1}) \qquad (20)$$

where $\Delta f$ is the frequency difference between the two points at which $|\delta| = 1$.  These points come at a height $\sigma'(\text{db})$ on the resonance curve,

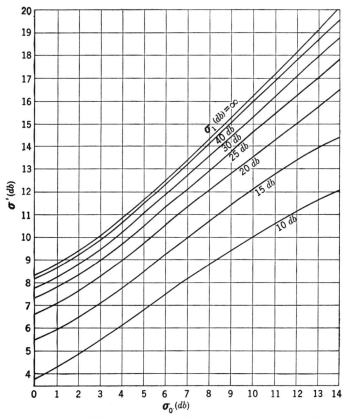

FIG. 15·4.—$\sigma'(\text{db})$ as function of $\sigma_0(\text{db})$ for various values of $\sigma_1$ db).

which can be computed from Eq. (19) as a function of $\sigma_0$ with $\sigma_1(\text{db})$ as a parameter, and using $\delta = 1$.  Curves computed in this way, for $\sigma_1(\text{db})$ between 10 and $\infty$, over the range of $\sigma_0(\text{db})$ up to 14 are given in Fig. 15·4.  In Case 2 it would be possible to find a value of $\sigma'(\text{db})$ such that Eq. (20) would apply, but this would involve taking the width of the curve so near the minimum that precision would be low.  Instead, it is more convenient to use the curves of Fig. 15·4 to find a value of $\sigma'(\text{db})$ corresponding to the observed $\sigma_0(\text{db})$ and $\sigma_1(\text{db})$ and then to ask where this value of $\Delta f/f$ leads. In this case, $\sigma_0$ is less than unity so that the curves of Fig. 15·4 give the value of $\sigma_1$(db) (with $\delta = \pm 1$) for which the reflection coefficient is given by

$$\overleftarrow{|\mathbf{r}|} = \sqrt{\frac{(\sigma_1 - 1)^2(1/\sigma_0 - \sigma_1)^2 + (1/\sigma_0 - 1)^2}{(\sigma_1 + 1)^2(1/\sigma_0 - \sigma_1)^2 + (1/\sigma_0 + 1)^2}}. \tag{21}$$

If numerator and denominator inside the radical are multiplied by $\sigma_0^2$, this equation may be written

$$\overleftarrow{|\mathbf{r}|} = \sqrt{\frac{(\sigma_1 - 1)^2(\sigma_0 - \sigma_1)^2\delta'^2 + (\sigma_0 - 1)^2}{(\sigma_1 + 1)^2(\sigma_0 - \sigma_1)^2\delta'^2 + (\sigma_0 - 1)^2}} \tag{22}$$

where

$$\delta' = \frac{1 - \sigma_0\sigma_1}{\sigma_0 - \sigma_1}. \tag{23}$$

By the use of Eqs. (15) and (17) it is evident that in Case 2 the width $\Delta f$ of the resonance curve at the height $\sigma'$(db) given by Fig. 15·4 is

$$\frac{\Delta f}{f} = \frac{1 - \sigma_0\sigma_1}{Q_0} \qquad \text{(Case 2)}. \tag{24}$$

Now it has been shown that the quantities $d_0$, $\sigma_1$, $\omega_0$, $Q_{\text{ext}}$, and $Q_0$ can all be determined by cold-test measurements. The only quantity pertaining to the resonator that cannot be determined in this way is the capacitance $C$, as was mentioned above. Although the details of the output coupling device remain completely unspecified, its effect on the behavior of the oscillator can be interpreted fully in terms of $d_0$, $\sigma_1$, and $Q_{\text{ext}}$. In designing a tube to cover a broad frequency band it would be necessary to consider in greater detail the nature of the output device; the problem is largely one of getting reasonable constancy of $Q_{\text{ext}}$ over the band in question.[1]

*Thermal Effects and Beam Loading.*—Before closing discussion on the subject of cold tests it is well to point out that in these experiments the tubes are literally, as well as figuratively, cold. This will have noticeable effects in general on $\omega_0$ and $Q_0$. Because of imperfect temperature compensation, $\omega_0$ will be appreciably different for a cold tube than for the same one at operating temperatures. Also, the resistivity of the cavity walls will increase with the temperature, and $Q_0$ will decrease somewhat from this cause. In addition to this purely thermal effect, it is to be expected that loading by the beam and by secondaries ejected from the grids will markedly decrease $Q_0$ in an operating tube. In

[1] A more complete discussion of this aspect of the problem, with particular application to the 2J51 magnetron, is given in J. C. Slater, "Cold Test Results on 2J51 and 725A Magnetrons," BTL Technical Memorandum, 44-180-3, Oct. 26, 1944.

principle it is possible to arrive at a more realistic $Q_0$ by making a "cold" test with a beam passing through the tube but with the reflector voltage adjusted to one of the special values ($\phi = \pm 90°$) between oscillating modes.

**15·4. Active Operation; the Ideal Rieke Diagram.**[1]—A distinctive feature of the cold tests outlined in the preceding sections is the use of a moving coordinate system, referred to the planes $d_0$, for expressing the results. Although this approach causes a welcome simplification of the expressions leading to determination of the cavity parameters, for tubes in active operation the problem is to predict the power (and frequency) delivered to various loads at a fixed physical distance from the oscillator. Thus it would be simple to equate $\overset{\leftarrow}{\mathbf{Z}}_{(d_0)}$ as given by Eq. (9) to $-\overset{\rightarrow}{\mathbf{Z}}_{(d_0)}$, where the latter is the load impedance referred to $d_0$, and obtain expressions for the power and frequency, but it would turn out to be troublesome always to have to refer loads to the moving plane $d_0$. For this reason it seems best to return to first principles—that is, the concepts of elementary reflex klystron theory (see Chap. 12) and the circuits of Fig. 15·1. At this time it is also convenient to shift from the use of impedances as in the preceding sections to admittances, which indeed might perfectly well have been used throughout.

*Behavior of Tube with Load Located at Gap.*—At the outset consider the load admittance $Y_L$ of Fig. 15·1a as located not in the output line but directly across the gap $C$. When the load is so situated the fundamental equation is

$$Y_e + j\omega C + jB_R + G_R + Y_L = 0 \tag{25}$$

where as usual

$$Y_e = -2G_e \frac{J_1(X)}{X} e^{-j\left(\theta + \frac{\pi}{2}\right)}.$$

In Chap. 12 and particularly in Sec. 12·2 the implications of this equation are discussed and it is shown that the real and imaginary parts yield the power and frequency respectively. These parts are

$$-2G_e \frac{J_1(X)}{X} \cos\left(\theta + \frac{\pi}{2}\right) + G_R + G_L = 0 \tag{26}$$

and

$$2G_e \frac{J_1(X)}{X} \sin\left(\theta + \frac{\pi}{2}\right) + \omega C + B_R + B_L = 0. \tag{27}$$

In computing power output, Eq. (26) is to be solved for $X$ and the value obtained substituted in

[1] J. C. Slater, "Operation and Testing of Reflex Oscillators," RL Report No. 742, June 18, 1945; J. B. H. Kuper and M. C. Waltz, "Notes on Load Effects in Reflex Oscillators," RL Report No. 717, May 29, 1945.

$$P_L = \frac{G_L}{G_L + G_R} \cdot \frac{2kI_0V_0}{\theta_e} XJ_1(X) \cos\left(\theta + \frac{\pi}{2}\right). \tag{28}$$

The frequency equation can be simplified by writing $\omega = \omega_0 + \Delta\omega$, where $\omega_0$ is the resonant frequency of the cavity alone.[1]   Then

$$B_R = -\frac{\omega_0 C}{1 + \dfrac{\Delta\omega}{\omega_0}} \approx -\omega_0 C + C\,\Delta\omega.$$

This approximation is safe for the high-$Q$ cavities generally employed. Equation (26) can also be used to eliminate the term involving $X$, resulting in

$$(G_R + G_L)\tan\left(\theta + \frac{\pi}{2}\right) + 2C\,\Delta\omega + B_L = 0. \tag{29}$$

In all these expressions the angle $\left(\theta + \dfrac{\pi}{2}\right)$ may be replaced by $\phi$.

Inspection of these expressions shows that the Rieke diagram for the tube having a load $Y_L = G_L + jB_L$ referred to the gap is extremely simple.   If rectangular coordinates are used for $B_L$ and $G = G_R + G_L$, the power contours will be straight lines parallel to the imaginary axis. These contours will be included between the values $G = G_R(G_L = 0)$ and $G = G_e \cos \phi$, on both of which the power output will be zero.   At $G = G_R$ the r-f voltage developed will be high but the circuit efficiency vanishes; at the other boundary the circuit efficiency will approach its maximum but because of overloading the r-f voltage will fall to zero.   Between these limiting values the power contours will be distributed in accordance with Eqs. (26) and (28).   The frequency contours will also be a family of straight lines equally spaced and making an angle $-\phi$ with the real axis.   The contour $\omega = \omega_0$ will cut the real axis at $G_R + G_L = 0$ (outside the region of oscillation), and $\Delta\omega$ for the other contours will be $-\dfrac{B_0}{2C}$, where $B_0$ is the intercept on the imaginary axis.

Figure 15·5 is a sample of this sort of diagram drawn for a hypothetical tube.   The small-signal conductance $G_e$ is taken as 500 $\mu$mhos, $G_R$ as 100 $\mu$mhos, and $C$ as 1 $\mu\mu$f.   This diagram assumes $\phi = +30°$, or reflector voltage somewhat less negative than optimum for the mode in use. The operating region is bounded on one side by $G = G_R = 100\ \mu$mhos, where the circuit efficiency is zero, and on the other by $G = G_e \cos 30°$, where oscillations cease because of overload.   The power contours between these boundaries are labelled in per cent of the maximum power output obtainable.   Note that loading for output reasonably close to the maximum is not particularly critical.   The frequency contours are

[1] Note that $\Delta\omega$ does not have the same meaning here as in Chap. 12.

labelled in Mc/sec shifts from the resonant frequency of the unperturbed cavity, and are drawn at 5-Mc/sec intervals.

*Deviations from the Ideal in Practical Diagrams.*—Aside from the obvious difficulty of there being no simple way of taking a diagram for a real tube under the conditions postulated here, there are several points in which a practical diagram would depart significantly from the simple one of Fig. 15·5. Chief among these is the assumption that the circuit efficiency can be represented by $\dfrac{G_L}{G_L + G_R}$ with no dependence on load susceptance. In any physical tube there will be losses in the output lead as represented by $\sigma_1$ in the preceding sections. With highly reac-

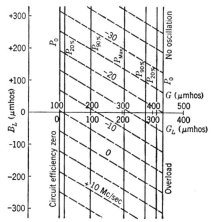

FIG. 15·5.—Ideal Rieke diagram in *B-G* plane for a hypothetical tube with load connected directly across the gap. $G_e = 500\ \mu\text{mhos}$, $G_R = 100\ \mu\text{mhos}$, $C = 1\ \mu\mu\text{f}$, $\phi = +30°$, $G = G_R + G_L$.

tive loads there will be, in general, a large standing wave in the output line that will greatly increase the importance of such small losses. This will distort Fig. 15·5 by drawing the power contours together at the top and bottom of the diagram with the result that the region of oscillation no longer extends to infinity. The second point of departure is the fact that it would be very difficult to keep a constant phase angle $\phi$ of the returning electrons while taking a diagram. Since the frequency will be changing because of the "pulling" effect of the load susceptance, it would be necessary to readjust the reflector voltage continually while taking the diagram. For the special condition of $\phi = 0$ it might be possible so to readjust the voltage, but in a case such as that considered here with $\phi = +30°$, it would almost be necessary to have all the information obtainable from the Rieke diagram in order to know how to set the voltage. The effect of keeping a constant reflector voltage would be to change $\phi$ by an amount

$$\Delta\phi = \left(\frac{\Delta\omega}{\omega_0}\right) \cdot 2\pi \left(n + \frac{3}{4}\right) \tag{30}$$

and to rotate the frequency contours accordingly so they would no longer be parallel.

*Change to Circle Diagram Representation.*—Before considering in detail the distortions of the ideal diagram, it is convenient to change from the

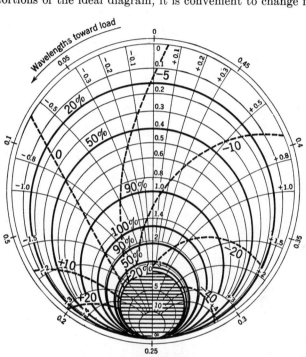

Fig. 15·6.—Ideal Rieke diagram in circle-diagram form for the same hypothetical tube as in Fig. 15·5. In Figs. 15·6 to 15·13 the power contours are shown as solid lines and the frequency contours as broken lines. The coordinates are conductance and susceptance.

rectangular coordinates for the admittance plane to the circle-diagram representation. The rectangular plot is the natural one to use at low frequencies where load impedances are measured on a bridge and line lengths are small in terms of wavelengths. At microwave frequencies, however, the impedances or admittances will, in general, not be measured directly. Instead, the experimental data will be standing-wave measurements—that is, magnitudes and phases of reflection coefficients. For data of this type the circle diagram representation is the natural and convenient one.

The idealized diagram of Fig. 15·5 is transformed to the circle chart form in Fig. 15·6, taking the unit of admittance as 100 μmhos.   Only the region presumed to be accessible to experiment, or $G_L$ positive, is shown in this diagram.   In contrast to Fig. 15·5, a rectangular plot of $G = G_R + G_L$ and $B_L$, the circle diagram is a plot of $G_L$ and $B_L$.   Accordingly, the region of Fig. 15·5 to the left of the boundary of the oscillation region marked "circuit efficiency zero" does not appear at all in Fig. 15·6.

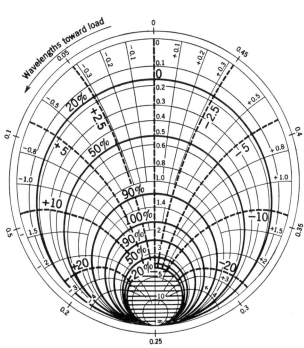

Fig. 15·7.—Ideal Rieke diagram for the same hypothetical tube as in Figs. 15·5 and 15·6, except that $\phi = 0$.

In Fig. 15·6 the boundaries of the oscillation region are the bounding circle of the diagram for the zero-circuit efficiency contour and a conductance circle at $G_{L_0} = G_e \cos \phi - G_R$ for the overload region.   This region is commonly called the "sink."   Between these boundaries the power contours are conductance circles that are tangent to the edge of the diagram at the point representing infinity.   Thus the "90 per cent power" contours enclose a crescent-shaped region tapering to infinitesimal thickness below the sink.   The frequency contours transform into arcs of circles that make an angle $-\phi$ with the susceptance coordinates. One of these arcs will be a straight line, but the fact that the straight contour happens to be the one for zero frequency shift in Fig. 15·6 is merely an accident of the choice of $G_R$ as 1 unit in this example.[1]

As is mentioned above, it would be almost impossible to obtain an experimental diagram at constant $\phi$ for any value of $\phi$ other than zero. Considerable interest is attached to this special case, and accordingly the rest of the diagrams will be drawn for $\phi = 0$, at least for a resistive load. Figure 15·7 corresponds exactly to Fig. 15·6 with the exception of the change from $\phi = 30°$ to $\phi = 0°$. Note that in addition to the effect on the frequency contours, which now follow the susceptance circles, the sink is smaller and a higher conductance is required for optimum output. Although it is not evident from the diagram, "100 per cent power" in this diagram actually represents considerably more power than the optimum in Fig. 15·6.

*Effect of Fixed Reflector Voltage.*—The next step in evolving a theoretical diagram from the zero-order theory for comparison with experiment is to use a fixed reflector voltage rather than attempt to maintain a constant $\phi$. The effect of this, as indicated in Eq. (30), will depend on the order of the mode used. Merely for convenience in computing, $2\pi(n + \frac{3}{4}) = 50$, which corresponds very nearly to $n = 7$, was chosen. This value of $n$ is rather larger than that used in most practical tubes, but will make the effects on the idealized Rieke diagram more readily visible. It is assumed that the reflector voltage is set for $\phi = 0$ with a purely resistive load, and then left unchanged. Substituting $\Delta\phi$ from Eq. (30) in (29) yields a rather unwieldy expression for $\Delta\omega$:

$$(G_R + G_L) \tan\left[\frac{\Delta\omega}{\omega_0} \cdot 2\pi\left(n + \frac{3}{4}\right)\right] + 2C\,\Delta\omega + B_L = 0. \qquad (31)$$

It can readily be seen that the effect of a fixed reflector voltage is to make the frequency pulling for a given load susceptance somewhat less than it would otherwise have been. The departure of the frequency contours from the susceptance circles will be least for light loads and small $n$, whereas in the vicinity of the sink the contours will be spread apart considerably. The power contours will also be affected, in a manner precisely similar to the effect of the equivalent amount of electronic tuning. Unfortunately, lacking inverse Bessel functions, the power variation with $\Delta\phi$ cannot be expressed by a single equation. In the diagram, the result is to close off the power contours rather than to permit them to extend to infinity below the sink, and also slightly to

[1] It is a property of the transformation that any straight line in the rectangular $G_L - B_L$ plot passing through the point $(-1, 0)$ and entering the region of positive conductance will be transformed into a straight line in the circle diagram. Furthermore, angles are preserved in the transformation. Straight lines not passing through $(-1, 0)$ are transformed into arcs of circles.

deform the sink from its original circular form. The sink will be defined by the relation

$$G_{L_0} = G_e \cos \Delta\phi - G_R. \tag{32}$$

These minor changes in the diagram are shown in Fig. 15·8.

In computing these diagrams it has been tacitly assumed that $G_e$ is strictly constant. Whether $\phi$ or the reflector voltage is held constant, there will be some change in $M$ and $\theta_e$, because the frequency is changing, with reactive loads. This change in $M$ and $\theta_e$ will cause small departures

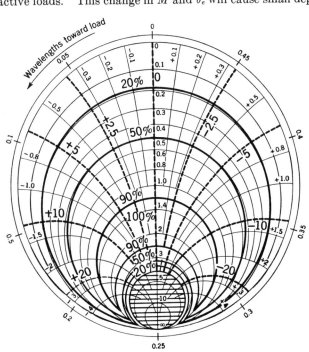

Fig. 15·8.—Ideal Rieke diagram for the same hypothetical tube as in Fig. 15·7 except that reflector voltage is held constant throughout, and assuming $2\pi(n + \frac{3}{4}) = 50$.

of the power contours in Fig. 15·7 from the conductance circles, but in practice these distortions will hardly be noticeable. The contours would tend to move upward slightly on the high-frequency side of the diagram and to be depressed at the lower frequencies. The neglect of this factor is equivalent to the assumption that the locus of the electronic conductance is an arc of a circle rather than a portion of a spiral.

*Diagrams of Electronic Tuning.*—Before proceeding to transform these idealized diagrams into more practical diagrams, it should be mentioned that another type of performance chart, strictly speaking not a Rieke diagram, is sometimes of interest. In this chart, power and electronic tuning range (normally measured between the half-power points) are plotted as functions of the load.   Since the power contours and sink have already been illustrated, it remains only to compute the tuning ranges.   Let $X_m$ be the value of $X$ at the center of the mode, $\phi = 0$. Then $X_m$ is a function of $G_e$ and the loss and load conductances only, for when $\phi = 0$, Eq. (26) reduces to

$$\frac{J_1(X_m)}{X_m} = \frac{G_R + G_L}{2G_e}.$$

The value of $X$ at the half-power points, $X_{\frac{1}{2}}$, will be $X_m/\sqrt{2}$, and the value of $\phi$ required to tune this far may be denoted by $\phi_{\frac{1}{2}}$.   This angle can be found from the relation

$$\cos \phi_{\frac{1}{2}} = \left[ \frac{J_1(X_m)}{X_m} \right] \Big/ \left[ \frac{J_1(X_m/\sqrt{2})}{(X_m/\sqrt{2})} \right],$$

and the frequency is then to be found by using Eq. (29).   Corrections similar to those discussed above will be required to take care of the variation of $G_e$ caused by pulling, consequently the contours of constant electrical tuning range will resemble strongly the power contours.   The tuning range between half-power points falls off much less rapidly than the power at light loads, goes through a very broad maximum at about the same loading as the power maximum, and drops off slowly until the overload becomes severe, after which it falls rapidly to zero at the sink. In contrast to this behavior, the tuning range between extinction points is a maximum for a vanishing load and decreases monotonically as the load becomes heavier (see Fig. 12·10).

**15·5. Transformation to the Practical Rieke Diagram.**—The obvious first step in transforming the preceding diagrams into practical ones is to shift the reference plane from the gap to a point that is accessible to experiment.   The making of this shift involves the changes indicated in Fig. 15·1b.   The load admittance $Y_L$, will no longer appear directly across the gap; there will now be a section of line between the gap and the output coupling or transducer and usually another section of line between the transducer and the reference point.   The cavity will be the first section of line (normally a radial transmission line) with the losses (mostly series resistance losses in actuality) represented by the shunt conductance $G_R$.   The output coupling will be most often a loop feeding a coaxial line, but it may be window to a waveguide; it will have an impedance-transformation ratio $m$ and, in general, will also have some losses.   The remaining section of line will be usually straightforward but in some tubes, for example the 723A/B, it may be necessary to consider lumped susceptance at the glass bead forming the vacuum seal and also possible discontinuities where the coaxial line is coupled to waveguide by an antenna.

*Effect of Output Coupling.*—The transformation from the ideal to a practical diagram can be calculated for very simple cavities, but this is unnecessary. The representation of Fig. 15·1b, omitting details of the output coupling other than to consider it as a slightly lossy transformer, will be adequate for all purposes, except perhaps the actual design of a coupling for a tube intended to cover a wide band.

In Fig. 15·1b it will be most convenient to consider the load admittance $Y'_L = G'_L + jB'_L$ in relative units with respect to the characteristic admittance $Y_0$ of the line or waveguide in which the load is measured, and to neglect for the moment losses in the output coupler. From this equivalent circuit it is clear that

$$Q_0 = \frac{\omega_0 C}{G_R} \tag{33}$$

and

$$Q_{\text{ext}} = \frac{\omega_0 C}{m Y_0}, \tag{34}$$

from the definition of $Q_{\text{ext}}$. Since $Y_L$ in Fig. 15·1a is assumed to be equivalent to $m Y_0 Y'_L$, apart from phase shifts due to the presence of a transmission line, it evidently will be possible to use the quantities determined in cold test to express Eqs. (26) to (29) in terms of $C$ and an easily measured load. In a simple case where the plane of reference for the diagram is an integral number of half waves from the gap the results are the following:

$$-\frac{2G_e}{\omega_0 C} \frac{J_1(X)}{X} \cos \phi + \frac{1}{Q_0} + \frac{G'_L}{Q_{\text{ext}}} = 0 \tag{35}$$

$$P_L = \frac{G'_L}{G'_L + \dfrac{Q_{\text{ext}}}{Q_0}} \frac{2k I_0 V_0}{\theta_e} X J_1(X) \cos \phi \tag{36}$$

and

$$\left( \frac{1}{Q_0} + \frac{G'_L}{Q_{\text{ext}}} \right) \tan \phi + \frac{2\Delta\omega}{\omega_0} + \frac{B'_L}{Q_{\text{ext}}} = 0. \tag{37}$$

In these expressions it is often convenient to introduce the loaded $Q$, $Q_L$, given by $1/Q_L = 1/Q_0 + G'_L/Q_{\text{ext}}$. The introduction of the cold-test quantities in this way obviates the necessity of an arbitrary choice of the unit for the diagrams (100 $\mu$mhos in the preceding examples) provided only that $C$ is known.

For any plane of reference other than one that is an integral number of half waves from the gap, the transformation from ideal to practical is easily made by rotating the family of contours comprising the diagram with respect to the coordinates of the Smith chart counterclockwise by the required amount, one complete revolution representing a half wavelength of line.

*Effect of Losses in Output Line.*—The presence of even moderate amounts of loss in the output line introduces marked changes in the diagrams. The most important are those resulting from the fact that Eqs. (35) and (36), which together determine the power output, will no longer involve only the load conductance but also the susceptance. The admittance $Y'_L = G'_L + jB'_L$ is to be taken as the load admittance when there is no loss in the output line, or $\sigma_1 = 0$. It will be convenient to introduce a new load admittance[1] $Y = G + jB$ to indicate the "disposable" load—that is, the load external to the tube and therefore subject to experimental variation. It is measured of course in relative units with respect to the characteristic admittance of the line or waveguide in which the standing-wave observations are made, and experimental Rieke diagrams will be plotted with respect to it.

With measurements referred to the planes $d_0$ as located by the procedure described in Sec. 15·3 it is clear by definition that

$$G'_L + jB'_L = \frac{1}{\overrightarrow{\mathbf{Z}}_{d_0} + \sigma_1} = \frac{1}{-\overleftarrow{\mathbf{Z}}_{d_0} + \sigma_1}. \tag{38}$$

Without line loss, the circuit efficiency $\eta_c$ is given by [see Eq. (36)]

$$\eta_c = \frac{G'_L}{G'_L + \dfrac{Q_{\text{ext}}}{Q_0}}.$$

Actually however the power will be dissipated in the series resistance $\sigma_1$ as well as in the real component of the load. If it is remembered that

$$\overrightarrow{\mathbf{Z}}_{d_0} + \sigma_1 = \frac{G'_L - jB'_L}{G'^2_L + B'^2_L}$$

and that the power dissipated in one of two resistances in series is proportional to that resistance, the circuit efficiency is

$$\eta_c = \frac{G'_L}{G'_L + \dfrac{Q_{\text{ext}}}{Q_0}} \cdot \frac{G'_L - \sigma_1(G'^2_L + B'^2_L)}{G'_L} = \frac{G'_L - \sigma_1(G'^2_L + B'^2_L)}{G'_L + \dfrac{Q_{\text{ext}}}{Q_0}}. \tag{39}$$

The power output will decrease as $B'_L$ increases; and at sufficiently high values of $B'_L$, namely when $B'_L = \sqrt{\dfrac{G'_L}{\sigma_1} - G'^2_L}$, it will fall to zero. In this

---

[1] The notation $Y = G + jB$ departs from that used by J. C. Slater in "Operation and Testing of Reflex Oscillators," RL Report No. 742, June 18, 1945. Slater used $G + jB$ in the sense $G'_L + jB'_L$ is used here.

condition, the load impedance $\vec{\mathbf{Z}}_{d_0}$ is a pure reactance and all the power that is not dissipated in the cavity is lost in the output lead.

From the definition of $G'_L + jB'_L$ in Eq. (38) it is evident that this quantity can be expressed in terms of the load admittance $G + jB$, provided the latter is measured at $d_0$, by the relations

$$\left.\begin{aligned}
\frac{B'_L}{G'^2_L + B'^2_L} &= \frac{B}{G^2 + B^2} \\
\frac{G'_L}{G'^2_L + B'^2_L} &= \frac{G}{G^2 + B^2} + \sigma_1,
\end{aligned}\right\}$$

which can be rearranged as

$$\left.\begin{aligned}
G'_L &= \frac{\dfrac{G}{G^2 + B^2} + \sigma_1}{\left(\dfrac{G}{G^2 + B^2} + \sigma_1\right)^2 + \left(\dfrac{B}{G^2 + B^2}\right)^2} \\
B'_L &= \frac{\dfrac{B}{G^2 + B^2}}{\left(\dfrac{G}{G^2 + B^2} + \sigma_1\right)^2 + \left(\dfrac{B}{G^2 + B^2}\right)^2}
\end{aligned}\right\}. \qquad (40)$$

If Eq. (36) for the power output is corrected as indicated in Eq. (39) to read

$$P_L = \frac{G'_L - \sigma_1(G'^2_L + B'^2_L)}{G'_L + \dfrac{Q_{\text{ext}}}{Q_0}} \cdot \frac{2kI_0V_0}{\theta_e} XJ_1(X)\cos\phi \qquad (41)$$

the development is complete, for with Eqs. (35), (37), and (41) together with the substitutions indicated in Eq. (40), the behavior is fully specified in terms of $G_e$, $\phi$, $C$, quantities determined in cold test, and the external load $G + jB$ as measured at the planes $d_0$. Equivalent results would have been obtained by using Eq. (38) in Eq. (9) and rearranging to yield

$$G'_L + jB'_L + \left[j\left(\frac{\omega}{\omega_0} - \frac{\omega_0}{\omega}\right) + \frac{1}{Q_0} + \frac{Y_e}{\omega_0 C}\right]Q_{\text{ext}} = 0. \qquad (42)$$

If this equation is separated into real and imaginary parts, the former will give Eq. (35) determining the bunching parameter $X$. The latter will determine the frequency and can be combined with Eq. (35) to yield Eq. (37) using the approximation

$$\frac{\omega}{\omega_0} - \frac{\omega_0}{\omega} \approx \frac{2\Delta\omega}{\omega_0}.$$

*Use of Transmission Line Calculator to Allow for Line Loss.*—Unfortunately Eqs. (40) are not particularly handy for performing the computations required. In practice, it seems much easier to make use of the transmission-line calculator in an alternative procedure. A transformation along a lossy line follows a spiral path instead of a simple rotation on the circle diagram. The observed $\sigma_1$ from cold test can be used to calculate the loss of the section of line (assumed to be evenly distributed) instead of considering it to represent a series resistance (in units of the characteristic impedance of the line) located immediately adjacent to the plane $d_0$.

The definition of $\sigma_1$ means that

$$\frac{1}{\sigma_1} = \frac{1 + |\mathbf{r}|}{1 - |\mathbf{r}|}$$

where $|\mathbf{r}|$ is the magnitude of the reflected voltage at the sending end of the line. Let the power $P_0$ at the receiving end of a length $l$ of lossy line be $P_0 = Pe^{-\alpha l}$ where $P$ is the sending-end power. Correspondingly, the amplitudes will be given by

$$v_0 = ve^{-\frac{\alpha l}{2}}.$$

Remembering that in reflection the length $l$ is traversed twice,

$$|\mathbf{r}| = e^{-\frac{\alpha l}{2}} \cdot e^{-\frac{\alpha l}{2}} = e^{-\alpha l};$$

then

$$\sigma_1 = \frac{1 - e^{-\alpha l}}{1 + e^{-\alpha l}}.$$

A solution of this equation for the power ratio (loss) yields

$$e^{-\alpha l} = \frac{P_0}{P} = \frac{1 - \sigma_1}{1 + \sigma_1}$$

or

$$\text{line loss (db)} = 10 \log_{10} \frac{1 - \sigma_1}{1 + \sigma_1}. \tag{43}$$

The typical case cited above in which $\sigma$(db) might be of the order of 35 db thus corresponds to a line loss of 0.156 db. A value of $\sigma_1$(db) of 10 db, as has been found in certain frequency regions for the 2K25 tube, indicates a line loss of 2.84 db. These losses apply where the line is terminated in a matched load; when standing waves are present on the line the dissipation is increased.

It is clear from the method of measurement of $\sigma_1$ that at the sending end of the line in question no standing-wave ratio higher than $\sigma_1$(db) can exist no matter what the termination at the receiving end. Therefore, there is an annular region extending inward from the boundary of the Smith chart which the tube can never see as a load; the width of this region depends on the line loss. The Rieke diagrams are plotted with respect to standing-wave ratios at the receiving end of the line; these may, in principle at least, cover the whole chart. This effect can be taken into account by imagining that the allowed region of the chart has been "stretched" radially enough to cover the whole circle. The amount of this stretch will vary with the radial distance (or standing-wave ratio). The idealized diagrams may be stretched in this way and then the power contours readjusted to allow for the attenuation, not forgetting the factor resulting from the standing waves.

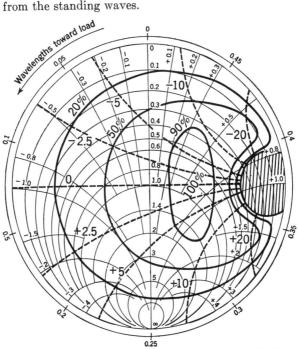

Fig. 15·9.—Ideal Rieke diagram for the same hypothetical tube as in Fig. 15·8 referred to a point in the line $2\frac{1}{4}$ wavelengths from the gap. Line loss 0.5 db, transformer ratio $\frac{1}{20}$.

*Ideal Rieke Diagram Including Line Loss.*—Alternatively, one may use the circular transmission-line calculator to make the entire transformation. Starting with any load point, in terms of magnitude and phase of the standing wave, the calculator is rotated to transform to the gap and the slider on the radial arm moved inward (according to the scale provided) to include the line loss. The new load, with a somewhat diminished standing-wave ratio and a new phase, is read off the chart in terms of conductance and susceptance, and these values are used to compute the frequency and the sending-end power. The latter must be corrected for the attenuation, including the standing-wave factor, and the results are then to be plotted at the original load point. This method is fairly rapid, particularly when a calculator with "dissipation" and "standing-wave-loss coefficient" scales on the radial arm is employed. It was used to construct the ideal diagram of Fig. 15·9, which applies to the hypothetical tube used in the previous examples. For this tube $G_e$ is assumed to be 500 $\mu$mhos, $C$ is 1 $\mu\mu f$, $G_r$ is 100 $\mu$mhos, and

$$2\pi(n + \tfrac{3}{4}) \approx 50.$$

The reflector voltage is assumed to be held constant at a value giving $\phi = 0$ for a pure resistance load at the gap. It is now time to assume a resonant frequency for the cavity, a line length from the grids to the point of measurement, and a line loss. Let these be, respectively, $\omega_0 = 6 \times 10^{10}$ cps., $2\tfrac{1}{8}$ wavelengths, and 0.5 db. Let it be further assumed that $Y_0 = 2000$ $\mu$mhos and that the transformer admittance stepup ratio $m = \tfrac{1}{20}$.

With these assumptions, the unloaded $Q$, $Q_0$, would be 600 [from Eq. (33)] and the external $Q$, $Q_{ext}$, would have the same numerical value [Eq. (34)]. Though not representing any particular tube type, these figures are of a reasonable order of magnitude. The line lengths in the 2K25 tubes seem to be about 2 to $2\tfrac{1}{4}$ wavelengths (depending on the frequency) from the grids to the plane in the waveguide containing the output antenna. This length varies from tube to tube over a range of about $\tfrac{1}{8}$ wavelength. The assumed loss of 0.5 db is also somewhere in the range encountered with that tube type.

In plotting Fig. 15·9 no "long-line effect" has been included; that is to say, the plane of reference is assumed to move as the frequency varies so that the electrical length remains constant. Apart from the obvious change in appearance that is due to the rotation, the change in shape of the power contours and of the sink is most striking. The sink has been "pushed outward" so that a portion of the circle is lost, and the horns of the power contours have been cut off so that they are kidney-shaped rather than crescents. The frequency contours are comparatively unaffected.

*Effect of Impedance Discontinuity in Output Line.*—In actual practice it may happen that there is an appreciable discontinuity in the output line. For example, there may be a noticeable reflection introduced by a glass bead forming the vacuum seal, or an output antenna may not be matched to the waveguide. In any event where there is appreciable loss between the cavity proper and such a discontinuity, it will be necessary to "tune out" the latter in order to obtain optimum power output. If there is no problem of multiple reflections, this situation can be handled readily by the method outlined in the preceding paragraphs. The procedure is to transform along the line from the load point to the discontinuity, to add the appropriate susceptance to the transformed load admittance, and then to transform the rest of the way to the grids calculating the frequency and sending-end power as before. An accurate calculation of the output power requires a knowledge of the distribution of the loss on the two sides of the discontinuity, but the purpose here is merely to give an idea of the kind of distortion of the Rieke diagram produced by a discontinuity. The appearance of the distorted diagram will naturally be sensitive to the location of the discontinuity. A

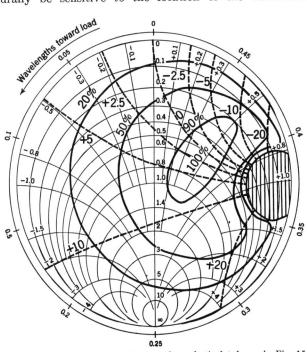

Fig. 15·10.—Ideal Rieke diagram for the same hypothetical tube as in Fig. 15·9, with a discontinuity of $-j1$ located $1\frac{1}{2}$ wavelengths from the gap.

typical case is illustrated in Fig. 15·10, drawn for the same conditions as those in Fig. 15·9, except that now there is a discontinuity of $-j1$ located in the line $1\frac{1}{2}$ wavelengths from the gap, or $\frac{5}{8}$ wavelength from the reference plane. The distortion is similar to that produced by failure to set the reflector voltage for $\phi = 0$, as in Fig. 15·6. However, in Fig. 15·6 maximum power will occur on or near a diameter of the chart that passes through the sink; but when there is a discontinuity, the optimum loading will be noticeably off this diameter. In addition, if the plane of reference is chosen an integral number of half wavelengths from the gap, the frequency contours will make an angle $-\phi$ with the susceptance circles. In practice, it may be difficult to get data that are sufficiently accurate to distinguish between a small discontinuity and a small error in setting the reflector voltage, but even a small discontinuity should show on cold test, provided that $\sigma_1$ is determined over an appreciable frequency range.

*Long-line Effects.*—Long-line effects will be noticeable in many practical applications of reflex klystrons, in which the load will normally be a device with an admittance that varies slowly with frequency and

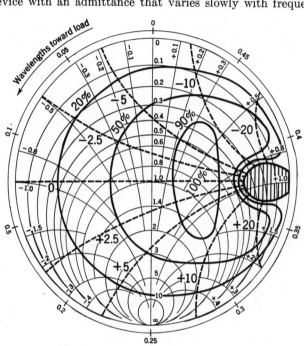

FIG. 15·11.—Ideal Rieke diagram for the same hypothetical tube as in Fig. 15·9, with long-line effect included. Line $2\frac{5}{8}$ wavelengths long.

that is located at a fixed distance from the tube. A diagram of the type illustrated in Fig. 15·9 is satisfactory for comparison between theory and experiment, except for the nuisance of using a slightly different line length for the reduction of each standing-wave observation. A diagram in which the physical line length is constant will make clearer some points of behavior. Phenomena such as split reflector-mode patterns (sometimes erroneously termed "double moding") and frequency discontinuities that make it impossible to tune to a specified frequency may arise from a mismatched load in combination with an excessive line length.

To transform a diagram drawn for a constant electrical length to a constant physical line, approximately $N$ wavelengths long, it is necessary to rotate every point except the zero frequency-shift contour through an angle $(\Delta f/f_0)N \cdot 720°$ with positive angles measured counterclockwise. The effect of this rotation will clearly be greatest in the neighborhood of the sink and, in fact, will alter the shape of the latter profoundly. For moderate amounts of long-line effect, such as is unavoidable in the 2K25 tube, the sink will be "pinched in" at the sides and bottom. With longer lengths of line the two boundaries "cross over" each other at the bottom of the sink, which is thus divided into two distinct regions. For

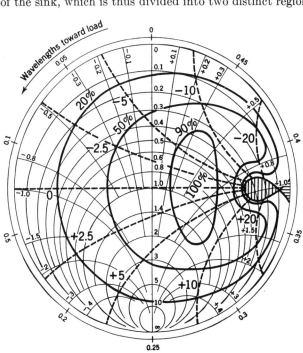

Fig. 15·12.—Ideal Rieke diagram for the same hypothetical tube as in Fig. 15·9 with long-line effect included. Line 5¼ wavelengths long.

still longer lines, this second region gets very much larger, while the original true sink shrinks to a point. This behavior is illustrated in Figs. 15·11, 15·12, and 15·13, which represent the diagram of Fig. 15·9 modified for line lengths of 2⅝, 5¼, and 10⅛ wavelengths respectively.

The second region of the sink, appearing in Figs. 15·12 and 15·13 and indicated by different shading, is of considerable interest. Unlike the first region within which no oscillation is possible at all, in the second region oscillation will occur, but both the power and frequency are double-valued. That is to say, in this second region the frequency and power contours originally on the high- and low-frequency side of the sink are now both present together.   If the tube is delivering power to a load represented by a point on the low-frequency side of the sink and the phase of the reflection is shifted clockwise so as to pass through the second region, the behavior will be regular as this region is entered, and the frequency will continue to decrease until the farther boundary of the region is reached.   At the boundary the frequency and power ouput will jump to values conforming to the contours outside the region on the high-

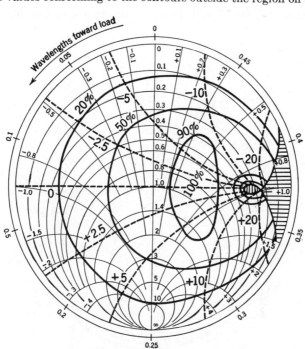

Fig. 15·13.—Ideal Rieke diagram for the same hypothetical tube as in Fig. 15·9, with long-line effect included.   Line 10⅛ wavelengths long.

frequency side.   In general, there will be a discontinuity in both frequency and power output although, for special cases, the change in power when crossing the line may be almost zero.   If an attempt is made to operate continuously in this region, the tube will shift erratically between the two possible sets of operating conditions.   For this reason it is very difficult to map this part of the sink.

Since the output in this second region depends on the previous history of the tube, this behavior might well be called a third type of hysteresis, not to be confused with those discussed in the preceding chapter caused by multiple transits or by transit angles varying with r-f voltage.   This terminology is particularly apt since the reflector characteristic patterns obtained when operating in this region may be very similar to those produced by the other types of hysteresis, which may of course be present simultaneously. This third type of hysteresis will be very sensitive to changes in loading and will appear only with overloads. By contrast, hysteresis arising from a dependence of $\phi$ on r-f voltage will be most severe at light loads and relatively insensitive to changes in loading. Multiple-transit hysteresis will be extremely sensitive to changes in resonator voltage, so it should always be easy to distinguish the different types.

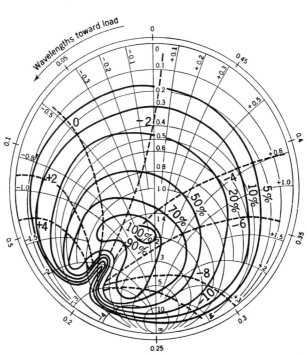

Fig. 15·14.—Experimental diagram for a typical 723A/B tube. Power and frequency plotted as functions of load admittance referred to the plane in the waveguide containing the output probe; resonator voltage 300; reflector voltage constant in the "160-volt" mode; wavelength 3.2 cm.

**15·6. Experimental Rieke Diagrams.**—Obtaining experimental Rieke diagrams with sufficient accuracy to permit comparison with theoretical results requires considerable patience and some practice on the part of the observer. Extreme care is necessary to avoid drifts in frequency (and, to a less extent, in power) resulting from drifts in applied voltages or from thermal changes. A skilled observer will require several hours to take the data for a detailed diagram; all drifts must be rigorously excluded during this time.

It is not often necessary to take a complete diagram; the location of the maximum power point and minimum standing-wave ratio to just reach the sink, or the sketching of a few frequency contours, may suffice, depending on the subject under investigation. After a little practice it is easy to accomplish these with a minimum of wasted effort, but the beginner will be well advised to start with a complete diagram.

Considerable labor can be avoided if the device used as a standing-wave introducer is of a type in which standing-wave ratio and phase

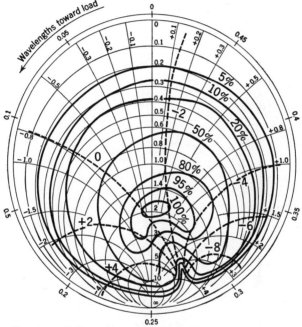

Fig. 15·15.—Experimental diagram for a typical 723A/B tube (as in Fig. 15·14) taken at a wavelength of 3.1 cm.

can be adjusted independently, or nearly so. Devices such as the double-slug tuner or sliding screw are desirable from this standpoint, although the former may not produce a sufficiently high standing-wave ratio for all purposes. Diagrams good enough for many practical purposes may be drawn from observations at the match point and suitably distributed around three standing-wave circles, a total of some two dozen points.

In drawing the contours it will usually be helpful to make separate auxiliary plots of power and frequency as a function of phase for the several standing-wave ratios used. Curves sketched in on these plots will assist in interpolation and will indicate clearly where additional observations may be needed. Without such interpolation curves the sketching-in of contours on the circle diagram will be very tedious.

Sample experimental diagrams taken on a typical 723A/B are shown in Figs. 15·14, 15·15, and 15·16. The tube was mounted in an adapter similar to that specified for testing the 2K25 tube. In this adapter the output antenna was thrust to its full length into the broad side of a standard ½- by 1-in. (outside) waveguide, with an r-f choke joint to the outer conductor. The point of insertion was 0.394 in. from a shorting

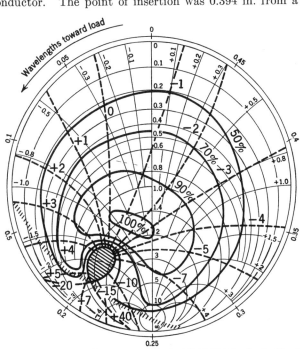

Fig. 15·16.—Experimental diagram for a typical 723A/B tube (as in Fig. 15·14) taken at a wavelength of 3.2 cm, with a line about 10 wavelengths long and the reflector voltage in the "250-volt" mode.

plug and 0.178 in. from the center line of the wave-guide. The resonator voltage was 300, and reflector voltage was held constant in either the 160-volt (nominal) or the "250-volt" mode. The diagrams were referred to the plane of the waveguide containing the output antenna, and no attempt was made to eliminate the long-line effect necessarily introduced by the slotted section and couplings to the standing-wave introducer. The unit admittance is naturally that of the ½- by 1-in. waveguide.

In Fig. 15·14 the tube was operated in the "160-volt" reflector mode at a wavelength of 3.2 cm. Note that the tube was definitely under-coupled for this condition; this undercoupling is a property of the adapter used, which was deliberately designed for light loading in order to secure more uniform output over the specified frequency band. Also, there was a noticeable long-line effect resulting from the almost unavoidable length of the waveguide involved in the measuring equipment. For Fig. 15·15 nothing was changed except the wavelength, which was 3.1 cm, and the reflector voltage, which was increased slightly. The diagram is similar to Fig. 15·14 except for the rotation caused by the increased electrical length of the output line.

Figure 15·16 illustrates an extreme long-line effect in which an attempt has been made to follow the frequency contours into the second region of the sink. The conditions were the same as for Fig. 15·14 except that the line length was increased to about 10 wavelengths and the tube was operated in the 250-volt reflector mode. The electronic conductance was thereby decreased so that the tube required a lighter load.

These diagrams were all taken with the reflector voltage set for the center of the mode, $\phi \approx 0$, at a matched load. In a diagram taken with the tube detuned electrically to one of the half-power points, the frequency contours would be skewed around as in Fig. 15·6 and the sink would come noticeably closer to the center of the diagram.

**15·7. Effects of a High-$Q$ Load.**—In the previous discussion it was assumed that the load was of such a nature that it could be described in terms of an admittance that was almost constant over the frequency range of interest. However, it is often necessary to use a high-$Q$ cavity, for example a reference wavemeter, in conjunction with a reflex oscillator. Depending on the line length from the r-f gap to the reference cavity, a variety of phenomena are possible: among these are stabilization by the external cavity in which the frequency shift produced by a given temperature change or a small displacement of the tuning mechanism is cut to a few per cent of its normal value, and discontinuities in tuning that make it impossible to set on particular frequencies. Stabilization by the method of "locking" to an external cavity has not come into general use, possibly because the modest improvement in frequency stability is not worth the difficulty inherent in keeping the line lengths correct; it is more common to use an external reference cavity and some form of automatic frequency control operating on the oscillator. Smooth and positive frequency control is important and requires the introduction of considerable loss in the line or attention to the loading of the cavity.[1]

*Admittance of a Cavity as a Function of Frequency.*—At the input to a cavity there will be an admittance $Y_c(f)$ that is a function of frequency

[1] R. V. Pound, "Frequency Discontinuities of Local Oscillator Tubes Due to High-$Q$ Load Circuits," RL Report No. 694, Feb. 27, 1945. See also R. V. Pound, "Electronic Frequency Stabilization of Microwave Oscillators," *Rev. Sci. Inst.*, **17**, 490, (1946).

of the form

$$Y_c(f) = g + jb(f), \tag{44}$$

where all quantities are in units of the characteristic admittance. At the resonant frequency $f_0$ the admittance will be a pure conductance $g$, determined by the input and output couplings, the load, and the internal losses. On a Smith chart the locus of $Y_c(f)$ will be a circle as drawn in Fig. 15·17$a$, traversed in the direction of the arrows as the frequency is increased. Clearly, this would be a most undesirable load for the tube,

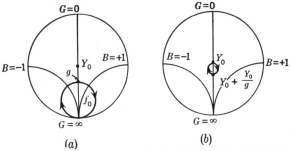

Fig. 15·17.—Locus of admittance of a cavity (in relative units): ($a$) at its input window, and ($b$) referred to a plane one-quarter wave back from the window at which there is a shunt conductance $Y_0$. Arrows indicate direction of traverse for increasing frequency.

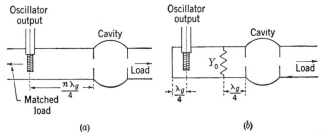

Fig. 15·18.—Two possible arrangements for approximately realizing conditions of Fig. 15·17($b$). In ($a$) the plane of reference is that containing the output antenna and $n$ is odd; in ($b$) the plane is that containing the lumped termination $Y_0$.

especially at frequencies remote from $f_0$; consequently it is expedient to put a terminating conductance $Y_0$ one quarter wavelength in front of the cavity. At the plane of this termination the new locus of the admittance will be simply the addition of $Y_0$ to the reciprocal of $Y_c/Y_0$ (provided $g \ll Y_0$ as indicated in Fig. 15·17$b$). At resonance the conductance will be $Y_0 + Y_0/g$ and the direction of traversing the circle is the same as before. A sufficient approximation to the conditions postulated here can be achieved with either of the arrangements sketched in Fig. 15·18. If no useful output is needed, other than that coming through the cavity, the scheme of Fig. 15·18$b$ is preferred. In Fig. 15·18$a$ the plane of reference for which Fig. 15·17b applies is that of the oscillator output antenna provided $n$ is odd, whereas in Fig. 15·18b the plane is that containing the lumped terminating resistance.

*Admittance of Oscillator Resonator and External Cavity.*—Since by hypothesis the external load has a $Q$ that is high in comparison with the oscillator resonator, the latter may be considered as consisting of a constant conductance $G_R$ and a susceptance $B_R$, which varies linearly with frequency, across the r-f gap. Then, when the plane of reference for Fig. 15·17b is an integral number of half wavelengths from the r-f gap, the total susceptance will vary with frequency as shown in Fig. 15·19. When the maximum negative slope of the dotted line representing the susceptance that is due to the external cavity is greater than the slope of the broken line representing the susceptance of the oscillator cavity, the tuning will be discontinuous, as is evidenced by the double-valued region of the solid line in Fig. 19·19a, which represents the sum

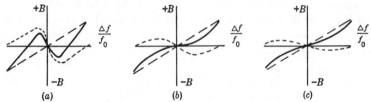

Fig. 15·19.—Susceptance at r-f gap. The dashed line is the contribution of oscillator resonator, dotted line the susceptance of external cavity, solid line the sum. Tuning is discontinuous in (a), barely continuous in (b), and smooth in (c).

of the susceptances. The other two sketches represent cases in which smooth tuning will be obtained.

*"Pulling" Parameter.*—A quantity somewhat similar to a "pulling figure" can be defined as follows. Let $K$ be the fractional frequency shift produced by a change of unit susceptance in the external load, at an integral number of half wavelengths from the gap. The ordinary pulling figure in magnetron practice is the frequency shift produced by a load with a voltage standing-wave ratio of 1.5 moved through 360° in phase, and is approximately $0.93f_0K$. From Eq. (37) it is evident that at the center of the electronic-tuning range $K$ will be just $1/2Q_{ext}$. In the cases of interest there will be some change in load conductance accompanying a change in susceptance, which will tend to increase $K$ provided $\phi \neq 0$. Also, loss in the output line, requiring the use of Eq. (40), will introduce an asymmetrical variation in $K$ with electrical tuning. Experimentally, in the 2K25 tube, $K$ is usually considerably larger at the low-frequency half-power point than at the center of the mode, and its variation with electronic tuning is complicated. From the definition of $K$ it is easy to see that the slope of the broken line in Fig. 15·19 will be merely $1/K$.

*Properties of a Cavity in Terms of Probability Functions.*—The behavior of the external cavity may be represented by $Q_0$, the dissipative $Q$ due to internal losses, and by $Q_1$ and $Q_2$, the $Q$'s of the windows (input and output respectively), which depend on the window sizes and on the admittances presented to them. For simplification of the algebra, it is convenient to use $\delta_0$, $\delta_1$, and $\delta_2$, the reciprocals of these $Q$'s, in the derivation.[1] The concept of the $\delta$'s may help to clarify the meaning of the term $Q$ when applied to the windows or coupling devices of a cavity, for the $\delta$'s are simply proportional to relative conductances of each of the three circuits associated with the cavity. They are sometimes called probability functions for they are related to the probability of energy dissipation per cycle in the respective parts of the circuits.

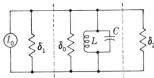

Fig. 15·20.—Equivalent circuit for a cavity in terms of "probability functions" $\delta_n = \dfrac{1}{Q_n}$.

If the equivalent circuit of Fig. 15·20 is considered, it is easy to show that, for a generator conductance $\delta_1$ representing a matched line as seen from the cavity input, Eq. (44) may be written as

$$Y_c(f) \approx \frac{\delta_0 + \delta_2}{\delta_1} + j\, \frac{2\Delta f}{f_0 \delta_1}. \tag{45}$$

Also, the power transmission through the cavity will be

$$T = \frac{P_0}{P_1} = \frac{4\delta_1\delta_2}{(\delta_1 + \delta_2 + \delta_0)^2} = \frac{4Q_L^2}{Q_1 Q_2} \tag{46}$$

where $P_0$ is the power dissipated in the load and $P_1$ is that available from the generator. The admittance presented to the oscillator in the conditions of Fig. 15·17b will be

$$Y_L = 1 + \frac{1}{Y_c} = 1 + \frac{\delta_1(\delta_0 + \delta_2) - j\, \dfrac{2\Delta f}{f_0}\, \delta_1}{(\delta_0 + \delta_2)^2 + 4\left(\dfrac{\Delta f}{f}\right)^2}. \tag{47}$$

As before, it is assumed that the plane of reference across which $Y_L$ is seen is an integral number of half wavelengths from the r-f gap. It can readily be shown that this is the most unfavorable situation for the avoidance of discontinuities, for the part of the small circle in Fig. 15·17b orthogonal to the constant-susceptance contours is the part in which the maximum rate of traverse with frequency is encountered.

*Choice of Parameters to Avoid Discontinuities.*—The maximum rate of change of the imaginary part of Eq. (47) with respect to $\Delta f/f_0$ is found

[1] Note that these $\delta$'s are not to be confused with the $\delta$ used in Sec. 15·3.

by differentiation to be

$$\frac{-2\delta_1}{(\delta_0 + \delta_2)^2}.$$

Hence the condition for continuous tuning—that the maximum slope of the dotted line in Fig. 15·19 be less than that of the broken line—may be written

$$\frac{2\delta_1}{(\delta_0 + \delta_2)^2} \geqq \frac{1}{K} \qquad (48a)$$

or, in the more familiar $Q$ notation,

$$\frac{\dfrac{2}{Q_1}}{\left(\dfrac{1}{Q_0} + \dfrac{1}{Q_2}\right)^2} \leqq \frac{1}{K}. \qquad (48b)$$

Thus the problem of avoiding discontinuities in an arrangement of the kind depicted in Fig. 15·18 is reduced to a suitable choice of the cavity

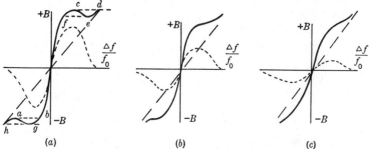

Fig. 15·21.—Susceptance at gap in case of stabilization.

parameters.   Note that $Q_0$ and $Q_2$ have relatively larger effects than $Q_1$; hence the common arrangement using identical input and output couplings will not be the most desirable.   The choice of values for the $Q$'s is, of course, to be made with due consideration of the desired loaded $Q$, $Q_L$, given by

$$\frac{1}{Q_L} = \delta_0 + \delta_1 + \delta_2 = \frac{1}{Q_0} + \frac{1}{Q_1} + \frac{1}{Q_2}$$

and of the power transmitted through the cavity as given by Eq. (46).

*Stabilization by an External Cavity.*—Frequency stabilization is obtained if the phase of the admittance at the r-f gap caused by the external circuit is the opposite to that shown in Fig. 15·17b.   This condition would be attained by making the distance from the reference plane to the gap an odd number of quarter wavelengths instead of a number of half wavelengths as before.   This situation is illustrated in Fig. 15·21, corresponding to Fig. 15·19.   In Fig. 15·21a there is good stabilization, as evidenced by the steepness of the curve of total suscept-ance with respect to frequency shift.    When stabilization is good there are two discontinuities.    Starting from the extreme negative end, the frequency changes continuously to $a$, jumps to $b$, changes smoothly from $b$ to $c$, and then jumps to $d$.    In the opposite direction the tube tunes continuously to $e$, jumps to $f$, goes continuously to $g$, and jumps to $h$. There are no discontinuities in Figs. 15·21$b$ and 15·21$c$; Fig. 15–21$b$ represents a borderline case.

This method of stabilization has not been very practical, partly because of the difficulty in keeping the correct line lengths but also because it has been found necessary, in order to achieve sufficient stabi-lization, to work in an extreme condition of the type illustrated in Fig. 15·21$a$.    Then, in order to get the tube "locked" to the cavity, a special tune-up procedure is required because the tube will lock when first turned on only if it happens to be tuned between points $b$ and $f$, but it will stay locked if tuned anywhere between $c$ and $g$.    In experimental cases the difference was much larger than is indicated in the illustration.

# CHAPTER 16

## REFLEX-KLYSTRON MODULATION

### By D. R. Hamilton

**16·1. Types of Modulation.**—Many of the modulation characteristics and possible types of modulation of the reflex klystron are indicated by the static operating characteristics shown in Figs. 12·4 and 12·17.

A simple type of modulation is the square-wave amplitude modulation produced by square-wave modulating the reflector voltage; this is a common technique in measurements work. Another simple modulation that has been used in microwave communications is small-amplitude modulation of the reflector voltage about the center of a mode; this gives a nearly linear frequency-modulation characteristic, with accompanying amplitude modulation to a degree dependent upon the excursion of the modulated voltage. The type of characteristic obtained with these two kinds of modulation is indicated in Fig. 16·1.

An equally important kind of modulation, always present although unintentionally so, is noise modulation by shot effect in the beam current. Here the beam-current noise components at frequencies adjacent to the oscillation frequency give rise to an output noise power at these adjacent frequencies. This subject is touched

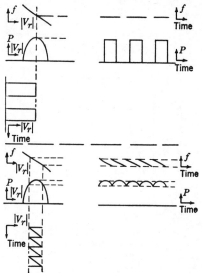

Fig. 16·1.—Commonly used reflex klystron modulation characteristics: output power $P$ and oscillation frequency $f$ as functions of time for slow reflector-voltage $(V_r)$ modulations.

upon briefly in the present chapter; the next chapter discusses in more detail the importance of this noise modulation and presents a detailed analysis and experimental data.

In addition to these commonly used or commonly occurring modulations, others suggest themselves for various purposes or simply for their

441

own intrinsic interest. Most of these may be grouped in the two categories of modulation of the reflector voltage and the beam current—or, more generally, modulation of the reflection phase and the small-signal electronic transconductance $G_e$. The effects of such modulation depend on whether the modulating frequency is comparable to or much smaller than the oscillation frequency. Another possible type of modulation with interesting characteristics is modulation by an external microwave signal coupled directly into the resonant circuit. In addition, there is

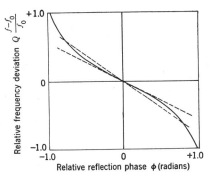

always the microphonic modulation of the resonant frequency of the cavity to contend with in actual tubes.

The general subject of modulation will also be taken to include transient phenomena; the most important of these transients is the initiation of oscillation when the oscillator is suddenly turned on.

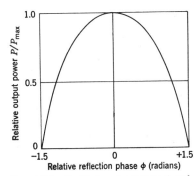

FIG. 16·2.—Oscillation frequency $f$ and relative output power $P/P_{max}$ as functions of relative reflection phase angle $\phi$, measured in radians: ideal oscillator $(G_e/G_{BR} \gg 1)$ operated at optimum load $(G_e/G = 2.3)$.

**16·2. Static Characteristics Relevant to Low-frequency Modulation.**—Before discussing the details of dynamic modulation and transient theory, it is worth while to review those static characteristics that are relevant to modulation at sufficiently low frequencies. These characteristics were treated by implication in Chap. 12, and were summarized there in Figs. 12·4, 12·5, and 12·17. The same information is presented in Fig. 16·2 in a slightly altered manner; here two universal curves illustrate the way in which oscillation frequency and relative output power depend upon the relative reflection transit angle $\phi$. The relation between $\phi$ and the actual electrode voltages has already been discussed in Chap. 13. Figure 16·2 and all the statements of this section refer to an oscillator for which $G_e/G_{BR} \gg 1$ and $n \gg 1$, and which is working into optimum load, that is $G_e/G = 2.3$. The analogous results for a nonideal oscillator with small $G_e/G_{BR}$ may be deduced from the general data given in Chap. 12 for this case.

Little need be said about the output-power characteristic in Fig. 16·2 beyond the fact that the half-power points are separated by a change in reflection transit angle of 1.76 radians. Above these half-power points the characteristic has essentially the shape of a resonance curve.

The points that need to be mentioned specifically about Fig. 16·2 relate to the frequency dependence shown there. The following numerical results may be obtained from that figure and should be noted:

1. The electronic tuning range $\Delta f_{\frac{1}{2}}$, or the difference in the oscillation frequencies at the two half-power points, is $1.21 f_0/Q$ or approximately the bandwidth of the klystron cavity when loaded for optimum output.

2. Since the mode has a reflection-transit-angle width of 1.76 radians between half-power points, the mean electronic-tuning rate averaged between half-power points is $-0.69 f_0/Q$ frequency units per radian.

3. Since $\tan \phi = -2Q(\omega/\omega_0 - 1)$ by Eq. (12·4), the center-of-mode tuning rate is $-f_0/2Q$ frequency units per radian.

The degree of linearity of frequency deviation with applied voltage is thus shown by the fact that the frequency deviation at the half-power point is 38 per cent larger than it would be if the center-of-mode tuning rate applied throughout. This nonlinearity diminishes as the frequency deviation diminishes; the frequency deviation which is half of that at the half-power points is only 11 per cent greater than would be expected from the center-of-mode tuning rate. Thus if a given frequency deviation is required from an oscillator, the only way to make the tuning linear with the applied voltage is to make the half-power tuning range as large as possible.

It can be seen from Fig. 16·2 that the same general prescription holds true if the minimum amplitude modulation for a given frequency modulation is desired. As a numerical example, suppose that it is desired to work between the 84 per cent power points; reference to Fig. 16·2 then shows that only the center half of the electronic-tuning range may be utilized.

It thus appears that anything that acts to make an oscillator operate with a low $Q$ at optimum load has the effect of simultaneously optimizing all the properties that are beneficial for frequency-modulated operation: namely, electronic-tuning range, rate and linearity of electronic tuning, and absence of associated amplitude modulation. As is seen in Chap. 12, this minimization of the value of $Q$ at optimum load corresponds to a maximization of $G_e/\omega C$, and, as far as concerns the choice of mode (value of $n$) is concerned, this maximization of $G_e/\omega C$ is associated with a sacrifice of output efficiency.

**16·3. Limitations on the Use of Static Characteristics; the Quasi-static Approximation in Modulation Theory.**—Static characteristics give no information regarding transients, and their implications as to periodic modulation become more and more faulty as the modulation frequency is raised. A more exact analysis of modulation[1] must be based upon an analysis of bunching and of circuit behavior when the relevant voltages and currents and parameters are not constants or single-frequency sinusoidal functions of time. This analysis is carried out in the next few sections. It is, however, considerably simplified by certain approximations; these are suggested and made palatable by considering what goes wrong with the static characteristics as the modulation frequency is increased or as transients are examined in greater detail.

Consider, for example, a sudden decrease in beam current or in small-signal electronic transconductance. The amplitude of oscillation approaches its new and lower value with the difference decaying exponentially as $e^{-\frac{\omega_0 t}{2Q}}$; the process requires a finite time because the surplus energy stored in the circuit must be dissipated before the new equilibrium amplitude is reached.

On the other hand, the consequence of a sudden change in reflection phase from $\phi_1$ to $\phi_2$ (and hence in the equilibrium value of oscillation frequency from $\omega_1$ to $\omega_2$) can not be deduced as simply from conservation of energy. In general, however, the initial output sine wave at frequency $\omega_1$ and the final equilibrium sine wave at $\omega_2$ do not correspond to the same values of voltages and currents (or zeroth and first derivatives of either variable) at the instant of change in $\phi$; and since these latter quantities must be physically continuous (by conservation of energy!), a transient oscillation described by $e^{\left(-\frac{1}{2Q}+j\right)\omega_0 t}$ is set up at the instant of change in $\phi$. Thus, the requirement of continuity in the voltages and currents has the consequence that the eventual pure sine wave at $\omega_2$ is initially mixed up with an exponentially damped sine wave at $\omega_0$, the resonant frequency of the cavity. Generalizing from these illustrations, any sudden change in conditions of oscillation is followed by an exponential approach to the new equilibrium. This is a general property of the differential equations of forced simple harmonic motion.

The consequences of sinusoidal modulation are less easily visualized in detail because they are essentially the consequences of an exponential pursuit of a continuously changing equilibrium point. It is clear, however, that if the modulation period becomes comparable to the circuit

[1] A large part of the remainder of this chapter is based on the following report: E. Feenberg and D. R. Hamilton, "Theory of Modulation of Reflex Klystrons," Report 5221.1040, Sperry Gyroscope Co. Research Laboratories, Garden City, N.Y., Aug. 30, 1945.

decay time, then with sinusoidal modulation, just as with discontinuous change, the r-f voltages and currents are not able to follow the applied electrode voltages instantaneously; static characteristics no longer necessarily describe the modulation. Since the time constant of the exponential approach to equilibrium is $2Q/\omega_0$, the higher the $Q$ the lower the modulation frequency at which dynamic effects begin to have an influence.

Thus, the customarily sizable circuit $Q$ necessitates an analysis of modulation from a dynamic, as distinguished from a static, point of view, but it also simplifies this analysis. The circuit $Q$ sets certain limits on those modulation frequencies that have appreciable effects; this limitation of the relevant modulation frequencies in turn permits the use of a convenient simplifying approximation and method of treatment.

The limitation comes about because, by an extension of the previous qualitative argument, the rate of variation of the r-f variables is limited by the circuit $Q$; if too high a modulation rate is used, the oscillator simply ignores the modulation. To say the same thing another way, a high-$Q$ circuit acts as a filter in suppressing any modulation sidebands that are far from the carrier frequency. Therefore there is little point in considering in detail any applied modulation for which all the generated sidebands lie far outside the pass band of the oscillator circuit.

Although modulation effects die out when the order of magnitude of the modulation frequency greatly exceeds $\omega/Q$, this does not mean that modulation at all higher frequencies produces negligible effects on the output signal; when the modulation frequency approaches $\omega(1 - 1/Q)$, modulation effects become important once more. To make this point clear by an illustration, suppose that the beam current is modulated at a circular frequency $\omega + \Omega$ separated by the low frequency $\Omega$ from the oscillation frequency $\omega$. Such modulation is later found to have the same effect as does the addition of small components, of frequency $\omega \pm \Omega$, to the bunched beam current. But this is exactly the effect that a modulation at the low frequency $\Omega$ would have. More generally, any modulation at a frequency $n\omega \pm \Omega$ near one of the harmonics of $\omega$ may be represented by an equivalent modulation at the low frequency $\Omega$.

This equivalence is later shown in detail for various specific modulations. For the moment, however, these considerations are only briefly introduced in order to delineate the resultant limitation of the relevant modulation frequencies.

As has already been stated, this limitation is the basis for a considerable simplification in the dynamic analysis of modulation and transients. The simplification arises from the fact that with modulation frequencies $\Omega$ and $n\omega \pm \Omega$—where $\Omega/\omega \ll 1$—all oscillator parameters and all r-f amplitudes and phases vary only slightly in one period of the oscillation or carrier frequency ω. This means, to a good approximation, that the relation between the momentary bunched beam current and the momentary r-f gap voltage is simply that of "static" bunching theory. Such an approximation, in which quantities that vary slowly with time are considered constant over a cycle, is referred to as the "quasi-static approximation." The detailed application of the quasi-static approximation may be seen in the remainder of the present chapter, in which this approximation is used. The eventual theoretical results should be accurate for $\Omega/\omega < 0.1$.

**16·4. Description of Modulation; the Small-signal Approximation.—** It is a standard procedure to describe a modulated wave in terms of the Fourier analysis into the carrier wave and the various sidebands. With the use of the Fourier integral this procedure becomes sufficiently general to allow the treatment of a wave modulated in any aperiodic way, as by a transient. The use of the quasi-static approximation suggests a slightly different and perhaps more intuitive description, which utilizes a simple generalization of the nomenclature used for the unmodulated wave.

Thus in Chap. 9 the instantaneous gap voltage $\mathcal{U}$ was given by

$$\mathcal{U} = \text{Re}\,(V_1 e^{j\omega t}) = \text{Re}\,(-jV e^{j\omega t}) \tag{1}$$

where $V$ was a real constant [see Eq. (9·1)]. If in the modulated or transient case ω is taken to be the equilibrium oscillation frequency, then the above expression for $\mathcal{U}$ still holds with $V$ a (complex) slowly varying function of time. As distinguished from $\mathcal{U}$, the instantaneous gap voltage, $V$ may be called the "momentary" vector amplitude of the r-f gap voltage.

The same generalization may be used to describe any other modulated r-f variable, such as the components of the bunched beam current; the discussion makes use of $V$ simply as representative of all these other variables. The general procedure omits further specification of the time-dependence of momentary voltage and current amplitudes in discussing quasi-static bunching and oscillator circuit relations. However, the remainder of this section is concerned with periodic modulation as distinct from transients. When periodic modulation is discussed as such, $V$ may be expressed as a Fourier series with components at the fundamental and various harmonics of the modulation (or equivalent low-frequency modulation) frequency, and these components are the unknowns of the problem.

In an analysis of periodic modulation, where $V$ may be expressed as a Fourier series in the modulation frequency, a further important simplification may be made if the modulation is assumed to be small. It is seen in later sections that the importance of this assumption lies in the manner in which it makes modulations at different modulation frequencies additive in their effects; at large modulation, nonlinearities in the bunching process make the situation more complicated. The preservation of linearity by the use of small signals means that any applied modulation may be analyzed into its Fourier components, each of which constitutes an isolated problem; thus only the question of an applied modulation consisting of a single pure sine wave need be considered. This small-signal approximation is introduced here with these sketchy comments because it is used in the immediately subsequent discussion; the statements about the bunching process are discussed in more detail in the next section.

A sine wave of circular frequency $\omega$, amplitude modulated at a circular frequency $\Omega$, may be Fourier-analyzed by simple trigonometric relations into a carrier wave at $\omega$ plus two sidebands occurring at the sum and difference frequencies $\omega \pm \Omega$. A similarly phase- or frequency-modulated sine wave is equivalent to a carrier at the frequency $\omega$ plus an infinite number of sidebands occurring at frequencies $\omega \pm n\Omega$ where $n = 1, 2, \cdots \infty$. But in the latter case, if the phase or frequency modulation is small enough, the only appreciable and relevant sidebands are those adjacent to the carrier at $\omega \pm \Omega$. Since the present discussions are to be confined to small-signal theory, any combination of amplitude and phase modulation will give rise to only two sidebands, at $\omega \pm \Omega$. Since the wave trains and sideband structures produced by phase and frequency modulation are identical, and since this type of modulation is most easily thought of as phase modulation in the present case, frequency modulation is not referred to further.

A carrier voltage with two completely arbitrary sidebands is described by Eq. (1) and the following equation:

$$V \equiv V_0\alpha = V_0(\alpha_0 + \alpha_+ e^{j\Omega t} + \alpha_- e^{-j\Omega t}). \tag{2}$$

(The various $\alpha$'s are an additional notation introduced here for convenience in the later development.) This equation is the Fourier analysis of $V$ as referred to earlier, with only two time-dependent terms because of the small-signal assumption. Just as $V/V_0$ is taken to be real in Chap. 9, so now $\alpha_0$ may be taken as real as a matter of convenience without affecting the final results. The relative phase and magnitude of the complex quantities $\alpha_+$ and $\alpha_-$ depend on the specific type of modulation that Eq. (2) serves to describe.

The complex instantaneous voltage $V_1 e^{j\omega t} = -jV e^{j\omega t}$ is thus the sum of three vectors rotating counter clockwise in the complex plane at angular frequencies $\omega$, $\omega \pm \Omega$. The physical significance of the normalized sideband voltages $\alpha_\pm$ is most easily seen by considering the motion of these two sideband vectors with respect to the normalized carrier voltage $\alpha_0$, as shown in Eq. (2); $\alpha_+e^{i\Omega t}$ and $\alpha_-e^{-i\Omega t}$ rotate counter clockwise and clockwise respectively at the angular modulation frequency $\Omega$ about $\alpha_0$, as shown in Fig. 16·3. This motion of $\alpha_+e^{i\Omega t} + \alpha_-e^{-i\Omega t}$ with respect to $\alpha_0$ is slow compared with the rotation of the total normalized voltage vector $-j\alpha e^{i\omega t}$ about the origin. Hence it is apparent from Fig. 16·3 that the instantaneous real part of $\alpha_+e^{i\Omega t} + \alpha_-e^{-i\Omega t}$ gives the momentary change in the voltage amplitude; the imaginary part of

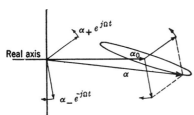

$(\alpha_+e^{i\Omega t} + \alpha_-e^{-i\Omega t})/\alpha_0$ gives the momentary phase shift in the voltage wave. These phase and amplitude deviations oscillate at the modulation frequency $\Omega$.

When $\alpha_+ = \alpha_-^*$, the amplitude but not the phase of $\alpha$ and of the instantaneous r-f gap voltage is modulated; when $\alpha_+ = -\alpha_-^*$, the phase but not the amplitude of $\alpha$ is modulated—at least to first order, which is all that matters in the

Fig. 16·3.—Composition of the complex normalized gap-voltage vector $\alpha$, in the presence of phase and amplitude modulation at the frequency $\Omega$. $\alpha = \alpha_0 + \alpha_+e^{i\Omega t} + \alpha_-e^{-i\Omega t}$.

small-signal applications in which these equations will be used. Thus it is convenient to define two new normalized voltages $\alpha_P$ and $\alpha_A$ ($P$ and $A$ for phase and amplitude) as follows:

$$\alpha_P^* \equiv \alpha_+ - \alpha_-^*; \qquad \alpha_A \equiv \alpha_+ + \alpha_-^*; \qquad (3a)$$
$$2\alpha_+ = \alpha_A + \alpha_P^*; \qquad 2\alpha_-^* = \alpha_A - \alpha_P^*. \qquad (3b)$$

The magnitudes and phases of $\alpha_P$ and $\alpha_A$ thus indicate the magnitude and phase of the amplitude and phase modulation of the instantaneous r-f gap voltage; $\alpha_P$ and $\alpha_A$ indicate the relative voltage response of phase-modulation and amplitude-modulation receivers receiving the output signal of the modulated oscillator.

The quantities $\alpha_A$ and $\alpha_P$ are proportional to the relative response of an amplitude-modulation or a hypothetical phase-modulation receiver. A given phase-modulated wave-train may be described either by a given excursion in phase or by an excursion in frequency that is equal to the product of this phase excursion and the modulation frequency; hence the response of a frequency-modulated receiver is proportional to $\Omega\alpha_P$. This suggests the definition of the quantity $\alpha_F$ to which the response of an f-m receiver is proportional:

$$\alpha_F \equiv \left(\frac{\Omega}{2\pi}\right)\alpha_P. \qquad (4)$$

The significance of $\alpha_A$ and $\alpha_P$ may be put in analytical form by expressing $\alpha$ in terms of $\alpha_P$ and $\alpha_A$ instead of $\alpha_\pm$:

$$\alpha = \alpha_0 \left[ 1 + \text{Re}\left( \frac{\alpha_A}{\alpha_0} e^{j\Omega t} \right) \right] e^{+j\text{Im}\left( \frac{\alpha_P{}^*}{\alpha_0} e^{j\Omega t} \right)}. \tag{5}$$

This relationship holds true only for $|\alpha_A| \ll \alpha_0$, $|\alpha_P| \ll \alpha_0$—that is, for the small-signal theory.

To this approximation, Eqs. (2) and (5) are exactly equivalent ways of expressing the value of $\alpha$ to use in Eq. (1). In Eq. (2) the voltages at the three frequencies $\omega$, $\omega \pm \Omega$ are explicitly separated in a form convenient for calculating the effect of the voltage modulation on the bunching process; this is therefore the form that is used in the bunching theory. The primary purpose of Eq. (5) is to emphasize the function of the normalized voltages $\alpha_A$ and $\alpha_P$ defined in Eqs. (3).

**16·5. Bunching in the Presence of Gap-voltage Modulation or Transients.**—Usually the reason for the existence of a modulation of the r-f gap voltage and of the output signal is a modulation of one of the oscillator parameters such as[1] $G_e$ or $\theta_0$. In the transient state when such modulation has just been initiated, the parameter modulation initially causes a bunched beam current modulation, which in turn causes r-f gap-voltage modulation; subsequently, or in the steady state, both r-f gap-voltage modulation and parameter modulation cause bunched-beam-current modulation simultaneously. Since small-signal modulation is assumed, the two modulations will not interfere with each other and may be calculated independently. The current modulation caused by a given gap-voltage modulation will be the same regardless of the original source of the over-all modulation, but that part of the current modulation arising directly from the modulation of applied electrode voltages (parameter modulation) must be calculated anew for each new type of applied modulation. It is convenient to use a different notation for these two contributions to the bunched beam current. Thus

$$I_1 = \text{Re}(i_1 e^{j\omega t}) \tag{6}$$

is the instantaneous value of the fundamental component of that part of bunched beam current caused by the modulated r-f gap voltage;

$$\Delta I_1 = \text{Re}(\Delta i_1 e^{j\omega t}) \tag{7}$$

is the corresponding contribution arising from the primary parameter modulation. Like $\alpha$, both $i_1$ and $\Delta i_1$ are slowly varying complex functions of time. The present section is concerned with deducing the properties of $i_1$ and $I_1$, the next section with those of $\Delta i_1$ and $\Delta I_1$.

In an oscillator in which an applied parameter has just been suddenly changed, with the result that the oscillator is in the transient state of

---

[1] In this chapter $\theta_0$ is the unmodulated value of reflection transit angle; the symbol $\theta$, used to denote this same quantity in Chap. 12, is reserved here for subsequent use as the modulated reflection transit angle.

approaching its new equilibrium, $\Delta i_1 = 0$ because the "applied parameter modulation" is only instantaneous. The calculation of $i_1$ is the same as it is when modulation is continuous, until detailed assumptions are made about the specific time dependence of $\alpha$.

*General Bunching Relations with an R-f Gap Voltage of Time-dependent Phase and Amplitude.*—To the limits of accuracy of the quasi-static approximation, the general relation between $i_1$ and $\alpha$ is a simple one.

The absolute value of $i_1$ is $2I_0 J_1(X)$, when $X = M\theta_0|\alpha|/2$. If $\alpha_0$ is used, in a sense somewhat broader than that of Eq. (2), to denote either the time-independent or final equilibrium value of $\alpha$, then the time-independent or final equilibrium value of $X$ may be denoted by $X_0$, where

$$X_0 = \frac{M\theta_0\alpha_0}{2}; \tag{8}$$

then $X$ is given by

$$X = \frac{X_0|\alpha|}{\alpha_0}. \tag{9}$$

Similarly the time-independent part of $i_1$, fundamental component of the bunched beam current, is denoted by $i_{10}$; by Eq. (9·9),

$$i_{10} = -je^{-i\phi}2I_0 J_1(X_0). \tag{10}$$

By the quasi-static assumption, the phase of $i_1$ is modified from that of $i_{10}$ by the factor $\alpha/|\alpha|$. Thus all told,

$$i_1 = -\frac{je^{-i\phi}2I_0 J_1(X)\alpha}{|\alpha|} \tag{11}$$

with $X$ given by Eq. (9).

*Effect of Steady-state Sinusoidal Modulation of R-f Gap Voltage.*—Equation (11), which is general as long as the quasi-static bunching limitation on modulation rate holds true, is now particularized somewhat for the case of a steady-state sinusoidal modulation of $\alpha$ at the frequency $\Omega$. For this purpose it is convenient to use the sideband expression for $\alpha$ in Eq. (2). The equivalent expression in terms of the degree of phase and amplitude modulation is given in Eq. (5). For small-signal modulation, that is, with

$$|\alpha_+| \ll \alpha_0, \qquad |\alpha_-| \ll \alpha_0,$$

it follows that

$$\frac{|\alpha|}{\alpha_0} \approx 1 + \text{Re}\left(\frac{\alpha_+}{\alpha_0}e^{i\Omega t} + \frac{\alpha_-}{\alpha_0}e^{-i\Omega t}\right) \tag{12}$$

$$\frac{\alpha}{|\alpha|} \approx 1 + j\,\text{Im}\left(\frac{\alpha_+}{\alpha_0}e^{i\Omega t} + \frac{\alpha_-}{\alpha_0}e^{-i\Omega t}\right).$$

Since

$$J_1(X) \approx J_1(X_0)\left[1 + \frac{J_1'(X_0)}{J_1(X_0)}(X - X_0)\right],$$

it follows from Eqs. (9), (11), and (12) that

$$\frac{i_1}{i_{10}} = 1 + \frac{J_1'(X_0)X_0}{J_1(X_0)}\operatorname{Re}\left(\frac{\alpha_+}{\alpha_0}e^{j\Omega t} + \frac{\alpha_-}{\alpha_0}e^{-j\Omega t}\right)$$
$$+ j\operatorname{Im}\left(\frac{\alpha_+}{\alpha_0}e^{j\Omega t} + \frac{\alpha_-}{\alpha_0}e^{-j\Omega t}\right). \quad (13)$$

Comparison of Eqs. (2) and (13) verifies that the phases of $i_1/i_{10}$ and $\alpha/\alpha_0$ are the same, as they should be; thus any phase modulation of $\alpha$ is reproduced in $i_1$. The relative amplitude modulation of $\alpha$ and $i_1$ are not the same in magnitude nor, for $X_0 > 1.84$, in sign; the reason, the nonlinear relation between $i_1$ or $J_1(X)$ and $X$, is obvious from Fig. 9·5. The deviation from unity of the function $X_0 J_1'(X_0)/J_1(X_0)$, which appears in Eq. (13), is a measure of this nonlinearity. It is convenient to specify this nonlinearity by the function $K(X_0)$:

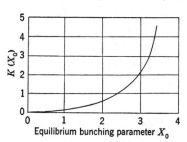

FIG. 16·4.—Dependence on equilibrium bunching parameter $X_0$ of the function $K(X_0)$.

$$K(X_0) \equiv \frac{1}{2}\left[1 - \frac{X_0 J_1'(X_0)}{J_1(X_0)}\right] \equiv 1 - \frac{X_0 J_0(X_0)}{2J_1(X_0)} \equiv \frac{X_0 J_2(X_0)}{2J_1(X_0)} \quad (14)$$

The function $K(X_0)$ is shown in Fig. 16·4. It is to be noted that $K(0) = 0$ and that $K(2.405) = 1$; $X_0 = 2.405$ is found in Chap. 12 to be the value of the bunching parameter at the center of a mode at optimum load with $G_e/G \gg 1$.

An analysis of $i_1$ into sideband components, corresponding to Eq. (2) for $\alpha$, shows some of the interesting consequences of the difference in the relative amplitude modulations of $\alpha$ and $i_1$. In a form similar to Eq. (2), $i_1$ may be written

$$\frac{i_1}{i_{10}} = 1 + \frac{i_{1+}}{i_{10}}e^{j\Omega t} + \frac{i_{1-}}{i_{10}}e^{-j\Omega t}. \quad (15)$$

A comparison of Eqs. (13) and (15) indicates, with the aid of Eq. (14) and some rearranging, that

$$\frac{i_{1+}}{i_{10}} = (1 - K)\frac{\alpha_+}{\alpha_0} - K\frac{\alpha_-^*}{\alpha_0} \quad (16a)$$

$$\left(\frac{i_{1-}}{i_{10}}\right)^* = -K\frac{\alpha_+}{\alpha_0} + (1 - K)\frac{\alpha_-^*}{\alpha_0}. \quad (16b)$$

Thus when $K \neq 0$—that is, when $X_0 > 0$—the two voltage side-bands do not act independently in producing the bunched beam current sidebands.[1] As already noted, $K = 1$ at loading for maximum output in a tube with $G_e/G \gg 1$; and at this particular operating point, by Eq. (16), each current sideband is produced solely by the opposite voltage sideband. This mixing of the sidebands by the nonlinearity of the bunching process has important consequences to be discussed later; it also provides an interesting example of the translation from phase-and-amplitude language into sideband language.

*Modulation of R-f Gap Voltage with a Spectrum of Modulation Frequencies.*—Another point of comparison between Eqs. (13) or (16) and Eq. (2) that should be noted, although it is mathematically trivial, is the fact that the voltage sidebands at $\omega \pm \Omega$ generate current sidebands only at $\omega \pm \Omega$ and at no other frequencies. This is simply a consequence of the assumption of small-signal modulation. For sizable modulation, such that $|\alpha_+| \ll \alpha_0$ no longer is true, comparable current sidebands occur at $\omega \pm \Omega$, $2\Omega$, $3\Omega$, $\cdots$ ; but for small modulation, the modulating signal may be decomposed into its components at various frequencies $\Omega$; each component has two sidebands at $\omega \pm \Omega$ and each acts independently of other component frequencies of the signal. Consequently, the theory of small-signal modulation at a single frequency is very easily generalized to cover any arbitrary small-signal modulation involving a spectrum of frequencies. This point is briefly commented upon in the preceding section.

**16·6. Effect of Primary Modulation of Oscillator Parameters.**—It has already been noted that an additional modulation of the bunched beam current also often arises from the primary modulation of oscillator parameters; the complex amplitude of this contribution, which is present only with continuous modulation, was denoted by $\Delta i_1$. As in gap-voltage modulation, this source contributes nothing to $i_{10}$; hence $\Delta i_1$ may be written

$$\Delta i_1 = \Delta i_{1+}e^{i\Omega t} + \Delta i_{1-}e^{-i\Omega t}. \tag{17}$$

The values of $\Delta i_\pm$ will now be calculated for a series of different primary parameter modulations.

*Low-frequency Beam-current Modulation.*—The first parameter modulation to be considered is the low-frequency modulation of the beam current at the frequency $\Omega$, as indicated thus:

$$I = I_0[1 + m \cos (\Omega t + \gamma)]. \tag{18}$$
$$= I_0 \left\{ 1 + \frac{m}{2} [e^{i(\Omega t + \gamma)} + e^{-i(\Omega t + \gamma)}] \right\}.$$

[1] This was first noted in J. K. Knipp, "Theory of Noise from the Reflex Oscillator," RL Report No. 873, Jan. 10, 1946. See also Chap. 17.

By the quasi-static assumption, the amplitude of the bunched beam current is modulated in the same manner as is the d-c beam current because the momentary value of any component of the bunched beam current is proportional to the momentary value of the beam current.  Thus

$$\frac{(i_{10} + \Delta i_{1+}e^{i\Omega t} + \Delta i_{1-}e^{-i\Omega t})}{i_{10}} = \frac{I}{I_0};$$

comparison with Eq. (18) shows that

$$\frac{\Delta i_{1\pm}}{i_{10}} = \frac{m}{2}\,e^{\pm i\gamma}. \tag{19}$$

*High-frequency Beam-current Modulation.*—By this term is meant the modulation of $I_0$ at a frequency $(n\omega + \Omega)$ distant by the small amount $\Omega$ from one of the harmonics, $n\omega$, of the oscillation frequency:

$$I = I_0\{1 + m\cos[(n\omega + \Omega)t + \gamma]\}. \tag{20}$$

Here the frequency $\Omega$ may be either positive or negative.  From the usual quasi-static viewpoint, the momentary values of $I$ and of the bunched beam current are those calculated on the basis of a modulation of $I_0$ at the harmonic frequency $n\omega$ and with the momentary phase $(\Omega t + \gamma)$.  This principle allows a direct application of the results of Sec. 9·9 where it is shown that a beam-current modulation

$$I = I_0[1 + m\cos(n\omega t + \gamma)] \tag{9·66}$$

gives rise to the following fundamental component of the bunched beam current:

$$i_1 = -2I_0 e^{-i\theta_0}\left\{J_1(X_0) - \frac{m}{2}[e^{i\gamma}J_{n-1}(X_0) + e^{-i\gamma}(-1)^{n+1}J_{n+1}(X_0)]\right\}. \tag{9·67}$$

By replacing, in these equations from Chap. 9, the constant phase $\gamma$ by the momentarily constant phase $(\Omega t + \gamma)$, it is apparent that

$$\frac{\Delta i_{1-}}{i_{10}} = \frac{m}{2}\frac{(-1)^n e^{-i\gamma}J_{n+1}(X_0)}{J_1(X_0)}.$$

The value of $\Delta i_{1+}/i_{10}$ is almost the same as for $\Delta i_{1-}/i_{10}$, except that in this latter quantity an additional factor must be taken into account.  This is the fact that when $n = 1$ the modulated beam current has a component at $\omega + \Omega$ even on the first passage of the beam through the r-f gap; this component, $mI_0 e^{i\gamma}$ in the complex notation, must be added to the second-transit component with reversed sign.  This process is carried out; then with the aid of the results of the preceding paragraph, it is found that

$$\frac{\Delta i_{1+}}{i_{10}} = \frac{[-je^{j\phi} - J_0(X_0)]}{2J_1(X_0)} me^{j\gamma}, \qquad (n = 1), \tag{21}$$

$$\frac{\Delta i_{1-}}{i_{10}} = \frac{-me^{-j\gamma}J_2(X_0)}{2J_1(X_0)},$$

$$\frac{\Delta i_{1+}}{i_{10}} = \frac{-me^{j\gamma}J_{n-1}(X_0)}{2J_1(X_0)}, \qquad (n > 1), \tag{22}$$

$$\frac{\Delta i_{1-}}{i_{10}} = \frac{(-1)^n e^{-j\gamma}mJ_{n+1}(X_0)}{2J_1(X_0)}.$$

*Low-frequency Reflection-time Modulation.*—The reflection time $\theta_0$ affects the components of the bunched beam current in two ways: through the dependence on $\theta_0$ of both the bunching parameter and the relative phase $\phi$. The bunching parameter is proportional to $\theta_0$, whereas $\phi$ is a small difference between the value of $\theta_0$ for a given electrode voltage and the value of $\theta_0$ at the center of the modes; since $\theta_0 \gg 1$ usually, a small change in $\theta_0$ makes a much larger change in $\phi$ than in $X$. Hence the effect of reflection-time modulation on the bunching parameter and the magnitude of the current components is ignored, and only the effects on the phase of the bunched current are considered.

The modulated value of $\theta_0$ is denoted by $\theta$ and is taken as

$$\theta = \theta_0[1 + m \cos (\Omega t + \gamma)];$$

hence if $\phi_0$ is the d-c value of $\phi$, the momentary value is

$$\phi = \phi_0 + (\theta - \theta_0) = \phi_0 + m\theta_0 \cos (\Omega t + \gamma). \tag{23}$$

For $m\theta_0 \ll 1$,

$$e^{-j\phi} = e^{-j\phi_0} \left\{ 1 - j\frac{m\theta_0}{2} [e^{j(\Omega t + \gamma)} + e^{-j(\Omega t + \gamma)}] \right\};$$

and since this is the only factor through which this modulation affects the bunched beam current,

$$\frac{\Delta i_{1\pm}}{i_{10}} = \frac{-jm\theta_0 e^{\pm j\gamma}}{2}. \tag{24}$$

*High-frequency Reflection-time Modulation.*—As in the discussion of low-frequency reflection-time modulation, amplitude effects are ignored; thus the effect of the modulation

$$\theta = \theta_0\{1 + m \cos [(n\omega + \Omega)t + \gamma]\}$$

is taken as equivalent to the modulation

$$\phi = \phi_0 + m\theta_0 \cos [(n\omega + \Omega)t + \gamma]. \tag{25}$$

Just as in high-frequency beam-current modulation, the quasi-static approximation allows representation of this modulation as modulation at the harmonic frequency $n\omega$ and the momentary phase $(\gamma + \Omega t)$. In Sec. 9·9, a phase modulation given by

$$\theta = \theta_0 + m\theta_0 \cos(n\omega t + \gamma),$$

where $\gamma$ is constant, is found to give the following fundamental component of the bunched beam current:

$$i_1 = -2I_0 e^{-i\theta_0} \left\{ J_1(X_0) + j\frac{m\theta_0}{2}[J_{n-1}(X_0)e^{-i\gamma} + (-1)^{n+1}J_{n+1}(X_0)e^{i\gamma})] \right\}.$$

By replacing, in these equations, the constant phase $\gamma$ by the momentarily constant phase $(\Omega t + \gamma)$, these equations are made applicable to the present case to the degree of accuracy of the quasi-static approximation. The result is

$$\frac{\Delta i_{1+}}{i_{10}} = \frac{jm\theta_0(-1)^{n+1}J_{n+1}(X_0)e^{i\gamma}}{2J_1(X_0)} \tag{26a}$$

$$\frac{\Delta i_{1-}}{i_{10}} = \frac{jm\theta_0 J_{n-1}(X_0)e^{-i\gamma}}{2J_1(X_0)}. \tag{26b}$$

Since the modulation is applied between the first and second gap-transits of the beam, there is no such sideband at $\omega + \Omega$ in the first gap-transit as there was in the case of high-frequency current modulation.

**16·7. Driving of a Resonant Circuit by a Slowly Changing R-f Current.**—Before considering the modulated oscillator as a whole, two necessary steps must be taken. The first of these, deduction of the bunched beam current generated by the modulated r-f gap voltage and by the primary parameter modulation, has just been discussed; the second step, investigation of the way in which such a time-varying r-f current drives a resonant circuit, is discussed in this section. The time dependence of the fundamental bunched beam current component $i_1$ will initially be left completely arbitrary, and will then be particularized to the case of a pure sine-wave modulation.

Any time-varying r-f current, periodic or aperiodic, may be Fourier-analyzed into its components at various frequencies; and the over-all response of the resonant circuit, since the latter is composed of linear elements, may be obtained by adding up the individual responses to each frequency component of the bunched beam. This approach is used in the next chapter in discussing noise modulation, but the present section continues with the perhaps more intuitive quasi-static procedure used so far in this chapter. Thus there is deduced a differential equation describing the way in which the momentary r-f gap voltage is determined by the momentary bunched beam current; this differential equation is applicable to transients and to continuous modulation alike. When particularized to the case of a sinusoidally modulated driving current·

the differential equation may be reduced to linear relations between the carrier and sideband amplitudes of the driving current and the r-f gap voltage. As has already been noted, the linearity of the circuit elements makes driving current sidebands at $\omega \pm \Omega$ produce voltage sidebands only at $\omega \pm \Omega$; hence no interaction between the effects of current sidebands at different values of $\Omega$ need be considered.

The present section is concerned solely with the driving of the resonant circuit, without any reference to the origin of the driving current. To forestall a suspicion of confused nomenclature, however, an anticipatory comment about the use of the results of Secs. 16·5 and 16·6 should be made. There it was found that when the over-all modulation is the result of continued modulation of one of the oscillator parameters (more concretely, one of the applied electrode voltages), then this parameter modulation adds a modulated current component $\Delta i_1$ to the modulated current $i_1$ that would be generated by the modulated gap voltage alone. There are other means of primary modulation—for example, the microphonic modulation of the circuit's resonant frequency or the excitation of the oscillator circuit from an external source at the frequency

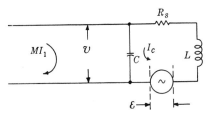

FIG. 16·5.—Equivalent circuit for resonant cavity, used in discussion of driving of resonant cavity by a modulated r-f current. $R_s = 1/GQ^2$; $MI_1 = \mathrm{Re}\,(Mi_1 e^{j\omega t})$; $\mathcal{U} = \mathrm{Re}\,(-jV e^{j\omega t})$; $\varepsilon = (1/Q)\,\mathrm{Re}\,(E e^{j\omega t})$.

$\omega + \Omega$, the effects of which may be described as being due to a voltage generator within the circuit itself. It is convenient to develop the circuit and oscillator equations in a unified manner in which the effect of the primary modulation is always represented by an equivalent voltage output, denoted by $E/Q$, of a generator located within the circuit, as shown in Fig. 16·5. Thus when the physical driving current is $i_1 + \Delta i_1$, the effect will be represented as due to a driving current $i_1$ and an output voltage $E/Q$ from the equivalent voltage generator. Cavity and load losses are for convenience represented as a series resistance $R_s$, given by $R_s = 1/GQ^2$ where $G$ is the corresponding shunt conductance.

The details of this equivalent voltage generator are discussed later. This brief discussion of the equivalent oscillator circuit of Fig. 16·4 has been carried out so as to make clear that the use of only $Mi_1$ to represent the driving current is not a conflict of notation with the previous section; this discussion is also intended to make temporarily palatable the introduction of the voltage generator. The topic of the moment is the following: Given a resonant circuit, driven as in Fig. 16·5 by shunt current and series voltage generators with instantaneous outputs

$$MI_1 = M \text{ Re } (i_1 e^{j\omega t}) \tag{27a}$$

$$\mathcal{E} = \frac{1}{Q} \text{ Re } (E e^{j\omega t}), \tag{27b}$$

in which $i_1$ and $E$ are slowly varying functions of time; what is the value of the instantaneous gap voltage $\mathcal{V}$ and the instantaneous circuit current $I_c$? Or more to the point, what is the time dependence of $\alpha$?

The instantaneous signal-generator current and circuit current of Fig. 16·5 are $MI_1$ and $I_c$ respectively. The latter may be immediately disposed of by noting that the rate of change of the instantaneous electromagnetic energy $\frac{1}{2}C\mathcal{V}^2$ stored in the capacitance $C$ is given by

$$\frac{d}{dt} \frac{1}{2} C\mathcal{V}^2 = C\mathcal{V} \frac{d\mathcal{V}}{dt} = \mathcal{V}(I_c + MI_1),$$

and hence that

$$I_c = C \frac{d\mathcal{V}}{dt} - MI_1. \tag{28}$$

The vanishing of the instantaneous voltage drop around the circuit of Fig. 16·1 may be written as follows:

$$0 = \mathcal{V} + \frac{I_c}{GQ^2} + L \frac{dI_c}{dt} - \mathcal{E}.$$

Utilizing the value of $I_c$ from Eq. (28), and writing $\mathcal{V}' \equiv d\mathcal{V}/d(\omega t)$, where as usual $\omega$ is taken to be the frequency of $I_1$ and $\mathcal{V}$ in the equilibrium state, the above equation becomes

$$\left(\frac{\omega}{\omega_0}\right)^2 \mathcal{V}'' + \frac{\omega}{\omega_0} \frac{1}{Q} \mathcal{V}' + \mathcal{V} = \mathcal{E} + \frac{M}{GQ} \left(\frac{I_1}{Q} + \frac{\omega}{\omega_0} I_1'\right). \tag{29}$$

Here $\omega_0^2 = 1/LC$.

Since Eq. (29) is linear with real coefficients, the real quantities therein may be replaced by the corresponding vector (complex) quantities of which the real parts are taken in Eqs. (1), (2), and (27). If this change is made and the differentiation indicated in Eq. (29) is carried out, the latter becomes

$$\left(\frac{\omega}{\omega_0}\right)^2 \alpha'' + \left(2j \frac{\omega}{\omega_0} + \frac{1}{Q}\right) \frac{\omega}{\omega_0} \alpha' + \left(1 - \frac{\omega^2}{\omega_0^2} + \frac{j}{Q} \frac{\omega}{\omega_0}\right) \alpha = \frac{j}{Q} \frac{E}{V_0}$$
$$+ \frac{jM}{GQV_0} \left[\frac{i_1}{Q} + \frac{\omega}{\omega_0} (i_1' + ji_1)\right].$$

Here $\omega/\omega_0$ may be set equal to unity except in the resonance term $(1 - \omega^2/\omega_0^2)$; and in the right-hand member of the equation, the driving term, $i_1'$ and $i_1/Q$ may be neglected compared with $i_1$; $i_1'/i_1$ is small because of the assumed slow rate of change of $i_1$.  Writing, as usual,

$$\delta = \frac{(\omega - \omega_0)}{\omega_0},$$

the above form of Eq. (29) becomes

$$\alpha'' + \left(2j + \frac{1}{Q}\right)\alpha' + \frac{j}{Q}(1 + 2jQ\delta)\alpha = \frac{j}{Q}\frac{E}{V_0} - \frac{M}{GQV_0}i_1. \qquad (30)$$

This, then, is a general equation giving the momentary gap voltage of a resonant circuit in terms of the momentary driving current and voltage shown in Fig. 16·5.  It holds not only for a reflex oscillator, but equally well for the output circuit of any klystron or of any other device described by Fig. 16·5.  In the equilibrium case (that is,

$$\alpha' = \alpha'' = E = 0),$$

this equation reduces to the familiar

$$V_1 = -j\alpha V_0 = \frac{Mi_1}{G(1 + 2jQ\delta)}.$$

In subsequent sections the circuit relations given by Eq. (30) are correlated with the bunching relations from Sec. 16·5 to determine the behavior of the oscillator as a whole.

**16·8. Transient Phenomena; Pulse Buildup.**—A transient state, as the expression is used in this chapter, refers to the approach to a new equilibrium after a sudden change in some oscillator parameter or applied voltage.  One of the most common transient phenomena in the reflex oscillator is the buildup of the amplitude of oscillation from zero when the various applied voltages or oscillator parameters are suddenly given values permitting oscillation.  Since in much common usage the duration of a condition allowing oscillation is very short, of the order of magnitude of a microsecond, the nature of the resultant output pulse is considerably influenced by the time taken for oscillation to build up initially.

The transient phenomena in such a "pulse buildup" are analyzed with the aid of the bunching relations and circuit relations of the preceding sections; such an analysis serves as an illustration of the method to be used with other transient phenomena.  The final results must, of course, be subjected to a requirement of self-consistency in that they must not indicate a buildup so rapid as to be out of line with the quasi-static approximation.  The results of the calculation meet this requirement, as is almost obvious from the beginning; and they are in good agreement with experiment, as a final illustrative comparison shows.

*General Oscillator Relations in Transient Phenomena.*—The necessary information for a discussion of transient phenomena is given in Eqs. (11) and (30), which show respectively the generation of $i_1$ by the processes of velocity modulation and bunching, and the driving of the oscillator circuit by $i_1$. These equations may be simplified somewhat before being combined to give the over-all oscillator behavior. Thus in transient phenomena, the parameter modulation is not continual but consists merely of the discontinuous change that initiates the transient; hence $\Delta i_1$ and $E$ are zero.

Another simplification may be made if the limiting form of Eqs. (11) and (30) in the equilibrium case is noted. Here $\alpha' = \alpha'' = 0$ in Eq. (30), and $i_1 = i_{10} = -je^{-i\phi}2I_0J_1(X_0)$ in Eq. (11). Combined, these two equations then give

$$\frac{2J_1(X_0)}{X_0} \frac{G_e}{G} e^{-i\phi} = 1 + 2jQ\delta,$$

which is simply Eq. (12·3) in slightly altered form, as it should be. Thus, the statement in the preceding section—that $\delta$ and $\omega$ refer to the time-independent or final equilibrium oscillator frequency—is justified. Using in Eq. (30) the above relation for $(1 + 2jQ\delta)$ and the value of $i_1$ from Eq. (11), and setting $E = 0$, the oscillator equation applicable to transient phenomena in general is found to be

$$\alpha'' + \left(2j + \frac{1}{Q}\right)\alpha' + \frac{je^{-i\phi}}{Q}\frac{G_e}{G}\left[\frac{2J_1(X_0)}{X_0} - \frac{2J_1(X)}{X}\right]\alpha = 0. \quad (31)$$

*Pulse Buildup.*—In the particular case of the transient buildup of oscillation when the oscillator is suddenly "turned on," the oscillation must start from a very low noise level, which is discussed later in more detail. During by far the largest portion of the buildup period $X \ll 1$, $2J_1(X)/X \approx 1$, and the coefficient of $\alpha$ in Eq. (31) is constant. In most practical instances a negligible error is made if the coefficient of $\alpha$ in Eq. (31) is assumed to be proportional to $[2J_1(X_0)/X_0 - 1]$ right up to the point when $X = X_0$. If this coefficient is written as $-jae^{-i\phi}$, where

$$a \equiv \frac{1}{Q}\frac{G_e}{G}\left[1 - \frac{2J_1(X_0)}{X_0}\right] = \frac{1}{Q}\left[\frac{G_e}{G} - \frac{1}{\cos\phi}\right], \quad (32)$$

Eq. (31) becomes

$$\alpha'' + \left(2j + \frac{1}{Q}\right)\alpha' - jae^{-i\phi}\alpha = 0. \quad (33)$$

This equation for the momentary normalized gap voltage $\alpha$ must now be solved subject to the proper boundary conditions. At the instant $t = 0$, taken as the time when $G_e$ or $\phi$ is suddenly given the value used in Eqs. (31) and (32), $\alpha$ has some value $\alpha_N$ determined by shot noise in the beam or thermal fluctuations in the circuit; $\alpha(0) = \alpha_N$, $\alpha'(0) = 0$. Since $\alpha(0)$ is a noise fluctuation voltage, the boundary condition $\alpha'(0) = 0$ is not especially significant; but this fact does not matter much, since the only effect of this latter boundary condition is to introduce a subtransient that decays exponentially. If only that part of the solution which builds up exponentially is written, $\alpha$ is given by

$$\alpha = \alpha_N e^{\frac{a}{2}\omega t(\cos\phi + j\sin\phi)}. \tag{34}$$

Thus, in addition to an exponential increase in $\alpha$ there is also a phase shift linear in time—or what is the same thing, a constant deviation of frequency from the equilibrium value. Since the instantaneous voltage is proportional to $\alpha e^{j\omega t}$, the frequency during buildup is

$$\omega \left(1 + \frac{a}{2} \sin \phi \right);$$

there is no frequency shift at the center of the mode. Both the exponential increase in $\alpha$ and the constant frequency shift taper off as $X$ approaches $X_0$.

By Eqs. (32) and (34), the exponential time constant $t_0$ is given by

$$\frac{1}{\omega t_0} = \frac{a}{2} \cos \phi = \frac{1}{2Q} \left(\frac{G_e}{G} \cos \phi - 1 \right). \tag{35}$$

For an oscillator in which $G_e/G_{BR} \gg 1$ and which is working at optimum load for maximum output, $G_e/G = 2.32$ and $Q \, \Delta f_{1/2}/f = 1.21$. Here and in what follows, $\Delta f_{1/2}$ is the half-power electronic tuning range. For this ideal oscillator,

$$\frac{1}{\omega t_0} = \frac{\Delta f_{1/2}}{f} (0.96 \cos \phi - 0.41). \tag{36}$$

Thus, the time in radians required for the oscillation to build up by a factor $e$ at $\phi = 0$ is approximately 2/(fractional electronic-tuning range). Since many practical oscillators deviate widely from the ideal oscillator, any actual numerical calculation should be based on Eq. (35); an example of such a calculation and a comparison of the result with experiment are given later.

If Eq. (34) is rewritten as

$$|\alpha| = \alpha_N e^{t/t_0}, \tag{37}$$

it is apparent that, if the final equilibrium value that $|\alpha|$ takes up is $\alpha_E$, the time $\tau$ required to build up from the initial $\alpha_N$ to the final $\alpha_E$ is given by

$$\omega \tau = \omega t_0 \ln \left(\frac{\alpha_E}{\alpha_N}\right). \tag{38}$$

*Initial Noise Level* is thus of considerable importance.   With no beam current at all, the mean-square fluctuation voltage across the r-f gap due to the Johnson thermal noise in the equivalent shunt conductance $G$ of the resonator is given by

$$\overline{V_T^2} = \left( \frac{4kT \, \Delta f_c}{G} \right) \quad \text{volts}^2,$$

where $\Delta f_c$ is now the cavity bandwidth, not the electronic-tuning range; $k$, Boltzmann's constant, is $1.4 \times 10^{-23}$ joules/degree and $G$ is measured in mhos.   To this $\overline{V_T^2}$ corresponds an $\alpha$, which may be denoted by $\alpha_T$, given by

$$\alpha_T = \sqrt{\frac{\overline{V_T^2}}{\overline{V_0^2}}} = \frac{2}{V_0} \sqrt{\frac{kT \, \Delta f_c}{G}}. \tag{39}$$

If, however, there is beam current passing through the resonator, the shot noise provides a fluctuation current $\overline{i^2} = 2eI_0 \, \Delta f_c$, where $e$ is the charge on the electron, $e = 1.6 \times 10^{-19}$ coulombs.   This fluctuation current induces an r-f gap voltage corresponding to an $\alpha$, denoted by $\alpha_S$, which is given by

$$\alpha_S = \frac{M\overline{i^2}}{GV_0} = \frac{M}{GV_0} \sqrt{2eI_0 \, \Delta f_c}. \tag{40}$$

In practical oscillators, $\alpha_S \gg \alpha_T$.   By application of Eq. (30) to the buildup of gap voltage that is due to shot noise it appears that this buildup is proportional to $(1 - e^{-\omega t/2Q})$—that is, $\alpha \approx \alpha_S$ after $Q/\pi$ cycles have elapsed from the time the beam current is turned on.   If $\alpha$ were building up from $\alpha_T$ by the process of oscillator buildup it would have increased by a factor of only about $e$ in this time.   Since $\alpha_T \ll \alpha_S$, it appears, then, that the initial noise level is effectively $\alpha_N = \alpha_S$; if any correction were made to Eq. (38) for the time required to go from $\alpha_T$ to $\alpha_S$ by shot noise excitation, Eq. (38) would read

$$\omega\tau = \omega t_0 \ln \left( \frac{\alpha_E}{\alpha_S} \right) + 2Q. \tag{41}$$

*Pulse Buildup in the 2K25.*—As an illustration of the foregoing relations, the type 2K25 reflex klystron may be considered.   For the 2K25, $M = 0.65$, $V_0 = 300$ volts, and $I_0 = 20$ ma.   For the ($n = 5$)-mode, allowing for absorption of beam current on grids, these numbers indicate

$$G_e = 1.9 \times 10^{-4} \text{ mhos.}$$

An observed starting current with zero external load of 7 to 10 ma, together with the above value of $G_e$, indicates that at load for maximum output $G_e/G = 1.5$ or $G \approx 1.3 \times 10^{-4}$ mhos.   From this same starting current may be deduced $Q \, \Delta f_{\frac{1}{2}}/f \approx 0.6$; for $\Delta f_{\frac{1}{2}} = 55$ Mc/sec at $f = 9400$ Mc/sec, this gives $Q = 100$, which also agrees with cold measurements, so these results are consistent so far. The above value of $G$ would be made falsely high by any reflector phase aberrations and therefore needs a little reducing. The end result for the ingredients of a numerical calculation are: $Q = 100$; $G = 1.0 \times 10^{-4}$ mhos; $\Delta f_c = 94$ Mc/sec; $f = 9400$ Mc/sec; $G_e/G = 1.5$; $I_0 = 13$ ma on first passage of the beam through the resonator.

These numbers give, with the foregoing equations,

$$\alpha_S = 1.35 \times 10^{-5},$$
$$\alpha_T = 4.2 \times 10^{-7},$$
$$\alpha_E = 0.17,$$
$$\omega t_0 = 400 \qquad \text{radians,}$$
$$\omega \tau = 400 \ln 12{,}600 + 200 = 4000 \qquad \text{radians,}$$
$$\tau = 640 \text{ cycles} = 0.07 \qquad \mu\text{sec.}$$

Since the starting time observed under comparable conditions varies between 0.1 and 0.05 $\mu$sec, the agreement is good.

**16·9. General Oscillator Relations with Sinusoidal Modulation.—** As has already been noted several times, any periodic modulation may, to the degree of accuracy of the small-signal approximation, be subjected to a Fourier analysis and the effects of each of its component frequencies considered separately. Thus the momentary amplitudes $\alpha$, $E$, and $i_1$ that appear in the circuit equation, Eq. (30), and the bunching equation, Eq. (11), have already been written in a form that covers the general case:

$$\alpha = \alpha_0 + \alpha_+ e^{j\Omega t} + \alpha_- e^{-j\Omega t}, \qquad (2)$$
$$i_1 = i_{10} + i_{1+} e^{j\Omega t} + i_{1-} e^{-j\Omega t}, \qquad (15)$$
$$E = E_+ e^{j\Omega t} + E_- e^{-j\Omega t}. \qquad (42)$$

In the discussion of the bunching theory in Secs. 16·5 and 16·6, the values of $i_{10}$, $i_{1\pm}$ for given $\alpha_0$, $\alpha_\pm$ have been determined [Eqs. (10) and (16)]; the current sidebands were found to be linear functions of the gap-voltage sidebands. If these values of $i_{10}$, $i_{1\pm}$ and the expressions for $i_1$ and $\alpha$ in Eqs. (15) and (2) are combined with the circuit equation, Eq. (30), the behavior of the modulated oscillator should be completely specified.

The resulting equation is really three separate equations arising from the time-independent portion, the coefficients of $e^{j\Omega t}$, and the coefficients of $e^{-j\Omega t}$. The equation derived from the time-independent terms is the ordinary equilibrium equation, Eq. (12), as has already been noted in the previous section. From the coefficients of $e^{\pm j\Omega t}$ there result the following equations:

$$K(X_0)(1 + 2jQ\delta)(\alpha_+ + \alpha_-^*) + 2jW\alpha_+ = \frac{E_+}{V_0},$$

$$K(X_0)(1 - 2jQ\delta)(\alpha_+ + \alpha_-^*) + 2jW\alpha_-^* = \frac{E_-^*}{V_0}. \tag{43}$$

Here $W$ is a measure of the modulation frequency in terms of the cavity bandwidth; $W$ is defined by the equation

$$W \equiv \frac{Q\Omega}{\omega}. \tag{44}$$

The Eqs. (43) may be solved for $\alpha_\pm$; if this is done and if the equilibrium relation

$$1 + 2jQ\delta = \frac{e^{-i\phi}}{\cos\phi}$$

is utilized as a means of slight simplification, then it is found that

$$4jW(K + jW)\alpha_+ V_0 = \left(\frac{Ke^{i\phi}}{\cos\phi} + 2jW\right) E_+ - \frac{Ke^{-i\phi}E_-^*}{\cos\phi}$$

$$4jW(K + jW)\alpha_-^* V_0 = \left(\frac{Ke^{-i\phi}}{\cos\phi} + 2jW\right) E_-^* - \frac{Ke^{i\phi}E_+}{\cos\phi}. \tag{45}$$

This is the basic oscillator relation, which shows how the gap-voltage sideband amplitudes $\alpha_\pm V_0$ are determined by the output $jE/Q$ of the equivalent voltage generator that represents the effect of the primary parameter modulation.

*Determination of the Equivalent Voltage Generator.*—In Fig. 16·1 the oscillator circuit is shown being driven by both the voltage $jE/Q$ and the current $Mi_1$. Only the former appears in Eq. (45) because, as has been already noted, $Mi_1$ includes the equilibrium r-f current and, in addition, only that part of the current sidebands which is the direct result of the gap-voltage modulation; this explicit dependence of $Mi_1$ on $\alpha$ has already been utilized in obtaining Eqs. (43) and (45). The equivalent-voltage-generator output is a catch-all used to describe any factor whose influence on the circuit equation, Eq. (30), cannot be explicitly calculated from $\alpha$. The most frequent source of this driving voltage $jE/Q$ is simply the additional r-f driving-current component $\Delta i_1$, which arises from the primary parameter modulation rather than from the gap-voltage modulation. Since $\Delta i_1 = \Delta i_{1+}e^{i\Omega t} + \Delta i_{1-}e^{-i\Omega t}$, it is apparent from Eq. (30) that the voltage-generator output, the effect of which is equivalent to the additional driving current $\Delta i_1$, is given by

$$E_\pm = \frac{jM\,\Delta i_{1\pm}}{G}. \tag{46}$$

If oscillator modulation is accomplished by some means other than the application of a modulation to the beam, $\Delta i_1$ is zero; $E$ may still be found as that term whose presence is required to maintain the form of Eq. (30).    Several illustrations serve to elucidate this point.

As an example, suppose that the resonant frequency of the oscillator circuit is modulated at the low frequency $\Omega$ by some means—this might occur by microphonics or it might be caused by a beam current modulation, which would in turn vary the space charge in the gap region and hence the resonant frequency.    Whatever the reason, the resonant frequency $\omega_0$ is given by

$$\omega_0 = \omega_{00}[1 + m \cos(\Omega t + \gamma)]. \tag{47}$$

If this new time-dependence of $\omega_0$ is inserted in Eq. (29), an additional term is eventually added to Eq. (30); the form of Eq. (30) remains unaltered if this additional term is absorbed in $E$, giving

$$E_\pm = jm\alpha_0 V_0 Q e^{\pm j\gamma}. \tag{48}$$

This illustration is of more pedagogic than practical interest because it is obvious from the quasi-static viewpoint that a given modulation of $\omega_0$ will produce the same modulation in the oscillation frequency $\omega$.

As another illustration, suppose that an externally supplied r-f signal at frequency $\omega + \Omega$ is introduced into the resonator circuit.    If the generator of this signal is isolated from the oscillator in question by sufficient attenuation, it is obvious, without discussing the details of the r-f input arrangement, that

$$\begin{aligned} E_+ &= \text{constant}, \\ E_- &= 0. \end{aligned} \tag{49}$$

*Phase and Amplitude Modulation.*—The specific values of $\Delta i_{1\pm}$ and of $E_\pm$ for specific modulations are shortly used to deduce oscillator-output characteristics such as are given by Eq. (45).    The latter equation, however, gives the relative amplitudes of the sidebands as they would be seen individually by a narrow-band receiver or a spectrum analyzer. In most practical cases the important thing is the way in which these sidebands and the carrier cooperate to produce an amplitude-modulated or phase-modulated wave train, the amplitude or phase modulation of which is then detected by a suitable wideband receiver.    Hence of more importance than $\alpha_\pm$ are the quantities $\alpha_A$, $\alpha_P$, and $W\alpha_P \equiv (Q/f)\alpha_F$ as defined in Eqs. (3) and (4), to which quantities are proportional the responses of receivers using amplitude modulation (AM), hypothetical phase modulation (PM), and frequency modulation (FM), respectively.

As an aid in rephrasing Eq. (45) in terms of amplitude and phase modulation, the amplitude and phase-modulation components of the output of the equivalent voltage generator may be defined as follows, by analogy to Eq. (3):

$$E_A = E_+ + E_-^*; \qquad E_P^* = E_+ - E_-^* \qquad (50a)$$
$$2E_+ = E_A + E_P^*; \qquad 2E_-^* = E_A - E_P^*. \qquad (50b)$$

In terms of these quantities, Eqs. (45) become

$$2(K + jW)\alpha_A V_0 = E_A,$$
$$2(K + jW)W\alpha_P^* V_0 = -j(K + jW)E_P^* + KE_A \tan \phi. \qquad (51)$$

These Eqs. (51) are used in the next sections to deduce the specific output characteristics resulting from the various specific modulations considered in this section and in Sec. 16·6.

**16·10. Low-frequency Modulation of Beam Current and Reflection Transit Time.**—The values of $\Delta i_{1\pm}$ for low-frequency modulation of the beam current and the reflection transit time have been found in Sec. 16·6, and are given in Eqs. (19) and (24). These values of $\Delta i_{1\pm}$ may be utilized in Eq. (46) to give the values of $E_\pm$ which characterize the equivalent voltage generators; the amplitude and phase-modulation components of the latter are then found by Eq. (50) to be the following:

1. Low-frequency beam-current modulation:

$$E_A = m\alpha_0 V_0 e^{j\gamma}, \qquad (52)$$
$$E_P^* = jm\alpha_0 V_0 e^{j\gamma} \tan \phi.$$

2. Low-frequency reflector-voltage modulation:

$$E_A = m\theta_0\alpha_0 V_0 e^{j\gamma} \tan \phi \qquad (53)$$
$$E_P^* = -jm\theta_0\alpha_0 V_0 e^{j\gamma}.$$

The significance of $\gamma$ as the phase of the applied modulation, and of $m$ as the peak fractional excursion of beam current or reflection transit time may be easily recalled by reference to the Eqs. (18) and (23) describing the applied modulation.

These values of $E_A$ and $E_P$ may now be used in the oscillator equation, Eq. (51), to give the values of the relative amplitude-, phase-, and frequency-modulation output-voltage signals, $\alpha_A$, $\alpha_P$, and $\alpha_F$, respectively. To simplify the resulting expression somewhat, only the absolute values of these output signals are given. They are:

1. Low-frequency beam-current modulation:

$$\frac{|\alpha_A|}{m\alpha_0} = \frac{1}{2\sqrt{K^2 + W^2}}, \qquad (54a)$$
$$\frac{(2\pi Q/\omega)|\alpha_F|}{m\alpha_0} = \frac{W|\alpha_P|}{m\alpha_0} = \frac{W \tan \phi}{2\sqrt{K^2 + W^2}}. \qquad (54b)$$

2. Low-frequency reflection-transit-time modulation:

$$\frac{|\alpha_A|}{m\alpha_0\theta_0} = \frac{\tan\phi}{2\sqrt{K^2+W^2}}, \tag{55a}$$

$$\left(\frac{2\pi Q}{\omega}\right)\frac{|\alpha_F|}{m\alpha_0\theta_0} = \frac{W|\alpha_P|}{m\alpha_0\theta_0} = \sqrt{\frac{K^2}{\cos^4\phi}+W^2}\Big/2\sqrt{K^2+W^2}. \tag{55b}$$

These equations possess a number of interesting features. The output-signal amplitude and phase modulation (AM and PM) produced by applied beam-current modulation ("$I_0$-modulation"), and the output PM produced by reflection transit time modulation ("$\theta_0$-modulation"), all depend on the modulation frequency $\Omega$ through the factor

$$\frac{1}{\sqrt{K^2+W^2}}.$$

(It will be recalled that $W = Q\Omega/\omega$.) The output PM produced by $\theta_0$-modulation has a somewhat more complicated dependence on $W$. Reference to Fig. 16·6, in which is shown the dependence of $K$ and $K/\cos^2\phi$ on $\phi$ for $G_e/G = 2.3$ (optimum load for an ideal oscillator), shows that

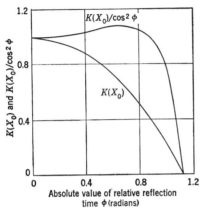

FIG. 16·6.—Dependence of $K(X_0)$ and $K(X_0)/\cos^2\phi$ on $\phi$ for ideal oscillator $(G_e/G_{BR} \gg 1)$ at optimum load $(G_e/G = 2.3)$.

$K \approx \cos^2\phi$ for $-0.95 \leq \phi \leq 0.95$—that is, for that part of the mode between the 39 per cent power points (see Fig. 16·2). Hence to a good approximation, for $\theta_0$-modulation Eq. (55b) becomes

$$\frac{|\alpha_P|}{m\alpha_0\theta_0} \approx \frac{\sqrt{1+W^2}}{2W\sqrt{K^2+W^2}}.$$

Thus, at large modulation frequencies, $|\alpha_A|$ and $|\alpha_P|$ are inversely proportional to $W$ for both types of applied modulation and are hence limited by the bandwidth of the oscillator circuit.

The static characteristics discussed in Sec. 16·2 predict the values that $|\alpha_A|$ and $|\alpha_F|$ should have at very low modulation frequencies. Without going into details, it may be stated that in the limit as $W \to 0$, Eqs. (54) and (55) predict the same AM and FM characteristics as do deductions from the static characteristics shown in Fig. 16·2 and discussed in Sec. 16·2. These static characteristics indicate nothing directly, however, about phase modulation. It is interesting, therefore, to note from Eq. (54b) that with $W = 0$, the output PM produced by $I_0$-modulation is given by

$$\frac{|\alpha_P|}{m\alpha_0} = \left(\frac{1}{2K}\right) \tan \phi \approx \frac{1}{2} \frac{\sin \phi}{\cos^3 \phi}.$$

It is at first sight surprising that there should be any output PM produced by a modulation in $I_0$.

As regards this phase modulation, Eq. (54b) effectively shows that no matter how slowly the current is changed, a certain constant shift

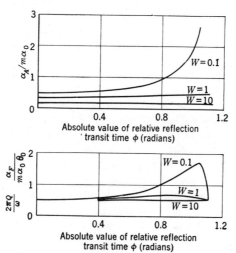

Fig. 16·7.—Dependence on $\phi$ and $W$ of the amplitude modulation produced by beam-current modulation $(\alpha_A/m\alpha_0)$ and the frequency modulation produced by reflection time modulation $\frac{2\pi Q}{\omega} \frac{\alpha_F}{m\alpha_0\theta_0}$; ideal oscillator, at optimum load.

in the phase of the output wave train is produced by a given change in beam current. This is exactly the same phenomenon as is observed in the discussion of pulse buildup in Sec. 16·8—namely, that while the amplitude is increasing there is, during buildup, a constant deviation of the oscillation frequency from its equilibrium value, which can be described equally well as a phase shift between the wave trains at different levels of oscillation; this phase shift is proportional to $\sin \phi$.

There are other interesting features about Eqs. (54) and (55), such as the symmetry between the output PM produced by $I_0$-modulation and the output AM produced by $\theta_0$-modulation. There is also a less apparent similarity between the variation with $\phi$ of the output AM produced by $I_0$-modulation and the output PM or FM produced by $\theta_0$-modulation. These similarities appear in Fig. 16·7, in which is shown the dependence on $\phi$ of $|\alpha_A|/m\alpha_0$ for $I_0$-modulation, and the dependence on $\phi$ of $W|\alpha_P|/m\alpha_0\theta_0$ for $\theta_0$-modulation. Curves are shown for $W = 0.1$, 1, and 10.

The most interesting and important aspect of the modulation phenomena discussed in this section, however, has to do with the output signal FM, and in particular with its dependence on modulation frequency.

First the output-signal FM produced by $\theta_0$-modulation is considered. By Eq. (55b), at the center of the mode ($\phi = 0$), $\alpha_F$ is completely independent of modulation frequency. Even at the half-power point (at which $K \approx \cos^2 \phi = 0.4$), the value of $\alpha_F$ at very high modulating frequencies is reduced to only 0.4 times its low-frequency value.

The output-signal FM produced by $I_0$-modulation is practically zero for $W \ll 1$, but, since the dependence of $\alpha_F$ on modulation frequency is given by $W/\sqrt{K^2 + W^2}$, $\alpha_F$ increases with increasing $W$ and eventually becomes independent of modulating frequency, just as is true of the $\theta_0$-modulation considered above. At any modulation frequency $\alpha_F$ is identically zero at the center of the mode, but it becomes important as soon as tan $\phi$ becomes comparable to unity. (Tan $\phi = 1$ at the equilibrium 69 per cent power point.) This production of a frequency-modulated output signal by beam-current modulation at high frequencies may be traced to the same change of phase during a change of amplitude that is discussed in connection with the residual PM at low frequencies and the change of frequency during pulse buildup.

These properties of the output-signal FM that appear as the modulation frequency is increased indicate that for FM, as distinguished from AM or PM, the modulation frequency is not limited by the bandwidth of the oscillator circuit. This fact can be stated more precisely in the following manner. For a given $Q$, the output FM has an almost constant value independent of modulation frequency, but for a given modulation frequency, the output FM signal is inversely proportional to $Q$. Thus, the minimization of the value of $Q$ for optimum load is still just as good a prescription for a good frequency-modulated oscillator as it was in Sec. 16·2.

It is not within the scope of the present discussion, which is based on small-signal theory, to discuss the linearity of the output FM with the input signal at high modulation frequencies.

The eventual limitation on the modulation frequency must come from phenomena neglected in the two principal approximations used in this chapter. The first of these approximations is the quasi-static bunching approximation; the second is the neglect, in applying this bunching approximation, of the finite transit time of electrons in the reflection space. With regard to this last point, a more exact treatment of Eq. (30) would have $\alpha(\omega t)$ in the left-hand member of the equation, and $i[\alpha(\omega t - \theta_0)]$ in the right-hand member.

**16·11. Modulation of $G_e$ and $\theta_o$ at Frequencies Comparable to $\omega$.—** This modulation is very important physically, not because it has been utilized intentionally, but because it occurs unintentionally in the form of noise modulation.    It is shown in Sec. 16·6 that such an applied modulation at a frequency $\omega + \Omega$ gives rise to bunched beam current and r-f gap-voltage sidebands at $\omega \pm \Omega$, which may be treated just as if they were produced by a low-frequency modulation at the modulation frequency $\Omega$.    This whole subject of noise in the reflex oscillator, including the associated modulation theory, is treated in the next chapter.    It is found to provide a good experimental confirmation of the modulation theory that is developed in the present chapter, although the mathematical formalism associated with the treatment of an infinite spectrum of noise modulation frequencies makes the correlation of the two chapters not too apparent.    (Note also in the next chapter that the quantity denoted by $\alpha$ and defined on page 485 is not related to the $\alpha$ of the present chapter.)

# CHAPTER 17

## NOISE IN REFLEX KLYSTRONS

### By J. B. H. Kuper and J. K. Knipp[1]

It is evident from the discussion of the preceding chapter, and of Chap. 3, that the output of a reflex oscillator is not a pure continuous wave without trace of frequency or amplitude modulation. A beam of electrons passing through the r-f gap of a resonator contains a continuous spectrum of noise currents arising from shot effect and from partition, and those frequencies for which the resonator has an appreciable shunt resistance appear as output voltages. Such direct excitation of the resonator has been used to some extent as a low-level noise generator for testing receiver sensitivity.[2] In the reflex oscillator there are, in addition, bunching effects that are due to noise voltages across the resonator and interactions with the returning electrons which can result in appreciable enhancement of the noise.

**17·1. Importance of Oscillator Noise.**—When a reflex klystron is used as a local oscillator, the resulting noise sidebands can mix with the desired oscillator frequency in the converter of a superheterodyne receiver. Two portions of these sidebands, equal in width to the i-f bandwidth of the receiver and located symmetrically with respect to the local oscillator frequency at a distance equal to the intermediate frequency, contribute noise to the receiver output. In the case of microwave receivers, where the intermediate frequency is a small fraction of the radio frequency, this source of noise can become the limiting factor in the over-all receiver noise figure.

Particularly with oscillator tubes designed for wide electronic tuning ranges the bandwidth of the loaded oscillator resonator is of the order of magnitude of the intermediate frequency, and a typical 3-cm receiver employing the conventional 2K25 or 723A/B tube at an intermediate frequency of 30 Mc/sec may lose 1 db or more in noise figure from oscillator noise. This limitation can be avoided by filtering the oscillator output with a suitable high-$Q$ cavity before feeding it to the mixer, or by the use of some form of balanced mixer. The latter is preferred since,

[1] Sections 17·1 through 17·5 by J. B. H. Kuper; the remainder of Chap. 17 by J. K. Knipp.

[2] J. B. H. Kuper and M. C. Waltz, "Simplified Measurements of Receiver Sensitivities (S-band Noise Source)," RL Report No. 443, Sept. 17, 1943.

with a high-$Q$ filter, manual tuning becomes very difficult and AFC is exceedingly complicated except in the case of fixed channel reception. The balanced mixer customarily employs a so-called "magic T" in an arrangement that is analogous to the balanced modulator used in carrier telephony. The cancellation is good enough to reduce the oscillator noise by roughly 20 db, so that it is no longer of practical concern. These mixers are discussed elsewhere in this series.[1]

It must be emphasized that these remarks apply only to the unavoidable noise modulation resulting from the finite charge and mass of the electron. Modulation arising from poorly filtered or unbypassed supplies may, of course, contribute tremendous amounts of i-f noise beyond that under consideration here. Most receivers for the bands above 3000 Mc/sec that do not have filters or balanced mixers are probably sacrificing a little in performance through neglect of this source of noise, the situation being worst for those with the highest ratio of r-f to i-f and employing tubes with large electronic tuning ranges. Designs employing balanced mixers seem destined to be used more widely in the future, since such mixers have numerous advantages beyond cancellation of oscillator noise, and accordingly this problem will presumably disappear. Nevertheless, although the practical importance of oscillator noise may diminish, it affords some interesting checks on our theoretical conclusions.

**17·2. Method of Measurement.** *Early Measurements.*—Early experiments[2] on oscillator noise were made in a simple and straightforward manner by measuring the noise figure of a receiver, with and without a filter in the line between oscillator tube and mixer. This method suffers from one serious disadvantage. Because of the insertion loss of the filter, it is necessary to readjust the coupling in the two cases in order to keep the mixer crystal at the same working level, and it is not easy to do this without changing the load seen by either the crystal or the oscillator.

In some cases there is enough power available to permit adequate padding on both sides of the filter and in such instances this method of measurement is satisfactory. Ordinarily, however, there is not enough power in the cases of greatest interest, namely at wavelengths of 3 cm and shorter. The apparatus needed is the same as that for measure-

[1] See Vol. 16, *Microwave Mixers*, of the Radiation Laboratory Series.

[2] E. Sherwood and E. Ginzton, "Some Studies of Noise Produced by Velocity Modulated Tubes of the Reflex Type," Sperry Gyroscope Co. Report 5220-107, Mar. 9, 1943. A. J. Rack, "Noise from the Beating Oscillator in Radar Systems," Bell Telephone Laboratory Report MM-42-130-85, Nov. 2, 1942. T. G. Roach, "Noise in S22A Valves," Standard Telephones and Cables, Ltd. Report WR571, Nov. 1942, published at Ilminster, Somerset, England. Y. Beers, "Noise from Local Oscillator," RL Report No. 304, June 8, 1943.

ments of mixer noise figures, that is, a good stable i-f amplifier with an attenuator and output meter, a mixer, and a signal or noise generator.

Measurements by this method have resulted in the general conclusion that with existing tubes oscillator noise can be ignored in the 10-cm region provided that the intermediate frequency is not much less than 30 Mc/sec, but that this noise is definitely present in the 3-cm region. It is further noticed that the noise does not behave symmetrically with electronic tuning. In the great majority of cases the noise at the half-power point on the high-frequency side of the reflector "mode" is considerably stronger than at the center of the mode, or at the low-frequency half-power point. In the early work this observation did not receive very much attention, possibly because there were high-$Q$ elements, such as T-R cells, present in the mixers used.

*Measurement Procedure.*—In some more recent measurements[1] every effort was made to avoid resonance effects and as far as possible to use a known load on the oscillator tube. In view of the scarcity of numerical data on local-oscillator noise, these results are summarized and some details of the procedure are given. Taking the case of the 723A/B as typical, the tube was mounted on a piece of waveguide with a plunger adjustment to permit varying the load for maximum output. An attenuator in the waveguide afforded padding as well as a means of adjusting crystal excitation to a standard level. The crystal (the same one was used throughout the measurements on one band) was matched to the guide and its output was fed by means of a coaxial-line transformer to one of three preamplifiers tuned to 30, 60, and 90 Mc/sec. A temperature-limited diode noise source associated with the crystal could be used to measure the noise figures of the various preamplifiers, and the transformers were so arranged that the crystal saw the same load regardless of which intermediate frequency was in use. The 60- and 90-Mc/sec preamplifiers were provided with converters to 30 Mc/sec so that the same i-f amplifiers, attenuator, and output meter could be used throughout.

The standard expression for the noise figure $\overline{NF}$ (expressed as a ratio) of a receiver is

$$\overline{NF} = \frac{(T_c + \overline{NF}_{\text{i-f}} - 1)}{G_c},$$

where $T_c$ and $G_c$ are the "temperature" and conversion gain of the mixer, and $\overline{NF}_{\text{i-f}}$ is the noise figure of the amplifier. If additional noise power from the local oscillator $P_{nx}$ (in watts for the bandwidth $\Delta f$) is fed to the input there results the expression

$$\overline{NF}' = \left(\frac{P_{nx}}{kT\Delta f}\right) + \frac{(T_c + \overline{NF}_{\text{i-f}} - 1)}{G_c},$$

---

[1] J. B. H. Kuper and M. C. Waltz, "Measurements on Noise from Reflex Oscillators," RL Report No. 872, Dec. 21, 1945.

where $\overline{NF}'$ is the resultant noise figure, $k$ is Boltzmann's constant, and $T$ is the absolute temperature of the input circuit.

For convenience in measurement an apparent crystal "temperature" $T_c'$, that includes the effects of oscillator noise, can be introduced so that

$$\overline{NF}' = \frac{(T_c' + \overline{NF}_{\text{i-f}} - 1)}{G_c},$$

and

$$T_c' = T_c + \left(\frac{G_c P_{nx}}{kT\Delta f}\right).$$

With this relation it is only necessary to measure the apparent crystal temperature by comparing the amplifier noise output with that obtained when the crystal is replaced by a resistor of equivalent i-f impedance. The conversion gain and temperature of the crystal are measured under standard conditions with oscillator noise filtered out, and rechecked occasionally. Barring accidents, both of these parameters seem to remain stable over extended series of measurements.

A "noise-to-signal ratio" for the oscillator itself can be defined as follows: Let $P_n$ be the total noise power in watts contained in the two portions of the noise sidebands of width $\Delta f$ centered on the frequencies, $f \pm f_i$, where $f$ is the oscillator frequency and $f_i$ is the intermediate frequency, and let $P$ be the oscillator power output. The ratio $P_n/P$ will naturally be a function of bandwidth and intermediate frequency. A bandwidth of 2.5 Mc/sec was used throughout the experiments under discussion.

If $P_x$ is the local-oscillator power fed to the crystal, and there is no high-$Q$ element in the oscillator line, $P_{nx}$ is given by

$$P_{nx} = \left(\frac{P_n}{P}\right)P_x.$$

When measurements are always made under standard conditions, say 0.5-ma crystal current, $P_x$ will vary roughly as $1/G_c$. Therefore, the increase in apparent temperature $T_c' - T_c$ will be directly proportional to $P_n/P$ and relatively independent of the properties of the particular crystal used for the measurement.

For many purposes such as evaluation of the deterioration in performance for a given receiver it is more convenient to work with $T_c'$ than the noise-to-signal ratio. The latter is, of course, required when comparing experiment with theory.

**17·3. Total Oscillator Noise.**—In Table 17·1 are shown sample measurements for a typical 723A/B tube operating at 3.2 cm. Measurements were made in five reflector modes, with the reflector voltage adjusted for the center and also for the high- and low-frequency half-power points in each mode, at each of the three intermediate frequencies. The power output at the center of the mode and electronic-tuning range between half-power points is also given. All data were taken with the attenuation adjusted for 0.5-ma crystal current, at which level the particular crystal used had a conversion gain of $-7$ db and a noise temperature of 1.2 times. Data for the half-power points were corrected for

TABLE 17·1.—SAMPLE NOISE MEASUREMENTS ON A TYPICAL 723A/B KLYSTRON

Wavelength = 3.2 cm, resonator voltage = 300 volts, loaded for maximum output in "160-volt" mode. Crystal conversion gain = $-7$ db, $T_c = -1.2$; $P_n$ is the sum of noise powers in the two sidebands 2.5 Mc/sec in width, measured at centers of modes and detuned to the half-power points.

| Reflector mode, volts | Power output (center), watts | Electronic tuning range, Mc/sec | $P_n$, $10^{-13}$ watts | | | | | | | | |
|---|---|---|---|---|---|---|---|---|---|---|---|
| | | | 30 Mc/sec | | | 60 Mc/sec | | | 90 Mc/sec | | |
| | | | center | ½ high | ½ low | center | ½ high | ½ low | center | ½ high | ½ low |
| 250 | $49 \times 10^{-3}$ | 20 | 156 | 202 | 122 | 63 | 63 | 41 | 14.7 | 17.1 | 12.2 |
| 160 | 47.5 | 32 | 91 | 215 | 98 | 48 | 68.5 | 44 | 9.6 | 16.6 | 14.2 |
| 105 | 22.8 | 39 | 45.5 | 137 | 44.5 | 27.5 | 51 | 29.5 | 6.9 | 14.7 | 13.7 |
| 70 | 7.4 | 55 | 22 | 55 | 19 | 15.5 | 31 | 16.4 | 7.4 | 13.2 | 10.8 |
| 45 | 0.86 | 57 | 137 | 304 | 198 | 62.5 | 60 | 56 | 31 | 19.7 | 29 |

this change in attenuation and so represent the noise that would be obtained with constant coupling as in a practical receiver. The noise power, $P_n$, is given in units of $10^{-13}$ watts for the sum of the two bands 2.5 Mc/sec wide. In calculating noise-to-signal ratios for the detuned conditions it is necessary to take account of the reduction in useful power.

The reduction in noise brought about by raising the intermediate frequency is shown clearly. As a matter of fact the noise at 90 Mc/sec is so weak that the experimental data cannot be considered trustworthy. Results for the 45-volt mode are doubtful for several reasons. The power is so low that it is impossible to use enough attenuation to eliminate resonance effects. The tube-mounting arrangements do not have sufficient range of adjustment to permit optimum loading for this mode, and bad electronic-tuning hysteresis is present. In all probability electrons penetrate so close to the reflector that focusing may be bad; furthermore, some electrons may strike the reflector. Otherwise the noise output has a regular trend downward as the transit angle is increased.

Again excluding the 45-volt mode, the noise-to-signal ratio remains comparatively constant with a minimum at the 160-volt mode. At the 250-volt mode the tube is somewhat overloaded, bringing the power down and the noise up, so $P_n/P$ rises rapidly. For the modes below

160 volts, the tube is progressively underloaded and both the noise and the useful power decrease, the latter dropping off faster than does the noise. This behavior is illustrated in Table 17·2, which shows $P_n/P$ for the same tube as in Table 17·1 for the centers of the various modes.

TABLE 17·2.—NOISE-TO-SIGNAL RATIOS

Values of $P_n/P$ computed from data in Table 17·1, for the centers of the modes

| Reflector mode, volts | $P_n/P$ | | |
|---|---|---|---|
| | 30 Mc/sec | 60 Mc/sec | 90 Mc/sec |
| 250 | $3.2 \times 10^{-10}$ | $1.3 \times 10^{-10}$ | $0.3 \times 10^{-10}$ |
| 160 | 1.9 | 1.0 | 0.2 |
| 105 | 2.0 | 1.2 | 0.3 |
| 70 | 3.0 | 2.1 | 1.0 |
| 45 | 159 | 73 | 36 |

Returning now to Table 17·1, the behavior of the noise with respect to electronic tuning shows a marked difference between the high- and low-frequency half-power points. With the single exception of the 45-volt mode at 90 Mc/sec intermediate frequency the high-frequency side is distinctly noisier. This asymmetry is generally observed except in cases of extremely light loading. Earlier theories[1] failed to predict this effect, which results from the "quasi-coherence" of noise that is due to the first and second passages of the electrons through the resonator—that is, for resonators with loaded $Q$'s of about 100 to 300 as used here, the time (a few cycles) spent by the electrons in the reflector space is not sufficient to destroy coherence. In a group of 21 tubes chosen to represent the widest possible range in other parameters, two cases were found in which the noise was worse on the low-frequency side in the 105-volt mode at 30 Mc/sec intermediate frequency. In this group $P_n$ was found to vary from 3.2 to 9.8 $\times 10^{-12}$ watts.

**17·4. Separation of Sidebands.**—Generally speaking, no attempt was made to separate the two sidebands contributing the noise. The separation was made, however, in a few cases in this series of measurements by use of a sharp rejection filter on a T-connection to the main line. When the sidebands were separated it was found they were not altogether symmetrical at the center of the electronic-tuning range. Actually, the point at which the two contributions were equal was noticeably displaced toward the high-frequency side of the center of the mode. Also, it was found that the high-frequency sideband went through rather minor variations with electronic tuning, while the low-frequency side-

[1] J. R. Pierce, "Noise Calculations for Reflex Oscillators," Bell Telephone Laboratory Report MM-44-140-4, Jan. 29, 1944.

band varied more rapidly. This behavior is illustrated in Figs. 17·1 and 17·2, which show the variations with electronic tuning of the separated sidebands as well as their sum for intermediate frequencies of

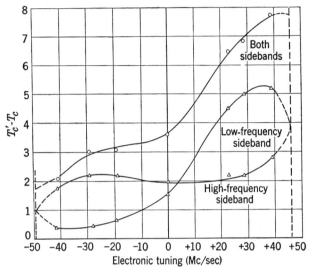

Fig. 17·1.—Noise sidebands from a 723A/B tube as a function of electronic tuning, 30-Mc/sec i-f, "105-volt" mode.

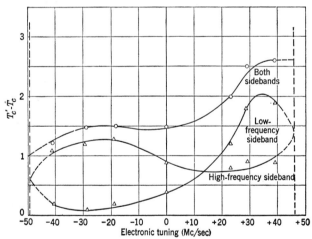

Fig. 17·2.—Noise sidebands from a 723A/B tube as a function of electronic tuning, 60-Mc/sec i-f, "105-volt" mode.

30 and 60 Mc/sec respectively. The scale of ordinates is $T'_c - T_c$. Points were taken at the $\frac{3}{4}$-, $\frac{1}{2}$-, and $\frac{1}{4}$-power points and corrected for the changes in attenuation required. The curves are sketched with an

attempt to follow the sort of variation predicted by the theory developed later in this chapter. The vertical dotted lines indicate the limits of oscillation, beyond which the concept of two sideband regions mixing with the main oscillation loses its meaning. There will, of course, be noise output in the nonoscillating state.

**17·5. Dependence of Noise on Load.**—The next point to be considered is the behavior of noise under variation of the load. For this purpose a representation in the form of a Rieke diagram is most useful. As indi-

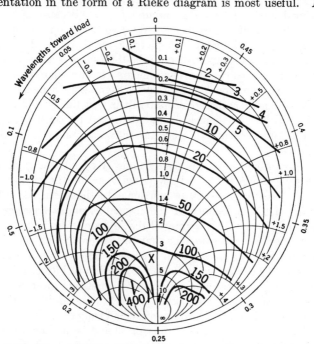

Fig. 17·3.—Noise output of a 723A/B tube plotted against load admittance, 30-Mc/sec i-f, "105-volt" mode. Contours labelled with $(T_c' - T) \times$ the per cent of maximum power, a quantity proportional to $P_n$.

cated in Chap. 15, the useful power output undergoes considerable change; therefore, large changes in attenuation are required to keep the measuring crystal at a constant level. For this reason contours were chosen, the numerical designations of which were obtained by multiplying the observed $T_c' - T_c$ by the per cent of maximum power output. These coordinates are directly proportional to $P_n$. The contours are plotted on an admittance diagram with the plane of reference an integral number of half-waves from the grids. The noise contours might be expected to be symmetrical because only the conductance component enters into the shunt impedance of the resonator; instead, however, they are found to bulge upward on the inductive (negative susceptance) side of the diagram. This phenomenon is illustrated in Fig. 17·3, taken on a 723A/B tube in the 105-volt mode at 30-Mc/sec intermediate frequency. The maximum power point is indicated by a cross.

The explanation for the distortion of the noise contours lies in the inevitable long-line effect coupled with the fact that the two noise contributions (from upper and lower sidebands) are not equal. In the present case each point on the diagram is actually the sum of the noise in the neighborhood of $f + f_i$ and that around $f - f_i$. Because of the long-line effect, the conductances seen by the two noise components are, in general, appreciably different. In plotting the diagram, the difference in the conductances is neglected; only the total noise is measured. Furthermore, theory predicts and experiments confirm that the two noise sidebands are asymmetrical, the degree of asymmetry depending on the load. Taken together, these factors result in just the type of distortion seen in Fig. 17·3. This conclusion was checked by constructing for a hypothetical tube a synthetic diagram that was found to exhibit the same features.

Apart from such matters as the asymmetry effects, the experimental results can be represented fairly well by a simple theory in which a mean-square noise-current, $\overline{i^2}$, proportional to the beam current flows through the shunt impedance of the resonator, and a fraction of the power is coupled out. If it is granted that a definite amount of power is required at the mixer, it is obvious that the accompanying noise is minimized by making the best possible use of the electron beam. Poor focusing, spread in transit angles, and losses due to interception at the grids—all of which reduce efficiency below theoretical expectations—may be expected to make the tube noisier. Overloading, and conditions that give rise to severe hysteresis, are also very bad from the noise standpoint. The loaded $Q$ of the oscillator resonator should be as high as possible, consistent with the electronic-tuning range required. This range is largely determined in the design of the tube, of course, and there is very little the circuit designer can do about it. Some improvement can be obtained by deliberate underloading in special cases where the increase in $P_n/P$ is more than compensated by the clipping of the sidebands. At the same time the intermediate frequency should be as high as practicable. Since the noise figure of the i-f amplifier usually increases with frequency, the choice of an optimum frequency for a given receiver may be rather difficult when a balanced mixer is not used.

It should be borne in mind that many mixers contain fairly high-$Q$ TR tubes that can make a considerable difference in the noise question. It is possible so to arrange the mixer that the desired oscillator power and one of the noise sidebands (the one at "image" frequency) are reflected from the TR tube back to the crystal, while the noise sideband at signal frequency passes through the TR tube and is radiated. In practical cases the noise entering the receiver is appreciably reduced by effects of this sort in comparison to the powers observed in the experiments. The very simple theory referred to here does not permit conclusions about the effects of electronic tuning on noise figures. For this, it is necessary to consider the more complete discussion presented in the following sections.

**17·6. Summary of Noise Behavior and Estimate of Noise Magnitude.** The measurements described in the preceding sections give the magnitude of reflex-oscillator noise and show how it changes with operating conditions.

*Observed Behavior.*—Noise behavior may be summarized as follows:

1. The total noise-power output at the center of the tuning range of a 723A/B 3.2-cm reflex oxcillator, operating with a beam potential of 300 volts in a 160-volt mode and loaded for optimum power output (about $\frac{1}{20}$ watt), is of the order of magnitude of $10^{-11}$ watts for an intermediate frequency of 30 Mc/sec and bandwidth of 2.5 Mc/sec.

2. On going to higher modes by using less negative reflector voltages, the noise-power output decreases; so does the oscillation power and at about the same rate. Hence the noise-to-signal ratio is roughly constant over a range of several modes; it is of the order of magnitude of $2 \times 10^{-10}$.

3. A change in the intermediate frequency from 30 Mc/sec to 60 Mc/sec decreases the noise output by a factor of about $\frac{1}{2}$; changing from 30 Mc/sec to 90 Mc/sec decreases it by a factor of about $\frac{1}{10}$.

4. The same tube when electronically detuned by varying the reflector voltage until the power output is reduced by $\frac{1}{2}$ has a total noise-power output that is altered very little at the low-frequency half-power point, but is larger by a factor of about 2 at the high-frequency half-power point. Thus, the total noise output is unsymmetrical with regard to electronic tuning although the oscillation-power output is nearly symmetrical.

5. The noise-power output from the two separate sidebands is different over the observed tuning range except at a crossover point that lies a few megacycles per second on the high-frequency side of the center of the tuning range. Below this crossover point the high-frequency sideband contributes the most noise; above the crossover point, the low-frequency sideband contributes the most. Extreme values of the noise from the low-frequency sideband differ by as much as a factor of 10; extreme values from the high-frequency sideband differ by a factor of about 2.

With the exception of 2, this behavior is understandable on the basis of a quantitative theory to be discussed shortly in which the noise arises from the shot effect in the injected current. The injected and reflected noise currents are partially coherent and the dissymmetry of the total noise with regard to electronic tuning is due to the change in relative phase of these two currents. The phase change is merely that arising from the change in time spent by the electrons in the reflector region due to the change in the reflector voltage. With regard to 2, the simple theory predicts the noise-power output to be approximately constant from one high mode to the next if the conductance is not changed. Consequently, the noise-to-signal ratio is expected to increase on going to modes beyond that for which the oscillation power output is a maximum, contrary to observation. This discrepancy is probably associated with the fact that the simple model does not give accurately the observed mode-to-mode changes in oscillation power output and electronic tuning.

*Gap-voltage Spectrum.*—In calculating the noise power of a reflex oscillator, it is to be remembered that the gap voltage $V(t)$ is composed of the oscillation potential, of amplitude $V$, and components that are due to noise. It is desirable, for frequencies near the oscillation frequency $f$, to define the spectral density of the gap potential as $G_V(f')$. This quantity is related to the time average of the square of the gap potential,

$$\overline{V(t)^2} = \frac{V^2}{2} + \int_0^\infty df' G_V(f'). \tag{1}$$

If $G$ is the gap conductance, the frequency dependence of which is usually negligible, the noise power produced in a sideband at $f'$ of width $\Delta f$ is $G\Delta f G_V(f')$. The oscillation power produced is $GV^2/2$. To obtain the power delivered to the load, these quantities must be multiplied by the circuit efficiency $G_L/G$, where $G_L$ is the load conductance measured at the gap.

The spectral density of the gap voltage bears a linear relation to the spectral functions characteristic of the injected electron stream. The most important of the latter is the spectral density of the injected current $G_i(f')$. The time average of the square of the injected current $i_i(0,t)$ is

$$\overline{i_i(0,t)^2} = I_0^2 + \int_0^\infty df' G_i(f'), \tag{2}$$

where $-I_0$ is the average injected current. For the spectral density of the injected current there is the relation

$$G_i(f') = 2eI_0\Gamma_i^2(f'), \tag{3}$$

where $\Gamma_i^2(f')$ is a factor determined by conditions in the acceleration region. For a temperature-limited cathode, $\Gamma_i^2\,(f') = 1$, except at very high frequencies. It can be much less than unity for a space-charge-limited cathode. This space-charge factor has been carefully studied for low frequencies but for high frequencies very little is known about its magnitude or behavior.[1]

*Noise Magnitude from Shot Formula and Gap Admittance.*—It is possible to estimate $G_V(f')$ from $G_i(f')$ by dividing the latter by the square of the absolute value of the admittance presented to the injected noise current at $f'$. At the oscillation frequency the circuit admittance is just canceled by the electronic admittance. In a noise sideband not far from the oscillation frequency $f$, the circuit admittance is different from that at the oscillation frequency by $4\pi j(f' - f)C$, where $C$ is the effective gap capacitance. Since the electronic admittance is a slowly varying function of frequency, it changes very little in passing to the sideband frequency. However, the original portion of the circuit admittance is not completely canceled for the noise current because for it the differential electronic admittance is effective. Still, $4\pi j(f' - f)C$ is a fair measure of the total admittance presented to the noise current. Hence an estimate of the spectral density of the gap voltage is

$$\frac{M^2 G_i(f')F_i(f')}{16\pi^2(f' - f)^2 C^2} = \frac{M^2 2eI_0\Gamma_i^2(f')F_i(f')}{16\pi^2(f' - f)^2 C^2}, \tag{4}$$

where $M$ is the beam-coupling coefficient and $F_i(f')$ is a factor of the order of magnitude of unity.

Reasonable values are $M^2 = \frac{1}{2}$, $I_0 = 2 \times 10^{-2}$ amp, and $C = 10^{-12}$ farad. With $\Gamma_i^2(f')F_i(f')$ made equal to unity, $e = 1.6 \times 10^{-19}$ coulomb, and an intermediate frequency $f_i = f' - f$ of 30 Mc/sec, the gap-voltage spectral density is estimated as $2 \times 10^{-14}$ (volts)$^2$ sec. If

$$G = 2 \times 10^{-4} \qquad \text{mho},$$

if the circuit efficiency is 40 per cent, and if the bandwidth is 2.5 Mc/sec, the total noise power from both bands is calculated to be $8 \times 10^{-12}$ watt, which is of the order of magnitude of the observed value.

It is possible to eliminate $C$ by introducing $Q = 2\pi f_0 C/G$, where $f_0$ is the resonant frequency of the circuit. It is convenient to introduce the conductance parameter defined by $G = \gamma G_{ne} = \gamma M^2\theta_{ne}kI_0/2V_0$ (see Chap. 12). In this expression $G_{ne}$ is the negative of the electronic admittance for zero gap voltage, $\theta_{ne}$ is the effective bunching angle at the center of the mode, $kI_0$ is the average current which returns to the gap, and $V_0$ is the beam potential. In high modes, for oscillation to take

---

[1] For a discussion of the space-charge factor, see Vol. 24, *Threshold Signals*, of this series, Chap. 4. Some experimental data are given in Sec. 6.4 of this book.

place, the conductance parameter must be less than unity.   Equation (4) becomes

$$\left(\frac{f_0}{2\gamma Q f_i}\right)^2 \left(\frac{2V_0}{\theta_{ne}M}\right)^2 \frac{2e}{k^2 I_0}\ \Gamma_i^2(f')F_i(f'), \tag{5}$$

where $f' = f \pm f_i$.   From this expression it is seen that, if $\gamma$, $Q$, and $V_0$ are kept constant, as is sometimes the case, the noise power increases with operating frequency for a given intermediate frequency and mode of operation; in addition, it decreases with increasing intermediate frequency and with increasing beam current.

**17·7. Discussion of Complicating Effects.**—*Nonlinear Effects of Bunching.*—The oscillation voltage causes bunching in the reflected current.   Besides introducing a discrete spectrum composed of all the harmonics of the oscillation frequency, the bunching action, which is nonlinear, affects the continuous noise spectrum by adding to any portion contributions from all portions of the continuous noise spectrum of the injected current separated from $f'$ by integral multiples of the oscillation frequency $f$.   The result is that the reflected noise current in the sideband of frequency $f' = f + f_i$, where $f_i$ is an intermediate frequency, contains not only a contribution from the injected noise current of the frequency $f'$ but also contributions from all higher and lower frequencies $f' - mf$, where $m$ is a positive or negative integer and negative frequencies are interpreted as being associated with exponential negative time factors.   Each contribution has an amplitude determined by the bunching action.   All have the common phase lag compared with the injected current associated with the time spent in the effective reflector region.   For $m = 1$ the harmonic contribution comes from the i-f portion of the spectrum and is termed "low-frequency noise."   It is small for a beam arising from a space-charge-limited cathode because

$$\Gamma_i^2(f' - f) = \Gamma_i^2(f_i) \ll 1.$$

It is very likely that the space-charge action is less effective in smoothing the beam in other portions of the spectrum.   Other contributions therefore probably have factors more nearly equal to unity, except possibly those from exceedingly high frequencies, where the amplitudes of the bunched current are small in any case.

*Coherence of Injected and Reflected Noise Currents.*—The portion of the reflected noise current that arises from $f'$ is coherent with the injected noise current, for the thermal spread in velocities is not sufficiently large to destroy that coherence.   Thus the spread in phase caused by a spread $\Delta v$ in the velocity is $\Delta\theta = \theta\ \Delta v/v$.   For thermal energies of $\frac{1}{10}$ electron-volt and a beam potential of 300 volts, $\Delta v/v = \frac{1}{6000}$.   Hence if $\theta = 40$, $\Delta\theta = \frac{1}{150}$, a spread that is small enough to have negligible effect on the coherence.   The two currents must be added with the proper phase.

This phase is subject to change under electronic tuning; hence, changing the reflector voltage changes the combined noise current in an unsymmetrical way about the center of the tuning range.

*Fluctuation in Velocity of Injection.*—The thermal spread in velocities does, however, have an important effect through the fluctuations that arise in the average velocity of injection of the electrons. This velocity $v_0(t)$ is a random variable, similar to the random variable $i_i(0,t)$, because of the discreteness of the electronic charge and the fact that the electrons do not all have the same velocity. It has a spectral density $G_v(f')$ for which

$$\overline{v_0(t)^2} = v_0^2 + \int_0^\infty df' G_v(f'), \tag{6}$$

where $v_0$ is the average velocity of injection. The spectral density $G_v(f')$ is written in the form,

$$G_v(f') = \frac{2e}{I_0}\left(\frac{2kT}{m}\right)\Gamma_v^2(f'), \tag{7}$$

where $k$ is Boltzmann's constant, $T$ is the absolute temperature of the cathode, and $\Gamma_v^2(f')$ is a factor of the order of magnitude of unity (or zero) in the absence of space-charge smoothing.[1]

Velocity fluctuations in the injected beam lead, through drift action (see Chaps. 3 and 12), to fluctuations in the reflected current proportional to $\dfrac{kI_0\theta_e}{v_0}$, where $\theta_e$ is the bunching angle (it is usually not greatly different from the phase angle $\theta$). The addition to the gap-voltage spectral density is estimated as

$$\frac{M^2k^2I_0^2\theta_e^2G_v(f')F_v(f')}{16\pi^2f_i^2C^2v_0^2}, \tag{8}$$

where $f' = f \pm f_i$ and $F_v(f')$ is of the order of magnitude of unity. Rewriting as before, this is

$$\left(\frac{f_0}{2\gamma Qf_i}\right)^2\left(\frac{2V_0}{\theta_e M}\right)^2\frac{2e}{k^2I_0}\left(\frac{\theta_e^2kT}{eV_0}\right)k^2\Gamma_v^2(f')F_v(f'). \tag{9}$$

If Eq. (9) is compared with Eq. (5), it is seen that the essential difference is the factor $(\theta_e^2kT/eV_0)k^2$. With $\theta_e = 40$, $kT/e = \frac{1}{10}$ volt, $V_0 = 300$ volts, and $k = \frac{1}{2}$, this factor is $\frac{4}{30}$. However, it increases rapidly with mode of operation; for sufficiently high modes, the noise from velocity fluctuation is larger than that arising from density fluctuation.

*Correlation between Current and Velocity Fluctuations.*—There is, furthermore, the possibility of correlation between the density and

---

[1] See, for example, J. K. Knipp, "Theory of Noise from the Reflex Oscillator," RL Report 873, Jan. 10, 1946, Appendix.

velocity fluctuations in the injected beam since they both arise from the shot effect. Such a correlation can be described in terms of a spectral function $G_{iv}(f')$ for which

$$\overline{i_i(0,t)v_0(t)} = -I_0v_0 + \tfrac{1}{2} \int_{-\infty}^{\infty} df'G_{iv}(f'). \qquad (10)$$

The spectral function $G_{iv}(f')$ is written in the form,

$$G_{iv}(f') = 2e \sqrt{\frac{2kT}{m}} \, \Gamma_{iv}(f'). \qquad (11)$$

For the pure shot effect, $\Gamma_{iv}(f') = 0$. The addition to the gap-voltage spectral density arising from such a correlation is estimated as

$$\left(\frac{f_0}{2\gamma Qf_i}\right)^2 \left(\frac{2V_0}{\theta_e M}\right)^2 \frac{2e}{k^2 I_0} \sqrt{\frac{\theta_e^2 kT}{eV_0}} \, k\Gamma_{iv}(f')F_{iv}(f'), \qquad (12)$$

where $F_{iv}(f')$ is of the order of magnitude of unity. Both $F_v(f')$ and $F_{iv}(f')$ contain harmonic contributions similar to those discussed in the first paragraph of this section.

*Mixing of Noise-voltage Effects.*—There is also bunching in the reflected current caused by the noise components of the gap voltage. This bunching is superposed on that due to the oscillation voltage. Because of the limited bandwidth of the resonator, the contributions to the reflected current are from the frequencies $f + f_i$ and $f - f_i$ only. The occurrence of such terms in the reflected current results in a mixing of the effects of the two gap-voltage sidebands. The circuit relations for the determination of the noise voltage amplitudes are a pair of simultaneous equations. Therefore the amplitude for each sideband is a linear combination of the effects of the total noise currents in these two bands.

**17·8. Summary of Results of Noise Calculation.**—In this section is presented, in advance of derivation, a discussion of the results of a detailed calculation of the spectral density of the gap voltage $G_v(f')$. As indicated in the preceding section, it is the infinite sum of terms containing factors $G_i(mf)$, $G_v(mf)$, and $G_{iv}(mf)$, which are functions characteristic of the primary spectra of the injected stream. Since these quantities are not known with any exactness for a stream originating from a space-charge-limited cathode such as is usually employed, a full discussion must await further research on the nature of the shot effect at high frequencies in the presence of space charge.

*Assumptions Regarding Primary Spectra.*—It is, however, instructive to study the results under the simple assumption that $G_{iv}(mf)$ is negligibly small for all frequencies and that $G_i(mf)$ and $G_v(mf)$ have their pure shot-effect values, except at low frequencies, where they are negligibly small. Stated in terms of the coefficients in Eqs. (3), (7), and (11),

$$
\begin{aligned}
\Gamma_{iv}(mf) &= 0, &&\text{for all } m; \\
\Gamma_i^2(0) &= 0, &\Gamma_v^2(0) &= 0; \\
\Gamma_i^2(mf) &= 1, &\Gamma_v^2(mf) &= 1, &&\text{for all } m \neq 0.
\end{aligned} \tag{13}
$$

The infinite summation occurring in $G_V(f')$, for which see Eq. (48), can then be carried out with the aid of the two identities

$$
\left.
\begin{aligned}
\sum_{-\infty}^{\infty} J_m^2(x) &= 1, \\[2mm]
\sum_{-\infty}^{\infty} J_{-m+1}(x) J_{m+1}(x) &= J_2(2x).
\end{aligned}
\right\} \tag{14}
$$

*Noise-power Spectrum.*—For the spectral density of the gap voltage for the high-frequency sideband there is found

$$
G_V(f+f_i) = \left(\frac{f_0}{2\gamma Q f_i}\right)^2 \left(\frac{2V_0}{\theta_e M}\right)^2 \frac{2e}{k^2 I_0}\left[F_i(f+f_i)\right.
$$
$$
\left. + \left(\frac{\theta_e^2 k T}{e V_0}\right) k^2 F_v(f+f_i)\right]. \tag{15}
$$

where $F_i(f+f_i)$ and $F_v(f+f_i)$ are now known factors. Explicitly,

$$
\left.
\begin{aligned}
F_i(f+f_i) &= \frac{1}{1+\alpha^2\cos^2\phi}\left[\left(1+\frac{\alpha^2}{2}+\alpha\sin\phi\right)(1-2kJ_0(x)\sin\phi)\right. \\
&\quad + 2kJ_2(x)\left(\frac{\alpha^2}{2}\sin\phi+\alpha\right) + \left(1+\frac{\alpha^2}{2}+\alpha\sin\phi\right)k^2(1-J_1^2(x)) \\
&\quad \left.- \left(\frac{\alpha^2}{2}+\alpha\sin\phi\right)k^2(J_2(2x)-J_1^2(x))\right]; \\
F_v(f+f_i) &= \frac{1}{1+\alpha^2\cos^2\phi}\left[\left(1+\frac{\alpha^2}{2}+\alpha\sin\phi\right)(1-J_1^2(x))\right. \\
&\quad \left.+ \left(\frac{\alpha^2}{2}+\alpha\sin\phi\right)(J_2(2x)-J_1^2(x))\right].
\end{aligned}
\right\} \tag{16}
$$

In these expressions

$$
\alpha = 2\left(\frac{f_0}{2\gamma Q f_i}\right) J_2(X), \tag{17}
$$

$X$ is the bunching parameter $\theta_e M V/2V_0$, and $\phi$ is the phase angle measured from the center of the tuning range; for the $n$th mode

$$
\phi = \theta - 2\pi(n+\tfrac{3}{4}).
$$

The conditions of oscillation are (see Chap. 12)

$$\left.\begin{array}{c} \gamma = \dfrac{2J_1(X)}{X} \cos\,\phi, \\[3mm] \dfrac{f_0 - f}{\dfrac{f_0}{2Q}} = \tan\,\phi. \end{array}\right\} \tag{18}$$

They determine $X$ and $\phi$ in terms of the conductance parameter $\gamma$, the frequency detuning $f - f_0$, and one-half the loaded resonator bandwidth $f_0/2Q$.

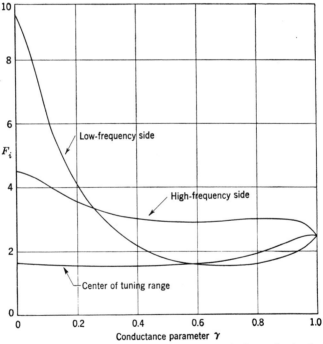

Fig. 17·4.—Factors for total noise from both i-f sidebands due to density fluctuations in injected current as functions of conductance parameter; $F_i = F_i(f + f_i) + F_i(f - f_i)$; $k = \frac{1}{2}$, $p = \frac{1}{2}$; $p = f_i/(f_0/2\gamma Q) = 4\pi f_i C/G_{ne}$.

The spectral density of the gap potential for the low-frequency side band is $G_v(f - f_i)$. The factors $F_i(f - f_i)$ and $F_v(f - f_i)$ are obtained from Eq. (16) by replacing $\alpha$ by $-\alpha$. The total noise power from both sidebands is $G\Delta f\,[G_v(f + f_i) + G_v(f - f_i)]$. The factors that occur are

$$F_i = F_i(f + f_i) + F_i(f - f_i)$$

$$= \frac{2}{1 + \alpha^2 \cos^2 \phi} \left[ \left(1 + \frac{\alpha^2}{2}\right)(1 - 2kJ_0(x) \sin \phi) + 2kJ_2(x) \frac{\alpha^2}{2} \sin \phi \right.$$

$$\left. + \left(1 + \frac{\alpha^2}{2}\right) k^2(1 - J_1^2(x)) \frac{\alpha^2}{2} k^2(J_2(2x) - J_1^2(x)) \right],$$

and

$$F_v = F_v(f + f_i) + F_v(f - f_i)$$

$$= \frac{2}{1 + \alpha^2 \cos^2 \phi} \left[ \left(1 + \frac{\alpha^2}{2}\right)(1 - J_1^2(x)) + \frac{\alpha^2}{2}(J_2(2x) - J_1^2(x)) \right]. \tag{19}$$

There are two sources of dissymmetry under electronic tuning. One is the dissymmetry in the admittance coefficients; the other is dissymmetry resulting from coherence between injected- and reflected-noise-current components. Terms that are due to the first source appear in $F_i(f + f_i)$, $F_i(f - f_i)$, $F_v(f + f_i)$, and $F_v(f - f_i)$, but drop out of $F_i$ and $F_v$ of Eq. (19).

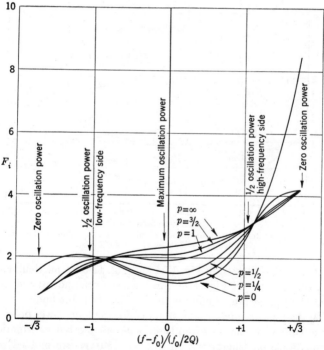

Fig. 17·5.—Factors for total noise from both i-f sidebands as functions of oscillation-frequency change under electronic tuning. $F_i = F_i(f + f_i) + F_i(f - f_i)$; $k = \frac{1}{2}$, $\gamma = \frac{1}{2}$, $p = 4\pi f_i C/G_{ne}$.

Terms that are due to the second source appear in $F_i(f + f_i)$ and $F_i(f - f_i)$, but not in $F_v(f + f_i)$ and $F_v(f - f_i)$ because velocity fluctuations require large drift times to be effective. Terms that are due to this source remain in $F_i$. As a consequence, the coherence causes the total noise that is due to density fluctuations to be unsymmetrical under electronic tuning. However, the total noise that is due to velocity fluctuations is symmetrical under electronic tuning, although the noise from the separate bands is unsymmetrical due to the admittance coefficients.

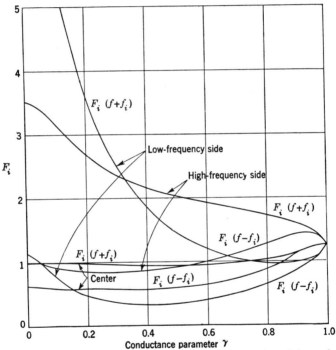

FIG. 17·6.—Factors for noise from the separate i-f sidebands as functions of the conductance parameter; $k = \frac{1}{2}$, $p = \frac{1}{2}$; $p = 4\pi f_i C / G_{ne}$.

The factor $F_i$ is plotted in Fig. 17·4 and Fig. 17·5 for particular values of the parameters. In Fig. 17·4 three curves are shown: one for the center of the tuning range, one for the half-power point under electronic tuning on the high-frequency side, and one for the half-power point under electronic tuning on the low-frequency side, all plotted as functions of the conductance parameter $\gamma$. In Fig. 17·4 curves are plotted against frequency change under electronic tuning for several values of the i-f parameter $p = 4\pi f_i C / G_{ne}$. The factors $F_i(f + f_i)$ and $F_i(f - f_i)$ are plotted in Figs. 17·6 and 17·7 for the same parameter values.

**17·9. Theory of Noise in Reflex Klystron.**[1]—The starting point in the calculation of noise is the assumption that the gap voltage can be expressed as a single oscillation term plus a continuous spectrum. In order to be able to express $V(t)$ with the aid of a Fourier integral, there is introduced a long time interval $T$ and $V(t)$ is taken as zero outside that inter-

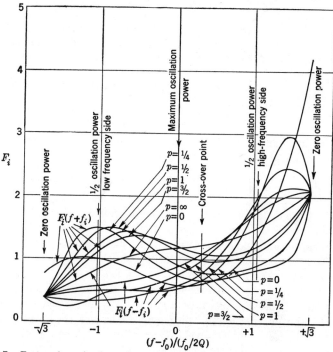

FIG. 17·7.—Factors for noise from the separate i-f sidebands as functions of oscillation-frequency change under electronic tuning; $k = \frac{1}{2}$, $\gamma = \frac{1}{2}$; $p = 4\pi f_i C / G_{ne}$.

val. Other quantities that are to be expressed as Fourier integrals are treated in a similar way. Thus the gap voltage is

$$V(t) = V \sin \omega t + \int_{-\infty}^{\infty} \frac{d\omega'}{2\pi} V_{\omega'} e^{j\omega' t}, \qquad (20)$$

where $V_{-\omega'}^{*} = V_{\omega'}$ since $V(t)$ is real, and $\omega = 2\pi f$, and $\omega' = 2\pi f'$. The gap-potential spectral density is

$$G_V(f') = \lim_{T \to \infty} \frac{2}{T} |V_{\omega'}|^2. \qquad (21)$$

The gap voltage is the result of excitation of the resonator by the electron beam. The driving current contains all harmonics of the oscil-

[1] J. K. Knipp, "Theory of Noise from the Reflex Oscillator," RL Report No. 873, Jan. 10, 1946.

lation frequency (see Chap. 12) as well as a continuous spectrum. It can be expressed in terms of the voltage amplitudes, with the aid of the gap admittance $Y_{\omega'}$, as

$$i(t) = -(1 - k)I_0 + \sum_{m \neq 0} Y_{m\omega} V_{m\omega} e^{jm\omega t} + \int \frac{d\omega'}{2\pi} Y_{\omega'} V_{\omega'} e^{j\omega' t}. \quad (22)$$

Since the gap admittance is very large for frequencies that are appreciably different from $\pm \omega_0 = \pm 2\pi f_0$, the voltage amplitudes are small for such frequencies even though the corresponding components of the driving current are not small.

In the reflex oscillator the driving current is the sum of the injected and reflected currents

$$i(t) = i^+(t) + i^-(t). \quad (23)$$

As shown in Chap. 12, it can be expressed in terms of the injected current $i^+(0,t)$ through the relation (Eq. 12.20)

$$i(t) = \int_{-\infty}^{\infty} \frac{d\omega'}{2\pi} e^{j\omega' t} \int_{-\infty}^{\infty} d\tau' i^+(0,\tau') \frac{1}{d} \int_0^d dx \left[ e^{-j\omega'\tau^+(x;\tau')} - k e^{-j\omega\tau^-(x;\tau')} \right], \quad (24)$$

where $d$ is the distance of separation of the grids of the gap, and $\tau^+(x;\tau')$ and $\tau^-(x;\tau')$ are the arrival times at the plane $x$ of electrons that were injected at $\tau'$ and have come directly or been reflected, respectively. The arrival times depend on the velocity of injection at $\tau'$ and the instantaneous field through which the electrons move.

*Primary Spectra.*—When the expressions for the arrival times derived from Newton's law are substituted in Eq. (24), it will contain the noise voltage amplitudes, which it is proposed to calculate, the injected current amplitudes, and the injected velocity amplitudes. The injected current and velocity amplitudes are defined by:

$$\left.\begin{array}{l} i^+(0,\tau') = -I_0 + \displaystyle\int \frac{d\omega'}{2\pi} i_{\omega'}^+ e^{j\omega'\tau'}, \\[2mm] v_0(\tau') = v_0 + \displaystyle\int \frac{d\omega'}{2\pi} v_{\omega'} e^{j\omega'\tau'}. \end{array}\right\} \quad (25)$$

The three spectral functions associated with these two quantities are

$$\left.\begin{array}{l} G_i\,(f') = \displaystyle\lim_{T \to \infty} \frac{2}{T} |i_{\omega'}^+|^2, \\[2mm] G_v(f') = \displaystyle\lim_{T \to \infty} \frac{2}{T} |v_{\omega'}|^2, \\[2mm] G_{iv}(f') = \displaystyle\lim_{T \to \infty} \frac{2}{T} i_{\omega'}^+ v_{\omega'}^*. \end{array}\right\} \quad (26)$$

These are the *primary* spectral functions.[1]

[1] They are discussed briefly in the appendix of RL Report **873**.

*Driving Current with Noise.*—If $v_d(\tau')$ is the speed with which an electron injected at $\tau'$ with the speed $v_0(\tau')$ leaves the gap after its first passage, for small voltage amplitudes (high modes),

$$\frac{1}{2} mv_d(\tau')^2 \approx \frac{1}{2} mv_0(\tau')^2 + MV \sin\left(\omega\tau + \frac{\theta_1}{2}\right) + \int \frac{d\omega'}{2\pi} M'V_{\omega'} e^{j\left(\omega'\tau' + \frac{\theta'_1}{2}\right)}, \tag{27}$$

where $M$ and $M'$ are the beam-coupling coefficients for the frequencies $\omega$ and $\omega'$, and $\theta_1$ and $\theta'_1$ are the corresponding gap-transit angles. Hence

$$\frac{v_d(\tau')}{v_0} \approx 1 + \frac{MV}{2V_0} \sin\left(\omega\tau' + \frac{\theta_1}{2}\right) + \int \frac{d\omega'}{2\pi} \left(\frac{v_{\omega'}}{v_0} + \frac{M'V_{\omega'}}{2V_0} e^{j\frac{\theta'_1}{2}}\right) e^{j\omega'\tau'}. \tag{28}$$

To this approximation the arrival times are

$$\left.\begin{aligned}
\tau^+(x;\tau') &= \tau' + \frac{x}{d} T_1, \\
\tau^-(x;\tau') &= \tau' + \left(\frac{d-x}{d}\right) T_1 + T_1 + 2T_2 + T_3 \\
&+ (-2T_2 + T_3)\left[\frac{MV}{2V_0} \sin\left(\omega\tau' + \frac{\theta_1}{2}\right) + \int \frac{d\omega'}{2\pi}\left(\frac{v_\omega}{v_0} + \frac{M'V_{\omega'}}{2V_0} e^{j\frac{\theta'_1}{2}}\right) e^{j\omega'\tau'}\right],
\end{aligned}\right\} \tag{29}$$

where $T_1$, $2T_2$, and $T_3$ are the transit times through the gap, through a possible field-free drift space (both ways), and in the reflector region, respectively, in the absence of the r-f field of an electron injected with the velocity $v_0$.

The space average of the phase factors required in the driving current are the expressions,

$$\left.\begin{aligned}
\frac{1}{d}\int_0^d dx\, e^{-j\omega'\tau^+(x,\tau')} &= M'e^{-j\left(\omega'\tau' + \frac{\theta'_1}{2}\right)}, \\
\frac{1}{d}\int_0^d dx\, e^{-j\omega\tau^-(x;\tau')} &= M'e^{-j\left(\omega'\tau' + \frac{\theta'_1}{2} + \theta'\right)} e^{-jZ'\sin\left(\omega\tau' + \frac{\theta_1}{2}\right)} \\
&\cdot \exp\left[-j(-2\theta'_2 + \theta'_3)\int \frac{d\omega''}{2\pi}\left(\frac{v_{\omega''}}{v_0} + \frac{M''V_{\omega''}}{2V_0} e^{-j\frac{\theta''_1}{2}}\right) e^{j\omega''\tau'}\right],
\end{aligned}\right\} \tag{30}$$

where $Z' = (-2\theta'_2 + \theta'_3)MV/2V_0$ and $\omega''$ is a frequency of integration. Because quadratic and higher terms in the noise amplitudes are to be discarded, the last exponential is expanded as follows:

$$\frac{1}{d}\int_0^d dx\, e^{-j\omega\tau^-(x;\tau')} \approx M'e^{-j\left(\omega'\tau' + \frac{\theta'_1}{2} + \theta'\right)} e^{-jZ'\sin\left(\omega\tau' + \frac{\theta_1}{2}\right)}$$
$$\cdot \left[1 - j(-2\theta'_2 + \theta'_3)\int \frac{d\omega''}{2\pi}\left(\frac{v_{\omega''}}{v_0} + \frac{M''V_{\omega''}}{2V_0} e^{-j\frac{\theta''_1}{2}}\right) e^{j\omega''\tau'}\right]. \tag{31}$$

The quantities just obtained are to be substituted into the expression for the driving current, Eq. (24). For the first portion of the driving current

$$i^+(t) = \int \frac{d\omega'}{2\pi} e^{j\omega t} \int d\tau' \left( -I_0 + \int \frac{d\omega''}{2\pi} i^+_{\omega''} e^{j\omega''\tau'} \right) M' e^{-j\left(\omega'\tau + \frac{\theta'_1}{2}\right)}. \quad (32)$$

Now

$$\int d\tau' \, e^{j(\omega''-\omega')\tau'} = 2\pi\delta(\omega'' - \omega') \quad (33)$$

is the integral representation of the Dirac delta function. Hence

$$i^+(t) = -I_0 + \int \frac{d\omega'}{2\pi} M' i^+_{\omega'} \, e^{j\left(\omega' t - \frac{\theta'_1}{2}\right)}. \quad (34)$$

This result is entirely reasonable because the electrons that contribute to this portion of the driving current are those with positive velocities which are at the instant within the gap. Their phases are spread uniformly over the range 0 to $\theta'_1$. On averaging over phases, one obtains the usual factor $M'e^{-j\frac{\theta'_1}{2}}$.

Considering next the reflected current,

$$i^-(t) = -k \int \frac{d\omega'}{2\pi} e^{j\omega' t} \int d\tau' \left( -I_0 + \int \frac{d\omega''}{2\pi} i^+_{\omega''} \, e^{j\omega''\tau'} \right) M' e^{-j\left(\omega'\tau + \frac{\theta'_1}{2} + \theta'\right)}$$
$$\cdot \, e^{-jZ' \sin\left(\omega\tau' + \frac{\theta_1}{2}\right)} \left[ 1 - j(-2\theta'_2 + \theta'_3) \int \frac{d\omega''}{2\pi} \left( \frac{v_{\omega''}}{v_0} + \frac{M'' V_{\omega''}}{2V_0} e^{j\frac{\theta''_1}{2}} \right) e^{j\omega''\tau'} \right]. \quad (35)$$

The Bessel function expansion is introduced,

$$e^{-jZ' \sin\left(\omega\tau' + \frac{\theta_1}{2}\right)} = \sum_{-\infty}^{\infty} J_m(Z')e^{jm\left(\omega\tau' + \frac{\theta_1}{2} - \pi\right)}; \quad (36)$$

and after dropping quadratic noise terms, the integrations over $\tau'$ and $\omega''$ are carried out. It is convenient to write

$$i^-_{\omega'} = e^{-j\theta'} \sum J_m(Z')e^{jm\left(\frac{\theta_1}{2} - \frac{\pi}{2}\right)} \left[ i^+_{\omega''} + jI_0(-2\theta'_2 + \theta'_3) \frac{v_{\omega''}}{v_0} \right]_{\omega''=\omega'-m\omega}. \quad (37)$$

Then

$$i^-(t) = kI_0 \sum J_m(mZ)M_m e^{-jm\left(\theta + \frac{\pi}{2}\right)} e^{jm\omega t} - \int \frac{d\omega'}{2\pi} M' k i^-_{\omega'} e^{j\left(\omega' t - \frac{\theta'_1}{2}\right)}$$
$$- jkI_0 \int \frac{d\omega'}{2\pi} e^{j\left(\omega' t - \frac{\theta'_1}{2} - \theta'\right)} M' \sum J_m(Z')e^{jm\left(\frac{\theta_1}{2} - \frac{\pi}{2}\right)}(-2\theta'_2 + \theta'_3) \frac{M'' V_{\omega''}}{2V_0} e^{j\frac{\theta''_1}{2}}. \quad (38)$$

By Eq. (23) the driving current with noise is the sum of Eq. (34) and Eq. (38).

*Noise Circuit Equations.*—On identifying coefficients of $e^{j\omega't}$ in Eqs. (22) and (24), there is obtained the equation,

$$Y_{\omega'}V_{\omega'} = M'e^{-j\frac{\theta_1'}{2}}(i_{\omega'}^{+} - ki_{\overline{\omega'}})$$
$$-ikI_0M'e^{-j\frac{\theta_1'}{2}}e^{-j\theta'}\sum J_m(Z')e^{jm\left(\frac{\theta_1}{2}-\frac{\pi}{2}\right)}(-2\theta_2' + \theta_3')\frac{M''V_{\omega''}}{2V_0}e^{j\frac{\theta_1''}{2}}. \quad (39)$$

Let $\omega''' = 2\omega - \omega'$, then since $\omega' - \omega = \omega - \omega'''$, $\omega'$ and $\omega'''$ are two frequencies located symmetrically about the oscillation frequency; they are the high and low sideband frequencies, respectively. In the summation the voltage amplitudes make all terms negligible except those with $m = 0$ and $m = 2$. For these values of $m$, $\omega''$ has the values $\omega'$ and $-\omega'''$, respectively. Hence

$$Y_{\omega'}V_{\omega'} = M'e^{-j\frac{\theta_1'}{2}}(i_{\omega'}^{+} - ki_{\overline{\omega'}}) - jkI_0M'e^{-j\theta'}\left[J_0(Z')(-2\theta_2' + \theta_3')\frac{MV_{\omega'}}{2V_0}\right.$$
$$\left. - J_2(Z')(-2\theta_2' + \theta_3')\frac{M'''V_{-\omega'''}}{2V_0}\right]. \quad (40)$$

Now

$$Y_{\omega'} = Y_\omega + 2j(\omega' - \omega)C = -Y_e + 2j(\omega' - \omega)C, \quad (41)$$

where $Y_e$ is the electronic admittance

$$Y_e = -\frac{2kI_0MJ_1(Z)}{V}e^{-j\left(\theta+\frac{\pi}{2}\right)}. \quad (42)$$

In the coefficients, the substitution $\omega' = \omega''' = \omega$ is made and $Z$ is replaced by $X = \theta_e MV/2V_0$, which are valid approximations (compare Chap. 12). Noting that $2J_1(X) - XJ_0(X) = XJ_2(X)$, Eq. (40) becomes

$$\left[\frac{kMI_0XJ_2(X)}{V}e^{-j\left(\theta+\frac{\pi}{2}\right)} + 2j(\omega' - \omega)C\right]V_{\omega'}$$
$$+ \left[\frac{kMI_0XJ_2(X)e^{-j\left(\theta+\frac{\pi}{2}\right)}}{V}\right]V_{-\omega'''} = Me^{-j\frac{\theta_1}{2}}(i_{\omega'}^{+} - ki_{\overline{\omega'}}). \quad (43)$$

The abbreviations,

$$A = \frac{2kMI_0XJ_2(X)}{V}, \quad \text{and} \quad B = 2(\omega' - \omega)C, \quad (44)$$

are then introduced. To obtain a second equation, $\omega'$ is substituted for $\omega'''$ in Eq. (4) (hence $B$ is replaced by $-B$). The two noise circuit equations are

$$\left.\begin{array}{l}\left(\dfrac{A}{2}e^{-j\theta} - B\right)V_{\omega'} + \dfrac{A}{2}e^{-j\theta}V_{-\omega'''} = jMe^{-j\frac{\theta_1}{2}}(i_{\omega'}^{+} - ki_{\overline{\omega'}}), \\[2mm] \dfrac{A}{2}e^{j\theta}V_{\omega'} + \left(\dfrac{A}{2}e^{j\theta} + B\right)V_{-\omega''} = -jMe^{j\frac{\theta_1}{2}}(i_{-\omega'''}^{-} - ki_{\omega'''}^{+})^*,\end{array}\right\} \quad (45)$$

where explicitly,

$$i_{\omega'}^+ - ki_{\overline{\omega'}} = i_{\omega+(\omega'-\omega)}^+ - ke^{-i\theta}\sum J_{-m+1}(X)e^{-j(m-1)\left(\frac{\theta_1}{2}-\frac{\pi}{2}\right)}\left[i_{m\omega+(\omega'-\omega)}^+\right.$$
$$\left.+\frac{jI_0\theta_e v_{m\omega+(\omega'-\omega)}}{v_0}\right], \quad (46)$$

and

$$(i_{\omega'''}^+ - ki_{\overline{\omega'''}})^* = i_{-\omega+(\omega'-\omega)}^+ - ke^{i\theta}\sum J_{m+1}(X)e^{-j(m+1)\left(\frac{\theta_1}{2}-\frac{\pi}{2}\right)}\left[i_{m\omega+(\omega'-\omega)}^+\right.$$
$$\left.-\frac{jI_0\theta_e v_{m\omega+(\omega'-\omega)}}{v_0}\right].$$

These equations give for $V_{\omega'}$,

$$-B[B + jA\sin\theta]V_{\omega'} = \left[\frac{A}{2}e^{i\theta} + B\right]jMe^{-j\frac{\theta_1}{2}}(i_{\omega'}^+ - ki_{\overline{\omega'}})$$
$$+\frac{A}{2}e^{-i\theta}jMe^{\frac{j\theta}{2}}(i_{\omega''}^+ - ki_{\overline{\omega'''}})^*. \quad (47)$$

After considerable manipulation there results

$$\frac{B^2(B^2 + A^2\sin^2\theta)G_V(f')}{M^2}$$

$$= \left[\left(\frac{A^2}{2} + B^2 + AB\cos\theta\right)(1 - 2kJ_0(X)\cos\theta)\right.$$
$$\left. + \left(\frac{A^2}{2}\cos\theta + AB\right)2kJ_2(X)\right]G_i(f)$$
$$-\left[\left(\frac{A^2}{2} + B^2 + AB\cos\theta\right)2kJ_0(x)\right.$$
$$\left. + \frac{A^2}{2}2kJ_2(x)\right]\frac{I_0\theta_e}{v_0}\frac{1}{2j}[G_{iv}(f)e^{i\theta} - G_{iv}^*(f)e^{-i\theta}]$$
$$-[AB2kJ_2(X)]\frac{I_0\theta_e}{v_0}\frac{1}{2j}[G_{iv}(f) - G_{iv}^*(f)]$$
$$+ k^2\left(\frac{A^2}{2} + B^2 + AB\cos\theta\right)\sum J_{m-1}^2(x)\left\{G_i(mf) + \frac{I_0^2\theta_e^2}{v_0^2}G_v(mf)\right.$$
$$\left. + \frac{2I_0\theta_e}{v_c}\frac{1}{2j}[G_{iv}(mf) - G_{iv}^*(mf)]\right\}$$
$$- k^2\left(\frac{A^2}{2} + AB\cos\theta\right)\sum J_{-m+1}(x)J_{m+1}(x)\left[G_i(mf) - \frac{I_0^2\theta_e^2}{v_0^2}G_v(mf)\right]$$
$$+ k^2\sum J_{-m+1}(x)J_{m+1}(x)\frac{2I_0\theta_e}{v_0}\left\{\frac{A^2}{2}\frac{1}{2j}[G_{iv}(mf) - G_{iv}^*(mf)] - AB\frac{1}{2j}\right.$$
$$\left. \cdot [G_{iv}^*(mf)e^{i\theta} - G_{iv}(mf)e^{-i\theta}]\right\}. \quad (48)$$

This expression is the basis of the discussion in Sec. 17·7.

# CHAPTER 18

## PRACTICAL REFLEX KLYSTRONS

### By J. B. H. Kuper

**18·1. Introduction.**—The main purpose of this chapter is to help the reader to select the correct type of reflex klystron for a given application. With this in mind some representative tubes have been chosen to illustrate a discussion of cavity design, methods of tuning, and other mechanical features in relation to the performance of the tube as an oscillator. In selecting types for discussion, consideration has been given to the illustrative value, rather than the popularity, of the tubes. Foreign types have been omitted because they are not widely known in this country.

Of many possible ways of classifying reflex oscillator types, perhaps the most obvious method depends on whether or not the tube requires an external cavity; a tube that is not a self-contained microwave oscillator requires the appendage of a cavity, in addition to the output lead and means of mechanical tuning. The next possible method of classification depends upon method of tuning, whether direct mechanical or thermal; then come electronic tuning range, power (input and output), and type of output lead. For many applications, frequency stability is so important that other factors in the choice of a tube are almost eliminated; in other instances output power or speed of tuning may be paramount.

Probably the best-known tube of the external cavity type is the 707B or its electronic equivalent, the 2K28. Designed primarily for the 3000-Mc/sec region, it can be used with suitable cavities at frequencies up to about 4000 Mc/sec and down to 2000 Mc/sec or lower. The classic examples of the integral cavity type are the 417A for the 3000-Mc/sec region, and the 723A/B (or its improved successor, the 2K25) for the range 8500 to 9660 Mc/sec. Both these tubes are mechanically tuned, but the 417A is capable of large output powers and has a very small electronic tuning range, whereas the 2K25/723A/B is designed specifically for use as a superheterodyne local oscillator and has a comparatively low power level but a wide electronic tuning range.

The integral-cavity tubes with thermal tuning are well represented by the 2K45, which is similar to the 2K25 as regards performance; the tuning, however, is controlled by the voltage applied to the grid of a triode section built inside the envelope. Expansion of the triode plate under bombardment is magnified and this magnified expansion is used for varying the separation between the grids that form the r-f gap. By using the thermal-tuner grid for coarse frequency adjustment and the reflector voltage for fine adjustment, the tube can be tuned easily from a remote location with negligible power required from the control circuit.

The 2K33 tube and the Sperry developmental tube designated as 2K57 (formerly SRC-2) have unusual combinations of features. The former, although it requires an external cavity, is tuned mechanically by flexing a diaphragm and altering the spacing of the r-f gap. The latter has an integral cavity tuned by mechanical variation of the "inductive" portion rather than by the gap spacing, and it also has a waveguide output; this tube is capable of markedly higher efficiency than is usual in reflex oscillators.

At frequencies above 5000 Mc/sec it becomes possible to build into a tube an output waveguide of convenient size, which seems to permit greater uniformity in loading from tube to tube than the more usual coupling loop and coaxial line. A good example of this construction, also incorporating a thermal tuning mechanism with grid control, is afforded by the 2K50.

Some of the most important characteristics of these types are summarized, for purposes of comparison, in Table 18·1. The numerical values given are neither specification limits nor maximum ratings; rather, an attempt has been made to give typical operating conditions. Many of the figures, particularly the reflector voltages, are to be taken only as rough indications. Of the types considered, only the 2K33 does not have grids at the r-f gap, having instead a pair of pinhole apertures 0.028 in. in diameter.

The reader should not be misled by the discussion of this chapter into thinking that the development of reflex klystrons is essentially a closed subject. Throughout most of the war years the emphasis was placed on producing types that were useful for superheterodyne local oscillators, and very little attention was paid to oscillator efficiency.

More recently, attempts have been made to come closer to realizing the theoretical efficiency of reflex klystrons with the intention of using them for transmitting tubes. Efficiency is a comparatively minor matter in local oscillator service where 25 mw of r-f power is usually adequate, and it makes little difference if 2.5 or even 5 watts is expended to obtain it. Where output powers of 5 to 10 watts are necessary for transmitter purposes, however, an efficiency of the order of magnitude of 1 per cent is hardly tolerable. Fortunately, by more careful design it seems practicable to attain efficiencies of 3 to 6 per cent in c-w operation and considerably higher efficiencies in pulsed applications. The 2K57 is one of the first reflex tubes designed specifically for transmitter service in c-w

TABLE 18·1.—CHARACTERISTICS OF SOME REPRESENTATIVE REFLEX KLYSTRONS

| Type | Cavity | Tuning means | Frequency range, per cent | Type of output | Beam voltage, volts | Beam current (approx), ma | Reflector voltage (approx), volts | R-f power output, mw | Electronic tuning range, per cent |
|---|---|---|---|---|---|---|---|---|---|
| 707B (2K28) | External | * | * | * | 300 | 25 | −175 | 150 | 0.7 |
| 417A | Integral | Mechanical coarse, screws; fine, knob | Coarse—20 fine—6 | Coaxial fitting | 1000 | 40 | −250 | 400 | 0.2 |
| 2K25/723A/B | Integral | Mechanical | 12 | Antenna into waveguide | 300 | 22 | −160 | 25 | 0.5 |
| 2K45 | Integral | Thermal, grid control | 12 | Antenna into waveguide | 300 | 22 +6 tuner | −160 | 30 | 0.5 |
| 2K33 | External | Mechanical | 5 | Waveguide | 1800 | 9 | −200 | 20 | 0.2 |
| 2K57 | Integral | Mechanical "inductive" | 5 | Waveguide | 700 | 70 | −200 | 1500 | 1.0 |
| 2K50 | Integral | Thermal, grid control | 6 | Waveguide | 300 | 15 +5 tuner | −100 | 15 | 0.3 |

* Depends on (or part of) external cavity.

applications. The remarkable difference shown in Table 18·1 between the 2K57 and the other tubes indicates that there is much room for improvement in most tube designs and it gives hope that satisfactory transmitter tubes will soon be available.

Tubes designed for pulse operation at very high recurrence rates—duty ratios of the order of magnitude of $\frac{1}{10}$ —may also be expected to become common in the future. The pioneer types in this field are the 2K54 and 2K55, which furnish a minimum pulse power of 7.5 watts.

**18·2. Resonator Design in Relation to Performance.** *Integral vs. External Cavity Construction.*—The choice between the integral and external cavity constructions can often be made on the basis of the intended service. From the standpoint of electronics only, the external cavity type, as exemplified by the 707B, offers advantages in simplicity and ease of exhaust that make the tube cheap to build. From the circuit standpoint it is not easy to devise a cavity that will be light and strong, make dependable contact to the tube, and at the same time permit quick and simple replacement of the tube. These questions depend to some extent on frequency, design of an external cavity being relatively easy for frequencies not exceeding 4000 Mc/sec. Circuit losses introduced by the glass envelope are another drawback in the external cavity type, but if a very wide tuning range is needed, it is usually chosen.

From the standpoint of temperature compensation there is little choice between the two types. With care either type can be made to work satisfactorily but the solution of the problem, at least in the case of the 2K28, seems a little easier with the external cavity. On the other hand, somewhat better heat dissipation can be obtained with the integral cavity construction. Barometric effects and sensitivity to acoustic disturbances should never be troublesome with an external cavity.

*Resonator Shape.*—A consideration of cavity proportions in their relation to power output, efficiency, and electronic tuning range is important for understanding reflex klystrons. The bunched beam in a klystron can best be considered as a current generator, and therefore a high-impedance load circuit is required as in the ordinary pentode. The problem is to choose a resonator that will present a high shunt impedance with a reasonable beam coupling coefficient. At this point it is helpful to repeat some of the results obtained in the theoretical discussions of Chaps. 3 and 4.

In practically all cases the resonator is a cylindrical container with a central post, as illustrated in cross section in Fig. 18·1. The top surface of the post and the corresponding portion of the top wall of the cavity must be perforated to permit the passage of the electron beam. The radius $a$ of the post must be large enough to permit the passage of the required current without causing difficulties with focusing, alignment, or the fundamental limits imposed by space-charge effects.  In any event, the dimension $a$ must be small compared with a quarter of the desired wavelength; otherwise a large part of the beam will interact with a negligible r-f voltage.  The length of the r-f gap $d$ must be small enough to give a satisfactory beam coupling coefficient at the desired beam voltage.  This dimension must not, however, be made too small or the gap capacitance will be high and the shunt resistance low, resulting in a small electronic tuning range and poor circuit efficiency.

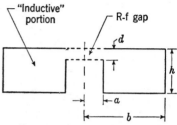

Fig. 18·1.—Section of typical klystron resonator; the complete resonator is a figure of revolution about the axis indicated.

The transit angle through the gap, $\omega T_1$, has an optimum value in the vicinity of $\pi$.  The exact optimum value is determined by two opposing effects: the decrease of shunt impedance with decreasing gap length, and the decrease of the beam coupling coefficient as $\omega T_1$ increases toward $2\pi$.  If $d$ is allowed to approach zero the capacitance approaches infinity; the circulating current, and hence the losses, must likewise approach infinity.

The beam coupling coefficient $M$, given by the equation

$$M = \frac{\sin \dfrac{\omega T_1}{2}}{\dfrac{\omega T_1}{2}}, \tag{1}$$

enters in the expressions for electronic efficiency in an involved way (see Chap. 12).  Its primary influence lies in the proportionality to $M$ of the efficiency at optimum load, but it enters as the square in the determination of optimum load.  It will be evident from the graph of Fig. 18·2, in which $M$ and $M^2$ are plotted as functions of $\omega T_1$, that the electronic efficiency will fall to zero at $\omega T_1 = 2\pi$.  The over-all efficiency will go through a maximum somewhere between 0 and $2\pi$, and in most cases the maximum will not be far from $\omega T_1 = \pi$.  For the present purposes it is sufficient to know that a maximum exists somewhere around this value.

Once the dimensions of the r-f gap have been fixed, it is necessary only to adjust the "inductive"[1] portion for optimum shunt impedance

---

[1] Quotation marks around the words "inductive" and "capacitive" are used here to call attention to the fact that in a cavity resonator a clean-cut separation of this sort is impossible, yet the two regions under consideration behave as though they were predominantly capacitive or inductive.

at the desired frequency. The proportions are not very critical, but there will be a broad maximum in shunt impedance when the cross section of the toroidal "inductive" region is square, that is, for $h = b - a$. This condition is not very critical, however, and is often violated for reasons of mechanical convenience. If $h$ is made very large, as is sometimes done when the necessity for a wide mechanical tuning range outweighs all other desiderata, the cavity degenerates into a short-circuited coaxial line loaded at the open end by the gap capacitance. The other extreme, the reduction of $h$ until the post disappears, is never used because tuning is difficult (the resonant frequency depends only on $b$) and the attainment of a reasonable shunt impedance requires a long r-f gap (shunt impedance varies approximately as the square of the height $d$).[1]

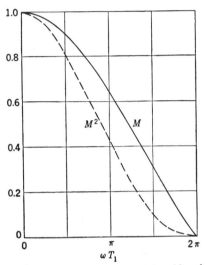

Fig. 18·2.—Beam coupling coefficient $M$, and its square, as functions of transit angle.

*Grids vs. Apertures.*—Important differences arise between cavities that have a simple aperture for the beam, as in the 2K33, and those provided with grids. When a cavity has an aperture, the transit times for electrons near the center may be sensibly different from those for electrons in the outer portions of the beam. This difference may lead to a spread in phase of the returning bunch. Also, because of the fringing of the fields, unless the r-f field is small compared with the d-c accelerating and retarding fields, a variation in focusing properties of the r-f gap during the cycle is to be expected. Depending on circumstances, a complication of this sort may or may not be harmful; that is, there may be some "sorting" in addition to reflex bunching, and it will be a matter of relative phases whether or not this is desirable. In general, however, it seems likely that phase shifts in the returning beam that are dependent on r-f voltage across the gap will lead to asymmetrical reflector characteristics (mode shape) and hysteresis.

Effects arising from fringing and interpenetration of the fields will be minimized by using a small aperture and a high beam velocity. Focusing and alignment difficulties, of course, set a lower limit to the practical

[1] A tabulation of $Q_0$ and shunt impedance for various resonator shapes is given in Figs. 4·8 to 4·12.

aperture diameter. Heat dissipation is much less of a problem because all the electrons eventually strike solid metal; the circuit losses are lower because no current has to flow on fine wires.

When the apertures are covered with grids, troubles with field penetration and spreads in transit angle are greatly reduced, and a lower beam voltage becomes practical. The disadvantages of using grids are beam losses by interception, higher circuit losses (caused by secondary electrons emitted from the grid and by resistance of the wires), and generally lower permissible input powers because of poor heat conduction. Since the electron beam must traverse a minimum of three grids (not counting the accelerator or "smoother" grid $G_1$, if it is used) in order to deliver energy to the resonator, a grid transmission of 80 per cent means that half the current injected is wasted. A transmission much less than 80 per cent for each grid is too wasteful for most applications. Circuit losses for a cavity with grids are increased because a large part of the charging current for the gap capacitance must flow on the grid wires. If the aperture size required to pass the necessary current becomes a large fraction of the total surface of the cavity, grid losses may be large enough to prevent oscillation. For example, the 2K50 probably would not oscillate if a parallel beam were used instead of one brought to a focus near the interaction gap; otherwise the grids would have to extend over too large a part of the cavity.

In scaling all dimensions of a cavity the unloaded $Q$ and the shunt impedance will vary as the square root of the wavelength. Therefore, as the wavelength is decreased, the beam current must be raised to maintain the same power production. If the proportions remain unchanged, it is clearly necessary to increase the current density in the beam. The maximum current density permitted by space charge, therefore, sets an upper limit to the attainable frequency.[1]

Losses in grids are increased by the fact that the temperature is usually high, and materials such as tungsten are required for mechanical reasons. Mesh grids may be less desirable than parallel wire construction because the second set of wires contributes less to the beam coupling coefficient than to the interception losses, and poor contacts at the wire crossings can increase the r-f losses. Loading by secondaries will also be more serious.

To sum up, a cavity without grids can probably be made to oscillate at frequencies higher than those that have been attained in tubes with grids, but at the cost of raising the voltage requirements and increasing the difficulties of focusing and alignment, thus tending to make the

---

[1] In most practical cases heat dissipation limits the current density before the space-charge limitation is reached. In high-power reflex oscillators space-charge effects in the reflector region may limit performance at low frequencies.

tube more expensive. This construction might also be valuable in tubes of comparatively high power at lower frequencies. For moderate powers, where the interception loss can be tolerated, the use of grids is almost universal. A large part of the excellent performance of the 2K57 is due to the use of a honeycomb grid, which combines low losses with high heat-dissipation capabilities.

**18·3. Tuning Methods.** *"Capacitive" vs "Inductive" Tuning.*—The method adopted for tuning the resonator has an important bearing on the performance of a reflex klystron, apart from the obvious considerations of the user's convenience. Tuning is most commonly accomplished by varying the length of the r-f gap and thus adjusting the capacitive portion of the resonator, but some tubes, most particularly the 707B and the 2K57, are tuned by altering the "inductive" portion. Capacitive tuning requires small motions for large frequency shifts, particularly near the low-frequency end of the range    It is entirely a matter of the circumstances of a given application whether this sensitivity is to be considered a drawback or an advantage. In general, it leads to extra trouble in attempting temperature compensation since there must be considerable reduction of motion by a mechanical linkage between the control knob and the gap itself.

In all cases, however, the use of capacitive tuning reduces the tuning range over which reasonable efficiency is obtained. As the frequency is raised by lengthening the gap, the transit angle through the gap increases rapidly because the electrons have farther to go and less time to make the trip. Thus, $\omega T_1$ varies faster than $\omega$, and conditions soon depart widely from the optimum referred to above. The frequency increases roughly as $\sqrt{d}$, and consequently $\omega T_1$ is proportional to $d^{3/2}$. As $M$ drops very rapidly when $\omega T_1$ exceeds $\pi$, a precipitous drop in power output is found at high frequencies. At frequencies below the center of the range, $\omega T_1$ becomes less than the optimum and the output again decreases, although not so rapidly as at the high-frequency limit.

A further difficulty with capacitive tuning as ordinarily employed is that a portion of the resonator must be flexible. This requirement often leads either to vacuum troubles and undue frequency modulation from sound waves impinging on the diaphragm, or to undesirable mechanical hysteresis in tuning if the diaphragm is too stiff.

Inductive tuning, on the other hand, is generally less sensitive in that larger mechanical motions are required. In the radial cavities customarily used with the 707B, radial screw plugs (four or six) are used for tuning. These prevent the fields from extending throughout the cavity volume and thus increase the frequency. The variation of shunt impedance with tuning of this kind is not wholly predictable, but, in any case, $\omega T_1$ varies only with $\omega$ and the useful operating range is wider than in the "capacitive" method. If efficiency is a minor matter, relatively enormous tuning ranges, 2 to 1 or more in frequency, can be obtained by use of a coaxial cavity.

*Thermal Tuning.*—Mechanical tuning, as distinct from thermal tuning which is exemplified by the 2K45 and 2K50, is employed in most applications. The exceptions occur where remote or automatic control of frequency is required over ranges larger than those obtained by reflector-voltage variations. A serious drawback to the general use of a thermally tuned tube is the complexity of its frequency control, but such tubes have been very successful in special signal generators sweeping over wide bands, systems involving control and stabilization of the frequency of an oscillator by means of a separate wavemeter cavity, and in radar systems permitting instantaneous frequency shifts with a single control knob.

Because the motion obtained is small, thermal tuning is always of the capacitive type. Some of the early experimental thermally tuned oscillators used resistive heating of a strut, or wire, through which a current is passed to actuate the tuner. Unless a heater design of inconveniently low impedance is employed, there will be some insulating material, which will add thermal capacity to the system. The result is a lag, or "overshoot," which prevents the direction of the frequency shift from reversing instantly when the heater current is cut off or suddenly applied. This lag is most marked in those cases where a construction resembling the familiar internally heated cathode sleeve is employed. This lag is most troublesome to the designer of a frequency-control circuit; the elimination of hunting without undue sacrifice in speed of response is very difficult. Therefore, in recent designs the tuning strut has been made the anode of an auxiliary triode that is heated by electron bombardment. In this case the strut can have good thermal contact to some fairly massive "sink" in order that the temperature will start to change as soon as the bombarding current is altered. In addition, this scheme automatically provides a high-impedance control electrode, which materially simplifies the design of the control circuit.

For a tuning strut, of length $l$ and thermal conductivity $K$, whose ends are maintained at a constant temperature, and to which heat is supplied uniformly along its length, the time constant $\tau$ is given approximately[1] by

$$\tau \approx \frac{l^2 \sigma \rho}{8K}, \tag{2}$$

where $\sigma$ and $\rho$ are the specific heat and specific density, respectively. The approximation here is the assumption that, in equilibrium, the

[1] For derivation see H. V. Neher, "A Low-voltage K-band Oscillator," RL Report No. 764, pp. 6–7, Sept. 17, 1945.

temperature will increase linearly from the ends to the middle of the strut. The product $\sigma\rho$ has a value close to 0.6 cal/cm$^3$ for most metals.

The power $P$ required to produce a useful motion $\Delta l$ is

$$P = \frac{\alpha \, \Delta l \sigma \rho F_{max}}{\lambda \tau S_{max}} \tag{3}$$

where $\alpha$ is the mechanical equivalent of heat, $\lambda$ is the linear thermal-expansion coefficient of the strut, $F_{max}$ is the maximum force against which the tuning mechanism will be expected to work, and $S_{max}$ is the maximum strain the material will take without creep at the highest temperatures expected. From the standpoint of low tuning power the material should be chosen for a maximum value of the product $\lambda S_{max}$, rather than for a large expansion alone. Comparison of Eqs. (2) and (3) points to the fact that a small time constant implies a large expenditure of power in the tuner; this conclusion might almost have been reached without resorting to mathematics. It should be noted that the cross-sectional area of the strut does not appear in either equation. It is necessary that the area be large enough to exert the required force without undue elastic deformation. A major problem in tuner design is to select a material for the struts that does not "creep" appreciably at the highest temperatures encountered in exhaust or operation. This requirement is necessary because the tuner must be set before assembly in order to cover the required range. Some recently developed stainless steels and Nichrome V have been found suitable.

*Speed of Thermal Tuning.*—The tuning speed of a thermally tuned tube is an important parameter because it enters into the design of the frequency-control circuits. In the case of the 2K45, from 4 to 8 sec are required to tune over the whole band (8500 to 9660 Mc/sec) in the direction of increasing frequency, and a slightly longer time is needed to cover the band in the other direction.

In practical tubes, heating and cooling curves do not follow a simple exponential law exactly, but show more than one time constant. This variation may be due either to heat loss by radiation in addition to conduction, or to the fact that the ends of the strut do not remain at a constant temperature. Manufacturing variations between tubes are large enough, however, to necessitate the use of a single average time constant in designing control circuits.

In order to have reasonably constant tuning speed over the entire operating frequency range, it is necessary to design the tuner mechanism for a much larger range as illustrated in Fig. 18·3. The "no heat" position of the tuner mechanism is determined by the ambient temperature and the input power to the oscillator section of the tube, and the "maximum heat" is fixed by the safe working temperature for the strut material.  Starting from the cold end with full heat applied, the temperature (and frequency to a first approximation) changes in accord with the curve marked "heating," and if the heat is suddenly cut off after equilibrium is reached at the hot extreme, the temperature follows the "cooling" curve.  Clearly, the speeds in the two directions will be very different near either end of the range, but over a considerable interval in the middle—for example, that indicated by broken lines—the speeds will be nearly enough constant to permit design of a satisfactory control circuit.  In the 2K45 and 2K50 it is found experimentally that the wavelength changes almost linearly with tuner cathode current,

or frequency increases more or less linearly with increasing negative grid bias on the tuner triode.

If an attempt is made to operate without automatic frequency control, it will ordinarily be necessary to regulate the heater voltage supply in addition to the reflector and resonator supplies.  For example, in the 2K45 a 10 per cent drop in heater voltage may cause a frequency increase of as much as 400 Mc/sec.  This difficulty comes partly from the fact that the state of activation of the tuner cathode, like any other oxide-coated cathode, depends on its history, and partly from the fact that as the cathode temperature is raised, there is a

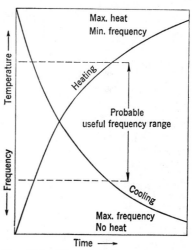

Fig. 18·3.—Thermal-tuning curves based on simple exponential law.

greater length of the sleeve emitting.  Presumably, this last effect could be reduced by coating only a central portion of the length of the cathode sleeve.  The design should minimize transfer of heat by radiation between cathode and anode.

It might appear that because of the light construction usual in thermal-tuning mechanisms, a tube of this type would give unusual trouble with microphonic response.  This fear seems to be groundless.  Although the mechanisms are light, they are of necessity well designed from the standpoint of strength and rigidity, with the result that thermally tuned tubes stand shock and vibration about as well as the corresponding mechanically tuned types.

*Thermal Compensation.*—In an integral-cavity tube, temperature compensation is obtained by a proper choice of materials (with regard to expansion coefficients) for the cavity and for the tuner mechanism.

The latter may incorporate struts housed in hollow screws as in the 417A, or it may have a fixed strut and a pair of bow springs as in the 723A/B. When the operating frequency range is small, it is possible to secure good compensation, but the manufacturing problem of keeping sufficiently tight tolerances on grid shaping and other critical dimensions is a severe one. For large frequency ranges with capacitive tuning, good thermal compensation is extremely difficult, if not impossible, to secure.

Compensation schemes in which the frequency-determining elements are partly within and partly outside the vacuum envelope have some inherent disadvantages. Obviously, there will be transient frequency shifts accompanying any change in ambient conditions, or input power, unless the thermal conductivity between the parts is very high, even though the frequency may return to the original value when the new equilibrium is attained.

This effect is quite marked in the 723A/B, which has satisfactory compensation for ambient changes, provided there is no attendant change in ventilation, but the presence of variable drafts leads to serious frequency fluctuations. If the temperature compensation is placed partly within and partly outside the envelope, there results also a barometric pressure effect on frequency that can be very objectionable in airborne equipment. The variation is due in part to a true pressure effect on the resonator considered as an anaeroid capsule, but the effect of changes in ventilation on the temperature distribution may be more serious. Although the 417A tube could be expected to suffer from this same difficulty, the effect is much smaller because of its more massive construction.

With an external-cavity tube such as the 707B, compensation for temperature changes may be achieved by choosing a suitable material for the cylinder supporting one resonator grid, by bending the annular portion of the disk between the cylinder and the glass, or by applying a bimetal ring to the lower side of the disk. The resulting temperature coefficient of frequency depends on the external cavity used. For a 707B in a thick-walled brass cavity the coefficient should not exceed $-0.2$ Mc/sec per degree centigrade at 3000 Mc/sec.

Thermal compensation is ordinarily not considered very important in a thermally tuned oscillator because some form of automatic frequency control is almost always employed, but it does enter into the question of warmup drift. Fortunately, when all vital parts are mounted within the envelope, it is not difficult to achieve satisfactory compensation. Measurement of the temperature coefficient is usually not even attempted because of the difficulty in maintaining adequate stability in the power supplies.

**18·4. Output Couplings.**—Tubes with integral resonators normally have built-in output circuits that consist essentially of a coupling device and an output transmission line. The most common coupling device is an inductive pickup loop formed on the end of a coaxial line and inserted in a region of the resonator where the magnetic field is high. This device is used on all the Sperry tubes of the 417A family and on the Bell Telephone Laboratories tubes of the 723A/B family, including the 2K45. Coupling by means of an aperture between the resonator and the output line, often referred to as "iris coupling," is used to a lesser extent, as in the 2K33, 2K50, and 2K57. A third type, the capacitive probe—or antenna feeding a coaxial line—is not often used except in external cavities of the coaxial-line type, where for optimum coupling a loop should be inserted in the tuning plunger, necessitating a flexible output line to permit tuning. Since a loop furnishes support to the center conductor, which otherwise would require a bead, and since the region of the resonator in which the electric field is strongest is already occupied by the electron beam, it is easy to see why the loop is generally preferred.[1]

The output lines are often small coaxial lines provided with beads, which are also vacuum seals, and carry either a fitting for making connections to another coaxial line or (as in the 2K25 and 2K45) an antenna that feeds a waveguide. Where it is desired to obtain maximum efficiency, waveguide output lines are used (as in the 2K33, 2K50, and the 2K57). This construction is more common for frequencies greater than 10,000 Mc/sec, where coaxial lines must be inconveniently small and waveguides are no longer awkwardly large. Whether or not there is an inherent reason, the experience has been that waveguide windows are held to closer tolerances than the coaxial-line bead seals. An aperture can be machined to much closer tolerances and will hold its dimensions through subsequent processing better than small coupling loops.

With a waveguide output line it is possible to "preplumb" a design so that all tubes will be loaded correctly by a matched guide, but except at comparatively low frequencies this is not satisfactory in the loop-to-coaxial line combination. Most tubes of the family typified by the 417A require individually adjusted transformers of some sort (usually a double-stub tuner) in order to deliver full power to a resistive load. The same is true to a considerable degree of the tubes in the 723A/B family, with the exception of the 726C, and especially the 2K29, which

---

[1] Where it is necessary, for mechanical reasons, to place a pickup in a region of weak magnetic field (where a loop would have to have excessive inductance) a probe with capacitive end loading may be used. This device may be considered as a very large loop whose self-inductance is to a large extent tuned out by the series capacitance between the button on the end of the probe and the opposite wall of the resonator.

work well into fixed loads. On the other hand, a 2K50 rarely delivers appreciably more power to a tuned load than to a simple terminated waveguide.

In the external-cavity construction it is easy to provide a simple coupling adjustment, which is a more desirable method of securing correct loading than the use of a separate tuner. When the adjustment is made by rotating a loop or by partially withdrawing it from the resonator, the load will be constant over a wide frequency range (limited mainly by the changing shunt impedance of the resonator). On the other hand, a device such as a double-stub tuner is frequency-sensitive in itself and is ordinarily located an appreciable distance (in wavelengths) along the line from the loop.

**18·5. Description of Some Representative Reflex Tubes.**—This section contains a more detailed description of the representative reflex-klystron tubes that are listed in Sec. 18·1 and are referred to in Secs. 18·2 to 18·4. Some of these tubes, particularly the 417A and 2K25/723A/B, are important as prototypes for whole series of tubes differing chiefly in frequency of oscillation. Others are included because their unusual features will assume more importance in future designs.

*The 707B.*—The 707B, which was developed at the Bell Telephone Laboratories and produced by the Western Electric Company, the Raytheon Manufacturing Company, and the Sylvania Electric Products, Inc., is illustrated in Fig. 18·4, which shows a photograph and an x-ray view. The grids $G_2$ and $G_3$ are supported by thin copper disks to which the glass is sealed. These disks are the means by which connection is made to the external cavity. Most commonly the external cavity is radial and is split to permit insertion of the tube (see Fig. 1.5c), although coaxial cavities are sometimes employed when very wide tuning ranges are required. The three grids are slightly bowed, for the purpose of avoiding erratic changes in spacing as a result of thermal expansion. The indirectly heated oxide cathode is a flat disk, with a projecting focusing cylinder at the same potential. The cathode is surrounded by a heat shield that supports the accelerating grid $G_1$. This electrode is normally operated at the same d-c potential as the resonator grids $G_2$ and $G_3$, but may be run at other potentials in order to adjust the power output by controlling the cathode current. The reflector is a shallow cup with slightly concave bottom.

Since the convergence of the beam resulting from curvature of the reflector field is not very strong, calculations of transit time and bunching on the basis of a parallel beam seem reasonably accurate. The permissible power input is limited by the temperature of the grids. Under normal operating conditions (6 to 8 watts input), the grids are a bright yellow.

The reflector voltage ranges in which oscillations are obtained at 3000 Mc/sec with a resonator voltage of +300 volts are −30 to −75 volts and −105 to −190 volts.[1]  These ranges correspond, respectively, to transit times of $3\frac{3}{4}$ and $2\frac{3}{4}$ cycles.  Somewhat larger negative reflector voltages are required at lower resonator voltages or at higher frequencies. The half-power electronic tuning range is roughly 20 Mc/sec; the tuning

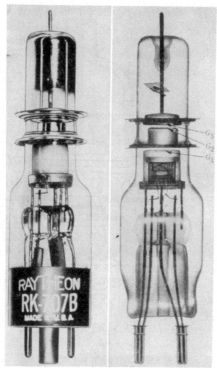

Fig. 18·4.—Photograph and x-ray of a 707B tube.

rate in Mc/sec per reflector volt depends largely on the external cavity and coupling loop.  Tubes of this type frequently suffer from excessive electronic tuning hysteresis, which is caused by multiple transits.

The 2K28, developed by the Raytheon Manufacturing Company, differs from the 707B chiefly in the fact that the lengths of the glass portions are reduced.  Electrically, the tubes are practically identical, but the temperature compensation is slightly better in the 2K28 than in the 707B.

[1] These voltage ranges result from manufacturing tolerances in spacings from tube to tube; for any one tube the regions of oscillation ("modes") are 20 to 40 volts wide.

*The* 417A.—The 417A, developed by the Sperry Gyroscope Company, Inc., and produced by them and by the Westinghouse Electric Company is illustrated in Fig. 18·5. In this tube the grids are made of radial vanes and have appreciable depth. As a result, heat is dissipated much better than in the 707B, and power inputs up to 75 watts (60 ma at 1250 volts) are possible with forced air cooling. The side of the cavity

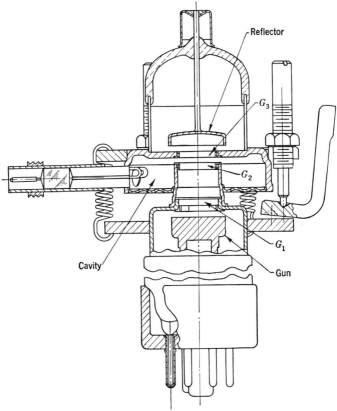

Fig. 18·5(a).—Cross section of a 417A tube mounted in tuner.

toward the cathode is a flexible diaphragm, and the spacing between the grids is controlled by three tuning struts. Coarse adjustment of frequency covering the range from 2650 to 3330 Mc/sec is made with screwdriver and pliers; fine adjustment is provided by a screw actuating a bent lever under one of the struts. Thus, the two parts of the tube are tilted slightly with respect to each other as the grid spacing is varied. This fine adjustment affords a minimum range of about 200 Mc/sec.

Temperature compensation is obtained by using metals of different coefficients of expansion for the struts and the hollow-screw strut-housings. By this scheme the frequency drift is held to less than 6 Mc/sec over the temperature range from $-10°$ to $+40°$C. In general, the reflector voltage should not exceed $-300$ volts. The electron gun is provided with a control electrode in the form of a grid in front of the flat oxide-coated emitting surface.[1] The control electrode is normally

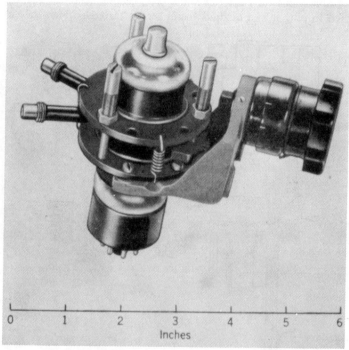

FIG. 18·5(b).—Photograph of a 417A tube mounted in tuner.

connected to the cathode, but if the maximum possible output is required, it may be run as much as 50 volts positive. Two coaxial output leads are provided, and r-f powers in excess of $\frac{1}{4}$ watt may be expected. Ordinarily, maximum output power will not be delivered directly to a 50-ohm line, and some form of transformer, usually a double-stub tuner, is required. The electronic tuning range between half-power points will be about 5 to 8 Mc/sec. Where comparatively low powers will suffice, as in local oscillator service, the 417A may be operated at a resonator potential of about 400 volts with a reduced beam current. Output

[1] A control grid is used only in the 417A; the other Sperry tubes have focusing rings operated at cathode potential or slightly negative.

powers of about 25 to 50 mw should be obtained.  Various other tubes employing a similar structure are made for frequency ranges up to 10,300 Mc/sec.

*The 723A/B (2K25).*—The 723A/B was developed by the Bell Telephone Laboratories and manufactured by Western Electric, Raytheon, and Ken-Rad.  It has been superseded by the 2K25, which is almost identical except for stricter test specifications.  Figure 18·6 shows a photograph of the tube exterior and a cross section sketch.  The tube is designed to plug into a modified octal socket through which the output

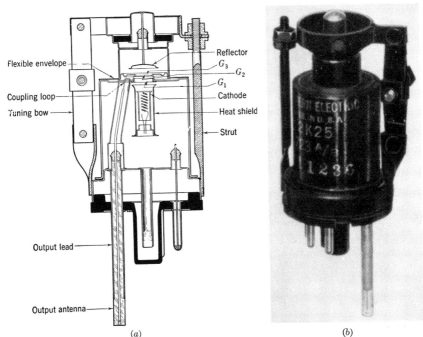

Flexible envelope

Coupling loop

Tuning bow

Reflector
$G_3$
$G_2$
$G_1$
Cathode
Heat shield
Strut

Output lead

Output antenna

(a)                                    (b)

Fig. 18·6.—A 2K25/723A/B tube: (*a*) cross section and (*b*) photograph.

lead (occupying the No. 4 pin position) projects into a waveguide. The center conductor of the output lead, protected by a polystyrene jacket, extends beyond the outer conductor to form an antenna.  A portion of the envelope forming the upper surface of the resonator is flexible. The spacing between $G_2$ and $G_3$ can then be varied by compressing the tuning bows and thereby tilting the upper part of the tube about the fixed strut as a pivot.

In an oscillator of this type the accelerator grid $G_1$ is mounted across the bottom of the cylinder supporting $G_2$; no independent control of its potential is possible.  The cathode is flat and is surrounded by a heat-shield trumpet at the same potential, which serves as a focusing electrode. The cathode current of any given tube can be varied only by changing the resonator voltage, and for a fixed voltage it varies from tube to tube as a result of differences in spacing. Moderately good heat conduction between the grids and the envelope permits the use of input powers up to 8 or 10 watts, although at these input levels the mesh grids are probably operating at a bright-red heat.

When operated at 300 volts on the resonator in the −160-volt (nominal) reflector mode, the 2K25 delivers a minimum of 20 mw at any frequency from 8500 to 9660 Mc/sec. Satisfactory operation over a band this wide requires careful attention to the loading of the tube. Correct loading is obtained, using standard 1-in. by $\frac{1}{2}$-in. (outside) waveguide, if the antenna is inserted to its full length at a point 0.394 in. from a short circuit and 0.178 in. from the center line of the broad face of the guide. In the region around 9375 Mc/sec, the electronic tuning range between half-power points will probably be at least 45 Mc/sec, and an output power of 35 to 40 mw is not unusual. At the ends of the band the electronic tuning range is somewhat less.

The 723A/B tube has served as the prototype for a whole series of tubes operating at various frequencies down to about 2700 Mc/sec. These tubes are similar in external appearance, with the exception that at the lower frequencies the output antenna is replaced by an extended center conductor that is plugged into a coaxial connector. The interior structure is much the same except that the lower side of the resonator is moved down toward the base and the cylindrical support for $G_2$ is correspondingly lengthened. Many of these tubes have also had alterations to the electron optics to discourage multiple transits.

*The* 2K45.—The 2K45, which also was developed at Bell Telephone Laboratories, is illustrated in Fig. 18·7. In regard to frequency range, output power, and output coupling, this type is similar to the 2K25, except that it frequently produces somewhat higher power. This higher power is very likely due to improvements in design of the resonator and coupling loop. The upper surface of the resonator is flexible and actuated by the thermal-tuning mechanism. Because this diaphragm does not form part of the vacuum envelope it can be made thin, and it is slotted radially and corrugated to reduce further the force required from the tuner. Both the gun structure and the reflector are mounted on mica disks supported from the cavity, and the reflector retains its position with respect to the cathode when $G_3$ is moved for tuning. Consequently, there is a greatly reduced variation in the reflector voltage required to produce oscillations over the band.

The cathode in a tube of this type is concave (with a central hole to eliminate the axial electrons) in order to produce a crossover. The aperture on the cathode side of the resonator covered with a grid ($G_2$ in the usual notation[1]) is about half the diameter of the grid ($G_3$) on the reflector side.   Thus, if the beam is brought to a focus below $G_2$ so as to diverge slightly on entering the resonator, it will continue to diverge after reflection, and most of the current will fail to pass through $G_2$ on the return trip.   By this means multiple-transit hysteresis is almost entirely eliminated.

The tuner mechanism consists essentially of a low-$\mu$ triode mounted from the resonator frame.   The anode of the triode is in the form of a

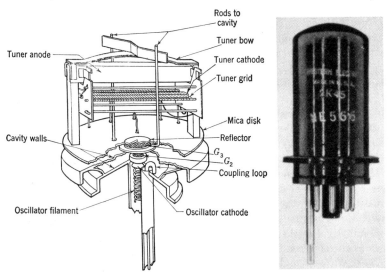

Fig. 18·7(a).—Cross section of part of a 2K45 tube.     Fig. 18·7(b).—Photograph of a 2K45 tube.

U-section, concave toward the cathode, and mounted so as to permit longitudinal expansion; it has good heat conduction from the ends.   A bow spring made of a stack of thin laminations is fastened by its ends to the ends of the anode.   When the latter expands as a result of electron bombardment, the spring, which is protected from bombardment and is fastened at the cool ends of the anode, is pulled down toward the anode. A yoke is fastened to the center of the spring and is connected to the diaphragm by a pair of rods.   Thus, expansion of the anode flattens the leaf spring and, by moving $G_3$ downward toward $G_2$, lowers the frequency.   The sign of the frequency shift produced by a change in tuner-

---

[1] The customary accelerating grid $G_1$ is omitted in this design.   An accelerating cylinder extends toward the cathode from the lower side of $G_2$.

grid potential is the same as that produced by a change of reflector potential; in each case, increasing the negative potential increases the frequency. Using the thermal-tuner grid alone, it is usually possible to

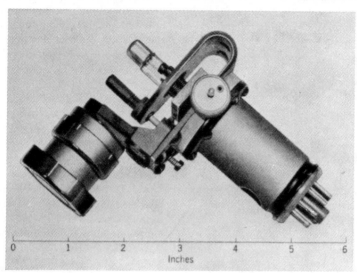

Fig. 18·8.—Photograph of a 2K33 tube mounted in tuner. Adjusting knob for tuning stub visible. Output waveguide on opposite side.

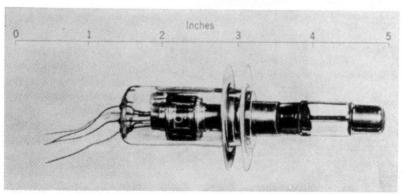

Fig. 18·9.—Photograph of a 2K33 tube without tuner.

tune at least 500 Mc/sec between half-power points without changing the reflector potential.

*The 2K33.*—The 2K33 tube was developed at the Clarendon Laboratory, Oxford, England, and with assistance from the Radiation Laboratory was put into production at the Raytheon Manufacturing Company. From Figs. 18·8, 18·9, and 18·10 it is apparent that, although the 2K33 is supplied with an external cavity (output waveguide and mechanical tuner put on at the factory), it really belongs with the 707B in the disk-seal class. Unlike the 707B, however, the frequency range is fixed by the internal cavity. The construction of the tube is unusual and will therefore be briefly described. The glass forming the cathode end is "dimpled" with three longitudinal creases in order to fit snugly on an arbor. An alignment tool fitting the dimples and carrying a 0.028-in. spike is inserted and the stamped disks and glass rings stacked up and sealed, the disks being held in alignment by the spike. The reflector is also provided with a hole so that it can be lined up with the same tool. After the reflector is sealed in, the tool is withdrawn and the gun assembly, centered in two mica rings, is forced in and held by the dimples.

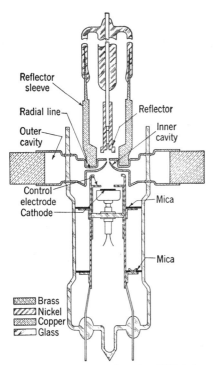

Reflector sleeve

Radial line

Reflector

Outer cavity

Inner cavity

Control electrode

Cathode

Mica

Mica

Brass
Nickel
Copper
Glass

Fig. 18·10.—Cross section of a 2K33 tube.

The use of apertures rather than grids requires the use of a high beam velocity to minimize variations in beam coupling coefficient and transit angle over the cross section of the beam. The 2K33 is operated normally with 1800 volts on the resonator. The gun, which is provided with a control electrode, produces a very fine focus in the gap region. The inner cavity is tuned by flexing the upper disk between the glass ring and the reflector sleeve, and is coupled to the outer cavity by a low-impedance radial line about a quarter wavelength long. This outer region, which ideally should not be resonant, is closed by the external cavity ring, which has two waveguides at opposite ends of a diameter. One of the waveguides is closed with an adjustable choke plunger to act as a tuning stub; the other is the output line. The loading of the resonator is strongly affected by the height of the radial coupling line, which not only varies from tube to tube but also is changed during tuning. As a result, it is sometimes difficult to get reasonably constant output power over a band from 23,500 to 24,500 Mc/sec.  From the electronic standpoint the tube should be capable of oscillating at any frequency from at least 25,000 down to 23,000 Mc/sec or lower, but, in practice, reflections from the glass restrict the range.

The tuner mechanism consists of a flat steel spring bent in the form of a U.  One arm is fastened to the external cavity block, the other carries a clamp for the reflector sleeve.  The free end of the spring is pushed upward by a strut and a screw-actuated bent lever similar to that used with the 417A tube.  Temperature compensation is achieved by proper choice of the strut material.  Because a surprisingly large force is required to flex the upper disk, the spring must be heavy, and mechanical tuning hysteresis is noticeable.

Early samples of this type gave considerable trouble because they had lopsided reflector characteristics and hysteresis.  This trouble has been remedied to a large extent by a modification of the reflector.  In its original form, the reflector had a hole of the same diameter as the apertures in the disks; however, it was found that a small spike (a tungsten wire 0.005 in. in diameter) mounted in the center of the hole reduced the excessive curvature of the reflector field while permitting the use of the spindle alignment technique (with a piece of tubing instead of a solid spike).  A redesign of the disks and a change in dimensions of the outer cavity apparently obviates the necessity of the tuning stub.

FIG. 18·11.—Photograph of a 2K57 tube.

When operated at 1800 volts and 9-ma cathode current, in the reflector mode in the region of −200 volts, output powers from 15 to 50 mw may be expected.  Under these conditions, the electronic tuning range between half-power points should be about 50 Mc/sec.  Considerable frequency shifts will occur if the beam current is varied by means of the focusing electrode.  These shifts result in large part from the thermal expansion of the nozzle or "trumpet" in the lower disk resulting from electron bombardment.  Since the trumpet tapers down to a thin wall at its top, a small change in current distribution over the trumpet can make a large difference in its temperature.

*The 2K57.*—The experimental type 2K57 developed at Sperry Gyroscope Company is an example of a tube designed for transmitting applications.  This tube is also of interest because of its novel tuning mechanism.  As is evident from the illustrations of Figs. 18·11 and 18·12, the 2K57 has a waveguide output that is iris-coupled to an integral resonator. The latter is tuned not by variation of the grid spacing, but by a plunger that varies the volume of the inductive portion. The grids are of a honeycomb construction, which permits improved heat conduction and reduced interception losses. An improved gun design with higher

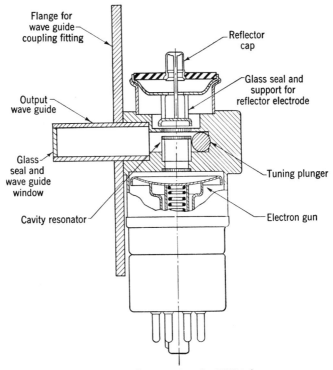

Fig. 18·12.—Cross section of a 2K57 tube.

perveance (note the typical rating of 70 ma at 700 volts as contrasted with 40 ma at 1000 volts for the 417A) is also an important factor.

Inasmuch as experimental tubes under the conditions set forth in Table 18·1 have given output powers of 2.5 watts, the 1.5 watts listed there is conservative. In achieving this greater efficiency, it has not been found necessary to sacrifice electronic tuning range. In fact, on a percentage basis this type has the largest range of those listed. Its great range is the result of the high current density achieved and of the minimizing of the parasitic or inactive capacitance across the r-f gap.

*The 2K50.*—The 2K50, which was developed at the Radiation Laboratory by H. V. Neher, and later improved and redesigned for production at the Bell Telephone Laboratories, is interesting in comparison with the 2K33.  Both tubes cover the same frequency range and have comparable output powers (perhaps 10 to 40 mw for the 2K50 in comparison with 15 to 50 mw for the 2K33), yet their power-supply requirements are very different.  The explanation is that the 2K33 was designed primarily with regard to simplicity in manufacture, whereas the 2K50 employs delicate parts and a relatively complicated assembly procedure to achieve exceptional performance.

Figures 18·13 and 18·14 are, respectively, a photograph of a completed tube and an enlarged sketch of the inner construction[1] of an early model that is essentially the same as the final version.  Referring to Fig. 18·14, 1 is the indirectly heated cathode, with a concave emitting surface, a focusing ring 2 at cathode potential, and an accelerator grid 3; the combination brings a beam of about 15 ma (at 300 volts or less) to a focus below the r-f gap formed by grids 4 and 13. Partly as a result of curvature of the grids, the beam enters the reflector space almost parallel.  The reflector 14 is given the same curvature as $G_3$ in its central region, and the curvature near the edges is increased by "cut and try" methods until about 90 per cent of the beam returns through $G_2$.  The

FIG. 18·13.—Photograph of a 2K50 tube.

cavity 5 is a hole in the block 6, closed on the lower side by the support for $G_2$ which has a conical nozzle, and on the upper side by a thin corrugated diaphragm to which $G_3$ and the reflector sleeve are fastened.

A portion of the cavity block is cut away to form the iris 18 coupling to the tapered waveguide 19, 21.  This waveguide is standard width throughout its length, with the height tapering from that of the cavity to standard height at the window.  The end of the waveguide is connected for radio frequency by a choke joint 22 to the Kovar cup 26 carrying the glass window 27.  In the completed tube an insulating flange is provided in order that the tube may be mounted with a slight modifica-

[1] For a more complete description see H. V. Neher, "A Low-voltage K-band Oscillator," RL Report No. 764, Sept. 17, 1945.

tion of the standard choke joint.  In the production design, the cavity is solidly connected to the tube envelope in order to improve the cooling.

In this tube, because of the small mechanical motion required to tune over the band, the thermal tuner is somewhat simpler than that employed in the 2K45.  The tuning element is formed by the two struts 8, which are metal strips creased longitudinally for most of their length to provide stiffening.  These are fastened at one end to an eyelet on the reflector sleeve, and at the other to the upper and lower sides of a rigid U-shaped support 7 welded to the resonator block.  The ends of the struts are kept cool by conduction through 7 and the flexible copper strap 12.  When the upper strut is heated by bombardment from the

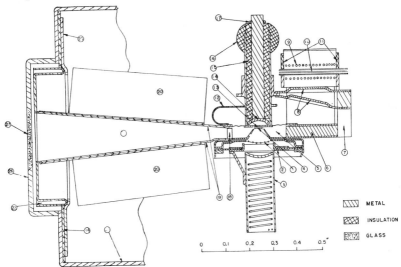

Fig. 18·14.—Cross section of an early version of the 2K50 tube.

cathode 10 (under control of the grid 9) it expands; the lower strut, which is protected from bombardment, retains its dimensions.  The junction of the two struts at the eyelet thus tends to describe an arc with the lower strut as radius.  For the small motions considered here, the resultant is practically a vertical motion of the whole reflector assembly and $G_3$, because the diaphragm will resist any lateral displacement.  It is evident that a tuner of this type tends to be self-compensating for ambient temperature changes if the cavity block, strut support, and reflector sleeve are all of the same material.  In the 2K50 tube temperature compensation, as evidenced by warmup drift, is very good indeed.

The speed of this thermal tuner is remarkable.  If the tube is allowed to reach equilibrium at one end of the 6 per cent tuning range centered on 24,000 Mc/sec, and the tuner power is cut off or applied full on as the case may be, the other end of the range will be reached in 1.2 to 2.6 sec. Near the middle of the range, tuning speeds of 600 to 800 Mc/sec/sec are obtained.

The grids are parallel wires rather than meshes, and are wound with 0.0006-in. tungsten wire, spaced 0.0037 in.; they are bowed to a radius of 0.10 in. A grid of this type will stand input powers up to 5 watts safely. Alignment of this tube is somewhat less critical than that of the 2K33 because the apertures are each 0.040 in. in diameter. The reflector shape is such that a lateral displacement of a few mils would probably not be very serious, but if the spread in transit angles of the returning beam is not to exceed $\pi/4$ radians, the tilt of the axis of the reflector must be less than 1 degree.

**18·6. Power Supplies.** *Pulse Operation.*—Reflex klystrons are often "keyed" to produce short bursts of r-f power at levels not far in excess of normal values, but they are seldom operated under pulse conditions with high peak input and output powers because magnetrons are superior in efficiency and power-handling ability. At duty ratios of the order of magnitude of $\frac{1}{1000}$, the performance of reflex klystrons has been disappointing, possibly because few have been designed for the requisite high voltages, but at duty ratios near $\frac{1}{10}$, which are of interest in pulse communication systems, they can be designed for appreciably higher efficiency than c-w tubes of the same general construction. For example, the 2K54 and 2K55 tubes, which physically resemble the 723A/B family, have a specification limit on output power of 7.5 watts minimum when pulsed at $\frac{1}{10}$ duty ratio at 1130 volts. Under these conditions the minimum efficiency is 5.6 per cent, and the average tube should do much better. Since tubes specially designed for this class of applications are not yet common, it does not appear worth while to consider detailed design of suitable pulse generators. The pulse voltage should be applied to the resonator, or simultaneously to the cathode and reflector, if a grounded resonator is desired. The applied voltage pulse must have a good flat top to avoid frequency modulation during the pulse. This requirement is considerably more severe than in magnetron practice because the electronic tuning rates for reflex tubes are larger. Questions of "jitter" and starting time are too specialized for discussion here; the latter was considered with reference to the 2K25 in Chap. 16. The balance of this section is devoted to general considerations applicable to power supplies for reflex tubes used as generators of continuous waves or modulated CW.

*C-w Operation. Polarity.* One of the first points to be settled in designing a power supply for a reflex oscillator is that of polarity. As in conventional vacuum tubes, it is customary to refer all voltages to the cathode, but it is often impractical to run a klystron with the cathode grounded. In applications such as signal generators, where a power supply is built for this purpose alone, it is generally desirable to operate with the resonator grounded in order that direct connections may be made to the r-f output terminals and that the resonator may be tuned without danger of shock. When the reflex klystron is used as the local oscillator in a microwave superheterodyne receiver, however, it is usually possible to obtain some, if not all, of the necessary regulated voltages from existing supplies and it may then become desirable to operate with the cathode grounded and the resonator at a positive d-c potential of hundreds of volts. This polarity is used most often with those types that operate normally with resonator voltages not over 300 volts. The 2K50 is provided with an insulating mounting flange especially for this purpose, and tubes like the 2K45 and 2K25/732A/B, which have output antennas, are usually operated with the cathode grounded. When this is done, an insulated shaft is needed on the tuning control. With external cavity tubes such as the 707B, it is easy to insulate the coupling loop, and with coaxial output tubes like the 726's, an insulating section can be designed in the coaxial-line adaptor.

*Necessity of Voltage Regulation.* Regulation will be needed for both the resonator and reflector voltages if the output power is to be reasonably free from amplitude and frequency modulation. Sometimes in superheterodyne local oscillator applications, where the reflector voltage is obtained from an automatic-frequency-control circuit, an unregulated supply is used for the resonator. This supply must have adequate filtering to keep the ripple negligible. A variation of the reflector voltage will be sufficient to compensate for any electronic tuning resulting from resonator-voltage variations, but unfortunately, in most reflex tubes, the power dissipated in the grids will vary as the $\frac{5}{2}$ power of the resonator voltage, and the resulting temperature changes will cause appreciable shifts in resonant frequency of the cavity. It then becomes necessary to sacrifice a portion of the useful electronic tuning range to compensate for the thermal tuning.[1] This practice may be satisfactory provided the fluctuations in line voltage are not severe.

*Compensating Circuits.* A method of compensating for line-voltage changes without complete regulation has been described by engineers of the Sperry Gyroscope Company.[2] Like the arrangement mentioned in the preceding paragraph, this method will compensate for the electronic tuning resulting from voltage variations but will not remove amplitude modulation or frequency shifts resulting from thermal effects.

---

[1] This point is discussed more fully in the RL Group Report 53-4/17/45, "Regulation of Resonator Voltage in Reflex Oscillators," by J. B. H. Kuper, D. N. Sands, and P. A. Cole.

[2] "Klystron Technical Manual," Sperry Gyroscope Co., Inc., 1944, pp. 65–66.

If $-V_0$ and $-(V_0 + |V_r|)$ are the cathode and reflector voltages, respectively, measured with reference to the resonator, the time of flight in the reflector region will be proportional to $\sqrt{V_0}/(V_0 + |V_r|)$, assuming a uniform retarding field and neglecting space charge. Electronic tuning effects will be eliminated if this time of flight is constant, apart from the small effects that are due to the variation of the transit time in the r-f gap. It is easy to show by differentiation that the time in an ideal reflector field will be constant if

$$\frac{\Delta(V_0 + |V_r|)}{(V_0 + |V_r|)} = \frac{1}{2}\frac{\Delta V_0}{V_0}, \tag{4}$$

or if the fractional change in reflector voltage is made half the fractional change in cathode voltage. This condition can be satisfied by supplying the reflector partly from a stable source and partly from the same unregulated supply furnishing the cathode-to-resonator voltage, as is illustrated

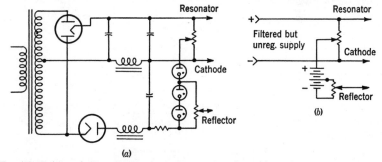

Fig. 18·15 (a) and (b).—Circuits for compensating electronic tuning resulting from line voltage variations.

schematically in Fig. 18·15. Figure 18·15a shows an arrangement using gas-discharge voltage-regulator tubes fed from an auxiliary half-wave rectifier operating on the same transformer as the main supply. A circuit of this type is reported to be satisfactory for line-voltage variations up to ±10 per cent. Batteries may also be used, as indicated in Fig. 18·15b, because the drain in the reflector circuit is infinitesimal. In practice, Eq. (4) is used only as a rough guide in setting up the circuit, and the constants are adjusted empirically for the particular reflex oscillator used. These circuits may need readjustment to restore good compensation after a major change in operating frequency has required a large change in reflector voltage. This necessity for individual adjustment, together with the residual amplitude modulation and thermal-tuning effects, has greatly restricted the application of this method, which appears most attractive in connection with high-power tubes.

*Electronically Regulated Supplies.* A discussion of the details of regulated power supply design is beyond the scope of this book, but some general remarks of particular interest in the present connection may be worth while. Regulators suitable for reflex klystron supplies may employ cold-cathode gas-discharge tubes or may be of the so-called "electronic" type in which the voltage drop in a series tube (ordinarily a triode) is controlled. This type, among others, has received extensive discussion by Hunt and Hickman,[1] and in spite of its apparent greater complexity, is usually more economical than the gas-discharge type. The reference voltage, however, will ordinarily be provided by one or more gas-discharge tubes that also regulate the reflector supply. Since

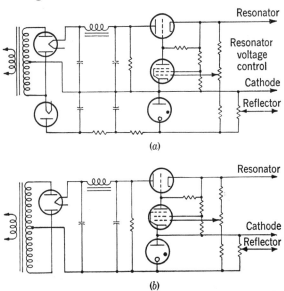

FIG. 18·16.—Schematics of typical electronically regulated supplies for reflex oscillators.

an electronic regulator is very effective in reducing ripple, a much smaller filter can be used than would otherwise be possible. Two versions of electronically regulated supplies are shown schematically in Fig. 18·16. In Fig. 18·16a an auxiliary supply furnishes the reference voltage and the reflector supply. Since the principal drain on this supply is the current drawn by the gas-discharge tube, the supply can be a simple halfwave arrangement with $RC$-filtering. In Fig. 18·16b only one rectifier and filter are used, but the voltage out of the filter must be the sum of the resonator and reflector supply voltages, plus the drop in the series tube. This higher voltage may increase the cost of the filter condensers and transformers enough to make circuit (a) preferable. Also, in cir-

---

[1] F. V. Hunt and R. W. Hickman, "On Electronic Voltage Stabilizers," *Rev. Sci. Inst.* **10**, 6, (1939).

cuit (*b*) the beam current in the oscillator plus the screen-divider current for the pentode must flow through the gas-discharge tube; consequently this scheme is restricted to those tubes having currents in the desirable working range of the gas-filled tubes.[1] This restriction is not severe because a great many reflex tubes have normal currents in the range 15 to 25 ma.

An annoying phenomenon that sometimes occurs in regulators of the types shown in Fig. 18·16 is a high-voltage surge occurring when the supply is first turned on. Such a surge results when the series tube, which is usually a quick-heating triode, starts to conduct before the pentode control tube has warmed up. The remedies are obvious: use of a slow-heating rectifier tube, or sequence switching with a time delay to prevent the application of the high voltage until the cathodes are warmed up. Generally, however, this surge applied to a cold oscillator tube does no harm.

Many tubes require, in addition to heater, resonator, and reflector voltages, a voltage for a control electrode (for example, the Sperry tubes of the 417A family and the 2K33) or a bias for a thermal-tuner grid (as in the 2K45 and the 2K50). Because supplies of the sort indicated in Fig. 18·16 have available regulated voltages both positive and negative with respect to cathode, one can obtain such extra voltages by a potentiometer arrangement. Most of the Sperry tubes operate satisfactorily with the control electrode at cathode potential, but the 417A requires a small positive bias for optimum performance. The rest of the Sperry reflex klystrons require zero or negative biases. Some of the higher-power tubes may have secondary emission from the control electrode and therefore require a low-impedance bias supply. The manufacturer's recommendations should be adhered to carefully in this respect.

*Reflector Supply Impedance.* Although normally no current other than leakage current and a small gas current will flow in the reflector circuit, it is inadvisable to have a very high impedance there. Many reflectors have secondary emission ratios greater than unity so that if the reflector momentarily goes positive as a result of some transient, and a high impedance is present, the reflector may bias itself positively and hold its bias. The condition is sometimes called "blocking," generally results in a considerable evolution of gas, and may ruin the tube. Such an accident is most likely to occur when the primary power is removed briefly and restored before the cathodes have cooled; it is much more probable with a grounded-resonator supply circuit than with a grounded

---

[1] Although series operation of gas-discharge regulator tubes is satisfactory and often employed, (the only precaution required being to shunt a high resistance across each tube but one), parallel operation is rarely attempted. Because equalizing resistors are necessary, the regulation obtained is poor.

cathode. Similar troubles may be encountered if too large a modulating voltage is applied to the reflector. In either case a diode connected between cathode and reflector so that the reflector is prevented from going positive is well worth the expense.

*Accuracy of Regulation.* The degree of regulation required is clearly a function of the frequency stability required in a particular application. Unfortunately, the electronic tuning rate—the frequency change per volt change on the reflector—cannot be specified for a particular tube unless the load is also specified. This fact is evidenced by the fact that the loaded $Q$ of the resonator appears in the expressions for electronic tuning derived in previous chapters. To give an idea of magnitudes, eighty out of one hundred 2K25 tubes tested in the load described in the preceding section had tuning rates at 9370 Mc/sec between 1.4 and 3.1 Mc/sec per reflector volt.[1]

With spreads as large as this, it is difficult to be specific about the regulation requirements in a given application, but it is safe to conclude that ripple and other fluctuations must be held to a small fraction of a volt. To the extent that the assumptions made in connection with Eq. (4) are valid (the neglect of thermal tuning effects is the most serious), it can be shown that the electronic tuning rate with respect to resonator voltage will be the rate with respect to reflector voltage multiplied by the factor $\frac{1}{2}(1 - |V_r|/|V_0|)$. Because $|V_r|$ is usually about half of $|V_0|$, the conclusion is that, provided thermal effects are absent, the regulation of the resonator voltage need be only about one quarter as good as that of the reflector supply on an absolute basis, or half as good as the reflector supply on a percentage basis.

More specific data and complete diagrams of typical power supplies may be found in Chap. 3, "Power Sources," of Vol. 11 in the Radiation Laboratory Series. The manufacturers' bulletins should be consulted for information on the peculiarities of specific types.

---

[1] J. B. H. Kuper and D. S. Beers, "Electronic Tuning of Reflex Oscillators," RL Report No. 774, Aug. 1, 1945.

# Index

CATALOGUE OF DOVER BOOKS

# PHYSICS

## General physics

**FOUNDATIONS OF PHYSICS, R. B. Lindsay & H. Margenau.** Excellent bridge between semi-popular works & technical treatises. A discussion of methods of physical description, construction of theory; valuable for physicist with elementary calculus who is interested in ideas that give meaning to data, tools of modern physics. Contents include symbolism, mathematical equations; space & time foundations of mechanics; probability; physics & continua; electron theory; special & general relativity; quantum mechanics; causality. "Thorough and yet not overdetailed. Unreservedly recommended," NATURE (London). Unabridged, corrected edition. List of recommended readings. 35 illustrations. xi + 537pp. 5⅜ x 8.
S377 Paperbound **$2.75**

**FUNDAMENTAL FORMULAS OF PHYSICS, ed. by D. H. Menzel.** Highly useful, fully inexpensive reference and study text, ranging from simple to highly sophisticated operations. Mathematics integrated into text—each chapter stands as short textbook of field represented. Vol. 1: Statistics, Physical Constants, Special Theory of Relativity, Hydrodynamics, Aerodynamics, Boundary Value Problems in Math. Physics; Viscosity, Electromagnetic Theory, etc. Vol. 2: Sound, Acoustics, Geometrical Optics, Electron Optics, High-Energy Phenomena, Magnetism, Biophysics, much more. Index. Total of 800pp. 5⅜ x 8.    Vol. 1 S595 Paperbound **$2.00**
Vol. 2 S596 Paperbound **$2.00**

**MATHEMATICAL PHYSICS, D. H. Menzel.** Thorough one-volume treatment of the mathematical techniques vital for classic mechanics, electromagnetic theory, quantum theory, and relativity. Written by the Harvard Professor of Astrophysics for junior, senior, and graduate courses, it gives clear explanations of all those aspects of function theory, vectors, matrices, dyadics, tensors, partial differential equations, etc., necessary for the understanding of the various physical theories. Electron theory, relativity, and other topics seldom presented appear here in considerable detail. Scores of definitions, conversion factors, dimensional constants, etc. "More detailed than normal for an advanced text . . . excellent set of sections on Dyadics, Matrices, and Tensors," JOURNAL OF THE FRANKLIN INSTITUTE. Index. 193 problems, with answers. x + 412pp. 5⅜ x 8.    S56 Paperbound **$2.00**

**THE SCIENTIFIC PAPERS OF J. WILLARD GIBBS.** All the published papers of America's outstanding theoretical scientist (except for "Statistical Mechanics" and "Vector Analysis"). Vol I (thermodynamics) contains one of the most brilliant of all 19th-century scientific papers—the 300-page "On the Equilibrium of Heterogeneous Substances," which founded the science of physical chemistry, and clearly stated a number of highly important natural laws for the first time; 8 other papers complete the first volume. Vol II includes 2 papers on dynamics, 8 on vector analysis and multiple algebra, 5 on the electromagnetic theory of light, and 6 miscellaneous papers. Biographical sketch by H. A. Bumstead. Total of xxxvi + 718pp. 5⅝ x 8⅜.
S721 Vol I Paperbound **$2.50**
S722 Vol II Paperbound **$2.00**
The set **$4.50**

**BASIC THEORIES OF PHYSICS, Peter Gabriel Bergmann.** Two-volume set which presents a critical examination of important topics in the major subdivisions of classical and modern physics. The first volume is concerned with classical mechanics and electrodynamics: mechanics of mass points, analytical mechanics, matter in bulk, electrostatics and magnetostatics, electromagnetic interaction, the field waves, special relativity, and waves. The second volume (Heat and Quanta) contains discussions of the kinetic hypothesis, physics and statistics, stationary ensembles, laws of thermodynamics, early quantum theories, atomic spectra, probability waves, quantization in wave mechanics, approximation methods, and abstract quantum theory. A valuable supplement to any thorough course or text.
Heat and Quanta: Index. 8 figures. x + 300pp. 5⅜ x 8½.    S968 Paperbound **$1.75**
Mechanics and Electrodynamics: Index. 14 figures. vii + 280pp. 5⅜ x 8½.
S969 Paperbound **$1.75**

**THEORETICAL PHYSICS, A. S. Kompaneyets.** One of the very few thorough studies of the subject in this price range. Provides advanced students with a comprehensive theoretical background. Especially strong on recent experimentation and developments in quantum theory. Contents: Mechanics (Generalized Coordinates, Lagrange's Equation, Collision of Particles, etc.), Electrodynamics (Vector Analysis, Maxwell's equations, Transmission of Signals, Theory of Relativity, etc.), Quantum Mechanics (the Inadequacy of Classical Mechanics, the Wave Equation, Motion in a Central Field, Quantum Theory of Radiation, Quantum Theories of Dispersion and Scattering, etc.), and Statistical Physics (Equilibrium Distribution of Molecules in an Ideal Gas, Boltzmann statistics, Bose and Fermi Distribution, Thermodynamic Quantities, etc.). Revised to 1961. Translated by George Yankovsky, authorized by Kompaneyets. 137 exercises. 56 figures. 529pp. 5⅜ x 8½. S972 Paperbound **$2.50**

**ANALYTICAL AND CANONICAL FORMALISM IN PHYSICS, André Mercier.** A survey, in one volume, of the variational principles (the key principles—in mathematical form—from which the basic laws of any one branch of physics can be derived) of the several branches of physical theory, together with an examination of the relationships among them. Contents: the Lagrangian Formalism, Lagrangian Densities, Canonical Formalism, Canonical Form of Electrodynamics, Hamiltonian Densities, Transformations, and Canonical Form with Vanishing Jacobian Determinant. Numerous examples and exercises. For advanced students, teachers, etc. 6 figures. Index. viii + 222pp. 5⅜ x 8½.    S1077 Paperbound **$1.75**

# Acoustics, optics, electricity and magnetism, electromagnetics, magneto-hydrodynamics

**THE THEORY OF SOUND, Lord Rayleigh.** Most vibrating systems likely to be encountered in practice can be tackled successfully by the methods set forth by the great Nobel laureate, Lord Rayleigh. Complete coverage of experimental, mathematical aspects of sound theory. Partial contents: Harmonic motions, vibrating systems in general, lateral vibrations of bars, curved plates or shells, applications of Laplace's functions to acoustical problems, fluid friction, plane vortex-sheet, vibrations of solid bodies, etc. This is the first inexpensive edition of this great reference and study work. Bibliography. Historical introduction by R. B. Lindsay. Total of 1040pp. 97 figures. 5⅜ x 8.
S292, S293, Two volume set, paperbound, **$4.70**

**THE DYNAMICAL THEORY OF SOUND, H. Lamb.** Comprehensive mathematical treatment of the physical aspects of sound, covering the theory of vibrations, the general theory of sound, and the equations of motion of strings, bars, membranes, pipes, and resonators. Includes chapters on plane, spherical, and simple harmonic waves, and the Helmholtz Theory of Audition. Complete and self-contained development for student and specialist; all fundamental differential equations solved completely. Specific mathematical details for such important phenomena as harmonics, normal modes, forced vibrations of strings, theory of reed pipes, etc. Index. Bibliography. 86 diagrams. viii + 307pp. 5⅜ x 8.
S655 Paperbound **$1.50**

**WAVE PROPAGATION IN PERIODIC STRUCTURES, L. Brillouin.** A general method and application to different problems: pure physics, such as scattering of X-rays of crystals, thermal vibration in crystal lattices, electronic motion in metals; and also problems of electrical engineering. Partial contents: elastic waves in 1-dimensional lattices of point masses. Propagation of waves along 1-dimensional lattices. Energy flow. 2 dimensional, 3 dimensional lattices. Mathieu's equation. Matrices and propagation of waves along an electric line. Continuous electric lines. 131 illustrations. Bibliography. Index. xii + 253pp. 5⅜ x 8.
S34 Paperbound **$2.00**

**THEORY OF VIBRATIONS, N. W. McLachlan.** Based on an exceptionally successful graduate course given at Brown University, this discusses linear systems having 1 degree of freedom, forced vibrations of simple linear systems, vibration of flexible strings, transverse vibrations of bars and tubes, transverse vibration of circular plate, sound waves of finite amplitude, etc. Index. 99 diagrams. 160pp. 5⅜ x 8.
S190 Paperbound **$1.35**

**LIGHT: PRINCIPLES AND EXPERIMENTS, George S. Monk.** Covers theory, experimentation, and research. Intended for students with some background in general physics and elementary calculus. Three main divisions: 1) Eight chapters on geometrical optics—fundamental concepts (the ray and its optical length, Fermat's principle, etc.), laws of image formation, apertures in optical systems, photometry, optical instruments etc.; 2) 9 chapters on physical optics—interference, diffraction, polarization, spectra, the Rayleigh refractometer, the wave theory of light, etc.; 3) 23 instructive experiments based directly on the theoretical text. "Probably the best intermediate textbook on light in the English language. Certainly, it is the best book which includes both geometrical and physical optics," J. Rud Nielson, PHYSICS FORUM. Revised edition. 102 problems and answers. 12 appendices. 6 tables. Index. 270 illustrations. xi +489pp. 5⅜ x 8½.
S341 Paperbound **$2.50**

**PHOTOMETRY, John W. T. Walsh.** The best treatment of both "bench" and "illumination" photometry in English by one of Britain's foremost experts in the field (President of the International Commission on Illumination). Limited to those matters, theoretical and practical, which affect the measurement of light flux, candlepower, illumination, etc., and excludes treatment of the use to which such measurements may be put after they have been made. Chapters on Radiation, The Eye and Vision, Photo-Electric Cells, The Principles of Photometry, The Measurement of Luminous Intensity, Colorimetry, Spectrophotometry, Stellar Photometry, The Photometric Laboratory, etc. Third revised (1958) edition. 281 illustrations. 10 appendices. xxiv + 544pp. 5½ x 9¼.
S319 Clothbound **$10.00**

**EXPERIMENTAL SPECTROSCOPY, R. A. Sawyer.** Clear discussion of prism and grating spectrographs and the techniques of their use in research, with emphasis on those principles and techniques that are fundamental to practically all uses of spectroscopic equipment. Beginning with a brief history of spectroscopy, the author covers such topics as light sources, spectroscopic apparatus, prism spectroscopes and graphs, diffraction grating, the photographic process, determination of wave length, spectral intensity, infrared spectroscopy, spectrochemical analysis, etc. This revised edition contains new material on the production of replica gratings, solar spectroscopy from rockets, new standard of wave length, etc. Index. Bibliography. 111 illustrations. x + 358pp. 5⅜ x 8½.    S1045 Paperbound **$2.25**

**FUNDAMENTALS OF ELECTRICITY AND MAGNETISM, L. B. Loeb.** For students of physics, chemistry, or engineering who want an introduction to electricity and magnetism on a higher level and in more detail than general elementary physics texts provide. Only elementary differential and integral calculus is assumed. Physical laws developed logically, from magnetism to electric currents, Ohm's law, electrolysis, and on to static electricity, induction, etc. Covers an unusual amount of material: one third of book on modern material: solution of wave equation, photoelectric and thermionic effects, etc. Complete statement of the various electrical systems of units and interrelations. 2 Indexes. 75 pages of problems with answers stated. Over 300 figures and diagrams. xix +669pp. 5⅜ x 8.    S745 Paperbound **$2.75**

*Catalogue of Dover Books*

**MATHEMATICAL ANALYSIS OF ELECTRICAL AND OPTICAL WAVE-MOTION, Harry Bateman.** Written by one of this century's most distinguished mathematical physicists, this is a practical introduction to those developments of Maxwell's electromagnetic theory which are directly connected with the solution of the partial differential equation of wave motion. Methods of solving wave-equation, polar-cylindrical coordinates, diffraction, transformation of coordinates, homogeneous solutions, electromagnetic fields with moving singularities, etc. Index. 168pp. 5⅜ x 8. S14 Paperbound **$1.75**

**PRINCIPLES OF PHYSICAL OPTICS, Ernst Mach.** This classical examination of the propagation of light, color, polarization, etc. offers an historical and philosophical treatment that has never been surpassed for breadth and easy readability. Contents: Rectilinear propagation of light. Reflection, refraction. Early knowledge of vision. Dioptrics. Composition of light. Theory of color and dispersion. Periodicity. Theory of interference. Polarization. Mathematical representation of properties of light. Propagation of waves, etc. 279 illustrations, 10 portraits. Appendix. Indexes. 324pp. 5⅜ x 8. S178 Paperbound **$2.00**

**THE THEORY OF OPTICS, Paul Drude.** One of finest fundamental texts in physical optics, classic offers thorough coverage, complete mathematical treatment of basic ideas. Includes fullest treatment of application of thermodynamics to optics; sine law in formation of images, transparent crystals, magnetically active substances, velocity of light, apertures, effects depending upon them, polarization, optical instruments, etc. Introduction by A. A. Michelson. Index. 110 illus. 567pp. 5⅜ x 8. S532 Paperbound **$2.45**

**ELECTRICAL THEORY ON THE GIORGI SYSTEM, P. Cornelius.** A new clarification of the fundamental concepts of electricity and magnetism, advocating the convenient m.k.s. system of units that is steadily gaining followers in the sciences. Illustrating the use and effectiveness of his terminology with numerous applications to concrete technical problems, the author here expounds the famous Giorgi system of electrical physics. His lucid presentation and well-reasoned, cogent argument for the universal adoption of this system form one of the finest pieces of scientific exposition in recent years. 28 figures. Index. Conversion tables for translating earlier data into modern units. Translated from 3rd Dutch edition by L. J. Jolley. x + 187pp. 5½ x 8¾. S909 Clothbound **$6.00**

**ELECTRIC WAVES: BEING RESEARCHES ON THE PROPAGATION OF ELECTRIC ACTION WITH FINITE VELOCITY THROUGH SPACE, Heinrich Hertz.** This classic work brings together the original papers in which Hertz—Helmholtz's protegé and one of the most brilliant figures in 19th-century research—probed the existence of electromagnetic waves and showed experimentally that their velocity equalled that of light, research that helped lay the groundwork for the development of radio, television, telephone, telegraph, and other modern technological marvels. Unabridged republication of original edition. Authorized translation by D. E. Jones. Preface by Lord Kelvin. Index of names. 40 illustrations. xvii + 278pp. 5⅜ x 8½. S57 Paperbound **$1.75**

**PIEZOELECTRICITY: AN INTRODUCTION TO THE THEORY AND APPLICATIONS OF ELECTROMECHANICAL PHENOMENA IN CRYSTALS, Walter G. Cady.** This is the most complete and systematic coverage of this important field in print—now regarded as something of scientific classic. This republication, revised and corrected by Prof. Cady—one of the foremost contributors in this area—contains a sketch of recent progress and new material on Ferroelectrics. Time Standards, etc. The first 7 chapters deal with fundamental theory of crystal electricity. 5 important chapters cover basic concepts of piezoelectricity, including comparisons of various competing theories in the field. Also discussed: piezoelectric resonators (theory, methods of manufacture, influences of air-gaps, etc.); the piezo oscillator; the properties, history, and observations relating to Rochelle salt; ferroelectric crystals; miscellaneous applications of piezoelectricity; pyroelectricity; etc. "A great work," W. A. Wooster, NATURE. Revised (1963) and corrected edition. New preface by Prof. Cady. 2 Appendices. Indices. Illustrations. 62 tables. Bibliography. Problems. Total of 1 + 822pp. 5⅜ x 8½.
S1094 Vol. I Paperbound **$2.50**
S1095 Vol. II Paperbound **$2.50**
Two volume set Paperbound **$5.00**

**MAGNETISM AND VERY LOW TEMPERATURES, H. B. G. Casimir.** A basic work in the literature of low temperature physics. Presents a concise survey of fundamental theoretical principles, and also points out promising lines of investigation. Contents: Classical Theory and Experimental Methods, Quantum Theory of Paramagnetism, Experiments on Adiabatic Demagnetization. Theoretical Discussion of Paramagnetism at Very Low Temperatures, Some Experimental Results, Relaxation Phenomena. Index. 89-item bibliography. ix + 95pp. 5⅜ x 8. S943 Paperbound **$1.25**

**SELECTED PAPERS ON NEW TECHNIQUES FOR ENERGY CONVERSION: THERMOELECTRIC METHODS; THERMIONIC; PHOTOVOLTAIC AND ELECTRICAL EFFECTS; FUSION, Edited by Sumner N. Levine.** Brings together in one volume the most important papers (1954-1961) in modern energy technology. Included among the 37 papers are general and qualitative descriptions of the field as a whole, indicating promising lines of research. Also: 15 papers on thermoelectric methods, 7 on thermionic, 5 on photovoltaic, 4 on electrochemical effect, and 2 on controlled fusion research. Among the contributors are: Joffe, Maria Telkes, Herold, Herring, Douglas, Jaumot, Post, Austin, Wilson, Pfann, Rappaport, Morehouse, Domenicali, Moss, Bowers, Harman, Von Doenhoef. Preface and introduction by the editor. Bibliographies. xxviii + 451pp. 6⅛ x 9¼. S37 Paperbound **$3.00**

**SUPERFLUIDS: MACROSCOPIC THEORY OF SUPERCONDUCTIVITY, Vol. I, Fritz London.** The major work by one of the founders and great theoreticians of modern quantum physics. Consolidates the researches that led to the present understanding of the nature of super-conductivity. Prof. London here reveals that quantum mechanics is operative on the macro-scopic plane as well as the submolecular level. Contents: Properties of Superconductors and Their Thermodynamical Correlation; Electrodynamics of the Pure Superconducting State; Relation between Current and Field; Measurements of the Penetration Depth; Non-Viscous Flow vs. Superconductivity; Micro-waves in Superconductors; Reality of the Domain Structure; and many other related topics. A new epilogue by M. J. Buckingham discusses developments in the field up to 1960. Corrected and expanded edition. An appreciation of the author's life and work by L. W. Nordheim. Biography by Edith London. Bibliography of his publica-tions. 45 figures. 2 Indices. xviii + 173pp. 5⅝ x 8⅜.                    S44 Paperbound **$1.45**

**SELECTED PAPERS ON PHYSICAL PROCESSES IN IONIZED PLASMAS, Edited by Donald H. Menzel, Director, Harvard College Observatory.** 30 important papers relating to the study of highly ionized gases or plasmas selected by a foremost contributor in the field, with the assistance of Dr. L. H. Aller. The essays include 18 on the physical processes in gaseous nebulae, covering problems of radiation and radiative transfer, the Balmer decrement, electron temperatures, spectrophotometry, etc. 10 papers deal with the interpretation of nebular spectra, by Bohm, Van Vleck, Aller, Minkowski, etc. There is also a discussion of the intensities of "forbidden" spectral lines by George Shortley and a paper concern-ing the theory of hydrogenic spectra by Menzel and Pekeris. Other contributors: Goldberg, Hebb, Baker, Bowen, Ufford, Liller, etc. viii + 374pp. 6⅛ x 9¼.       S60 Paperbound **$2.95**

**THE ELECTROMAGNETIC FIELD, Max Mason & Warren Weaver.** Used constantly by graduate engineers. Vector methods exclusively: detailed treatment of electrostatics, expansion meth-ods, with tables converting any quantity into absolute electromagnetic, absolute electrostatic, practical units. Discrete charges, ponderable bodies, Maxwell field equations, etc. Introduc-tion. Indexes. 416pp. 5⅜ x 8.                                                  S185 Paperbound **$2.00**

**THEORY OF ELECTRONS AND ITS APPLICATION TO THE PHENOMENA OF LIGHT AND RADIANT HEAT, H. Lorentz.** Lectures delivered at Columbia University by Nobel laureate Lorentz. Unabridged, they form a historical coverage of the theory of free electrons, motion, absorption of heat, Zeeman effect, propagation of light in molecular bodies, inverse Zeeman effect, optical phenomena in moving bodies, etc. 109 pages of notes explain the more advanced sections. Index. 9 figures. 352pp. 5⅜ x 8.                          S173 Paperbound **$1.85**

**FUNDAMENTAL ELECTROMAGNETIC THEORY, Ronold P. King,** Professor Applied Physics, Harvard University. Original and valuable introduction to electromagnetic theory and to circuit theory from the standpoint of electromagnetic theory. Contents: Mathematical Description of Matter—stationary and nonstationary states; Mathematical Description of Space and of Simple Media—Field Equations, Integral Forms of Field Equations, Electromagnetic Force, etc.; Transformation of Field and Force Equations; Electromagnetic Waves in Unbounded Regions; Skin Effect and Internal Impedance—in a solid cylindrical conductor, etc.; and Electrical Circuits—Analytical Foundations, Near-zone and quasi-near zone circuits, Balanced two-wire and four-wire transmission lines. Revised and enlarged version. New preface by the author. 5 appendices (Differential operators: Vector Formulas and Identities, etc.). Problems. Indexes. Bibliography. xvi + 580pp. 5⅜ x 8½.                  S1023 Paperbound **$2.75**

# Hydrodynamics

**A TREATISE ON HYDRODYNAMICS, A. B. Basset.** Favorite text on hydrodynamics for 2 genera-tions of physicists, hydrodynamical engineers, oceanographers, ship designers, etc. Clear enough for the beginning student, and thorough source for graduate students and engineers on the work of d'Alembert, Euler, Laplace, Lagrange, Poisson, Green, Clebsch, Stokes, Cauchy, Helmholtz, J. J. Thomson, Love, Hicks, Greenhill, Besant, Lamb, etc. Great amount of docu-mentation on entire theory of classical hydrodynamics. Vol I: theory of motion of frictionless liquids, vortex, and cyclic irrotational motion, etc. 132 exercises. Bibliography. 3 Appendixes. xii + 264pp. Vol II: motion in viscous liquids, harmonic analysis, theory of tides, etc. 112 exercises, Bibliography. 4 Appendixes. xv + 328pp. Two volume set. 5⅜ x 8.
·S724 Vol I Paperbound **$1.75**
S725 Vol II Paperbound **$1.75**
The set **$3.50**

**HYDRODYNAMICS, Horace Lamb.** Internationally famous complete coverage of standard refer-ence work on dynamics of liquids &. gases. Fundamental theorems, equations, methods, solutions, background, for classical hydrodynamics. Chapters include Equations of Motion, Integration of Equations in Special Gases, Irrotational Motion, Motion of Liquid in 2 Dimen-sions, Motion of Solids through Liquid-Dynamical Theory, Vortex Motion, Tidal Waves, Surface Waves, Waves of Expansion, Viscosity, Rotating Masses of liquids. Excellently planned, ar-ranged; clear, lucid presentation. 6th enlarged, revised edition. Index. Over 900 footnotes, mostly bibliographical. 119 figures. xv + 738pp. 6⅛ x 9¼.            S256 Paperbound **$3.75**

**HYDRODYNAMICS, H. Dryden, F. Murnaghan, Harry Bateman.** Published by the National Research Council in 1932 this enormous volume offers a complete coverage of classical hydrodynamics. Encyclopedic in quality. Partial contents: physics of fluids, motion, turbulent flow, compressible fluids, motion in 1, 2, 3 dimensions; viscous fluids rotating, laminar motion, resistance of motion through viscous fluid, eddy viscosity, hydraulic flow in channels of various shapes, discharge of gases, flow past obstacles, etc. Bibliography of over 2,900 items. Indexes. 23 figures. 634pp. 5⅜ x 8. S303 Paperbound **$2.75**

# Mechanics, dynamics, thermodynamics, elasticity

**MECHANICS, J. P. Den Hartog.** Already a classic among introductory texts, the M.I.T. professor's lively and discursive presentation is equally valuable as a beginner's text, an engineering student's refresher, or a practicing engineer's reference. Emphasis in this highly readable text is on illuminating fundamental principles and showing how they are embodied in a great number of real engineering and design problems: trusses, loaded cables, beams, jacks, hoists, etc. Provides advanced material on relative motion and gyroscopes not usual in introductory texts. "Very thoroughly recommended to all those anxious to improve their real understanding of the principles of mechanics." MECHANICAL WORLD. Index. List of equations. 334 problems, all with answers. Over 550 diagrams and drawings. ix + 462pp. 5⅜ x 8.
S754 Paperbound **$2.00**

**THEORETICAL MECHANICS: AN INTRODUCTION TO MATHEMATICAL PHYSICS, J. S. Ames, F. D. Murnaghan.** A mathematically rigorous development of theoretical mechanics for the advanced student, with constant practical applications. Used in hundreds of advanced courses. An unusually thorough coverage of gyroscopic and baryscopic material, detailed analyses of the Coriolis acceleration, applications of Lagrange's equations, motion of the double pendulum, Hamilton-Jacobi partial differential equations, group velocity and dispersion, etc. Special relativity is also included. 159 problems. 44 figures. ix + 462pp. 5⅜ x 8.
S461 Paperbound **$2.25**

**THEORETICAL MECHANICS: STATICS AND THE DYNAMICS OF A PARTICLE, W. D. MacMillan.** Used for over 3 decades as a self-contained and extremely comprehensive advanced undergraduate text in mathematical physics, physics, astronomy, and deeper foundations of engineering. Early sections require only a knowledge of geometry; later, a working knowledge of calculus. Hundreds of basic problems, including projectiles to the moon, escape velocity, harmonic motion, ballistics, falling bodies, transmission of power, stress and strain, elasticity, astronomical problems. 340 practice problems plus many fully worked out examples make it possible to test and extend principles developed in the text. 200 figures. xvii + 430pp. 5⅜ x 8. S467 Paperbound **$2.00**

**THEORETICAL MECHANICS: THE THEORY OF THE POTENTIAL, W. D. MacMillan.** A comprehensive, well balanced presentation of potential theory, serving both as an introduction and a reference work with regard to specific problems, for physicists and mathematicians. No prior knowledge of integral relations is assumed, and all mathematical material is developed as it becomes necessary. Includes: Attraction of Finite Bodies; Newtonian Potential Function; Vector Fields, Green and Gauss Theorems; Attractions of Surfaces and Lines; Surface Distribution of Matter; Two-Layer Surfaces; Spherical Harmonics; Ellipsoidal Harmonics; etc. "The great number of particular cases . . . should make the book valuable to geophysicists and others actively engaged in practical applications of the potential theory," Review of Scientific Instruments. Index. Bibliography. xiii + 469pp. 5⅜ x 8. S486 Paperbound **$2.50**

**THEORETICAL MECHANICS: DYNAMICS OF RIGID BODIES, W. D. MacMillan.** Theory of dynamics of a rigid body is developed, using both the geometrical and analytical methods of instruction. Begins with exposition of algebra of vectors, it goes through momentum principles, motion in space, use of differential equations and infinite series to solve more sophisticated dynamics problems. Partial contents: moments of inertia, systems of free particles, motion parallel to a fixed plane, rolling motion, method of periodic solutions, much more. 82 figs. 199 problems. Bibliography. Indexes. xii + 476pp. 5⅜ x 8. S641 Paperbound **$2.50**

**MATHEMATICAL FOUNDATIONS OF STATISTICAL MECHANICS, A. I. Khinchin.** Offering a precise and rigorous formulation of problems, this book supplies a thorough and up-to-date exposition. It provides analytical tools needed to replace cumbersome concepts, and furnishes for the first time a logical step-by-step introduction to the subject. Partial contents: geometry & kinematics of the phase space, ergodic problem, reduction to theory of probability, application of central limit problem, ideal monatomic gas, foundation of thermo-dynamics, dispersion and distribution of sum functions. Key to notations. Index. viii + 179pp. 5⅜ x 8.
S147 Paperbound **$1.50**

**ELEMENTARY PRINCIPLES IN STATISTICAL MECHANICS, J. W. Gibbs.** Last work of the great Yale mathematical physicist, still one of the most fundamental treatments available for advanced students and workers in the field. Covers the basic principle of conservation of probability of phase, theory of errors in the calculated phases of a system, the contributions of Clausius, Maxwell, Boltzmann, and Gibbs himself, and much more. Includes valuable comparison of statistical mechanics with thermodynamics: Carnot's cycle, mechanical definitions of entropy, etc. xvi + 208pp. 5⅜ x 8. S707 Paperbound **$1.45**

**PRINCIPLES OF MECHANICS AND DYNAMICS, Sir William Thomson (Lord Kelvin) and Peter Guthrie Tait.** The principles and theories of fundamental branches of classical physics explained by two of the greatest physicists of all time. A broad survey of mechanics, with material on hydrodynamics, elasticity, potential theory, and what is now standard mechanics. Thorough and detailed coverage, with many examples, derivations, and topics not included in more recent studies. Only a knowledge of calculus is needed to work through this book. Vol. I (Preliminary): Kinematics; Dynamical Laws and Principles; Experience (observation, experimentation, formation of hypotheses, scientific method); Measures and Instruments; Continuous Calculating Machines. Vol. II (Abstract Dynamics): Statics of a Particle—Attraction; Statics of Solids and Fluids. Formerly Titled "Treatise on Natural Philosophy." Unabridged reprint of revised edition. Index. 168 diagrams. Total of xlii + 1035pp. 5⅜ x 8½.
Vol. I: S966 Paperbound **$2.35**
Vol. II: S967 Paperbound **$2.35**
Two volume Set Paperbound **$4.70**

**INVESTIGATIONS ON THE THEORY OF THE BROWNIAN MOVEMENT, Albert Einstein.** Reprints from rare European journals. 5 basic papers, including the Elementary Theory of the Brownian Movement, written at the request of Lorentz to provide a simple explanation. Translated by A. D. Cowper. Annotated, edited by R. Fürth. 33pp. of notes elucidate, give history of previous investigations. Author, subject indexes. 62 footnotes. 124pp. 5⅜ x 8.
S304 Paperbound **$1.25**

**MECHANICS VIA THE CALCULUS, P. W. Norris, W. S. Legge.** Covers almost everything, from linear motion to vector analysis: equations determining motion, linear methods, compounding of simple harmonic motions, Newton's laws of motion, Hooke's law, the simple pendulum, motion of a particle in 1 plane, centers of gravity, virtual work, friction, kinetic energy of rotating bodies, equilibrium of strings, hydrostatics, sheering stresses, elasticity, etc. 550 problems. 3rd revised edition. xii + 367pp. 6 x 9. S207 Clothbound **$4.95**

**THE DYNAMICS OF PARTICLES AND OF RIGID, ELASTIC, AND FLUID BODIES; BEING LECTURES ON MATHEMATICAL PHYSICS, A. G. Webster.** The reissuing of this classic fills the need for a comprehensive work on dynamics. A wide range of topics is covered in unusually great depth, applying ordinary and partial differential equations. Part I considers laws of motion and methods applicable to systems of all sorts; oscillation, resonance, cyclic systems, etc. Part 2 is a detailed study of the dynamics of rigid bodies. Part 3 introduces the theory of potential; stress and strain, Newtonian potential functions, gyrostatics, wave and vortex motion, etc. Further contents: Kinematics of a point; Lagrange's equations; Hamilton's principle; Systems of vectors; Statics and dynamics of deformable bodies; much more, not easily found together in one volume. Unabridged reprinting of 2nd edition. 20 pages of notes on differential equations and the higher analysis. 203 illustrations. Selected bibliography. Index. xi + 588pp. 5⅜ x 8. S522 Paperbound **$2.45**

**A TREATISE ON DYNAMICS OF A PARTICLE, E. J. Routh.** Elementary text on dynamics for beginning mathematics or physics student. Unusually detailed treatment from elementary definitions to motion in 3 dimensions, emphasizing concrete aspects. Much unique material important in recent applications. Covers impulsive forces, rectilinear and constrained motion in 2 dimensions, harmonic and parabolic motion, degrees of freedom, closed orbits, the conical pendulum, the principle of least action, Jacobi's method, and much more. Index. 559 problems, many fully worked out, incorporated into text. xiii + 418pp. 5⅜ x 8.
S696 Paperbound **$2.25**

**DYNAMICS OF A SYSTEM OF RIGID BODIES (Elementary Section), E. J. Routh.** Revised 7th edition of this standard reference. This volume covers the dynamical principles of the subject, and its more elementary applications: finding moments of inertia by integration, foci of inertia, d'Alembert's principle, impulsive forces, motion in 2 and 3 dimensions, Lagrange's equations, relative indicatrix, Euler's theorem, large tautochronous motions, etc. Index. 55 figures. Scores of problems. xv + 443pp. 5⅜ x 8. S664 Paperbound **$2.50**

**DYNAMICS OF A SYSTEM OF RIGID BODIES (Advanced Section), E. J. Routh.** Revised 6th edition of a classic reference aid. Much of its material remains unique. Partial contents: moving axes, relative motion, oscillations about equilibrium, motion. Motion of a body under no forces, any forces. Nature of motion given by linear equations and conditions of stability. Free, forced vibrations, constants of integration, calculus of finite differences, variations, precession and nutation, motion of the moon, motion of string, chain, membranes. 64 figures. 498pp. 5⅜ x 8. S229 Paperbound **$2.45**

**DYNAMICAL THEORY OF GASES, James Jeans.** Divided into mathematical and physical chapters for the convenience of those not expert in mathematics, this volume discusses the mathematical theory of gas in a steady state, thermodynamics, Boltzmann and Maxwell, kinetic theory, quantum theory, exponentials, etc. 4th enlarged edition, with new material on quantum theory, quantum dynamics, etc. Indexes. 28 figures. 444pp. 6⅛ x 9¼.
S136 Paperbound **$2.65**

**THE THEORY OF HEAT RADIATION, Max Planck.** A pioneering work in thermodynamics, providing basis for most later work, Nobel laureate Planck writes on Deductions from Electrodynamics and Thermodynamics, Entropy and Probability, Irreversible Radiation Processes, etc. Starts with simple experimental laws of optics, advances to problems of spectral distribution of energy and irreversibility. Bibliography. 7 illustrations. xiv + 224pp. 5⅜ x 8.
S546 Paperbound **$1.75**

**FOUNDATIONS OF POTENTIAL THEORY, O. D. Kellogg.** Based on courses given at Harvard this is suitable for both advanced and beginning mathematicians. Proofs are rigorous, and much material not generally avaliable elsewhere is included. Partial contents: forces of gravity, fields of force, divergence theorem, properties of Newtonian potentials at points of free space, potentials as solutions of Laplace's equations, harmonic functions, electrostatics, electric images, logarithmic potential, etc. One of Grundlehren Series. ix + 384pp. 5⅜ x 8.
S144 Paperbound **$1.98**

**THERMODYNAMICS, Enrico Fermi.** Unabridged reproduction of 1937 edition. Elementary in treatment; remarkable for clarity, organization. Requires no knowledge of advanced math beyond calculus, only familiarity with fundamentals of thermometry, calorimetry. Partial Contents: Thermodynamic systems; First & Second laws of thermodynamics; Entropy; Thermodynamic potentials: phase rule, reversible electric cell; Gaseous reactions: van't Hoff reaction box, principle of LeChatelier; Thermodynamics of dilute solutions: osmotic & vapor pressures, boiling & freezing points; Entropy constant. Index. 25 problems. 24 illustrations. x + 160pp. 5⅜ x 8.
S361 Paperbound **$1.75**

**THE THERMODYNAMICS OF ELECTRICAL PHENOMENA IN METALS and A CONDENSED COLLECTION OF THERMODYNAMIC FORMULAS, P. W. Bridgman.** Major work by the Nobel Prizewinner: stimulating conceptual introduction to aspects of the electron theory of metals, giving an intuitive understanding of fundamental relationships concealed by the formal systems of Onsager and others. Elementary mathematical formulations show clearly the fundamental thermodynamical relationships of the electric field, and a complete phenomenological theory of metals is created. This is the work in which Bridgman announced his famous "thermomotive force" and his distinction between "driving" and "working" electromotive force. We have added in this Dover edition the author's long unavailable tables of thermodynamic formulas, extremely valuable for the speed of reference they allow. Two works bound as one. Index. 33 figures. Bibliography. xviii + 256pp. 5⅜ x 8. S723 Paperbound **$1.65**

**TREATISE ON THERMODYNAMICS, Max Planck.** Based on Planck's original papers this offers a uniform point of view for the entire field and has been used as an introduction for students who have studied elementary chemistry, physics, and calculus. Rejecting the earlier approaches of Helmholtz and Maxwell, the author makes no assumptions regarding the nature of heat, but begins with a few empirical facts, and from these deduces new physical and chemical laws. 3rd English edition of this standard text by a Nobel laureate. xvi + 297pp. 5⅜ x 8.
S219 Paperbound **$1.75**

**THE MATHEMATICAL THEORY OF ELASTICITY, A. E. H. Love.** A wealth of practical illustration combined with thorough discussion of fundamentals—theory, application, special problems and solutions. Partial Contents: Analysis of Strain & Stress, Elasticity of Solid Bodies, Elasticity of Crystals, Vibration of Spheres, Cylinders, Propagation of Waves in Elastic Solid Media, Torsion, Theory of Continuous Beams, Plates. Rigorous treatment of Volterra's theory of dislocations, 2-dimensional elastic systems, other topics of modern interest. "For years the standard treatise on elasticity," AMERICAN MATHEMATICAL MONTHLY. 4th revised edition. Index. 76 figures. xviii + 643pp. 6⅛ x 9¼. S174 Paperbound **$3.25**

**STRESS WAVES IN SOLIDS, H. Kolsky,** Professor of Applied Physics, Brown University. The most readable survey of the theoretical core of current knowledge about the propagation of waves in solids, fully correlated with experimental research. Contents: Part I—Elastic Waves: propagation in an extended plastic medium, propagation in bounded elastic media, experimental investigations with elastic materials. Part II—Stress Waves in Imperfectly Elastic Media: internal friction, experimental investigations of dynamic elastic properties, plastic waves and shock waves, fractures produced by stress waves. List of symbols. Appendix. Supplemented bibliography. 3 full-page plates. 46 figures. x + 213pp. 5⅜ x 8½.
S1098 Paperbound **$1.75**

## Relativity, quantum theory, atomic and nuclear physics

**SPACE TIME MATTER, Hermann Weyl.** "The standard treatise on the general theory of relativity" (Nature), written by a world-renowned scientist, provides a deep clear discussion of the logical coherence of the general theory, with introduction to all the mathematical tools needed: Maxwell, analytical geometry, non-Euclidean geometry, tensor calculus, etc. Basis is classical space-time, before absorption of relativity. Partial contents: Euclidean space, mathematical form, metrical continuum, relativity of time and space, general theory. 15 diagrams. Bibliography. New preface for this edition. xviii + 330pp. 5⅜ x 8.
S267 Paperbound **$2.00**

**ATOMIC SPECTRA AND ATOMIC STRUCTURE, G. Herzberg.** Excellent general survey for chemists, physicists specializing in other fields. Partial contents: simplest line spectra and elements of atomic theory, building-up principle and periodic system of elements, hyperfine structure of spectral lines, some experiments and applications. Bibliography. 80 figures. Index. xii + 257pp. 5⅜ x 8.
S115 Paperbound **$2.00**

# Catalogue of Dover Books

**THE PRINCIPLE OF RELATIVITY, A. Einstein, H. Lorentz, H. Minkowski, H. Weyl.** These are the 11 basic papers that founded the general and special theories of relativity, all translated into English. Two papers by Lorentz on the Michelson experiment, electromagnetic phenomena. Minkowski's SPACE & TIME, and Weyl's GRAVITATION & ELECTRICITY. 7 epoch-making papers by Einstein: ELECTROMAGNETICS OF MOVING BODIES, INFLUENCE OF GRAVITATION IN PROPAGATION OF LIGHT, COSMOLOGICAL CONSIDERATIONS, GENERAL THEORY, and 3 others. 7 diagrams. Special notes by A. Sommerfeld. 224pp. 5⅜ x 8.
S81 Paperbound **$1.75**

**EINSTEIN'S THEORY OF RELATIVITY, Max Born.** Revised edition prepared with the collaboration of Gunther Leibfried and Walter Biem. Steering a middle course between superficial popularizations and complex analyses, a Nobel laureate explains Einstein's theories clearly and with special insight. Easily followed by the layman with a knowledge of high school mathematics, the book has been thoroughly revised and extended to modernize those sections of the well-known original edition which are now out of date. After a comprehensive review of classical physics, Born's discussion of special and general theories of relativity covers such topics as simultaneity, kinematics, Einstein's mechanics and dynamics, relativity of arbitrary motions, the geometry of curved surfaces, the space-time continuum, and many others. Index. Illustrations, vii + 376pp. 5⅜ x 8. S769 Paperbound **$2.00**

**ATOMS, MOLECULES AND QUANTA, Arthur E. Ruark and Harold C. Urey.** Revised (1963) and corrected edition of a work that has been a favorite with physics students and teachers for more than 30 years. No other work offers the same combination of atomic structure and molecular physics and of experiment and theory. The first 14 chapters deal with the origins and major experimental data of quantum theory and with the development of conceptions of atomic and molecular structure prior to the new mechanics. These sections provide a thorough introduction to atomic and molecular theory, and are presented lucidly and as simply as possible. The six subsequent chapters are devoted to the laws and basic ideas of quantum mechanics: Wave Mechanics, Hydrogenic Atoms in Wave Mechanics, Matrix Mechanics, General Theory of Quantum Dynamics, etc. For advanced college and graduate students in physics. Revised, corrected republication of original edition, with supplementary notes by the authors. New preface by the authors. 9 appendices. General reference list. Indices. 228 figures. 71 tables. Bibliographical material in notes, etc. Total of xxiii + 810pp. 5⅜ x 8⅜.
S1106 Vol. I Paperbound **$2.50**
S1107 Vol. II Paperbound **$2.50**
Two volume set Paperbound **$5.00**

**WAVE MECHANICS AND ITS APPLICATIONS, N. F. Mott and I. N. Sneddon.** A comprehensive introduction to the theory of quantum mechanics; not a rigorous mathematical exposition it progresses, instead, in accordance with the physical problems considered. Many topics difficult to find at the elementary level are discussed in this book. Includes such matters as: the wave nature of matter, the wave equation of Schrödinger, the concept of stationary states, properties of the wave functions, effect of a magnetic field on the energy levels of atoms, electronic spin, two-body problem, theory of solids, cohesive forces in ionic crystals, collision problems, interaction of radiation with matter, relativistic quantum mechanics, etc. All are treated both physically and mathematically. 68 illustrations. 11 tables. Indexes. xii + 393pp. 5⅜ x 8½. S1070 Paperbound **$2.25**

**BASIC METHODS IN TRANSFER PROBLEMS, V. Kourganoff,** Professor of Astrophysics, U. of Paris. A coherent digest of all the known methods which can be used for approximate or exact solutions of transfer problems. All methods demonstrated on one particular problem —Milne's problem for a plane parallel medium. Three main sections: fundamental concepts (the radiation field and its interaction with matter, the absorption and emission coefficients, etc.); different methods by which transfer problems can be attacked; and a more general problem—the non-grey case of Milne's problem. Much new material, drawing upon declassified atomic energy reports and data from the USSR. Entirely understandable to the student with a reasonable knowledge of analysis. Unabridged, revised reprinting. New preface by the author. Index. Bibliography. 2 appendices. xv + 281pp. 5⅜ x 8½.
S1074 Paperbound **$2.00**

**PRINCIPLES OF QUANTUM MECHANICS, W. V. Houston.** Enables student with working knowledge of elementary mathematical physics to develop facility in use of quantum mechanics, understand published work in field. Formulates quantum mechanics in terms of Schroedinger's wave mechanics. Studies evidence for quantum theory, for inadequacy of classical mechanics, 2 postulates of quantum mechanics; numerous important, fruitful applications of quantum mechanics in spectroscopy, collision problems, electrons in solids; other topics. "One of the most rewarding features . . . is the interlacing of problems with text," Amer. J. of Physics. Corrected edition. 21 illus. Index. 296pp. 5⅜ x 8. S524 Paperbound **$2.00**

**PHYSICAL PRINCIPLES OF THE QUANTUM THEORY, Werner Heisenberg.** A Nobel laureate discusses quantum theory; Heisenberg's own work, Compton, Schroedinger, Wilson, Einstein, many others. Written for physicists, chemists who are not specialists in quantum theory, only elementary formulae are considered in the text; there is a mathematical appendix for specialists. Profound without sacrifice of clarity. Translated by C. Eckart, F. Hoyt. 18 figures. 192pp. 5⅜ x 8. S113 Paperbound **$1.25**

# PHYSICS, HISTORIES AND CLASSICS

**A HISTORY OF PHYSICS: IN ITS ELEMENTARY BRANCHES (THROUGH 1925), INCLUDING THE EVOLUTION OF PHYSICAL LABORATORIES, Florian Cajori.** Revised and enlarged edition. The only first-rate brief history of physics. Still the best entry for a student or teacher into the antecedents of modern theories of physics. A clear, non-mathematical, handy reference work which traces in critical fashion the developments of ideas, theories, techniques, and apparatus from the Greeks to the 1920's. Within each period he analyzes the basic topics of mechanics, light, electricity and magnetism, sound, atomic theory and structure of matter, radioactivity, etc. A chapter on modern research: Curie, Kelvin, Planck's quantum theory, thermodynamics, Fitzgerald and Lorentz, special and general relativity, J. J. Thomson's model of an atom, Bohr's discoveries and later results, wave mechanics, and many other matters. Much bibliographic detail in footnotes. Index. 16 figures. xv + 424pp. 5⅜ x 8.                T970 Paperbound **$2.00**

**A HISTORY OF THE MATHEMATICAL THEORIES OF ATTRACTION AND THE FIGURE OF THE EARTH: FROM THE TIME OF NEWTON TO THAT OF LAPLACE, I. Todhunter.** A technical and detailed review of the theories concerning the shape of the earth and its gravitational pull, from the earliest investigations in the seventeenth century up to the middle of the nineteenth. Some of the greatest mathematicians and scientists in history applied themselves to these questions: Newton ("Principia Mathematica"), Huygens, Maupertuis, Simpson, d'Alembert, etc. Others discussed are Poisson, Gauss, Plana, Lagrange, Boit, and many more. Particular emphasis is placed on the theories of Laplace and Legendre, several chapters being devoted to Laplace's "Mécanique Céleste" and his memoirs, and several others to the memoirs of Legendre. Important to historians of science and mathematics and to the specialist who desires background information in the field. 2 volumes bound as 1. Index. xxxvi + 984pp. 5⅜ x 8.
S148 Clothbound **$7.50**

**OPTICKS, Sir Isaac Newton.** In its discussions of light, reflection, color, refraction, theories of wave and corpuscular theories of light, this work is packed with scores of insights and discoveries. In its precise and practical discussion of construction of optical apparatus, contemporary understandings of phenomena it is truly fascinating to modern physicists, astronomers, mathematicians. Foreword by Albert Einstein. Preface by I. B. Cohen of Harvard University. 7 pages of portraits, facsimile pages, letters, etc. cxvi + 414pp. 5⅜ x 8.
S205 Paperbound **$2.25**

**TREATISE ON LIGHT, Christiaan Huygens.** The famous original formulation of the wave theory of light, this readable book is one of the two decisive and definitive works in the field of light (Newton's "Optics" is the other). A scientific giant whose researches ranged over mathematics, astronomy, and physics, Huygens, in this historic work, covers such topics as rays propagated in straight lines, reflection and refraction, the spreading and velocity of light, the nature of opaque bodies, the non-spherical nature of light in the atmosphere, properties of Iceland Crystal, and other related matters. Unabridged republication of original (1912) English edition. Translated and introduced by Silvanus P. Thompson. 52 illustrations. xii + 129pp. 5⅜ x 8.                S179 Paperbound **$1.50**

**FARADAY'S EXPERIMENTAL RESEARCHES IN ELECTRICITY.** Faraday's historic series of papers containing the fruits of years of original experimentation in electrical theory and electrochemistry. Covers his findings in a variety of areas: Induction of electric currents, Evolution of electricity from magnetism, New electrical state or condition of matter, Explication of Arago's magnetic phenomena, New law of electric conduction, Electro-chemical decomposition, Electricity of the Voltaic Pile, Static Induction, Nature of the electric force or forces, Nature of electric current, The character and direction of the electric force of the Gymnotus, Magneto-electric spark, The magnetization of light and the illumination of magnetic lines of force, The possible relation of gravity to electricity, Sub-terranean electrotelegraph wires, Some points of magnetic philosophy, The diamagnetic conditions of flame and gases, and many other matters. Complete and unabridged republication. 3 vols. bound as 2. Originally reprinted from the Philosophical Transactions of 1831-8. Indices. Illustrations. Total of 1463pp. 5⅜ x 8.                S783-4, Clothbound **$17.50** (tentative)

**REFLECTIONS ON THE MOTIVE POWER OF FIRE, Sadi Carnot,** and other papers on the 2nd law of thermodynamics by E. Clapeyron and R. Clausius. Carnot's "Reflections" laid the groundwork of modern thermodynamics. Its non-technical, mostly verbal statements examine the relations between heat and the work done by heat in engines, establishing conditions for the economical working of these engines. The papers by Clapeyron and Clausius here reprinted added further refinements to Carnot's work, and led to its final acceptance by physicists. Selections from posthumous manuscripts of Carnot are also included. All papers in English. New introduction by E. Mendoza. 12 illustrations. xxii + 152pp. 5⅜ x 8.

S661 Paperbound **$1.50**

**DIALOGUES CONCERNING TWO NEW SCIENCES, Galileo Galilei.** This classic of experimental science, mechanics, engineering, is as enjoyable as it is important. A great historical document giving insights into one of the world's most original thinkers, it is based on 30 years' experimentation. It offers a lively exposition of dynamics, elasticity, sound, ballistics, strength of materials, the scientific method. "Superior to everything else of mine," Galileo. Trans. by H. Crew, A. Salvio. 126 diagrams. Index. xxi + 288pp. 5⅜ x 8.
S99 Paperbound **$1.75**

**TREATISE ON ELECTRICITY AND MAGNETISM, James Clerk Maxwell.** For more than 80 years a seemingly inexhaustible source of leads for physicists, mathematicians, engineers. Total of 1082pp. on such topics as Measurement of Quantities, Electrostatics, Elementary Mathematical Theory of Electricity, Electrical Work and Energy in a System of Conductors, General Theorems, Theory of Electrical Images, Electrolysis, Conduction, Polarization, Dielectrics, Resistance, etc. "The greatest mathematical physicist since Newton," Sir James Jeans. 3rd edition. 107 figures, 21 plates. 1082pp. 5⅜ x 8. S636-7, 2 volume set, paperbound **$4.00**

**A HISTORY OF THE THEORY OF ELASTICITY AND THE STRENGTH OF MATERIALS, I. Todhunter and K. Pearson.** For over 60 years a basic reference, unsurpassed in scope or authority. Both a history of the mathematical theory of elasticity from Galileo, Hooke, and Mariotte to Saint Venant, Kirchhoff, Clebsch, and Lord Kelvin and a detailed presentation of every important mathematical contribution during this period. Presents proofs of thousands of theorems and laws, summarizes every relevant treatise, many unavailable elsewhere. Practically a book apiece is devoted to modern founders: Saint Venant, Lamé, Boussinesq, Rankine, Lord Kelvin, F. Neumann, Kirchhoff, Clebsch. Hundreds of pages of technical and physical treatises on specific applications of elasticity to particular materials. Indispensable for the mathematician, physicist, or engineer working with elasticity. Unabridged, corrected reprint of original 3-volume 1886-1893 edition. Three volume set. Two indexes. Appendix to Vol. I. Total of 2344pp. 5⅜ x 8⅜. S914-916 The set, Clothbound **$15.00**

**DE MAGNETE, William Gilbert.** This classic work on magnetism founded a new science. Gilbert was the first to use the word "electricity", to recognize mass as distinct from weight, to discover the effect of heat on magnetic bodies; invent an electroscope, differentiate between static electricity and magnetism, conceive of the earth as a magnet. Written by the first great experimental scientist, this lively work is valuable not only as an historical landmark, but as the delightfully easy to follow record of a perpetually searching, ingenious mind. Translated by P. F. Mottelay. 25-page biographical memoir. 90 figures. lix +368pp. 5⅜ x 8. S470 Paperbound **$2.00**

# ASTRONOMY

**THE INTERNAL CONSTITUTION OF THE STARS, Sir A. S. Eddington.** Influence of this has been enormous; first detailed exposition of theory of radiative equilibrium for stellar interiors, of all available evidence for existence of diffuse matter in interstellar space. Studies quantum theory, polytropic gas spheres, mass-luminosity relations, variable stars, etc. Discussions of equations paralleled with informal exposition of intimate relationship of astrophysics with great discoveries in atomic physics, radiation. Introduction. Appendix. Index. 421pp. 5⅜ x 8. S563 Paperbound **$2.75**

**PLANETARY THEORY, E. W. Brown and C. A. Shook.** Provides a clear presentation of basic methods for calculating planetary orbits for today's astronomer. Begins with a careful exposition of specialized mathematical topics essential for handling perturbation theory and then goes on to indicate how most of the previous methods reduce ultimately to two general calculation methods: obtaining expressions either for the coordinates of planetary positions or for the elements which determine the perturbed paths. An example of each is given and worked in detail. Corrected edition. Preface. Appendix. Index. xii + 302pp. 5⅜ x 8½. S1133 Paperbound **$2.25**

**CANON OF ECLIPSES (CANON DER FINSTERNISSE), Prof. Theodor Ritter von Oppolzer.** Since its original publication in 1887, this has been the standard reference and the most extensive single volume of data on the calculation of solar and lunar eclipses, past and future. A comprehensive introduction gives a full explanation of the use of the tables for the calculations of the exact dates of eclipses, etc. Data furnished for the calculation of 8,000 solar and 5,200 lunar eclipses, going back as far as 1200 B.C. and giving predictions up to the year 2161. Information is also given for partial and ring eclipses. All calculations based on Universal (Greenwich) Time. An unsurpassed reference work for astronomers, scientists engaged in space research and developments, historians, etc. Unabridged republication, with corrections. Preface to this edition by Donald Menzel and Owen Gingerich of the Harvard College Observatory. Translated by Owen Gingerich. 160 charts. lxx + 538pp. 8⅜ x 11¼. S114 Clothbound **$10.00**

**THEORY OF THE MOTION OF THE HEAVENLY BODIES MOVING ABOUT THE SUN IN CONIC SECTIONS, Karl Friedrich Gauss.** A landmark of theoretical astronomy by the great German scientist. Still authoritative and invaluable to the practicing astronomer. Part I develops the relations between the quantities on which the motion about the sun of the heavenly bodies depends—relations pertaining simply to position in the orbit, simply to position in space, between several places in orbit, and between several places in space. The calculation methods of Part I based on the groundwork of Part I include: determination of an orbit from 3 complete observations, from 4 observations (of which only two are complete), determination of an orbit satisfying as nearly as possible any number of observations whatever, and determination of orbits, taking into account the perturbations. Translation of "Theoria Motus" and with an appendix by C. H. Davis. Unabridged republication. Appendices and tables. 13 figures. xviii + 376pp. 6½ x 9¼. S1056 Paperbound **$2.95**

**THE GALACTIC NOVAE, C. Payne-Gaposchkin,** Prof. of Astronomy, Harvard Univ. A work that will be the standard reference source for years to come. Gathers together all the pertinent data, results recorded by countless observers of galactic novae over the centuries, in order to formulate a valid starting point for an interpretation of the nova process. Covers information and statistics on known novae, their variations in luminosity, distribution in the sky, spectral changes, etc.; symbiotic novae; frequently-recurring variables of the U Geminorum and Z Camelopardis class; supernovae; comparison of spectral changes; theories and interpretations of these phenomena, etc. "A comprehensive summary of everything that is now known about these stars," SCIENCE. Bibliographical references. Preface. Indices. 49 figures. 6 plates. 101 tables. x + 336pp. 5⅜ x 8⅜.                                S1170 Paperbound **$2.45**

**BINARY STARS, R. G. Aitken.** Still the definitive work in the field of double star astronomy. Written by the director of the Lick Observatory (considered the father of the modern study of binary star systems), this book sums up the results of 40 years of experience in the field, plus the work of centuries of research. Includes historical survey of major discoveries and contributions of the past, observational methods for visual binary stars, the radial velocity of a star (by Dr. J. H. Moore), eclipsing binary stars, known orbits of binary stars, some binary systems of special interest, the origin of binary stars. Much information on methods of spectrum analysis, orbit plotting, use of the telescope, and other practical matters. Useful for classroom study and advanced hobbyists, etc. Revised edition, corrected and with additional notes by Prof. J. T. Kent. New preface. 50 tables, 13 figures, 4 full-page plates. Bibliographies. Appendix. Indices. xii + 309pp. 5⅜ x 8½.
S1102 Paperbound **$2.00**

**THE NATURE OF COMETS, N. B. Richter.** An authority on comets presents a concise, but thorough survey of the state of our present-day knowledge of comets and cometary activity. Based on over 20 years of research, this is a middle-level account that even the layman can appreciate, providing a fund of information on historical theories (from 1700 to the present); statistical research on total number of comets, orbital forms, perturbations caused by Jupiter, comet groups, etc.; the structure of a comet; comets as processes of cosmic decay; origin and formation of comets; etc. Also: a lengthy introduction on modern theories by Dr. R. A. Lyttleton, much technical data and observational material of specific comets, supplementary tables, and the like. Revised (1963) edition. Translated and revised by Arthur Beer. 69 illustrations, including 54 photographs of comets, tails, spectra. 41 tables. Bibliography. Index. xli + 221pp.                                S1111 Clothbound **$10.00**

**CELESTIAL OBJECTS FOR COMMON TELESCOPES, Rev. T. W. Webb.** Classic handbook for the use and pleasure of the amateur astronomer. Of inestimable aid in locating and identifying thousands of celestial objects. Vol. I, The Solar System: discussions of the principle and operation of the telescope, procedures of observations and telescope-photography, spectroscopy, etc., precise location information of sun, moon, planets, meteors. Vol. II, The Stars: alphabetical listing of constellations, information on double stars, clusters, stars with unusual spectra, variables, and nebulae, etc. Nearly 4,000 objects noted. Edited and extensively revised by Margaret W. Mayall, director of the American Assn. of Variable Star Observers. New Index by Mrs. Mayall giving the location of all objects mentioned in the text for Epoch 2000. New Precession Table added. New appendices on the planetary satellites, constellation names and abbreviations, and solar system data. Total of 46 illustrations. Total of xxxix + 606pp. 5⅜ x 8.
Vol. I: T917 Paperbound **$2.25**
Vol. II: T918 Paperbound **$2.25**
Two Volume Set Paperbound **$4.50**

**ASTRONOMY AND COSMOGONY, Sir James Jeans.** A modern classic which is still of enormous value to everyone in astronomy, etc., this is Jean's last and most famous exposition. The summation of a lifetime's devotion to science, it presents his final conclusions on a host of problems ranging over the whole of descriptive astronomy, astrophysics, stellar dynamics, and cosmology. Contents: The Light from the Stars, Gaseous Stars, the Source of Stellar Energy, Liquid Stars, The Evolution of the Stars, The Configuration of Rotating Masses, The Evolution of Binary Systems, The Ages of the Stars, The Great Nebulae, The Galactic Systems, Variable Stars, etc. New preface by L. Motz, Columbia U. 16 full-page photographic illustrations. xv + 428pp. 5⅝ x 8⅜.                                S923 Paperbound **$2.45**

**ASTRONOMY OF STELLAR ENERGY AND DECAY, Martin Johnson.** Middle level treatment of astronomy as interpreted by modern atomic physics. Part One is non-technical, examines physical properties, source of energy, spectroscopy, fluctuating stars, various models and theories, etc. Part Two parallels these topics, providing their mathematical foundation. "Clear, concise, and readily understandable," American Library Assoc. Bibliography. 3 indexes. 29 illustrations. 216pp. 5⅜ x 8.                                S537 Paperbound **$1.50**

**MATHEMATICAL THEORIES OF PLANETARY MOTIONS, Otto Dziobek.** Translated by Mark W. Harrington and William J. Hussey. Lucid account of the principles of mathematical astronomy. It examines that part of celestial mechanics which deals with the motions of heavenly bodies considered as material points. Contents: Solution of the Problem of Two Bodies; Formation of the General Integrals for Problem of n Bodies . . . including discussions of elliptic, parabolic, and hyperbolic orbits, the solution of Kepler's equation, etc.; and sections headed The General Properties of the Integrals and The Theory of Perturbations . . . which deals with the theory of absolute perturbations, analytical development of the perturbing function, the variation of the elements, the secular variation of the mean longitude, etc. vi + 294pp. 5⅜ x 8½.                                S129 Paperbound **$2.00**

**A COMPENDIUM OF SPHERICAL ASTRONOMY, S. Newcomb.** Long a standard collection of basic methods and formulas most useful to the working astronomer, and clear full text for students. Includes the most important common approximations; 40 pages on the method of least squares; general theory of spherical coordinates; parallax; aberration; astronomical refraction; theory of precession; proper motion of the stars; methods of deriving positions of stars; and much more. Index. 9 Appendices of tables, formulas, etc. 36 figures. xviii + 444pp. 5⅜ x 8.
S690 Paperbound **$2.25**

**PRINCIPLES OF STELLAR DYNAMICS, S. Chandrasekhar.** A leading astrophysicist here presents the theory of stellar dynamics as a branch of classical dynamics, clarifying the fundamental issues and the underlying motivations of the theory. He analyzes the effects of stellar encounters in terms of the classical 2-body problem, and investigates problems centering about Liouville's theorem and the solutions of the equations of continuity. This edition also includes 4 important papers by the author published since "Stellar Dynamics," and equally indispensable for all workers in the field: "New Methods in Stellar Dynamics" and "Dynamical Friction," Parts I, II, and III. Index. 3 Appendixes. Bibliography. 50 illustrations. x + 313pp. 5⅜ x8.
S659 Paperbound **$2.25**

**AN INTRODUCTION TO THE STUDY OF STELLAR STRUCTURE, Subrahmanyan Chandrasekhar.** Outstanding treatise on stellar dynamics by one of world's greatest astrophysicists. Uses classical & modern math methods to examine relationship between loss of energy, the mass, and radius of stars in a steady state. Discusses thermodynamic laws from Carathéodory's axiomatic standpoint; adiabatic, polytropic laws; work of Ritter, Emden, Kelvin, others; Stroemgren envelopes as starter for theory of gaseous stars; Gibbs statistical mechanics (quantum); degenerate stellar configuration & theory of white dwarfs, etc. "Highest level of scientific merit," BULLETIN, AMER. MATH. SOC. Bibliography. Appendixes. Index. 33 figures. 509pp. 5⅜ x 8.
S413 Paperbound **$2.75**

**STATISTICAL ASTRONOMY, Robert J. Trumpler and Harold F. Weaver,** University of California. Standard introduction to the principles and techniques of statistical astronomy, a field of rapidly growing importance in this space age. An extensive section, "Elements of Statistical Theory," provides the astronomer with the tools for solving problems of descriptive astronomy, observational errors, constitution of extra-galactic nebulae, etc. Procedures used in statistical astronomy are related to basic mathematical principles of statistics such as unvariate distribution, integral equations, general theory of samples, etc. Other sections deal with: Statistical Description of the Galactic System; Stellar Motions in the Vicinity of the Sun; Luminosity—Spectral Type Distribution; Space Distribution of Stars; and Galactic Rotation. List of symbols. Appendix (10 tables). 2 Indexes. Extensive bibliography. 31 tables. 97 figures. xxi + 644pp. 5⅜ x 8½.
S301 Paperbound **$3.00**

**AN INTRODUCTORY TREATISE ON DYNAMICAL ASTRONOMY, H. C. Plummer.** Unusually wide connected and concise coverage of nearly every significant branch of dynamical astronomy, stressing basic principles throughout: determination of orbits, planetary theory, lunar theory, precession and nutation, and many of their applications. Hundreds of formulas and theorems worked out completely, important methods thoroughly explained. Covers motion under a central attraction, orbits of double stars and spectroscopic binaries, the libration of the moon, and much more. Index. 8 diagrams. xxi + 343pp. 5⅜ x 8⅜.
S689 Paperbound **$2.35**

**AN INTRODUCTORY TREATISE ON THE LUNAR THEORY, E. W. Brown.** Indispensable for all scientists and engineers interested in orbital calculation, satellites, or navigation of space. Only work in English to explain in detail 5 major mathematical approaches to the problem of 3 bodies, those of Laplace, de Pontécoulant, Hansen, Delaunay, and Hill. Covers expressions for mutual attraction, equations of motion, forms of solution, variations of the elements in disturbed motion, the constants and their interpretations, planetary and other disturbing influences, etc. Index. Bibliography. Tables. xvi + 292pp. 5⅜ x 8⅜.
S666 Paperbound **$2.00**

**SPHERICAL AND PRACTICAL ASTRONOMY, W. Chauvenet.** First book in English to apply mathematical techniques to astronomical problems is still standard work. Covers almost entire field, rigorously, with over 300 examples worked out. Vol. 1, spherical astronomy, applications to nautical astronomy; determination of hour angles, parallactic angle for known stars; interpolation; parallax; laws of refraction; predicting eclipses; precession, nutation of fixed stars; etc. Vol. 2, theory, use, of instruments; telescope; measurement of arcs, angles in general; electro-chronograph; sextant, reflecting circles; zenith telescope; etc. 100-page appendix of detailed proof of Gauss' method of least squares. 5th revised edition. Index. 15 plates, 20 tables. 1340pp. 5⅜ x 8.
Vol. 1 S618 Paperbound **$2.75**
Vol. 2 S619 Paperbound **$2.75**
The set **$5.50**

**RADIATIVE TRANSFER, S. Chandrasekhar.** Definitive work in field provides foundation for analysis of stellar atmospheres, planetary illumination, sky radiation; to physicists, a study of problems analogous to those in theory of diffusion of neutrons. Partial contents: equation of transfer, isotropic scattering, H-functions, diffuse reflection and transmission, Rayleigh scattering, X, Y functions, radiative equilibrium of stellar atmospheres. Extensive bibliography. 3 appendices. 35 tables. 35 figures. 407pp. 5⅜ x 8⅜.
S599 Paperbound **$2.25**

# GEOLOGY, GEOGRAPHY, METEOROLOGY

**PRINCIPLES OF STRATIGRAPHY, A. W. Grabau.** Classic of 20th century geology, unmatched in scope and comprehensiveness. Nearly 600 pages cover the structure and origins of every kind of sedimentary, hydrogenic, oceanic, pyroclastic, atmoclastic, hydroclastic, marine hydroclastic, and bioclastic rock; metamorphism; erosion; etc. Includes also the constitution of the atmosphere; morphology of oceans, rivers, glaciers; volcanic activities; faults and earthquakes; and fundamental principles of paleontology (nearly 200 pages). New introduction by Prof. M. Kay, Columbia U. 1277 bibliographical entries. 264 diagrams. Tables, maps, etc. Two volume set. Total of xxxii + 1185pp. 5⅜ x 8.
S686 Vol I Paperbound **$2.50**
S687 Vol II Paperbound **$2.50**
The set **$5.00**

**TREATISE ON SEDIMENTATION, William H. Twenhofel.** A milestone in the history of geology, this two-volume work, prepared under the auspices of the United States Research Council, contains practically everything known about sedimentation up to 1932. Brings together all the findings of leading American and foreign geologists and geographers and has never been surpassed for completeness, thoroughness of description, or accuracy of detail. Vol. 1 discusses the sources and production of sediments, their transportation, deposition, diagenesis, and lithification. Also modification of sediments by organisms and topographical, climatic, etc. conditions which contribute to the alteration of sedimentary processes. 220 pages deal with products of sedimentation: minerals, limestones, dolomites, coals, etc. Vol. 2 continues the examination of products such as gypsum and saline residues, silica, strontium, manganese, etc. An extensive exposition of structures, textures and colors of sediments: stratification, cross-lamination, ripple mark, oolitic and pisolitic textures, etc. Chapters on environments or realms of sedimentation and field and laboratory techniques are also included. Indispensable to modern-day geologists and students. Index. List of authors cited. 1733-item bibliography. 121 diagrams. Total of xxxiii + 926pp. 5⅜ x 8½.
Vol. I: S950 Paperbound **$2.50**
Vol. II: S951 Paperbound **$2.50**
Two volume set Paperbound **$5.00**

**THE EVOLUTION OF THE IGNEOUS ROCKS, N. L. Bowen.** Invaluable serious introduction applies techniques and chemistry to explain igneous rock diversity in terms of chemical composition and fractional crystallization. Discusses liquid immiscibility in silicate magmas, crystal sorting, liquid lines of descent, fractional resorption of complex minerals, petrogenesis, etc. Of prime importance to geologists & mining engineers, also to physicists, chemists working with high temperatures and pressures. "Most important," TIMES, London. 3 indexes. 263 bibliographic notes. 82 figures. xviii + 334pp. 5⅜ x 8.
S311 Paperbound **$2.25**

**INTERNAL CONSTITUTION OF THE EARTH, edited by Beno Gutenberg.** Completely revised. Brought up-to-date, reset. Prepared for the National Research Council this is a complete & thorough coverage of such topics as earth origins, continent formation, nature & behavior of the earth's core, petrology of the crust, cooling forces in the core, seismic & earthquake material, gravity, elastic constants, strain characteristics and similar topics. "One is filled with admiration . . . a high standard . . . there is no reader who will not learn something from this book," London, Edinburgh, Dublin, Philosophic Magazine. Largest bibliography in print: 1127 classified items. Indexes. Tables of constants. 43 diagrams. 439pp. 6⅛ x 9¼.
S414 Paperbound **$3.00**

**HYDROLOGY, edited by Oscar E. Meinzer.** Prepared for the National Research Council. Detailed complete reference library on precipitation, evaporation, snow, snow surveying, glaciers, lakes, infiltration, soil moisture, ground water, runoff, drought, physical changes produced by water, hydrology of limestone terranes, etc. Practical in application, especially valuable for engineers. 24 experts have created "the most up-to-date, most complete treatment of the subject," AM. ASSOC. of PETROLEUM GEOLOGISTS. Bibliography. Index. 165 illustrations. xi + 712pp. 6⅛ x 9¼.
S191 Paperbound **$3.50**

**SNOW CRYSTALS, W. A. Bentley and W. J. Humphreys.** Over 200 pages of Bentley's famous microphotographs of snow flakes—the product of painstaking, methodical work at his Jericho, Vermont studio. The pictures, which also include plates of frost, glaze and dew on vegetation, spider webs, windowpanes; sleet; graupel or soft hail, were chosen both for their scientific interest and their aesthetic qualities. The wonder of nature's diversity is exhibited in the intricate, beautiful patterns of the snow flakes. Introductory text by W. J. Humphreys. Selected bibliography. 2,453 illustrations. 224pp. 8 x 10¼.
T287 Paperbound **$2.95**

**PHYSICS OF THE AIR, W. J. Humphreys.** A very thorough coverage of classical materials and theories in meteorology . . . written by one of this century's most highly respected physical meteorologists. Contains the standard account in English of atmospheric optics. 5 main sections: Mechanics and Thermodynamics of the Atmosphere, Atmospheric Electricity and Auroras, Meteorological Acoustics, Atmospheric Optics, and Factors of Climatic Control. Under these headings, topics covered are: theoretical relations between temperature, pressure, and volume in the atmosphere; composition, pressure, and density; circulation; evaporation and condensation; fog, clouds, thunderstorms, lightning; aurora polaris; principal ice-age theories; etc. New preface by Prof. Julius London. 226 illustrations. Index. xviii + 676pp. 5⅜ x 8½.
S1044 Paperbound **$3.00**

# ENGINEERING AND TECHNOLOGY

## General and mathematical

**ENGINEERING MATHEMATICS, Kenneth S. Miller.** A text for graduate students of engineering to strengthen their mathematical background in differential equations, etc. Mathematical steps very explicitly indicated. Contents: Determinants and Matrices, Integrals, Linear Differential Equations, Fourier Series and Integrals, Laplace Transform, Network Theory, Random Function . . . all vital requisites for advanced modern engineering studies. Unabridged republication. Appendices: Borel Sets; Riemann-Stieltjes Integral; Fourier Series and Integrals. Index. References at Chapter Ends. xii + 417pp. 6 x 8½. S1121 Paperbound **$2.00**

**MATHEMATICAL ENGINEERING ANALYSIS, Rufus Oldenburger.** A book designed to assist the research engineer and scientist in making the transition from physical engineering situations to the corresponding mathematics. Scores of common practical situations found in all major fields of physics are supplied with their correct mathematical formulations—applications to automobile springs and shock absorbers, clocks, throttle torque of diesel engines, resistance networks, capacitors, transmission lines, microphones, neon tubes, gasoline engines, refrigeration cycles, etc. Each section reviews basic principles of underlying various fields: mechanics of rigid bodies, electricity and magnetism, heat, elasticity, fluid mechanics, and aerodynamics. Comprehensive and eminently useful. Index. 169 problems, answers. 200 photos and diagrams. xiv + 426pp. 5⅜ x 8½. S919 Paperbound **$2.50**

**MATHEMATICS OF MODERN ENGINEERING, E. G. Keller and R. E. Doherty.** Written for the Advanced Course in Engineering of the General Electric Corporation, deals with the engineering use of determinants, tensors, the Heaviside operational calculus, dyadics, the calculus of variations, etc. Presents underlying principles fully, but purpose is to teach engineers to deal with modern engineering problems, and emphasis is on the perennial engineering attack of set-up and solve. Indexes. Over 185 figures and tables. Hundreds of exercises, problems, and worked-out examples. References. Two volume set. Total of xxxiii + 623pp. 5⅜ x 8.
S734 Vol I Paperbound **$1.85**
S735 Vol II Paperbound **$1.85**
The set **$3.70**

**MATHEMATICAL METHODS FOR SCIENTISTS AND ENGINEERS, L. P. Smith.** For scientists and engineers, as well as advanced math students. Full investigation of methods and practical description of conditions under which each should be used. Elements of real functions, differential and integral calculus, space geometry, theory of residues, vector and tensor analysis, series of Bessel functions, etc. Each method illustrated by completely-worked-out examples, mostly from scientific literature. 368 graded unsolved problems. 100 diagrams. x + 453pp. 5⅝ x 8⅜. S220 Paperbound **$2.00**

**THEORY OF FUNCTIONS AS APPLIED TO ENGINEERING PROBLEMS, edited by R. Rothe, F. Ollendorff, and K. Pohlhausen.** A series of lectures given at the Berlin Institute of Technology that shows the specific applications of function theory in electrical and allied fields of engineering. Six lectures provide the elements of function theory in a simple and practical form, covering complex quantities and variables, integration in the complex plane, residue theorems, etc. Then 5 lectures show the exact uses of this powerful mathematical tool, with full discussions of problem methods. Index. Bibliography. 108 figures. x + 189pp. 5⅜ x 8.
S733 Paperbound **$1.35**

## Aerodynamics and hydrodynamics

**AIRPLANE STRUCTURAL ANALYSIS AND DESIGN, E. E. Sechler and L. G. Dunn.** Systematic authoritative book which summarizes a large amount of theoretical and experimental work on structural analysis and design. Strong on classical subsonic material still basic to much aeronautic design . . . remains a highly useful source of information. Covers such areas as layout of the airplane, applied and design loads, stress-strain relationships for stable structures, truss and frame analysis, the problem of instability, the ultimate strength of stiffened flat sheet, analysis of cylindrical structures, wings and control surfaces, fuselage analysis, engine mounts, landing gears, etc. Originally published as part of the CALCIT Aeronautical Series. 256 Illustrations. 47 study problems. Indexes. xi + 420pp. 5⅜ x 8½.
S1043 Paperbound **$2.25**

**FUNDAMENTALS OF HYDRO- AND AEROMECHANICS, L. Prandtl and O. G. Tietjens.** The well-known standard work based upon Prandtl's lectures at Goettingen. Wherever possible hydrodynamics theory is referred to practical considerations in hydraulics, with the view of unifying theory and experience. Presentation is extremely clear and though primarily physical, mathematical proofs are rigorous and use vector analysis to a considerable extent. An Enginering Society Monograph, 1934. 186 figures. Index. xvi + 270pp. 5⅜ x 8.
S374 Paperbound **$1.85**

**THE SOLUBILITY OF NONELECTROLYTES, Joel H. Hildebrand and Robert L. Scott.** The standard work on the subject; still indispensable as a reference source and for classroom work. Partial contents: The Ideal Solution (including Raoult's Law and Henry's Law, etc.); Nonideal Solutions; Intermolecular Forces; The Liquid State; Entropy of Athermal Mixing; Heat of Mixing; Polarity; Hydrogen Bonding; Specific Interactions; "Solvation" and "Association"; Systems of Three or More Components; Vapor Pressure of Binary Liquid Solutions; Mixtures of Gases; Solubility of Gases in Liquids; of Liquids in Liquids; of Solids in Liquids; Evaluation of Solubility Parameters; and other topics. Corrected republication of third (revised) edition. Appendices. Indexes. 138 figures. 111 tables. 1 photograph. iv + 488pp. 5⅜ x 8½.
S1125 Paperbound **$2.50**

**TERNARY SYSTEMS: INTRODUCTION TO THE THEORY OF THREE COMPONENT SYSTEMS, G. Masing.** Furnishes detailed discussion of representative types of 3-components systems, both in solid models (particularly metallic alloys) and isothermal models. Discusses mechanical mixture without compounds and without solid solutions; unbroken solid solution series; solid solutions with solubility breaks in two binary systems; iron-silicon-aluminum alloys; allotropic forms of iron in ternary system; other topics. Bibliography. Index. 166 illustrations. 178pp. 5⅝ x 8⅜.
S631 Paperbound **$1.50**

**THE KINETIC THEORY OF GASES, Leonard B. Loeb,** University of California. Comprehensive text and reference book which presents full coverage of basic theory and the important experiments and developments in the field for the student and investigator. Partial contents: The Mechanical Picture of a Perfect Gas, The Mean Free Path—Clausius' Deductions, Distribution of Molecular Velocities, discussions of theory of the problem of specific heats, the contributions of kinetic theory to our knowledge of electrical and magnetic properties of molecules and its application to the conduction of electricity in gases. New 14-page preface to Dover edition by the author. Name, subject indexes. Six appendices. 570-item bibliography. xxxvi + 687pp. 5⅜ x 8½.
S942 Paperbound **$2.95**

**IONS IN SOLUTION, Ronald W. Gurney.** A thorough and readable introduction covering all the fundamental principles and experiments in the field, by an internationally-known authority. Contains discussions of solvation energy, atomic and molecular ions, lattice energy, transferral of ions, interionic forces, cells and half-cells, transference of electrons, exchange forces, hydrogen ions, the electro-chemical series, and many other related topics. Indispensable to advanced undergraduates and graduate students in electrochemistry. Index. 45 illustrations. 15 tables. vii + 206pp. 5⅜ x 8½.
S124 Paperbound **$1.50**

**IONIC PROCESSES IN SOLUTION, Ronald W. Gurney.** Lucid, comprehensive examination which brings together the approaches of electrochemistry, thermodynamics, statistical mechanics, electroacoustics, molecular physics, and quantum theory in the interpretation of the behavior of ionic solutions—the most important single work on the subject. More extensive and technical than the author's earlier work (IONS IN SOLUTION), it is a middle-level text for graduate students and researchers in electrochemistry. Covers such matters as Brownian motion in liquids, molecular ions in solution, heat of precipitation, entropy of solution, proton transfers, dissociation constant of nitric acid, viscosity of ionic solutions, etc. 78 illustrations. 47 tables. Name and subject index. ix + 275pp. 5⅜ x 8½.
S134 Paperbound **$1.75**

**CRYSTALLOGRAPHIC DATA ON METAL AND ALLOY STRUCTURES, Compiled by A. Taylor and B. J. Kagle,** Westinghouse Research Laboratories. Unique collection of the latest crystallographic data on alloys, compounds, and the elements, with lattice spacings expressed uniformly in absolute Angstrom units. Gathers together previously widely-scattered data from the Power Data File of the ATSM, structure reports, and the Landolt-Bornstein Tables, as well as from other original literature. 2300 different compounds listed in the first table. Alloys and Intermetallic Compounds, with much vital information on each. Also listings for nearly 700 Borides, Carbides, Hydrides, Oxides, Nitrides. Also all the necessary data on the crystal structure of 77 elements. vii + 263pp. 5⅜ x 8.
S1013 Paperbound **$2.25**

**MATHEMATICAL CRYSTALLOGRAPHY AND THE THEORY OF GROUPS OF MOVEMENTS, Harold Hilton.** Classic account of the mathematical theory of crystallography, particularly the geometrical theory of crystal-structure based on the work of Bravais, Jordan, Sohncke, Federow, Schoenflies, and Barlow. Partial contents: The Stereographic Projection, Properties Common to Symmetrical and Asymmetrical Crystals, The Theory of Groups, Coordinates of Equivalent Points, Crystallographic Axes and Axial Ratios, The Forms and Growth of Crystals, Lattices and Translations, The Structure-Theory, Infinite Groups of Movements, Triclinic and Monoclinic Groups, Orthorhombic Groups, etc. Index. 188 figures. xii + 262pp. 5⅜ x 8½.
S1058 Paperbound **$2.00**

**CLASSICS IN THE THEORY OF CHEMICAL COMBINATIONS. Edited by O. T. Benfey.** Vol. I of the Classics of Science Series, G. Holton, Harvard University, General Editor. This book is a collection of papers representing the major chapters in the development of the valence concept in chemistry. Includes essays by Wöhler and Liebig, Laurent, Williamson, Frankland, Kekulé and Couper, and two by van't Hoff and le Bel, which mark the first extension of the valence concept beyond its purely numerical character. Introduction and epilogue by Prof. Benfey. Index. 9 illustrations. New translation of Kekulé paper by Benfey. xiv + 191pp. 5⅜ x 8½.
S1066 Paperbound **$1.85**

**FLUID MECHANICS FOR HYDRAULIC ENGINEERS, H. Rouse.** Standard work that gives a coherent picture of fluid mechanics from the point of view of the hydraulic engineer. Based on courses given to civil and mechanical engineering students at Columbia and the California Institute of Technology, this work covers every basic principle, method, equation, or theory of interest to the hydraulic engineer. Much of the material, diagrams, charts, etc., in this self-contained text are not duplicated elsewhere. Covers irrotational motion, conformal mapping, problems in laminar motion, fluid turbulence, flow around immersed bodies, transportation of sediment, general charcteristics of wave phenomena, gravity waves in open channels, etc. Index. Appendix of physical properties of common fluids. Frontispiece + 245 figures and photographs. xvi + 422pp. 5⅜ x 8. S729 Paperbound **$2.25**

**WATERHAMMER ANALYSIS, John Parmakian.** Valuable exposition of the graphical method of solving waterhammer problems by Assistant Chief Designing Engineer, U.S. Bureau of Reclamation. Discussions of rigid and elastic water column theory, velocity of waterhammer waves, theory of graphical waterhammer analysis for gate operation, closings, openings, rapid and slow movements, etc., waterhammer in pump discharge caused by power failure, waterhammer analysis for compound pipes, and numerous related problems. "With a concise and lucid style, clear printing, adequate bibliography and graphs for approximate solutions at the project stage, it fills a vacant place in waterhammer literature," WATER POWER. 43 problems. Bibliography. Index. 113 illustrations. xiv + 161pp. 5⅜ x 8½. S1061 Paperbound **$1.65**

**AERODYNAMIC THEORY: A GENERAL REVIEW OF PROGRESS, William F. Durand, editor-in-chief.** A monumental joint effort by the world's leading authorities prepared under a grant of the Guggenheim Fund for the Promotion of Aeronautics. Intended to provide the student and aeronautic designer with the theoretical and experimental background of aeronautics. Never equalled for breadth, depth, reliability. Contains discussions of special mathematical topics not usually taught in the engineering or technical courses. Also: an extended two-part treatise on Fluid Mechanics, discussions of aerodynamics of perfect fluids, analyses of experiments with wind tunnels, applied airfoil theory, the non-lifting system of the airplane, the air propeller, hydrodynamics of boats and floats, the aerodynamics of cooling, etc. Contributing experts include Munk, Giacomelli, Prandtl, Toussaint, Von Karman, Klemperer, among others. Unabridged republication. 6 volumes bound as 3. Total of 1,012 figures, 12 plates. Total of 2,186pp. Bibliographies. Notes. Indices. 5⅜ x 8. S328-S330 Clothbound, The Set **$17.50**

**APPLIED HYDRO- AND AEROMECHANICS, L. Prandtl and O. G. Tietjens.** Presents, for the most part, methods which will be valuable to engineers. Covers flow in pipes, boundary layers, airfoil theory, entry conditions, turbulent flow in pipes, and the boundary layer, determining drag from measurements of pressure and velocity, etc. "Will be welcomed by all students of aerodynamics," NATURE. Unabridged, unaltered. An Engineering Society Monograph, 1934. Index. 226 figures, 28 photographic plates illustrating flow patterns. xvi + 311pp. 5⅜ x 8. S375 Paperbound **$1.85**

**SUPERSONIC AERODYNAMICS, E. R. C. Miles.** Valuable theoretical introduction to the supersonic domain, with emphasis on mathematical tools and principles, for practicing aerodynamicists and advanced students in aeronautical engineering. Covers fundamental theory, divergence theorem and principles of circulation, compressible flow and Helmholtz laws, the Prandtl-Busemann graphic method for 2-dimensional flow, oblique shock waves, the Taylor-Maccoll method for cones in supersonic flow, the Chaplygin method for 2-dimensional flow, etc. Problems range from practical engineering problems to development of theoretical results. "Rendered outstanding by the unprecedented scope of its contents . . . has undoubtedly filled a vital gap," AERONAUTICAL ENGINEERING REVIEW. Index. 173 problems, answers. 106 diagrams. 7 tables. xii + 255pp. 5⅜ x 8. S214 Paperbound **$1.45**

**HYDRAULIC TRANSIENTS, G. R. Rich.** The best text in hydraulics ever printed in English . . . by one of America's foremost engineers (former Chief Design Engineer for T.V.A.). Provides a transition from the basic differential equations of hydraulic transient theory to the arithmetic intergration computation required by practicing engineers. Sections cover Water Hammer, Turbine Speed Regulation, Stability of Governing, Water-Hammer Pressures in Pump Discharge Lines, The Differential and Restricted Orifice Surge Tanks, The Normalized Surge Tank Charts of Calame and Gaden, Navigation Locks, Surges in Power Canals—Tidal Harmonics, etc. Revised and enlarged. Author's prefaces. Index. xiv + 409pp. 5⅜ x 8½. S116 Paperbound **$2.50**

**HYDRAULICS AND ITS APPLICATIONS, A. H. Gibson.** Excellent comprehensive textbook for the student and thorough practical manual for the professional worker, a work of great stature in its area. Half the book is devoted to theory and half to applications and practical problems met in the field. Covers modes of motion of a fluid, critical velocity, viscous flow, eddy formation, Bernoulli's theorem, flow in converging passages, vortex motion, form of effluent streams, notches and weirs, skin friction, losses at valves and elbows, siphons, erosion of channels, jet propulsion, waves of oscillation, and over 100 similar topics. Final chapters (nearly 400 pages) cover more than 100 kinds of hydraulic machinery: Pelton wheel, speed regulators, the hydraulic ram, surge tanks, the scoop wheel, the Venturi meter, etc. A special chapter treats methods of testing theoretical hypotheses: scale models of rivers, tidal estuaries, siphon spillways, etc. 5th revised and enlarged (1952) edition. Index. Appendix. 427 photographs and diagrams. 95 examples, answers. xv + 813pp. 6 x 9. S791 Clothbound **$8.00**

**GASEOUS CONDUCTORS: THEORY AND ENGINEERING APPLICATIONS, J. D. Cobine.** An indispensable text and reference to gaseous conduction phenomena, with the engineering viewpoint prevailing throughout. Studies the kinetic theory of gases, ionization, emission phenomena; gas breakdown, spark characteristics, glow, and discharges; engineering applications in circuit interrupters, rectifiers, !ight sources, etc. Separate detailed treatment of high pressure arcs (Suits); low pressure arcs (Langmuir and Tonks). Much more. "Well organized, clear, straightforward," Tonks, Review of Scientific Instruments. Index. Bibliography. 83 practice problems. 7 appendices. Over 600 figures. 58 tables. xx + 606pp. 5⅜ x 8.
S442 Paperbound **$2.95**

**INTRODUCTION TO THE STATISTICAL DYNAMICS OF AUTOMATIC CONTROL SYSTEMS, V. V. Solodovnikov.** First English publication of text-reference covering important branch of automatic control systems—random signals; in its originel edition, this was the first comprehensive treatment. Examines frequency characteristics, transfer functions, stationary random processes, determination of minimum mean-squared error, of transfer function for a finite period of observation, much more. Translation edited by J. B. Thomas, L. A. Zadeh. Index. Bibliography. Appendix. xxii + 308pp. 5⅜ x 8.
S420 Paperbound **$2.25**

**TENSORS FOR CIRCUITS, Gabriel Kron.** A boldly original method of analyzing engineering problems, at center of sharp discussion since first introduced, now definitely proved useful in such areas as electrical and structural networks on automatic computers. Encompasses a great variety of specific problems by means of a relatively few symbolic equations. "Power and flexibility . . . becoming more widely recognized," Nature. Formerly "A Short Course in Tensor Analysis." New introduction by B. Hoffmann. Index. Over 800 diagrams. xix + 250pp. 5⅜ x 8.
S534 Paperbound **$2.00**

**SELECTED PAPERS ON SEMICONDUCTOR MICROWAVE ELECTRONICS, edited by Sumner N. Levine and Richard R. Kurzrok.** An invaluable collection of important papers dealing with one of the most remarkable devolopments in solid-state electronics—the use of the p-n junction to achieve amplification and frequency conversion of microwave frequencies. Contents: General Survey (3 introductory papers by W. E. Danielson, R. N. Hall, and M. Tenzer); General Theory of Nonlinear Elements (3 articles by A. van der Ziel, H. E. Rowe, and Manley and Rowe); Device Fabrication and Characterization (3 pieces by Bakanowski, Cranna, and Uhlir, by McCotter, Walker and Fortini, and by S. T. Eng); Parametric Amplifiers and Frequency Multipliers (13 articles by Uhlir, Heffner and Wade, Matthaei, P. K. Tien, van der Ziel, Engelbrecht, Currie and Gould, Uenohara, Leeson and Weinreb, and others); and Tunnel Diodes (4 papers by L. Esaki, H. S. Sommers, Jr., M. E. Hines, and Yariv and Cook). Introduction. 295 Figures. xiii + 286pp. 6½ x 9¼.
S1126 Paperbound **$2.25**

**THE PRINCIPLES OF ELECTROMAGNETISM APPLIED TO ELECTRICAL MACHINES, B. Hague.** A concise, but complete, summary of the basic principles of the magnetic field and its applications, with particular reference to the kind of phenomena which occur in electrical machines. Part I: General Theory—magnetic field of a current, electromagnetic field passing from air to iron, mechanical forces on linear conductors, etc. Part II: Application of theory to the solution of electromechanical problems—the magnetic field and mechanical forces in non-salient pole machinery, the field within slots and between salient poles, and the work of Rogowski, Roth, and Strutt. Formery titled "Electromagnetic Problems in Electrical Engineering." 2 appendices. Index. Bibliography in notes. 115 figures. xiv + 359pp. 5⅜ x 8½.
S246 Paperbound **$2.25**

# Mechanical engineering

**DESIGN AND USE OF INSTRUMENTS AND ACCURATE MECHANISM, T. N. Whitehead.** For the instrument designer, engineer; how to combine necessary mathematical abstractions with independent observation of actual facts. Partial contents: instruments & their parts, theory of errors, systematic errors, probability, short period errors, erratic errors, design precision, kinematic, semikinematic design, stiffness, planning of an instrument, human factor, etc. Index. 85 photos, diagrams. xii + 288pp. 5⅜ x 8.
S270 Paperbound **$2.00**

**A TREATISE ON GYROSTATICS AND ROTATIONAL MOTION: THEORY AND APPLICATIONS, Andrew Gray.** Most detailed, thorough book in English, generally considered definitive study. Many problems of all sorts in full detail, or step-by-step summary. Classical problems of Bour, Lottner, etc.; later ones of great physical interest. Vibrating systems of gyrostats, earth as a top, calculation of path of axis of a top by elliptic integrals, motion of unsymmetrical top, much more. Index. 160 illus. 550pp. 5⅜ x 8.
S589 Paperbound **$2.75**

**MECHANICS OF THE GYROSCOPE, THE DYNAMICS OF ROTATION, R. F. Deimel,** Professor of Mechanical Engineering at Stevens Institute of Technology. Elementary general treatment of dynamics of rotation, with special application of gyroscopic phenomena. No knowledge of vectors needed. Velocity of a moving curve, acceleration to a point, general equations of motion, gyroscopic horizon, free gyro, motion of discs, the damped gyro, 103 similar topics. Exercises. 75 figures. 208pp. 5⅜ x 8.
S66 Paperbound **$1.75**

**STRENGTH OF MATERIALS, J. P. Den Hartog.** Distinguished text prepared for M.I.T. course, ideal as introduction, refresher, reference, or self-study text. Full clear treatment of elementary material (tension, torsion, bending, compound stresses, deflection of beams, etc.), plus much advanced material on engineering methods of great practical value: full treatment of the Mohr circle, lucid elementary discussions of the theory of the center of shear and the "Myosotis" method of calculating beam deflections, reinforced concrete, plastic deformations, photoelasticity, etc. In all sections, both general principles and concrete applications are given. Index. 186 figures (160 others in problem section). 350 problems, all with answers. List of formulas. viii + 323pp. 5⅜ x 8. **S755 Paperbound $2.00**

**PHOTOELASTICITY: PRINCIPLES AND METHODS, H. T. Jessop, F. C. Harris.** For the engineer, for specific problems of stress analysis. Latest time-saving methods of checking calculations in 2-dimensional design problems, new techniques for stresses in 3 dimensions, and lucid description of optical systems used in practical photoelasticity. Useful suggestions and hints based on on-the-job experience included. Partial contents: strained and stress-strain relations, circular disc under thrust along diameter, rectangular block with square hole under vertical thrust, simply supported rectangular beam under central concentrated load, etc. Theory held to minimum, no advanced mathematical training needed. Index. 164 illustrations. viii + 184pp. 6⅛ x 9¼. **S720 Paperbound $2.00**

**APPLIED ELASTICITY, J. Prescott.** Provides the engineer with the theory of elasticity usually lacking in books on strength of materials, yet concentrates on those portions useful for immediate application. Develops every important type of elasticity problem from theoretical principles. Covers analysis of stress, relations between stress and strain, the empirical basis of elasticity, thin rods under tension or thrust, Saint Venant's theory, transverse oscillations of thin rods, stability of thin plates, cylinders with thin walls, vibrations of rotating disks, elastic bodies in contact, etc. "Excellent and important contribution to the subject, not merely in the old matter which he has presented in new and refreshing form, but also in the many original investigations here published for the first time," NATURE. Index. 3 Appendixes. vi + 672pp. 5⅜ x 8. **S726 Paperbound $3.25**

**APPLIED MECHANICS FOR ENGINEERS, Sir Charles Inglis, F.R.S.** A representative survey of the many and varied engineering questions which can be answered by statics and dynamics. The author, one of first and foremost adherents of "structural dynamics," presents distinctive illustrative examples and clear, concise statement of principles—directing the discussion at methodology and specific problems. Covers fundamental principles of rigid-body statics, graphic solutions of static problems, theory of taut wires, stresses in frameworks, particle dynamics, kinematics, simple harmonic motion and harmonic analysis, two-dimensional rigid dynamics, etc. 437 illustrations. xii + 404pp. 5⅜ x 8½. **S1119 Paperbound $2.00**

**THEORY OF MACHINES THROUGH WORKED EXAMPLES, G. H. Ryder.** Practical mechanical engineering textbook for graduates and advanced undergraduates, as well as a good reference work for practicing engineers. Partial contents: Mechanisms, Velocity and Acceleration (including discussion of Klein's Construction for Piston Acceleration), Cams, Geometry of Gears, Clutches and Bearings, Belt and Rope Drives, Brakes, Inertia Forces and Couples, General Dynamical Problems, Gyroscopes, Linear and Angular Vibrations, Torsional Vibrations, Transverse Vibrations and Whirling Speeds (Chapters on vibrations considerably enlarged from previous editions). Over 300 problems, many fully worked out. Index. 195 line illustrations. Revised and enlarged edition. viii + 280pp. 5⅝ x 8¾. **S980 Clothbound $5.00**

**THE KINEMATICS OF MACHINERY: OUTLINES OF A THEORY OF MACHINES, Franz Reuleaux.** The classic work in the kinematics of machinery. The present thinking about the subject has all been shaped in great measure by the fundamental principles stated here by Reuleaux almost 90 years ago. While some details have naturally been superseded, his basic viewpoint has endured; hence, the book is still an excellent text for basic courses in kinematics and a standard reference work for active workers in the field. Covers such topics as: the nature of the machine problem, phoronomic propositions, pairs of elements, incomplete kinematic chains, kinematic notation and analysis, analyses of chamber-crank trains, chamber-wheel trains, constructive elements of machinery, complete machines, etc., with main focus on controlled movement in mechanisms. Unabridged republication of original edition, translated by Alexander B. Kennedy. New introduction for this edition by E. S. Ferguson. Index. 451 illustrations. xxiv + 622pp. 5⅜ x 8½. **S1124 Paperbound $3.00**

**ANALYTICAL MECHANICS OF GEARS, Earle Buckingham.** Provides a solid foundation upon which logical design practices and design data can be constructed. Originally arising out of investigations of the ASME Special Research Committee on Worm Gears and the Strength of Gears, the book covers conjugate gear-tooth action, the nature of the contact, and resulting gear-tooth profiles of: spur, internal, helical, spiral, worm, bevel, and hypoid or skew bevel gears. Also: frictional heat of operation and its dissipation, friction losses, etc., dynamic loads in operation, and related matters. Familiarity with this book is still regarded as a necessary prerequisite to work in modern gear manufacturing. 263 figures. 103 tables. Index. x + 546pp. 5⅜ x 8½. **S1073 Paperbound $2.75**

## Optical design, lighting

**THE SCIENTIFIC BASIS OF ILLUMINATING ENGINEERING, Parry Moon,** Professor of Electrical Engineering, M.I.T. Basic, comprehensive study. Complete coverage of the fundamental theoretical principles together with the elements of design, vision, and color with which the lighting engineer must be familiar. Valuable as a text as well as a reference source to the practicing engineer. Partial contents: Spectroradiometric Curve, Luminous Flux, Radiation from Gaseous-Conduction Sources, Radiation from Incandescent Sources, Incandescent Lamps, Measurement of Light, Illumination from Point Sources and Surface Sources, Elements of Lighting Design. 7 Appendices. Unabridged and corrected republication, with additions. New preface containing conversion tables of radiometric and photometric concepts. Index. 707-item bibliography. 92-item bibliography of author's articles. 183 problems. xxiii + 608pp. 5⅜ x 8½.
S242 Paperbound **$2.85**

**OPTICS AND OPTICAL INSTRUMENTS: AN INTRODUCTION WITH SPECIAL REFERENCE TO PRACTICAL APPLICATIONS, B. K. Johnson.** An invaluable guide to basic practical applications of optical principles, which shows how to set up inexpensive working models of each of the four main types of optical instruments—telescopes, microscopes, photographic lenses, optical projecting systems. Explains in detail the most important experiments for determining their accuracy, resolving power, angular field of view, amounts of aberration, all other necessary facts about the instruments. Formerly "Practical Optics." Index. 234 diagrams. Appendix. 224pp. 5⅜ x 8.
S642 Paperbound **$1.65**

**APPLIED OPTICS AND OPTICAL DESIGN, A. E. Conrady.** With publication of vol. 2, standard work for designers in optics is now complete for first time. Only work of its kind in English; only detailed work for practical designer and self-taught. Requires, for bulk of work, no math above trig. Step-by-step exposition, from fundamental concepts of geometrical, physical optics, to systematic study, design, of almost all types of optical systems. Vol. 1: all ordinary ray-tracing methods; primary aberrations; necessary higher aberration for design of telescopes, low-power microscopes, photographic equipment. Vol. 2: (Completed from author's notes by R. Kingslake, Dir. Optical Design, Eastman Kodak.) Special attention to high-power microscope, anastigmatic photographic objectives. "An indispensable work," J., Optical Soc. of Amer. "As a practical guide this book has no rival," Transactions, Optical Soc. Index. Bibliography. 193 diagrams. 852pp. 6⅛ x 9¼.
Vol. 1 S366 Paperbound **$3.50**
Vol. 2 S612 Paperbound **$2.95**

## Miscellaneous

**THE MEASUREMENT OF POWER SPECTRA FROM THE POINT OF VIEW OF COMMUNICATIONS ENGINEERING, R. B. Blackman, J. W. Tukey.** This pathfinding work, reprinted from the "Bell System Technical Journal," explains various ways of getting practically useful answers in the measurement of power spectra, using results from both transmission theory and the theory of statistical estimation. Treats: Autocovariance Functions and Power Spectra; Direct Analog Computation; Distortion, Noise, Heterodyne Filtering and Pre-whitening; Aliasing; Rejection Filtering and Separation; Smoothing and Decimation Procedures; Very Low Frequencies; Transversal Filtering; much more. An appendix reviews fundamental Fourier techniques. Index of notation. Glossary of terms. 24 figures. XII tables. Bibliography. General index. 192pp. 5⅜ x 8.
S507 Paperbound **$1.85**

**CALCULUS REFRESHER FOR TECHNICAL MEN, A. Albert Klaf.** This book is unique in English as a refresher for engineers, technicians, students who either wish to brush up their calculus or to clear up uncertainties. It is not an ordinary text, but an examination of most important aspects of integral and differential calculus in terms of the 756 questions most likely to occur to the technical reader. The first part of this book covers simple differential calculus, with constants, variables, functions, increments, derivatives, differentiation, logarithms, curvature of curves, and similar topics. The second part covers fundamental ideas of integration, inspection, substitution, transformation, reduction, areas and volumes, mean value, successive and partial integration, double and triple integration. Practical aspects are stressed rather than theoretical. A 50-page section illustrates the application of calculus to specific problems of civil and nautical engineering, electricity, stress and strain, elasticity, industrial engineering, and similar fields.—756 questions answered. 566 problems, mostly answered. 36 pages of useful constants, formulae for ready reference. Index. v + 431pp. 5⅜ x 8.
T370 Paperbound **$2.00**

**METHODS IN EXTERIOR BALLISTICS, Forest Ray Moulton.** Probably the best introduction to the mathematics of projectile motion. The ballistics theories propounded were coordinated with extensive proving ground and wind tunnel experiments conducted by the author and others for the U.S. Army. Broad in scope and clear in exposition, it gives the beginnings of the theory used for modern-day projectile, long-range missile, and satellite motion. Six main divisions: Differential Equations of Translatory Motion of a projectile; Gravity and the Resistance Function; Numerical Solution of Differential Equations; Theory of Differential Variations; Validity of Method of Numerical Integration; and Motion of a Rotating Projectile. Formerly titled: "New Methods in Exterior Ballistics." Index. 38 diagrams. viii + 259pp. 5⅜ x 8½.
S232 Paperbound **$1.75**

**LOUD SPEAKERS: THEORY, PERFORMANCE, TESTING AND DESIGN, N. W. McLachlan.** Most comprehensive coverage of theory, practice of loud speaker design, testing; classic reference, study manual in field. First 12 chapters deal with theory, for readers mainly concerned with math. aspects; last 7 chapters will interest reader concerned with testing, design. Partial contents: principles of sound propagation, fluid pressure on vibrators, theory of moving-coil principle, transients, driving mechanisms, response curves, design of horn type moving coil speakers, electrostatic speakers, much more. Appendix. Bibliography. Index. 165 illustrations, charts. 411pp. 5⅜ x 8. **S588 Paperbound $2.25**

**MICROWAVE TRANSMISSION, J. C. Slater.** First text dealing exclusively with microwaves, brings together points of view of field, circuit theory, for graduate student in physics, electrical engineering, microwave technician. Offers valuable point of view not in most later studies. Uses Maxwell's equations to study electromagnetic field, important in this area. Partial contents: infinite line with distributed parameters, impedance of terminated line, plane waves, reflections, wave guides, coaxial line, composite transmission lines, impedance matching, etc. Introduction. Index. 76 illus. 319pp. 5⅜ x 8.
**S564 Paperbound $1.50**

**MICROWAVE TRANSMISSION DESIGN DATA, T. Moreno.** Originally classified, now rewritten and enlarged (14 new chapters) for public release under auspices of Sperry Corp. Material of immediate value or reference use to radio engineers, systems designers, applied physicists, etc. Ordinary transmission line theory; attenuation; capacity; parameters of coaxial lines; higher modes; flexible cables; obstacles, discontinuities, and injunctions; tunable wave guide impedance transformers; effects of temperature and humidity; much more. "Enough theoretical discussion is included to allow use of data without previous background," Electronics. 324 circuit diagrams, figures, etc. Tables of dielectrics, flexible cable, etc., data. Index. ix + 248pp. 5⅜ x 8. **S459 Paperbound $1.65**

**RAYLEIGH'S PRINCIPLE AND ITS APPLICATIONS TO ENGINEERING, G. Temple & W. Bickley.** Rayleigh's principle developed to provide upper and lower estimates of true value of fundamental period of a vibrating system, or condition of stability of elastic systems. Illustrative examples; rigorous proofs in special chapters. Partial contents: Energy method of discussing vibrations, stability. Perturbation theory, whirling of uniform shafts. Criteria of elastic stability. Application of energy method. Vibrating systems. Proof, accuracy, successive approximations, application of Rayleigh's principle. Synthetic theorems. Numerical, graphical methods. Equilibrium configurations, Ritz's method. Bibliography. Index. 22 figures. ix + 156pp. 5⅜ x 8. **S307 Paperbound $1.50**

**ELASTICITY, PLASTICITY AND STRUCTURE OF MATTER, R. Houwink.** Standard treatise on rheological aspects of different technically important solids such as crystals, resins, textiles, rubber, clay, many others. Investigates general laws for deformations; determines divergences from these laws for certain substances. Covers general physical and mathematical aspects of plasticity, elasticity, viscosity. Detailed examination of deformations, internal structure of matter in relation to elastic and plastic behavior, formation of solid matter from a fluid, conditions for elastic and plastic behavior of matter. Treats glass, asphalt, gutta percha, balata, proteins, baker's dough, lacquers, sulphur, others. 2nd revised, enlarged edition. Extensive revised bibliography in over 500 footnotes. Index. Table of symbols. 214 figures. xviii + 368pp. 6 x 9¼. **S385 Paperbound $2.45**

**THE SCHWARZ-CHRISTOFFEL TRANSFORMATION AND ITS APPLICATIONS: A SIMPLE EXPOSITION, Miles Walker.** An important book for engineers showing how this valuable tool can be employed in practical situations. Very careful, clear presentation covering numerous concrete engineering problems. Includes a thorough account of conjugate functions for engineers—useful for the beginner and for review. Applications to such problems as: Stream-lines round a corner, electric conductor in air-gap, dynamo slots, magnetized poles, much more. Formerly "Conjugate Functions for Engineers." Preface. 92 figures, several tables. Index. ix + 116pp. 5⅜ x 8½. **S1149 Paperbound $1.25**

**THE LAWS OF THOUGHT, George Boole.** This book founded symbolic logic some hundred years ago. It is the 1st significant attempt to apply logic to all aspects of human endeavour. Partial contents: derivation of laws, signs & laws, interpretations, eliminations, conditions of a perfect method, analysis, Aristotelian logic, probability, and similar topics. xviii + 424pp. 5⅜ x 8. **S28 Paperbound $2.00**

**SCIENCE AND METHOD, Henri Poincaré.** Procedure of scientific discovery, methodology, experiment, idea-germination—the intellectual processes by which discoveries come into being. Most significant and most interesting aspects of development, application of ideas. Chapters cover selection of facts, chance, mathematical reasoning, mathematics, and logic; Whitehead, Russell, Cantor; the new mechanics, etc. 288pp. 5⅜ x 8. **S222 Paperbound $1.35**

**FAMOUS BRIDGES OF THE WORLD, D. B. Steinman.** An up-to-the-minute revised edition of a book that explains the fascinating drama of how the world's great bridges came to be built. The author, designer of the famed Mackinac bridge, discusses bridges from all periods and all parts of the world, explaining their various types of construction, and describing the problems their builders faced. Although primarily for youngsters, this cannot fail to interest readers of all ages. 48 illustrations in the text. 23 photographs. 99pp. 6⅛ x 9¼. **T161 Paperbound $1.00**

# Differential equations, ordinary and partial; integral equations

**INTRODUCTION TO THE DIFFERENTIAL EQUATIONS OF PHYSICS, L. Hopf.** Especially valuable to the engineer with no math beyond elementary calculus. Emphasizing intuitive rather than formal aspects of concepts, the author covers an extensive territory. Partial contents: Law of causality, energy theorem, damped oscillations, coupling by friction, cylindrical and spherical coordinates, heat source, etc. Index. 48 figures. 160pp. 5⅜ x 8.
S120 Paperbound **$1.25**

**INTRODUCTION TO THE THEORY OF LINEAR DIFFERENTIAL EQUATIONS, E. G. Poole.** Authoritative discussions of important topics, with methods of solution more detailed than usual, for students with background of elementary course in differential equations. Studies existence theorems, linearly independent solutions; equations with constant coefficients; with uniform analytic coefficients; regular singularities; the hypergeometric equation; conformal representation; etc. Exercises. Index. 210pp. 5⅜ x 8.
S629 Paperbound **$1.65**

**DIFFERENTIAL EQUATIONS FOR ENGINEERS, P. Franklin.** Outgrowth of a course given 10 years at M. I. T. Makes most useful branch of pure math accessible for practical work. Theoretical basis of D.E.'s; solution of ordinary D.E.'s and partial derivatives arising from heat flow, steady-state temperature of a plate, wave equations; analytic functions; convergence of Fourier Series. 400 problems on electricity, vibratory systems, other topics. Formerly "Differential Equations for Electrical Engineers." Index 41 illus. 307pp. 5⅜ x 8.
S601 Paperbound **$1.65**

**DIFFERENTIAL EQUATIONS, F. R. Moulton.** A detailed, rigorous exposition of all the non-elementary processes of solving ordinary differential equations. Several chapters devoted to the treatment of practical problems, especially those of a physical nature, which are far more advanced than problems usually given as illustrations. Includes analytic differential equations; variations of a parameter; integrals of differential equations; analytic implicit functions; problems of elliptic motion; sine-amplitude functions; deviation of formal bodies; Cauchy-Lipschitz process; linear differential equations with periodic coefficients; differential equations in infinitely many variations; much more. Historical notes. 10 figures. 222 problems. Index. xv + 395pp. 5⅜ x 8.
S451 Paperbound **$2.00**

**DIFFERENTIAL AND INTEGRAL EQUATIONS OF MECHANICS AND PHYSICS (DIE DIFFERENTIAL-UND INTEGRALGLEICHUNGEN DER MECHANIK UND PHYSIK), edited by P. Frank and R. von Mises.** Most comprehensive and authoritative work on the mathematics of mathematical physics available today in the United States: the standard, definitive reference for teachers, physicists, engineers, and mathematicians—now published (in the original German) at a relatively inexpensive price for the first time! Every chapter in this 2,000-page set is by an expert in his field: Carathéodory, Courant, Frank, Mises, and a dozen others. Vol I, on mathematics, gives concise but complete coverages of advanced calculus, differential equations, integral equations, and potential, and partial differential equations. Index. xxiii + 916pp. Vol. II (physics): classical mechanics, optics, continuous mechanics, heat conduction and diffusion, the stationary and quasi-stationary electromagnetic field, electromagnetic oscillations, and wave mechanics. Index. xxiv + 1106pp. Two volume set. Each volume available separately. 5⅝ x 8⅜.
S787 Vol I Clothbound **$7.50**
S788 Vol II Clothbound **$7.50**
The set **$15.00**

**LECTURES ON CAUCHY'S PROBLEM, J. Hadamard.** Based on lectures given at Columbia, Rome, this discusses work of Riemann, Kirchhoff, Volterra, and the author's own research on the hyperbolic case in linear partial differential equations. It extends spherical and cylindrical waves to apply to all (normal) hyperbolic equations. Partial contents: Cauchy's problem, fundamental formula, equations with odd number, with even number of independent variables; method of descent. 32 figures. Index. iii + 316pp. 5⅜ x 8.   S105 Paperbound **$1.75**

**THEORY OF DIFFERENTIAL EQUATIONS, A. R. Forsyth.** Out of print for over a decade, the complete 6 volumes (now bound as 3) of this monumental work represent the most comprehensive treatment of differential equations ever written. Historical presentation includes in 2500 pages every substantial development. Vol. 1, 2: EXACT EQUATIONS, PFAFF'S PROBLEM; ORDINARY EQUATIONS, NOT LINEAR: methods of Grassmann, Clebsch, Lie, Darboux; Cauchy's theorem; branch points; etc. Vol. 3, 4: ORDINARY EQUATIONS, NOT LINEAR; ORDINARY LINEAR EQUATIONS: Zeta Fuchsian functions, general theorems on algebraic integrals, Brun's theorem, equations with uniform periodic coefficients, etc. Vol. 4, 5: PARTIAL DIFFERENTIAL EQUATIONS: 2 existence-theorems, equations of theoretical dynamics, Laplace transformations, general transformation of equations of the 2nd order, much more. Indexes. Total of 2766pp. 5⅜ x 8.   S576-7-8 Clothbound: the set **$15.00**

**PARTIAL DIFFERENTIAL EQUATIONS OF MATHEMATICAL PHYSICS, A. G. Webster.** A keystone work in the library of every mature physicist, engineer, researcher. Valuable sections on elasticity, compression theory, potential theory, theory of sound, heat conduction, wave propagation, vibration theory. Contents include: deduction of differential equations, vibrations, normal functions, Fourier's series, Cauchy's method, boundary problems, method of Riemann-Volterra. Spherical, cylindrical, ellipsoidal harmonics, applications, etc. 97 figures. vii + 440pp. 5⅜ x 8.
S263 Paperbound **$2.00**

# MATHEMATICS, HISTORIES AND CLASSICS

**HISTORY OF MATHEMATICS, D. E. Smith.** Most comprehensive non-technical history of math in English. Discusses lives and works of over a thousand major and minor figures, with footnotes supplying technical information outside the book's scheme, and indicating disputed matters. Vol I: A chronological examination, from primitive concepts through Egypt, Babylonia, Greece, the Orient, Rome, the Middle Ages, the Renaissance, and up to 1900. Vol 2: The development of ideas in specific fields and problems, up through elementary calculus. Two volumes, total of 510 illustrations, 1355pp. 5⅜ x 8. Set boxed in attractive container.
T429, 430 Paperbound, the set **$5.00**

**A SHORT ACCOUNT OF THE HISTORY OF MATHEMATICS, W. W. R. Ball.** Most readable non-technical history of mathematics treats lives, discoveries of every important figure from Egyptian, Phoenician mathematicians to late 19th century. Discusses schools of Ionia, Pythagoras, Athens, Cyzicus, Alexandria, Byzantium, systems of numeration; primitive arithmetic; Middle Ages, Renaissance, including Arabs, Bacon, Regiomontanus, Tartaglia, Cardan, Stevinus, Galileo, Kepler; modern mathematics of Descartes, Pascal, Wallis, Huygens, Newton, Leibnitz, d'Alembert, Euler, Lambert, Laplace, Legendre, Gauss, Hermite, Weierstrass, scores more. Index. 25 figures. 546pp. 5⅜ x 8.
S630 Paperbound **$2.00**

**A HISTORY OF GEOMETRICAL METHODS, J. L. Coolidge.** Full, authoritative history of the techniques which men have employed in dealing with geometric questions . . . from ancient times to the modern development of projective geometry. Critical analyses of the original works. Contents: Synthetic Geometry—the early beginnings, Greek mathematics, non-Euclidean geometries, projective and descriptive geometry; Algebraic Geometry—extension of the system of linear coordinates, other systems of point coordinates, enumerative and birational geometry, etc.; and Differential Geometry—intrinsic geometry and moving axes, Gauss and the classical theory of surfaces, and projective and absolute differential geometry. The work of scores of geometers analyzed: Pythagoras, Archimedes, Newton, Descartes, Leibniz, Lobachevski, Riemann, Hilbert, Bernoulli, Schubert, Grassman, Klein, Cauchy, and many, many others. Extensive (24-page) bibliography. Index. 13 figures. xviii + 451pp. 5⅜ x 8½.
S1006 Paperbound **$2.25**

**THE MATHEMATICS OF GREAT AMATEURS, Julian Lowell Coolidge.** Enlightening, often surprising, accounts of what can result from a non-professional preoccupation with mathematics. Chapters on Plato, Omar Khayyam and his work with cubic equations, Piero della Francesca, Albrecht Dürer, as the true discoverer of descriptive geometry, Leonardo da Vinci and his varied mathematical interests, John Napier, Baron of Merchiston, inventor of logarithms, Pascal, Diderot, l'Hospital, and seven others known primarily for contributions in other fields. Bibliography. 56 figures. viii + 211pp. 5⅜ x 8½.
S1009 Paperbound **$1.50**

**ART AND GEOMETRY, Wm. M. Ivins, Jr.** A controversial study which propounds the view that the ideas of Greek philosophy and culture served not to stimulate, but to stifle the development of Western thought. Through an examination of Greek art and geometrical inquiries and Renaissance experiments, this book offers a concise history of the evolution of mathematical perspective and projective geometry. Discusses the work of Alberti, Dürer, Pelerin, Nicholas of Cusa, Kepler, Desargues, etc. in a wholly readable text of interest to the art historian, philosopher, mathematician, historian of science, and others. x + 113pp. 5⅜ x 8⅜.
T941 Paperbound **$1.00**

**A SOURCE BOOK IN MATHEMATICS, D. E. Smith.** Great discoveries in math, from Renaissance to end of 19th century, in English translation. Read announcements by Dedekind, Gauss, Delamain, Pascal, Fermat, Newton, Abel, Lobachevsky, Bolyai, Riemann, De Moivre, Legendre, Laplace, others of discoveries about imaginary numbers, number congruence, slide rule, equations, symbolism, cubic algebraic equations, non-Euclidean forms of geometry, calculus, function theory, quaternions, etc. Succinct selections from 125 different treatises, articles, most unavailable elsewhere in English. Each article preceded by biographical, historical introduction. Vol. I: Fields of Number, Algebra. Index. 32 illus. 338pp. 5⅜ x 8. Vol. II: Fields of Geometry, Probability, Calculus, Functions, Quaternions. 83 illus. 432pp. 5⅜ x 8.
Vol. 1: S552 Paperbound **$1.85**
Vol. 2: S553 Paperbound **$1.85**
2 vol. set, boxed **$3.50**

**A COLLECTION OF MODERN MATHEMATICAL CLASSICS, edited by R. Bellman.** 13 classic papers, complete in their original languages, by Hermite, Hardy and Littlewood, Tchebychef, Fejér, Fredholm, Fuchs, Hurwitz, Weyl, van der Pol, Birkhoff, Kellogg, von Neumann, and Hilbert. Each of these papers, collected here for the first time, triggered a burst of mathematical activity, providing useful new generalizations or stimulating fresh investigations. Topics discussed include classical analysis, periodic and almost periodic functions, analysis and number theory, integral equations, theory of approximation, non-linear differential equations, and functional analysis. Brief introductions and bibliographies to each paper. xii + 292pp. 6 x 9.
S730 Paperbound **$2.00**

**THE WORKS OF ARCHIMEDES, edited by T. L. Heath.** All the known works of the great Greek mathematician are contained in this one volume, including the recently discovered Method of Archimedes. Contains: On Sphere & Cylinder, Measurement of a Circle, Spirals, Conoids, Spheroids, etc. This is the definitive edition of the greatest mathematical intellect of the ancient world. 186-page study by Heath discusses Archimedes and the history of Greek mathematics. Bibliography. 563pp. 5⅜ x 8.
S9 Paperbound **$2.25**

**THE THIRTEEN BOOKS OF EUCLID'S ELEMENTS,** edited by **Sir Thomas Heath.** Definitive edition of one of the very greatest classics of Western world. Complete English translation of Heiberg text, together with spurious Book XIV. Detailed 150-page introduction discussing aspects of Greek and Medieval mathematics. Euclid, texts, commentators, etc. Paralleling the text is an elaborate critical apparatus analyzing each definition, proposition, postulate, covering textual matters, mathematical analysis, commentators of all times, refutations, supports, extrapolations, etc. This is the full Euclid. Unabridged reproduction of Cambridge U. 2nd edition. 3 volumes. Total of 995 figures, 1426pp. 5⅜ x 8.
S88,89,90, 3 volume set, paperbound **$6.75**

**A CONCISE HISTORY OF MATHEMATICS, D. Struik.** Lucid study of development of mathematical ideas, techniques from Ancient Near East, Greece, Islamic science, Middle Ages, Renaissance, modern times. Important mathematicians are described in detail. Treatment is not anecdotal, but analytical development of ideas. "Rich in content, thoughtful in interpretation," U.S. QUARTERLY BOOKLIST. Non-technical; no mathematical training needed. Index. 60 illustrations, including Egyptian papyri, Greek mss., portraits of 31 eminent mathematicians. Bibliography. 2nd edition. xix + 299pp. 5⅜ x 8.
T255 Paperbound **$1.75**

**A HISTORY OF THE CALCULUS, AND ITS CONCEPTUAL DEVELOPMENT, Carl B. Boyer.** Provides laymen and mathematicians a detailed history of the development of the calculus, from early beginning in antiquity to final elaboration as mathematical abstractions. Gives a sense of mathematics not as a technique, but as a habit of mind, in the progression of ideas of Zeno, Plato, Pythagoras, Eudoxus, Arabic and Scholastic mathematicians, Newton, Leibnitz, Taylor, Descartes, Euler, Lagrange, Cantor, Weierstrass, and others. This first comprehensive critical history of the calculus was originally titled "The Concepts of the Calculus." Foreword by R. Courant. Preface. 22 figures. 25-page bibliography. Index. v + 364pp. 5⅜ x 8.
S509 Paperbound **$2.00**

**A MANUAL OF GREEK MATHEMATICS, Sir Thomas L. Heath.** A non-technical survey of Greek mathematics addressed to high school and college students and the layman who desires a sense of historical perspective in mathematics. Thorough exposition of early numerical notation and practical calculation, Pythagorean arithmetic and geometry, Thales and the earliest Greek geometrical measurements and theorems, the mathematical theories of Plato, Euclid's "Elements" and his other works (extensive discussion), Aristarchus, Archimedes, Eratosthenes and the measurement of the earth, trigonometry (Hipparchus, Menelaus, Ptolemy), Pappus and Heron of Alexandria, and detailed coverage of minor figures normally omitted from histories of this type. Presented in a refreshingly interesting and readable style. Appendix. 2 Indexes. xvi + 552pp. 5⅜ x 8.
S279 Paperbound **$2.25**

**THE GEOMETRY OF RENÉ DESCARTES.** With this book Descartes founded analytical geometry. Excellent Smith-Latham translation, plus original French text with Descartes' own diagrams. Contains Problems the Construction of Which Requires Only Straight Lines and Circles; On the Nature of Curved Lines; On the Construction of Solid or Supersolid Problems. Notes. Diagrams. 258pp. 5⅜ x 8.
S68 Paperbound **$1.60**

**A PHILOSOPHICAL ESSAY ON PROBABILITIES, Marquis de Laplace.** This famous essay explains without recourse to mathematics the principle of probability, and the application of probability to games of chance, natural philosophy, astronomy, many other fields. Translated from the 6th French edition by F. W. Truscott, F. L. Emory, with new introduction for this edition by E. T. Bell. 204pp. 5⅜ x 8.
S166 Paperbound **$1.35**

*Prices subject to change without notice.*

*Dover publishes books on art, music, philosophy, literature, languages, history, social sciences, psychology, handcrafts, orientalia, puzzles and entertainments, chess, pets and gardens, books explaining science, intermediate and higher mathematics, mathematical physics, engineering, biological sciences, earth sciences, classics of science, etc. Write to:*

*Dept. catrr.*
*Dover Publications, Inc.*
*180 Varick Street, N.Y. 14, N.Y.*

Date Due